D0914800

Frontispiece

The Old Slater Mill at Pawtucket, R. I., as It Appeared in 1850. The Inset Shows It as It Appeared Originally in 1793 and Practically as It Exists Today. (From Field's History of Rhode Island.) (*See Art. 18.*)

Frontispiece

THE WORKS OF THE GENERAL ELECTRIC CO. AT SCHENECTADY EMPLOYING 25,000 WORKERS.

PRINCIPLES

OF

INDUSTRIAL ORGANIZATION

BY

DEXTER S. KIMBALL, A.B., M.E., Dr.Sc., Dr.Eng., LL.D.

Professor Emeritus of Industrial Engineering and Dean Emeritus of the College of Engineering, Cornell University; Fellow and Past President American Society of Mechanical Engineers; Past President American Engineering Council; Author (with J. H. Barr), "Elements of Machine Design," "Industrial Education," "Cost Finding," "Industrial Economics," etc.

AND

DEXTER S. KIMBALL, Jr., M.E., M.M.E.

Technical Assistant to the Production Manager, Agfa Ansco Corp.; Formerly Assistant Professor of Industrial Engineering, Cornell University; Production Manager, General Household Utilities; Member American Society of Mechanical Engineers

Fifth Edition
Second Impression

McGRAW-HILL BOOK COMPANY, Inc.

NEW YORK AND LONDON

1939

PRINTED IN THE UNITED STATES OF AMERICA

THE MAPLE PRESS COMPANY, YORK, PA.

PREFACE TO THE FIFTH EDITION

The kindly reception that this book has received has led to the belief that its scope and size have been found to be well adapted to the purposes of instruction. At the same time it has been, apparently, of considerable service outside the classroom. No marked changes have been made, therefore, in the general plan of the book in this edition, but an earnest effort has been made to bring the subject matter fully up to date. New material treating of the effect of recent federal legislation upon industry has been included and all statistical data have been carefully revised.

When the fourth edition was issued, I was greatly assisted by my son, Dexter S. Kimball, Jr., who has had experience not only as a teacher of industrial engineering but also an extended experience in modern methods of production. He has again assisted me in this revision, and I am therefore associating him with me as coauthor. We shall be grateful for any suggestions or corrections that will make the book more useful or more accurate.

DEXTER S. KIMBALL.

CORNELL UNIVERSITY,
ITHACA, N. Y.,
October, 1939.

PREFACE TO THE FIRST EDITION

As industrial enterprises have grown in magnitude, as processes have become more refined and competition more keen, the problems of organization have steadily grown in importance. Just as the tools and processes of our forefathers became inadequate as enterprises grew in magnitude, so the simple administrative methods formerly in use have long since been outgrown by modern plants. Aside, however, from these reasons there are other factors affecting organization, which, while of little importance in former times, promise to be of great importance in the organizations of the future.

The ideals that man has held before him in his toilsome journey from savagery to civilization have varied with changing time and place. Among many of the older nations war was the central thought, the country was an armed camp, and predatory methods were an approved means of national support. In other cases some form of religion was the predominating influence, and the social and industrial organization was modeled accordingly. In a few of the older civilizations industry was held in high esteem; but for the most part labor was considered menial, and industry was adjudged by standards that now seem strange indeed.

But as the humanistic side of civilization has made progress we have attained higher ideals regarding industry. Never before in the history of mankind has it been so universally acknowledged that physical, mental, and moral well-being rest upon, and are solely supported by, labor. Industry is the *business* of the civilized world, and the greater part of our problems—national, state, and home—center around the great industrial questions. Furthermore, industry is being looked upon more and more, not as an incidental matter, or merely as a means of securing personal profits, but as the great basic feature of our civilization.

And with this new evaluation of industry have come new and higher ideals regarding service to humanity. No longer is it considered necessary merely to *tell* people how to improve themselves mentally, morally, and materially, but there is a cry for a remodeling of our industrial structure that will put the material basis, on which these improvements rest, into the hands of all.

It is for these reasons that the ideas embodied in so-called scientific management are coming in for such close scrutiny. Changes of a similar character and as far-reaching in their effects have been made in our industrial methods in times past with little or no comment from any quarter. But today changes of this character cannot be made, as formerly, on the basis or plea of *increased production* alone. The specter of *distribution of profit*, the bugbear of our industrial system, stands constantly in the background, and the question that it ever raises—What will be the effect of these changes on humanity?—can no longer be ignored.

An intelligent appreciation of even the simpler problems of factory organization and operation cannot be attained without some knowledge of the origin and trend of these modifying factors. Already the effects of many of them are rapidly passing from the transitory stage of public sentiment into the more permanent form of state or national legislation. This is the writer's excuse, if any is needed, for the first four chapters of the book. It is not the purpose of the book to exploit any form of industrial management or any specific remedy for industrial evils, but it is an endeavor to set before young men entering the industrial field the salient facts regarding the most important movements with which they are sure to be brought into contact, and to explain the origin and growth of the important features of industrial organization.

To the engineer whose ever-widening circle of usefulness brings him more and more in contact with economic problems these are matters of peculiar importance, and it is for the needs of young engineers primarily that the book has been written, being based on a course of lectures given by the writer for a number of years past to the senior class in Sibley College of Mechanical Engineering, Cornell University. It is hoped, however, that the practicing engineer or manager who wishes to know something of the fundamental principles of organization, without regard to some specific system of management, may also find it of interest.

It has been the writer's endeavor to deal as far as possible with general principles only, and no effort has been made to illustrate the many kinds of cards and forms used in industrial management, only such cards and forms having been shown as were necessary to illustrate the principles discussed. These documents are so varied in character that they possess little educational value except as they illustrate principles, though instruction in this subject is greatly aided by collections of the cards and forms used in representative systems of management. Such documents, also, grow naturally out of the needs of the business concerned, and the form or blank that is best for one industry may be entirely unsuited for the same purpose in another. If the need is clearly defined there is usually no trouble in making a card or form that will be exactly suited to the work, though the practical man can, of course, obtain help and suggestions from collections of such documents.

The writer has availed himself freely of the works of other writers, and had endeavored to give full credit for this assistance where such help has been used. The subject matter is necessarily much condensed, but ample references have been included to provide collateral reading. In fact any book that would do full justice to this great subject would be many times too large for the purpose for which this work is intended.

The writer is greatly indebted to Mr. John H. Barr, Consulting Engineer for the Remington Typewriter Co., Mr. F. P. Halsey, Editor Emeritus of the American Machinist, Mr. L.P. Alford, Editor of the American Machinist, Mr. E. E. Barney, Superintendent of the Remington Typewriter Works, Mr. F. R. Whittlesey of the General Electric Co., and Professors A. E. Wells, C. D. Albert, and John Bauer of Cornell University for assistance in reading the manuscript and for helpful criticisms. The author will be grateful for suggestions or criticisms that will make the book more useful, or for corrections that will make it more accurate.

DEXTER S. KIMBALL.

ITHACA, N. Y.,
September, 1913.

CONTENTS

PRINCIPLES OF INDUSTRIAL ORGANIZATION

CHAPTER I

THE BACKGROUND OF INDUSTRY

1. The Sources of Wealth.—As we peer backward into the remote past as far as the dim light of history illuminates our vision, we see great civilizations like that of ancient Egypt comparable in many ways with present-day existence. These ancient organizations supported a highly cultured ruling class, a numerous and very powerful priesthood, large and well-equipped armies and navies, and in their periods of respite from wars built monuments and temples whose size and grandeur are still a source of wonder and amazement. And this amazement is augmented when it is considered that the tools of production which these ancient Egyptians possessed were of the most primitive type and, consequently, the personal efficiency must have been very low. The rich Nile Valley furnished an abundance of food with comparatively small effort and provided sustenance not only for those who worked the soil, but also for the army of laborers who built the monuments and temples, as well as for the ruling classes and the armed forces. Probably hunger was not common in normal times. But the output of farmer and artisan was so small that when the great national needs were satisfied there was little remaining for the producer. The comforts and refinements of life were for the ruling classes and not for him, and his status if not that of actual slavery was little better.

The pattern of this great and interesting Egyptian civilization has been repeated many times in other places and the glories of all of these ancient nations stand out against a background of countless thousands of handicraft workers whose economic status was little better than that of the beasts of the field and whose only hope for ease and comfort lay in another world. It may be considered axiomatic that in any civilized community the state of the actual worker approaches that of slavery as his tools are more and more primitive, even though the upper or non-producing classes may enjoy a high state of mental development and physical comfort. And all economic history indicates the truth of the following statements.

The *total* wealth that any people can create is governed primarily by two factors: (1) the natural resources of the country that they inhabit, and (2) the tools and methods of production, mental and physical, which they possess for developing these resources.

Thus savages living in a rich and fertile territory do not rise above the level permitted by their tools of production, while nations such as Switzerland and Germany, with comparatively limited resources, may easily occupy a foremost position among civilized peoples. The progress of civilization, in fact, is measured by the character of the tools which man has developed and, in general, this is recognized when the Stone Age, the Bronze Age, the Age of Iron, and the Age of Steel are mentioned. It is not unbelievable that another metallic basis may be developed which will serve as an index for a still higher plane of civilization.

The *distribution* of wealth—that is, the degree to which all people share the proceeds of industry and the consequent individual physical comfort and mental development which any nation can enjoy—is governed, for given natural resources and given productive powers, by the *industrial system* under which production is carried on. And the industrial system in all cases is closely interwoven with the *ideals* of the ruling classes and the organization of society. The older nations were, of necessity, supported by vast numbers of low-paid producers whose economic state bordered upon or actually was that of slavery; but civilization possessing the highest type of tools and operating them by slave labor can be readily conceived. *Highly developed tools of production make possible a high average state of mental development and physical comfort; but the realization of this average depends upon national ideals and the social and industrial organization by which the wealth is distributed.* Civilization, therefore, presents two great problems: (1) that of *producing* sufficient wealth to insure proper living conditions and (2) that of *distributing* this wealth in an equitable manner. Considerable progress has been made in solving the first problem but the second still presents many difficulties. This book deals primarily with the problems of production.

2. National Ideals.—It is of the greatest importance to understand and appreciate the influence that man's economic needs have always exerted upon his ideas and ideals of existence. Every people as it has emerged from savagery has brought with it many and curious regulations governing religion, industry, family life, etc. These regulations are the result of long experiments and are very powerful in their effects. Furthermore, they differ widely with conditions and geographical location. Practices and customs that are good form in one place are unthinkable in another. Thus, in India the caste system for countless years prohibited all forms of factories and all production was by simple handicraft, definite kinds of work being assigned to particular classes of people. Under the Roman system, the armorers or *fabricæ* were a class of artisans set apart for this sole purpose. They were branded with a "stigma" and could not change their calling nor could their children do so. It was a form of state-supported and regulated slavery. History abounds in similar instances of the effect of public opinion or national necessity upon the method by which the nation provided itself with the necessities of life. National ideals whether of civilized or uncivilized peoples are always more or less *ideals of necessity.* The cannibal could make an excellent argument for eating his enemy. Both Plato and Aristotle believed that slavery was a good institution, and the great statesman Pitt condoned the exploitation of little children in the early factories of England in a time of great national stress.

Fortunately, as economic stress becomes less pressing, higher ethical standards and more human practices seem to develop naturally. The last half century has seen a tremendous change in our ideas and practices concerning the conditions under which men and women earn their living, and there has been a steady growth in the sensitiveness of the public conscience toward industrial abuses. Much credit, of course, must be given to the many uplifting moral forces of the present day. But it should be remembered that these have been rendered much more effective through the vast increase in our productive efficiency. Modern industrial methods have made *possible* a higher civilization mentally and morally by removing many of the old limitations that so greatly hampered former civilizations. As we have abolished slavery so we may, if we will, abolish compulsory poverty.

And because of these higher ideals, business and industry have become more dignified callings in the public esteem. In ancient times and in the foolish, yet much admired, age of chivalry, these matters were considered to be menial and were left to those "who were unfitted by birth or spirit for the princely vocations of warfare and pillage." There are no doubt many who still hold a semblance of this view. But modern business and industry demand the best brains of the nation and this has necessarily brought about a wider vision and a more humane viewpoint on the part of those who manage industry. In this more enlightened viewpoint lies the hope of the future. Undoubtedly industry was made for man and not man for industry. While, therefore, the essential features of our modern industrial system will probably continue for a long time, it need not be a matter of surprise or alarm that many changes and regulations have been made, and will be made, in deference to public opinion or national necessity.

The truth of these statements will be made more obvious by a consideration of the status of agriculture and industry under the dictatorships in Italy and Germany, the experiment in communism in Soviet Russia and the corresponding status of these activities in the democracies of Great Britain, France, and the United States. In the latter, in recent years, there has been a marked growth of governmental regulation of both agriculture and industry and an extension of governmental ownership somewhat at variance with its historical development. These relations will be referred to again in a later section (see Chap. VII).

3. The Basic Industrial Discoveries.—The basic industrial discoveries that man has uncovered in his long march from savagery to civilization are remarkably few in number considering the vast amount of speculation and investigation that has occupied his mind. The most important are as follows:

1. The use of tools.
2. The economic gains that result from specialization in the use of tools.
3. The control and use of fire particularly in the making of metallic tools.
4. The use of power other than that supplied by bodily strength.
5. The use of scientific methods as contrasted with magic and empirical methods. While scientific methods are not applicable alone to industrial matters they have been most important in industrial development.

The use and development of tools will be quite fully discussed in succeeding sections. Specialization is defined as the concentration of effort upon a limited field of endeavor. Thus, carpenters, masons, farmers, physicians, etc., are specialists as opposed to a worker who may try to practice several of these callings. All experience shows that when a man specializes he becomes more expert in his chosen field than one who practices in several callings. This principle will also be fully discussed in succeeding sections. The control and use of fire need no discussion as its importance is axiomatic. The development of power is manifestly a large subject by itself and will be discussed here only as it has affected industrial development. Similarly, it will be assumed that scientific methods are understood and in the following sections reference will be made to such methods only as they are related to the problems of production and management.

Of course the effects of these principles have been closely interrelated. Thus, when a man specializes in the use of some particular tool he may, and frequently does, try to improve it. He may, in fact, develop the "science" of the particular tool or operation under consideration. That is, he may analyze and set in order all basic facts pertaining to it so that these become matters of permanent record for future use. Again, specialization of workers into the several trades and callings, such as carpenters, masons, sailors, etc., made necessary some form of commercial **organization** and also the necessity of a medium of exchange. Hence came the use of money, which must also be accounted a great discovery or rather a great development, since its use came gradually. The development of new tools and processes in turn creates new callings and new types of specialists. It has been said that *science* and *organization* are the most important factors in modern industry. They have, at least, profoundly affected industry and have greatly modified our ideas as to methods of production.

Plate I.—Scenes from the tomb of Rekhmara, prefect of Thebes about 1600 B.C.

Above, a man cuts strands of leather which are then twisted into a rope, while two others are engaged in the manufacture of sandals. Below, carpenters are making a small shrine, and blocks of wood are being sawn and hewn, while inlayers decorate a larger shrine with mystic symbols. In the lowest band of painting all the processes in the smelting and casting of gold are shown—the furnaces, the bellows, and the gold being poured into moulds. (*By permission of J. A. Hammerton from Wonders of the Past.*)

4. Handicraft Production.—It is obvious that, in general, for a given result the skill of the worker must be increasingly great as his tools become decreasingly primitive and inefficient. It is customary to speak of production with primitive tools and high manual skill as **handicraft.** Highly developed manual skill has been practically universal with primitive people in all times. The Indian women of the Pacific Northwest, for instance, wove baskets which for skill and artistry rank with the best work of the ancient Egyptians. It has been assumed also that the manual skill of these primitive peoples is vastly superior to anything existing in modern industry. Nothing could be further from the truth. The skill of hand required in modern tool making is utterly beyond that possessed by the primitive handworker mainly because it is *different in character*. The ancient worker who could make a beautiful canoe or carve a beautiful column would be useless in operating a modern high-precision lathe until he had acquired sufficient practice. Usually the term handicraft is interpreted as synonymous with *hand tools* but even in very ancient times machines such as looms were in use, though their operation required skill of hand. In general, however, even such machines as were in use were within financial reach of all and industry under the handicraft system is essentially *individual* and not dependent upon *congregated* effort. The true relation of skill of hand and machine production is more fully discussed in a succeeding section.

5. Factory System.—The term *manufacturing* is generally used to refer to the production of goods by means of *congregated labor* and the use of *machinery*. These characteristics are not, however, distinctive of modern methods as both can be and were used[1] by handicraftsmen before the modern era of production began. The Egyptians and Romans were well aware of the advantage of congregated labor, and machinery was in use in England and on the Continent before the birth of modern methods. Nor does the principle of *division of labor* explain the difference between old and new methods, though some modern writers have fallen into the error of this assumption. Division of labor is as old as humanity; it is an essential feature of civilization and was used in some detail by the old handicraftsman. The new methods have enabled mankind to utilize more fully the advantages of congregated labor and division of labor, but these are not the essential features of the change, which will be discussed more fully later on. Handicraft does, however, carry with it the idea of a limited output because of the primitive nature of the tools employed, while manufacturing is essentially synonymous with production in quantity. Handicraft, moreover, carries with it the idea of a *permanent* state of tools and production, and a consequent permanent social structure. Manufacturing, on the other hand, is synonymous

[1] TAYLOR, R. W. COOKE, "Modern Factory System," p. 3, and "History of the Factory System."

with rapid change in productive methods and consequent change in the social and economical conditions.

The term "factory system" refers particularly to the modern method by which men organize labor and tools for the production of commodities. There have been other forms of industrial organization, however, which have varied greatly with changing time and place. Previous to about 150 years ago, all productive organizations of which there is any record were based on handicraft. In most instances the organization was extremely simple, because handicraft is essentially individual. The Egyptians, however, had factories such as that at Canopus where pottery was manufactured, and the Romans had a well-organized system of factories for the making of armor. Factories of considerable size also existed in England and on the Continent during the Middle Ages.[1] These factories, while possessing the characteristics of congregated labor and perhaps in many instances including machines, were, after all, simple collections of handicraft processes with some division of labor. They were not comparable with modern factories so far as the systematic organization of labor or of processes is concerned.

6. Industrial Systems Preceding Present Methods.—As has been noted, the methods by which industry is conducted have varied widely with time and place. Any account of these variations is beyond the scope of this book, but it should be noted that until the modern era all industrial systems were based upon handicraft. Our present industrial methods, as has been noted, originated in England during the latter part of the eighteenth century, and it is important to understand the industrial methods in use there just preceding the change to modern methods. Under the Feudal System of the Middle Ages men were either bound to the landed proprietors of the soil or, if independent craftsmen, they were held together by the strong bonds of trade guilds (the ancient trades unions). These influences, while hampering the personal freedom of the workman, protected him in a measure against the oppression of influences external to his calling or surroundings. With the decline of the Feudal System, and the growth of personal liberty, these restraining and protective influences gradually disappeared. A most potent influence toward this end was the principle of *commutation of service* by which those bound to the soil were permitted to pay rent in money instead of labor and even eventually to buy their complete freedom from the domination of their feudal chiefs. There was, therefore, an ever-increasing tendency to pay dues and reward labor, not by labor or by the direct product of labor, but in money; and long before the rise of the modern system of production this had resulted in a considerable wage-earning class. It is to be specially noted that this wage-earning class, while free to sell their labor as they pleased, were totally unpro-

[1] TAYLOR, R. W. COOKE, "The History of the Factory System."

tected either by law or by mutual organizations of any kind such as had formerly existed or have since come into existence.

Immediately prior to the modern era, industry had not as yet assumed a definite form, but was passing through a transitional stage in which there existed three clearly defined methods of production. First, there was the ancient method of isolated handicraft which had existed from earliest times. This form of labor had just been rendered unorganized and free from restraint or protection by the downfall of feudal influences. In this method the producing unit was (and still is, for the system still survives in a feeble way) the workman himself, and he and his family were dependent solely on his efforts.

Second, there was what has been called the Domestic System which, as can readily be seen, grew directly out of the decay of the Feudal System. In this form of industry the householder was primarily an agriculturist and he and his family tilled their small farm. At such times, however, as he, or any member of his family, was not so engaged they practiced some handicraft calling, as weaving, or spinning, implements for which were installed in some part of his house, and were his own property. He might even hire assistance for either or both of his activities, and the product of his spinning wheels or looms, in excess of what was needed at home, was disposed of to dealers. This system was a very natural outgrowth of the changed conditions, and was the most important method of production just previous to the great change.

The third form of industrial organization then existing was the forerunner of our modern factory system. In this method the production was carried on by a controlling owner, or principal, who hired employees to operate machines or furnish hand labor in exchange for wages. The fact that the industry was usually carried on in the employer's house does not alter the fact that these establishments were *factories* in the full sense. There are well-authenticated records of some of these old factories, as for instance, that of "Jack of Newbury,"[1] whose works employed over one thousand persons. This form of industry grew up by the side of the Domestic System and perhaps grew out of a natural extension of that system. It is not to be confused, however, with its successor, the modern factory system. True, it had many of the defects of the modern system and ample record can be found of legislation aimed at the oppressive methods of master cloth makers before the present era. It is possible that in time this system would have supplanted the Domestic System entirely in all forms of manufacturing industry with consequent increased discontent of the masses and capitalistic troubles similar to those now existing.

The condition of the common people just previous to the great change to be discussed should also be carefully noted. Economic conditions

[1] TAYLOR, R. W. COOKE, "Modern Factory System," p. 49.

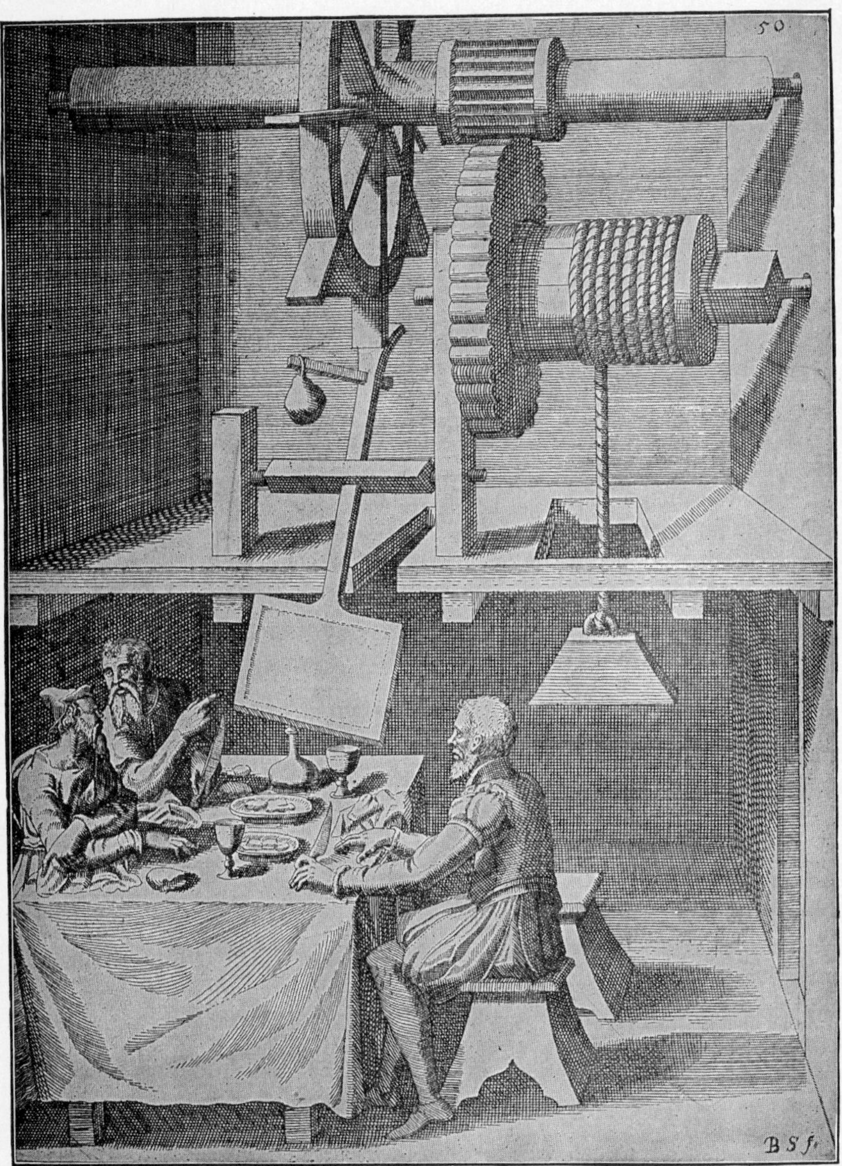

PLATE II.—A table fan of 1614.

were such that they found a ready market for their output, the demand exceeding the supply, and hence they were relatively prosperous. They enjoyed a large measure of personal freedom and independence, since they were *free wage-earners* and the tools of production were more easily obtainable by the individual than at present. These apparently satisfactory conditions have been much exaggerated in making comparisons with present-day conditions. Many writers and poets[1] have written and sung of this so-called "Golden Age" as one of pastoral delight and content. As a matter of fact and history, the condition of the common working people, viewed from a present-day standpoint, was wretched indeed.[2] Housed in unsanitary hovels, uneducated and loose in morals, a prey to epidemics and plagues, their condition would be envied by few workmen today.[3] Whatever evils the modern factory system has brought in its train, it must be credited with making possible a vast improvement in the workers' environment. It cannot be said, however, that it has always improved the workers' bodily vigor; but this has not been the fault of the system so much as it has been due to the ignorance and greed of those controlling it.

It is not likely that improvement in the economic status of these workers could ever have been brought about to a degree comparable with modern conditions, since these old factories were based on *handicraft*, the limitations of which have already been discussed. Nevertheless, enough experience was had with handicraft factories to show that certain social changes, for which the modern factory system is wholly blamed, were even then under way, and that they are an integral part of the change from the state where agriculture was the principal occupation with manufacturing industry a subsidiary matter, to one where these two great branches are entirely divorced and manufacturing is carried on as a separate venture with congregated labor, a wage-earning class, and capitalistic support and control.

References

Bogart, E. L., and C. E. Landon: "Modern Industry."
Cowdrick, E. S.: "Industrial History of the United States."
Gibbins, H. deB.: "The Industrial History of England."
Sumner, W. G.: "Folkways."
Taylor, R. W. Cooke: "History of the Factory System."
———: "Modern Factory System."
Usher, A. P.: "A History of Mechanical Inventions."

[1] Goldsmith, Oliver, "The Deserted Village."

[2] Wright, Carroll D., "The Factory System of the United States," *Report on Manufactures* of the United States at the tenth census.

[3] Jessupp, Augustus, "Village Life in Norfolk Six Hundred Years Ago," in "The Coming of the Friars," p. 53.

CHAPTER II

THE INDUSTRIAL REVOLUTION

7. Characteristics of Tools of Production.—An inventory of the tools, processes, and methods of modern industry will show that progress has developed along three principal lines or channels, namely, **labor-saving machinery, time-saving machinery**, and **machinery for communicating** intelligence. These fields necessarily overlap and interlock, but it will be helpful to keep this classification in mind and to consider the progress that had been made in these fields up to the beginning of the modern era in the eighteenth century.

From earliest times man had appreciated his own bodily weakness and had used domesticated animals to aid him in his work. He had also tried to increase his productive effort by calling natural forces to his aid. He had discovered how to use the wind for pumping water and grinding corn and he had succeeded in harnessing water power for industrial purposes in a primitive manner. But the total amount of such aid was extremely small and the burden of doing the world's work fell upon men and beasts with frightful weight. Labor-saving machinery in a large sense, as illustrated by the steam engine and the internal-combustion engine and their applications, was still unknown.

A distinction should be made between labor-saving machinery and time-saving machinery. Time-saving machinery[1] enables the worker to increase his output per unit of time. Thus the person who operates a sewing machine can do more sewing per unit of time than he can with the hand needle, though the work of operating the machine for a given time may be as great as or greater than in hand sewing. If the machine is power driven it will also be a labor-saving machine. A farmer might work as hard using a modern steel spade as he would with an ancient wooden spade, but the amount of spading accomplished per hour would be greatly increased. Brief reflection will reveal that all handicraft tools are essentially time-saving devices.

The problem of transmitting information quickly and accurately is one that has occupied men's mind from earliest antiquity. Our North American Indians used puffs of smoke quite successfully for this purpose and the Greeks and Romans employed heliographs and semaphores for such work. It has remained for recent generations to solve this problem in a most successful and impressive manner. The telegraph, the telephone, and the radio, in conjunction with the printing press, constitute

[1] The man-hours expended in producing a modern automobile are between 200 and 300, depending upon circumstances.

the most remarkable means of disseminating information the world has ever witnessed. Basically, these developments are classified as time-saving devices. They have *accelerated* the entire industrial field to a much greater degree than is usually realized and their influence in increasing production has been profound. Because of its great and growing importance the transmission of intelligence is entitled to be considered as one of the major branches of industry.

8. The Great Inventions.—The industrial conditions described in the preceding chapter prevailed in England, and for that matter in many parts of continental Europe, up to about the middle of the eighteenth century. It is a somewhat remarkable fact that mankind had dwelt on the earth in a civilized state so long and yet had made such a very small advance in industrial methods. The great callings were agriculture and the textile industries and in both of these the implements were exceedingly primitive, most of them having changed but little in countless thousands of years, though in use (and still in use, for that matter) by all civilized and by many semicivilized nations. About this time (1750), however, there began a simultaneous movement in England and on the Continent looking toward the improvement of the implements of spinning and weaving. It is difficult to fix exact dates or even to give proper credit for the early conceptions of these improvements. Undoubtedly, many men had independently stumbled upon or thought out these new methods but had been unable to develop them into practical operating machines. In England, a great incentive was given to invention by the offer by the government of prizes of £50 and £25, respectively, for the first and next best improved method of spinning. The government's interest lay in the fact that the policy of foreign expansion, then under way, made it very desirable to secure more textiles for export, and the weak part of the industry was the spinning, which was then done on the primitive wheel. The many unsuccessful efforts to improve spinning and weaving culminated in the latter part of the century in what are usually known as the "four great inventions." In 1770 James Hargreaves, a weaver, patented the "spinning jenny," which consisted of a frame with a number of spindles side by side so that many threads could be spun at once. In 1771 Richard Arkwright, originally a barber, operated a spinning mill in which he successfully used his "water frame," so called because it was driven by water power, and the term "water twist" as the name of the product, still survives. In 1779 both these inventions were superseded by the invention of the "mule" by Samuel Crompton, a spinner, whose machine combined all the good features of its predecessors and was so called as being a hybrid offspring of these former inventions. Finally, the invention of the power loom, in 1785, by Dr. Edmund Cartwright, a Kentish parson, gave to the weaving industry what these other inventions had given to the spinning industry.

PLATE III.—The Hargreaves Spinning Jenny now preserved in the Kensington Museum, London.

PLATE IV.—An early Arkwright spinning machine now preserved in the Kensington Museum, London.

PLATE V.—The original Crompton Mule-Jenny now in the Kensington Museum, London.

These inventions of themselves would in time have revolutionized the textile industry; but the process was greatly hastened by the development of the steam engine by James Watt, in 1769. This new motor gave unlimited power and permitted the choice of location that allowed these new methods to spread with great rapidity, and the overthrow of the old methods of textile production was thereby greatly accelerated. In many places this overthrow was violent and complete though handicraft production continued elsewhere on a large scale for some time after the introduction of the new methods. In fact, handicraft production is as yet not entirely extinct though almost negligible as a competitive factor. This very significant change in manufacturing is known as the **Industrial Revolution** and the principles involved, although first applied extensively to the textile industry only, spread with amazing rapidity to all kinds of industry, changing and stimulating them to a very remarkable degree.

9. The Character of These Inventions.—Viewed from the standpoint of modern machine construction, these new machines were neither complex nor efficient, and their great importance lies in the application of the principles they involved. These principles are, as a rule, not well understood and are often confused with other phenomena incident to the change. For instance, this change is often spoken of as a change to *machine industry*. Now, as has been seen, machines were in use in the textile industry preceding the great inventions, and factories and factory systems of manufacture had already appeared. Nor is the extension of the principle of *division of labor* the fundamental change, but rather a corollary of the new methods. The real change in manufacturing methods can perhaps be best studied by taking a simple fundamental case as follows:

Suppose it be desired to drill four holes h, h, h, h, in a number of plates like A (Fig. 1) so that they bear a certain fixed relation to the edges of the plate; and suppose the operator to be equipped with the ordinary drilling machine which guides the drill so that it pierces the plate squarely. To drill these holes in *one* plate, with any degree of accuracy, requires a high degree of skill on the part of the operator; and to drill any number of such plates so that the spacing of the holes in them will correspond closely with those in the first plate requires a very high degree of manual skill, considerable time per plate, and is a costly operation.

Suppose, however, a skilled workman makes a so-called "drilling jig" (B, Fig. 1) in which the plate A can be securely clamped by set screws S, and in which all the plates can in turn be clamped in exactly the same position. The plate B contains four holes h', h', h', h', which have been very carefully located to correspond with the required location of the holes in A, and when A is held in B these holes h', h', h', h', are directly above the required location of holes h, h, h, h. The holes in B are surrounded by hardened steel rings or so-called "bushings" to prevent the drill D from wearing them unduly, and D fits the holes in these bushings accurately and closely.

Now, it is evident that almost any *unskilled* person can drill the plate A, when held in B, as accurately as the most skilled workman can without it. Further, he cannot drill the plate *inaccurately* if B is accurately made. True, he must have a slight amount of training in handling

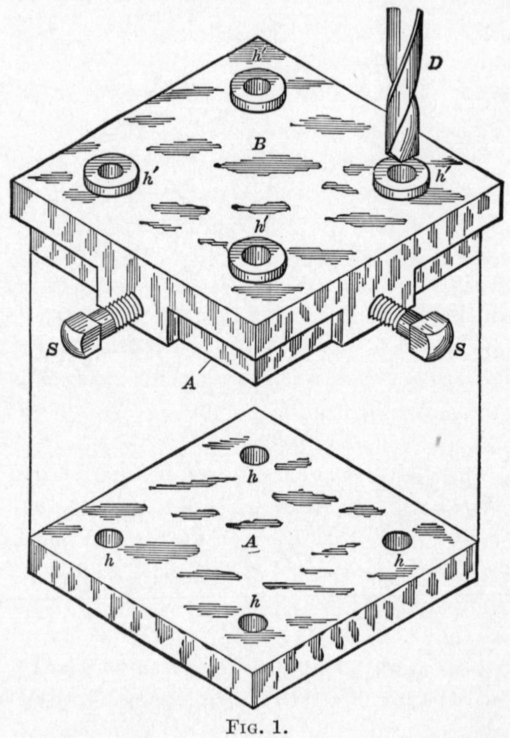

Fig. 1.

the drilling machine, but this is small and soon acquired. *The accuracy of the work no longer depends on the skill of the operator but on the accuracy of his tools.*

The principles illustrated above had been aptly called the "transfer of skill"[1] and it is to be especially noted that this principle has nothing to do with division of labor, though, as can be seen, it allows an extension of the same. Nor is the principle inherently applicable to *machines* alone; it can be and is applied to hand methods. True, most machines are constructed with this end in view, the drilling machine mentioned above, for instance, having this characteristic in so far as guiding the drill vertically is concerned. Transfer of skill is, in fact, the basic idea in all tool con-

[1] Strictly speaking, the term "skill" refers to either mental or manual ability. It has seemed expedient here to use it in the more commonly accepted sense of skill of hand.

struction. It was embodied in the first stone axe, and all succeeding improvements in tools of production were, essentially, advances in transfer of skill. Thus it was common practice in the early days of mass production in this country to apply the principle to hand work as follows: In making flat irregular-shaped pieces, such as are found in the locks of rifles, it was the practice first to make one such piece with great accuracy out of carbon steel. This piece was then hardened so that it could not be cut with the ordinary file, forming what is known as a "templet." If, now, this templet were held firmly against a piece of unhardened steel of somewhat greater outline dimensions, it formed a guide for filing this larger piece down to the exact outline of the templet. Since the file could not cut the templet, the workman could with speed and ease reduce the larger piece to the exact outline of the templet. He could not make it smaller than the templet in the plane where it adjoined the templet, though, of course, if the piece were very thick the surface which did not adjoin the templet might not be true to form because of inaccurate filing.

It is evident that for a given operation the more skill that is transferred to the machine the less is required in the operator. When nearly all the skill has been so transferred, but the machine still requires an attendant, it is called a "semiautomatic" machine. Turret lathes are excellent examples of this class of machinery.

In drilling the plate *A* without the jig the skilled mechanic must expend *thought* as well as skill in properly locating the holes. The unskilled operator using the jig need expend no thought regarding the location of the holes. That part of the mental labor has been done once for all by the tool maker. It appears, therefore, that a **transfer of thought or intelligence** can also be made from a person to a machine. If the quantity of parts to be made is sufficiently large to justify the expenditure, it is possible to make machines to which all the required skill and thought have been transferred and the machine does not require even an attendant, except to make adjustments. Such machines are known as **full automatic machines.** Automatic screw machines are excellent examples of a complete transfer of skill and thought.

Strictly speaking, there is no such thing as an automatic machine. All machines require constant attention of some kind, all require repairs at some time or another, and all require more or less adjustment. Many machines, however, will function properly, if once adjusted to their work, over considerable periods of time without human aid. But the fear held by some that self-perpetuating automatons may be created is without foundation scientifically or mechanically. The modern player piano is an excellent example of transfer of skill and thought. The thought of the composer is transferred quite accurately, but the transfer of playing skill is somewhat imperfect. It should be noted that composing and playing are not necessarily the accomplishments of any one man.

Care should be taken to distinguish clearly between *transmission* of intelligence, as illustrated in drawings, specifications, and written or spoken communication, in general, between *men* and the transfer of intelligence or thought from a skilled man to a *machine.* These principles, transfer of skill and transfer of thought, lie at the bottom of modern industrial methods. Under former and simpler methods of manufacture the machine was an aid to the worker's skill, the amount of skill that had been transferred being very small. In the new machines the transfer of skill and thought may be so great that little or none of these are required of the attendant worker. *The true significance of the Industrial Revolution, therefore, is that prior to that time the tool was always an adjunct to the skill of the worker. The great inventions carried transfer of skill to the point where the skill of the worker became an adjunct to the tool or machine.*

10. Extension of These Principles.—As before noted, it is difficult to ascribe exact credit for these improvements. They assumed great importance first in the textile industries, since these were the most important manufacturing interests in England at that time. But similar changes took place either simultaneously, or shortly after, in all lines of work, especially in the metal-working industries. In a series of articles in the *Engineering Magazine,* for 1899, Henry Roland gives a very interesting and instructive account of the rise of these principles in machine tools in which he credits Samuel Bentham with first completely comprehending the full significance of the tool maker's art about 1791. The application of these principles to the design of **machine tools,** so called, is of greatest importance since the production of all machinery is dependent upon these **master tools of industry.** No doubt the mechanical problems involved in building the steam engine did much to facilitate the development of these new tools and the progress made in the tool makers' art since the invention of the steam engine of itself distinguishes this era from all others that have preceded it. These machine tools are the lathe and its derivatives (the boring mill and the drilling machine) the planing machine, the milling machine, and the modern precision grinding machine which has made refined measurements possible. The development of the lathe is the most striking example of this progress and will serve best to illustrate the application of transfer of skill in these implements.

Figure *A* (Plate VI) shows the original oriental lathe in which the piece of work to be "turned" into a circular shape is rotated alternately from and toward the operator by means of a bow the string of which is passed once around the piece. The cutting is performed only during rotation toward the operator, the tool being held by the hand and steadied upon a "rest." Figure *B* shows the occidental adaptation of this machine which probably reached Europe through the Moors. The

Plate VI.—Increase of transfer of skill as illustrated in the development of the lathe.

reciprocating rotary motion is obtained through a treadle and the overhead spring pole, both hands being thus free for holding the turning tool. Lathes of this kind were quite common in New England 80 years ago. The next great improvement, which is not illustrated, was the introduction of continuous rotation through the use of the crank, the connecting rod, and the belt as seen in the ordinary sewing machines. By these means the reciprocating motion of the treadle is transformed into continuous rotation of the flywheel from which the spindle upon which the work is mounted can be driven by a belt as in all modern foot-power lathes.

Even with this improvement, considerable skill of hand was still required to hold and direct the cutting tool. The first great step in transfer of skill in this machine is found in the small lathe built by Henry Maudslay about 1800, illustrated in Fig. *C* (Plate VI) and carefully preserved in the Kensington Museum in London. The machine is made entirely of iron. The cutting tool, as can be seen, is clamped firmly to a carriage or saddle which, in turn, is guided longitudinally along the bed so that it can move only in a direction parallel to the axis of the piece to be machined. The cutting tool is adjustable at right angles to this axis. The saddle is moved longitudinally along the bed by a "lead" screw so that if the tool is once set and the lead screw put into operation, a true cylinder is formed automatically, whereas it required a high degree of skill to produce the same cylinder with the hand tool. This little lathe, in fact, embodies all of the fundamental principles of modern standard lathes of whatever size. The next great step in transfer of skill was the turret of Henry Stone, of New Hampshire, illustrated in Fig. *D* (Plate VI). In this machine a series of tools is securely fastened equidistantly upon a revolving turret so that any tool can be brought into operation upon the work which is fed through the hollow spindle while the required series of operations is performed upon it. *The skill necessary to set and adjust the tools is performed once for all by a skilled mechanic and thereafter almost anyone can do the required work.* This was the first **semiautomatic** lathe and corresponds in point of development to the Hargreaves spinning jenny. The next and last great step in this development was the application by Christopher Miner Spencer, of Connecticut, of an adjustable cam wheel or **brain wheel,** as it is sometimes called, to the automatic operation of the turret, thus obviating the need of an attendant and making the machine fully automatic through *transfer of intelligence.* One of Spencer's first automatics is shown in Fig. *E* (Plate VI) where the brain wheel is easily recognizable. A modern automatic lathe is shown in Fig. *F* (Plate VI). Though more highly developed than that shown in Fig. *E*, basically it is identical and depends for its principal functions upon Maudslay's slide rest, Stone's turret, and Spencer's cam wheel.

These were the great epoch-making inventions in machine construction. Perhaps invention is not the correct term to use in this connection, as no doubt all of these elements had been thought of long before by other people; but to these three men, at least, belongs the credit of making them working possibilities. These three elements, namely the

Plate VII.—A turret-type drilling and boring machine performing a total of 38 drilling, core-drilling, countersinking, rough and finish boring, rough and finish reaming, counterboring, spot facing and milling operations upon 120 single-bore cylinder blocks per hour. The machine has 5 vertical and 3 horizontal drilling heads and one milling unit. Seventy-six operations, 38 on each of two blocks, are performed with every cycle of the machine. (*Courtesy of National Automatic Tool Company.*)

slide rest, the turret, and Spencer's brain wheel for operating the combination of the first two are, perhaps, more used in complex automatic and semiautomatic machinery than any other machine elements. Plate VII shows a modern application of these principles. In this machine the work is mounted on the several *stations* of the turret. The drilling heads, each of which carries several drills, are mounted upon the sliding members, some of which in this machine are placed in a vertical position and some in a horizontal position. The brain wheel, which is enclosed in the framework, controls the vertical and horizontal movements of the drilling heads and rotates the turret at the proper time. The attendant is required simply to take the finished work from the turret at the end of the cycle of operations and to fasten two unfinished cylinders in place. Of course, it will not pay to operate such a machine unless the number of holes to be drilled is very great.

As has been noted, such machinery is often spoken of as "labor-saving" machinery but this term is not quite correct. It may be more laborious work to operate a semiautomatic lathe than it would be to do the same operations upon a standard lathe. The output of the semi-automatic machine is, however, much greater, hence, speaking accurately, it is a *time-saving* machine. It is labor-saving only because it is driven by a power-producing prime mover. The full automatic machine is both a *time-saving* and a *labor-saving* machine, that is to say, the parallel development of transfer of skill and of sources of power as noted in Art. 7 should be kept clearly in mind. As will be shown later, just as there may be time-saving machines so there may also be *time-saving methods.*

11. The Inventions of the Nineteenth and Twentieth Centuries.—The "great inventions" and that of the steam engine were followed by a series of inventions and applications of scientific discoveries unparalleled in rapidity in the history of mankind. Between the construction of the Morse telegraph in 1844 and the development of wireless telephony in 1914 there appeared the sewing machine, the knitting machine, the telephone, the electric generator, the electric motor, the electric transformer, the electric light, the gas engine, the Diesel engine, the steam turbine, the automobile, the submarine, the airplane, the Bessemer converter, the harvester, wireless telegraphy, the phonograph, the linotype, rayon, and so on, through an almost endless list of new devices and scientific applications.

Many of these inventions are interdependent and cumulative. Thus the automobile consists of a number of important inventions such as the gas engine, the pneumatic tire, electric ignition, etc. And one invention may render obsolete others in the same field. Thus Watts's reciprocating steam engine, on the development of which an infinite amount of time and energy were expended, reached its maximum size and efficiency about 1900, and has been pushed into the background, except for small sizes and special conditions, by the gas engine, the Diesel engine, and the steam turbine. The sewing machine, on the other hand, has changed but little in its basic principles in many years.

While it is not likely that this rate of inventive progress will continue predictions are unwise. Thus the field of synthetic chemistry is making rapid strides. The production of synthetic cloth is now commonplace and the production of synthetic foods, on which a start has been made, might cause a serious dislocation in some of our agricultural and industrial methods.

References

GASKELL, P.: "The Manufacturing Population of England."
GIBBINS, H. DEB.: "The Industrial History of England."
ROE, JOSEPH: "English and American Tool Builders."
ROLAND, HENRY: "The Revolution in the Machine Shop," *Eng. Mag.*, 1899.
TAYLOR, R. W. COOKE: "History of the Factory System."
———: "Modern Factory System."
USHER, A. P.: "A History of Mechanical Inventions."

CHAPTER III

THE ECONOMIC AND SOCIAL EFFECTS OF INVENTIONS

12. Division of Industry.—The effects of the great inventions and the inventions that followed and of the steam engine were many and far-reaching as well as complex. A consideration of the most important of these changes is necessary to a full understanding of modern conditions. One of the first and most significant effects was the completion of the separation of agriculture from the field of mechanic arts, which had already started under handicraft production. Today this separation is quite complete, practically all of the tools and appliances used by the farmer being now made in factories, and at present it appears that even the farmer's faithful helper, the horse, may be superseded by the factory-made tractor. The cotton and wool which the farmer raises are manufactured into clothing by the mechanic-arts group and returned to the farmer through a complex system of middlemen. Much of the food that he produces is preserved in factories before being put upon the market where he and others may purchase it. The roads and bridges over which he travels are built by engineers and mechanics, as are also the automobiles and trucks in which he traverses them. His house and furniture, his machinery for pumping and conveying water are built by the mechanic-arts workers. He is even dependent upon scientific workers for much of his necessary knowledge concerning crops and pests that prey upon them. This separation, therefore, is not merely a mechanical division of employment; it involves intricate economic problems. The legislation that may be helpful to the mechanic may be hurtful to the farmer and vice versa. Agriculture, of course, has been rendered more efficient through the advances made in the industrial arts and the farmer has shared, in some degree, the general uplift in living conditions. But obviously there is much to be done before the agriculturist is elevated to the economic level of some of our industrial workers.

The development of the steam engine, the steam turbine, and the internal-combustion engine and their application to railroads, steamships, and other means of transportation have greatly accentuated the importance of transportation as an industrial factor. In common with agriculture, the tools and appliances of transportation are built by the mechanic-arts group, but the actual work of transportation has become so vast and so important as to constitute an independent function. This has resulted in a class-conscious group of workers and has also necessitated special governmental regulation in an effort to insure fair conditions within and without the field. The mechanical growth in the machinery of transportation is noteworthy. The first locomotives weighed 3 or 4 tons, while a modern freight locomotive of largest size weighs from 300 to 400 tons. Yet these larger machines require no more men for their operation than did the original machines. The economic gain in haulage is self-evident. In a similar manner, the telegraph, the telephone, and the radio have created a field of service that already stands apart from all other industrial activities as an economic factor. Modern life would be impossible without these means of communication, and this development has consequently come also under more or less governmental regulation.

Lastly, the great development in central stations supplying light, heat, and power should be noted. The total prime-mover capacity actually installed in the United States, including automobiles, is well over one billion horse power. This is sufficient to give every man, woman, and child physical service equivalent to that which could be rendered by 150 slaves. And the power-operated machinery in the United States alone is doing more work daily than could be performed by all the able-bodied men in the world working industriously from sunrise to sunset. Statistics show that national per capita wealth is closely connected with developed prime-mover capacity. The per capita wealth of the United States bears the same ratio to the per capita wealth of Great Britain as the developed horse power here does to the developed horse power there —a result that might be expected. The prime-mover capacity of the United States is four times as great as that of Great Britain or Germany and ten times as great as that of France. These are significant figures and obviously the field of power production is of the greatest economic significance. This field also is separating itself from the main stem of industry as formerly conceived, and because of its great importance to the national welfare it also is being subjected to close governmental scrutiny and regulation. At present, therefore, the outstanding divisions of productive industry are **agriculture, manufacturing, transportation, communication,** and **power production.** There are, of course, many other important callings that greatly affect our productive capacity. Without preventive medicine and its ally, sanitary engineering, modern cities would not be habitable. But for the purpose of this work the foregoing classification will be found to be sufficient.

13. Separation of the Worker from the Tools of Industry.—The changes outlined in the preceding article were changes in the fabric of industry itself. Equally great and more important changes have been made by the new methods in the status of the worker. The first and most significant change was that regarding the ownership of the tools of industry. Until the Industrial Revolution the tools of handicraft industry were simple and, in general, it was possible for anyone to secure the implements of his calling. But *capital* was necessary to build the new textile machinery, the lathe, the boring mill, the steam engine or the water-driven textile mill. No longer was it possible for almost anyone to secure the implements of his trade. The new methods, therefore, hastened the changes foreshadowed by the old handicraft factories where the industry was supported and controlled by capital and the worker was a wage-earner pure and simple, and unsupported by an auxiliary calling such as agriculture. In agriculture, the worker, for the most part, still owns the implements of his calling, but he no longer *makes* them himself. And in the basic mechanic-arts industries, the worker becomes increasingly dependent upon capital for his tools. A few years ago an ordinary machinist could make his own outfit of hand tools such as squares, calipers, etc., with satisfaction to himself and his employer. Today the basic standards of measurement, gages, and micrometers are highly specialized products and so costly that they must be furnished by the employer. Indeed, in some instances, the employer prefers to furnish all hand tools in order to be sure they are of first-class quality. Nor is this movement confined to the factory. Office equipment in the form of typewriters, adding and computing machines, and even bookkeeping machines have widened the gap between the office worker and ownership of equipment. The office worker of today does not even supply or own the pencil with which he works.

This feature of modern industry has been very severely criticized and there is no doubt much justification for this criticism. The gap between the industrial worker and the ownership of the tools with which he earns his daily bread has steadily widened until today the vast majority of industrial workers are wholly dependent upon capital for employment. The industrial worker is no longer an independent self-supporting economic unit as in handicraft days, but is dependent upon others for a *chance* to exist. If this is to continue, capital must see to it that this chance to exist is assured and safeguarded. Industry must be conducted from a somewhat broader and more humane standpoint than the simple acquisition of profits. And fortunately, there appears to be a growing sentiment among employers of labor in this direction.

During the prosperous years before 1929, a large number of working people invested their savings in stocks and bonds of corporations. In many cases this was made possible through very advantageous opportunities offered by the owners to their employees. It is sometimes stated that through this method workers may again control, in some degree, the tools of industry. There is little, however, in our experience with American stock corporations to warrant great hope that this may come about, though no doubt the tendency is a hopeful sign.

It should be remarked in passing that this separation of the worker from the ownership of his tools is the center of attack by socialists and communists upon our present industrial and social order. The student of American industrial organization should watch and study with care the vast experiment now being tried by the Soviet government in Russia with state-owned and -controlled industrial and agricultural equipment. Similar experiments upon a small scale have, in general, proved to be failures and there are reasons for believing that the Soviet experiment will go the way of all others. But it should be remembered that industry and government have both been socialized not a little in this country, and should the Soviet effort succeed in even a partial degree it may have strong repercussive effects upon our social and industrial order. It is equally important to study the results of the dictatorships in Italy and Germany, where free enterprise has been severely checked, since the tendency of federal legislation at the present time is in that direction.

Equally important is the tendency for ownership to divorce itself from the actual management of industry. As productive industry becomes more scientific and more highly organized it becomes increasingly necessary to intrust the management of such enterprises to technical men and specialists who have been specially trained for such duties. As a result there has grown up in this country a sort of "absentee landlordism" wherein those who actually operate industries and to whom the worker must look for employment may have little or no share in the ownership of the plant. This is particularly the case where the industry for one reason or another is controlled by a bank, whose primary interest is usually that of securing dividends.

14. Degradation of Labor.—Following closely upon the introduction of the new textile machinery the old handicraft workman found that the skill he had acquired was almost useless as a marketable product, since the new machines could be operated by unskilled workmen. In many cases, young boys and girls were sufficiently strong and intelligent to master the operations quickly. Since industry was limited and, furthermore, since it is difficult for a mechanic to change his calling, practically the entire textile-producing population was **degraded;** that is, the market value of their skill and labor was reduced to that of unskilled girls and boys who could operate the new machines. In some cases, in fact, the handicraft trade soon ceased to be an industrial factor, so radical was the change. This so-called "degradation of labor" is one of the first results of the introduction of transfer of skill. Thus, in introducing the drilling jig illustrated in Fig. 1, the skilled mechanic who formerly drilled the plates is brought into direct economic competition with the boy who can use the jig.

In the beginning of the new industrial era, this effect was much more marked than at any time since, because practically the entire industrial field, which was limited, was very quickly affected. But as the field of industry has broadened, it has become more and more difficult to make any radical change that will affect all of industry. Nevertheless, the same effect is still produced in some degree whenever transfer of skill or advanced methods of production or management are introduced. As will appear, all classes of men are benefited, in the long run, by methods that multiply productive power; but these beneficial effects often affect others outside of the industry in which the change is made at the expense of those directly concerned, and for this reason the worker is naturally opposed to the introduction of labor-saving or time-saving machinery that directly affects his calling. Thus Hargreave's house was mobbed and his first machine was destroyed by his neighbors, and the industrial worker of today, instinctively feeling hostility to new methods, is often inclined to be no less opposed to them. It is of little use to tell him that posterity will be benefited by the improved methods; he is concerned more largely with his present economic and social status.

As has been pointed out in Art. 13, these tendencies are inherent in all advances in the tools of industry. The extreme of such advances appears when the new processes are entirely automatic in character and even the operator is no longer needed. In such a case the industry passes into the hands of an entirely different class of workers, namely, those who can *build* and *adjust* such machinery, and the displacement of the former workers is complete. The term **technological unemployment** has come into use to designate the displacement of industrial workers by new and advanced processes and methods.

The problem is intensified by the difficulty experienced in transferring skilled or even semiskilled workers to new kinds of industry. Machinists for instance cannot and do not wish to do carpentry work. Once a skilled man has worked for some time at any specialized productive process he loses adaptability to other processes, unless they are closely related to his former calling. This difficulty increases with increase in skill and diminishes with decrease in skill upon the part of the worker. When, therefore, a calling is eliminated, as it may be by advanced mechanical or chemical processes, the situation of the displaced workers may be desperate indeed and degradation of the worst kind may befall them.

15. The Extension of the Field of Labor.—A consideration of the use of the drilling jig in Fig. 1 will make evident the fact that the unskilled person who is thus brought into the industry could otherwise have no part in such productive processes. His contribution would necessarily be confined to such manual work as requires brawn, but little or no skill.

The new methods of production have enabled many unskilled people to take an important part in many industrial fields formerly occupied solely by skilled workers. Today, in nearly every large manufacturing industry, the unskilled or semiskilled labor greatly outnumbers the skilled, and products of great accuracy and high finish are turned out by such organizations. This principle of **extension of the field of labor** is a broad one. As more and more skill and thought have been transferred to hand and machine tools, it has become increasingly easy for men and women to take part in what was formerly entirely skilled industry. The *actual* production of shoes, automobiles, watches, typewriters, etc., is conducted almost entirely by semiskilled labor.

This influence has not been confined to industries that already existed but has made possible the existence of many new industries. The automobile, the telephone, the sewing machine, and countless other articles now considered necessities of daily life are obtainable by the majority of people solely because the new methods of production have multiplied and cheapened production, the demand for these articles opening up new fields of manufacturing, with consequent further extension of the field of labor. It is fortunate that this is so because, as the tools and methods of production become increasingly efficient and as transfer of skill is still further extended, it is obvious that fewer and fewer men are required, proportionately, to produce the volume of goods of any one kind that can be consumed. The excess workers must be absorbed in new fields of production and this is exactly what is taking place, as illustrated by the growth of such industries as automobile manufacture. The query naturally arises as to the extent to which this movement can be carried. Several limiting influences may be noted. (1) No doubt there are limits to the efficiency of modern productive methods. These limits have already appeared in some industries and they will be discussed in a succeeding section. (2) There may be a decrease in the rate at which population will increase; in fact this has already occurred in this country. And (3) the movement may go on until we reach the limit of our land and other resources on which life itself is based; or combinations of these influences may limit the expansion.

16. The Elevation of Labor.—While the introduction of these new methods may degrade certain classes of labor, they may, on the other hand, **elevate** others. The skilled mechanic that has been engaged in drilling the plate in Fig. 1 is not necessarily degraded by the introduction of the drilling jig, because his skill can be utilized to *make* such tools; and this class of labor, namely, the skilled workers in the metal trades, has, on the whole, usually been benefited, rather than otherwise, by the new methods, though at times trying periods of readjustment have ensued upon the introduction of labor-saving machinery into their own industry.

Again, the unskilled worker who is taken from low-paid menial employment and taught to operate a semiautomatic machine can usually earn more money than formerly and be elevated to a higher plane. The history of manufacturing in New England shows very clearly the absorption into the manufacturing industries of the successive waves of immigration of unskilled labor that have from time to time moved into these states. The descendants of immigrants who entered New England industry as laborers and machine tenders now form a large part of the substantial middle class of that section. Of course there are limits to the absorbing power of industry, and there can be no doubt but that the present policy of restricting immigration is a wise one.

17. Increased Production and Decreased Cost.—Manifestly, these new methods have multiplied man's productive power manyfold, enabling him to produce more per unit of time, with a corresponding reduction in the cost of production. This feature, and the principles of elevation of labor and the extension of the field of labor, more than compensate, *in the long run,* for the effects of degradation of labor, though, as before noted, the many benefit at the expense of the few. These new methods, furthermore, tend constantly to tear old trades and methods apart, substituting other methods, operated perhaps by a different class of workers. Old trades and methods tend constantly to disintegrate or disappear with consequent hardship, perhaps, to those affected. New processes, new products, and, consequently, new callings are constantly appearing and no trade or calling is exempt from the probability of being modified or even destroyed. Consider the introduction of rayon for silk, the kerosene lamp for the tallow candle, and again the electric light for the gas jet and the kerosene lamp, and the rapidity of these changes is obvious. At the present moment, electric welding threatens to make marked changes in the callings of pattern making, foundry work, and structural steel working, and the automobile has largely superseded the horse in a quarter of a century.

All such changes draw in their wake significant industrial and social changes. Human progress, apparently, cannot take place without someone's suffering.[1] Theoretically, all should be greatly benefited by these improved methods, and one important reason why this has not always been the case lies, not in the processes themselves, but in the fact that their net result is solely to *increase production.* They do not carry with them inherently any influences tending to rearrange the *distribution* of the increased profits derived from them, or to offset the effects of the fierce competition rendered possible because of this increase in productive capacity. Invention and its results always act quickly; social and political changes move more slowly. The law of supply and demand operated quickly under the older and simpler methods. The complexity of modern methods tends to make these laws act much more sluggishly. From the very beginning of the industrial revolution there has been a constant struggle to secure equitable methods of distributing

[1] TAYLOR, R. W. COOKE, "The Factory System and Factory Acts"; and "Modern Factory System," Chaps. VI and VII.

industrial benefits against constant distortion of these methods by new inventions and industrial changes. And the struggle still persists.

18. Immediate Results of the Industrial Revolution.—It will be remembered that at the time of this great industrial change, the laborer was unprotected by either legal statutes or mutual protective societies of any kind. The first effect of the new methods, therefore, was a heartless enforcement of the first two principles enumerated above, the worker being torn suddenly from the tools of production, and degradation of labor of the worst kind resulting. No slavery that ever existed could have been worse than that into which the textile workers of England were quickly thrown, and it is difficult, even allowing for the hard spirit of the times, to account for the atrocities inflicted upon them by those into whose hands the control of industry fell. An account of these inflictions is out of place in this treatise, but the history of the change should be carefully read and pondered by every man before expressing too positive an opinion regarding labor matters. Some little extenuation can be found for the government and the better classes which allowed this free "exploitation of labor" in the situation in which England was placed at the time. First, she was continually engaged in foreign wars which not only occupied the attention of the ruling class, but made necessary large sums of money which were more readily available under the new methods. Second, but no less important, were the peculiar views on political economy then in vogue.

National ideals, no doubt, entered largely into the apparently complacent attitude assumed by many people toward conditions that would be considered atrocious judged by any modern standards. It was the day of *laissez-faire*, and people apparently believed that these conditions were necessary, or, if curable, they would cure themselves. As will be seen, it was exceedingly difficult for the reformer, who naturally appeared, to get a hearing, even looking to the amelioration of the hardships of the working classes.

Darwin's law of the "survival of the fittest" and the Malthusian doctrine of overpopulation seem also at later times to have made a deep impression on the existing national ideals.

The effects of these new methods have not been so swift or so drastic in other lines of industry. As the field of industry broadened it became more stable and possessed of greater inertia against sudden changes. A generation ago, even, the old methods were still to be seen in competition with the new. But eventually the new ideas have prevailed and handicraft as an important factor in production has practically ceased to exist.

19. The Industrial Revolution in the United States.—It was quite natural that the early settlers in this country should bring with them the simple handicraft methods in use in Europe when they migrated. It was equally natural that the methods introduced by the Industrial Revolution should also find their way across the Atlantic. The British government was quick to see the great commercial advantage of the new machines, and stringent laws were passed prohibiting the exportation of machines or drawings to the British colonies or foreign countries. Several attempts were made in America, however, to establish the new methods, but with indifferent success, until Samuel Slater, a young Englishman who had worked for Strutt, a former partner of Arkwright, built, in 1790, some Arkwright spinning machines for the firm of Almy and Brown of Pawtucket, Rhode Island. These machines operated 72 spindles and were housed in the building shown in the Frontispiece. While other spinning machines were built at about the same time, the success of the Slater mill was so pronounced that it has usually been taken as marking the introduction of the new factory system into this country, and Slater has been called "the father of American manufactures." The first mill[1] in the world wherein textiles were produced from the raw material under one roof was built in Waltham in 1814.

These early mills and factories were, naturally, modeled after their English prototypes, and, like them, their size was usually governed by the available water power. Handicraft and handicraft factories flourished for many years in other callings, though the colonists very early developed that great skill in manufacturing which has made New England famous, and the progress of the factory system during the first part of the nineteenth century was comparatively slow.

The first authoritative information on this point is found in the Census of the United States of 1850. At that time the term "manufacturing" was broadly defined as including any mechanical operations, and in addition to organized factories it included the building trades and hand manufactures. The gross value of these products was recorded as half a billion dollars and the average output for all establishments for 1849 is recorded as $4,300. During this early period, also, other features of our industrial life became firmly rooted. A merchant class, carrying on trade both at home and abroad, developed rapidly and, as a consequence, there arose in connection with manufacturing the combination of manufacturer, transporter, wholesaler, and retailer that is so marked a feature of our industrial life. As trade increased and factories grew in size, the problems of financing gave rise to a group whose sole business it is to provide financial means for carrying on manufacturing and mercantile operations.

The second half of the nineteenth century saw a tremendous expansion of American industry, during which the United States rose from an inferior industrial position to the foremost place among the nations of the world, as to both value and range of product. There were several

[1] WRIGHT, CARROLL D., "The Industrial Revolution of the United States," p. 131.

reasons for this great growth. (1) A rapidly growing population created an ever-expanding home market. (2) During this period the country was more fully explored and found to be exceedingly rich in natural resources, particularly in fruitful land and in deposits of coal and iron. (3) More important still has been the avidity with which American inventors, engineers, and manufacturers have grasped the significance of transfer of skill and the openness of mind with which they have received the best talent from other countries. Mass production, which utilizes to the full these new manufacturing methods and makes possible the extended use of division of labor, is essentially an American development. The American method of manufacturing in large quantities standardized, interchangeable parts, as illustrated in the production of watches, sewing machines, harvesting machinery, automobiles, etc., is the most striking departure that American manufacture has made from European methods, which still depend to a large degree upon skill of hand. By 1899 the value of the manufactured products of the United States had risen to ten billions of dollars, of which only one-tenth was produced by hand trades. The day of large enterprises had arrived. In 1904, 79.3 per cent of the manufactured product of the United States came from factories whose annual output was valued at $100,000 or more, while in 1929, the output of such factories had risen to 93.8 per cent of the national production. This phase of American industry is discussed more fully later on.

A most important factor in the rise of the factory system during this period was the development of the steam engine, which removed the limitations on the size of the plant. The influence of this prime mover was particularly marked after the introduction of the dynamo and the electrical distribution of energy. This, with the electric light, has revolutionized factory construction as compared to the small, water-driven plants of a century ago. The application of the steam engine to rail and water transportation has also been of great importance, not only as regards the marketing of finished goods but also as a means of bringing the raw materials of production to manufacturing centers. Obviously, the new power-driven spinning and weaving machines had, in the beginning, to be grouped close to the source of power. In the beginning, water power was the only source available, but as steam power came into use the location of factories was not so restricted. With improved means of transportation the congregation of men and machines was not only rendered economically possible, but to the increased efficiency of productive methods was added much more effective means of distributing the product. Local competition of handicraftsmen, at a distance from the factory that would have protected them under the old methods of transportation, was thus obliterated. Improvements in methods of transportation have kept pace with improvement in productive processes, since the new productive methods themselves were soon applied to the making of machinery of transportation.

To these influences have been added those of the telegraph, the telephone, the radio, and other improved methods of communication. The latest addition to our industrial machinery, namely, the airplane, is still too young to be truly evaluated. But unless all signs fail it also will take its place as one of the most advanced methods of transportation for certain purposes. These are commercial possibilities, and of almost universal use and convenience, solely because of modern productive methods. Improvements in facilities for transportation or communicating intelligence, therefore, aid productive processes, and these in turn make transportation and communication more efficient, the entire system of production and distribution constituting a most remarkable development unlike anything that has ever gone before. It should be noted that the *development of tools of production*, the development of *sources of power*, and the *development of means of rapid communication* are three of man's most ancient problems that have constantly challenged his efforts. The present-day simultaneous development of these three fields to a degree undreamed of by our ancestors has produced an industrial system as marvelously efficient as it is difficult to control.

20. The Human Element in American Industry.—The evil effects of the new system were never so bad in America as in England, for obvious reasons. The freedom of a new country and the temper of the people were both opposed to such a state of affairs; and before the arrival of large numbers of helpless aliens, labor organization and labor legislation had come to the rescue and the beneficial effects of the new methods enumerated above began to be felt. Nevertheless, as the older states became more and more thickly populated, the evil effects became more pressing, and the highest of statesmanship will be needed to show a way out of these difficulties if the system is to remain and fair and equitable distribution of its advantages is to be instituted.

These oppressive influences and effects are, of course, not so marked as formerly, partly because the industrial field is much larger and hence not so easily disturbed; but they still are, and must always remain, characteristic features of transfer of skill and transfer of thought, and must always be reckoned with in judging the effects of labor-saving machines or processes. A brief review of the progress of human relations in our factory system may be of interest at this point.

The early factories, as has been noted, were modeled after those in England. Textile mills naturally were located at water-power sites and around these grew up the "mill village" so typical of New England a century ago. When factories of other kinds grew up in the towns, they were, of necessity, small in size, and in the beginning rather primitive in character. The owner was usually the manager also, and his personality dominated the enterprise. He superintended production and disposed of the product. He knew personally every man in his employ and often the members of every family as well. The workers and their families were permanent residents of the town and migration of workers as seen today was little known. Personal relations between the manager and his men were necessarily close, since handicraft skill was still important. Industry was still regarded as largely vocational, with the manager as the directing mind; scientific methods as now understood not having, as yet, developed.

When such management was enlightened and kindly the workers were, no doubt, happy and contented. But such was not always the case. The hours of labor were long, factories were cheerless, and the management often only too arbitrary and overbearing. Labor troubles were frequent even in colonial days, though usually local in character. Trade associations similar to those that had long existed in the mother country had also long existed in America and foreshadowed the modern labor unions of today. For many years after the introduction of the new methods, however, the door of opportunity stood open to the more efficient of the workers. It was still possible for the thrifty and skillful to rise to be master workers and owners. It was only when the influences discussed in the first section of this chapter began to be effective in a large way, and many workers found themselves separated from the ownership of the tools of industry, that modern labor unionism really began. The first labor union that involved more than one trade was the Mechanics' Union of Trade Associations, organized in Philadelphia in 1827, and was the result of a strike among the carpenters to obtain a 10-hour day.

It should be remembered that the first half of the nineteenth century was a period of great agitation for reform, with a certain amount of real moral awakening. The communistic doctrines of Robert Owen and his experimental village at New Harmony, Indiana, no doubt did much to stir men's minds to strive for better conditions, and such problems as suffrage, slavery, the militia system, schools, bankruptcy laws, and many others were much discussed and legislation concerning them enacted. This broadening view undoubtedly led eventually to the Civil War. During this first half of the century, labor problems were also prominent, but labor organizations led a somewhat checkered career. When times were good and work plentiful they naturally strengthened themselves and, when business was depressed, they quite as naturally declined in power, and there was much confusion as to what were the best methods of organization and what the aims of such organizations should be. In fact this confusion still exists.

The second half of the nineteenth century, however, ushered in a new era in industry. The expansion of the entire industrial field and the increase in the size of factories soon made it evident that industry was to be owned and largely controlled by capital. The door of opportunity, so far as individual ownership was concerned, was closed to the vast majority of workers. By the end of the century this was fully recognized. A famous labor leader, John Mitchell, writing about that time, said:

> The average wage-earner has made up his mind that he must remain a wage-earner. He has given up the hope of a kingdom to come where he himself will be a capitalist, and he asks the reward for his work to be given him as a workingman. Singly, he has been too weak to enforce his just demands, and he has sought strength in union and has associated himself into labor organizations.

This new point slowly impressed upon the worker's mind during the early days of the new era became a conviction by 1850, and modern trade unionism began to take form. The issues of shorter hours, higher pay, the closed shop, the restriction of apprentices, and secrecy of proceedings which now form the major gospel of unionism rose above all other reform efforts of the first half century, with the strike and boycott as the principal offensive measures. Isolated unions were organized into national bodies and these again into consolidated groups culminating in such organizations as the American Federation of Labor. Obviously, this movement was accelerated by the fact that the new and larger enterprises brought together larger groups of workers with common needs and problems. The result was inevitable. The writer is neither defending nor advocating labor unionism, but simply desires to point out that it is a perfectly natural result of the new industrial day and no man should assume to judge this or any other movement in the industrial field without careful study of the causes that gave rise to it.

An important factor in the development of industry during the last 80 years has been the immigration of foreigners, who found ready employment in our great basic industries. This, also, was a considerable factor in the growth of labor unionism, since in this immigration lay, also, the possibilities of "degradation" (see Art. 14) in connection with new and modern processes. The extent of the migration should be noted, since it is an important factor in our industrial background.

The U. S. Census of 1930 reports the total number of persons "gainfully employed" as 48,829,920 out of a total population of 122,775,046. Of these 35,173,370 were native-born, 7,411,127 were born in other countries, and 6,245,423 were negroes and other non-whites. Many of our native-born are, of course, of foreign parentage. A study made in 1917 reported that 56[1] distinct nationalities were represented in American industry. These immigrants have no doubt contributed much to our

[1] LAUCK, W. J., and E. SYDENSTRICKER, "Conditions of Labor in American Industries."

general culture and they have made our mass-production industries possible. The percentage of persons of foreign birth is probably much higher in the basic industries, such as steel, automobile construction, and other mass-production enterprises than the foregoing data would indicate. The presence of this large and, as yet, unassimilated foreign population has, however, introduced industrial problems that fully justify the limitation of immigration.

21. Modern Ownership and Management.—The new industrial methods quite naturally affected the ownership of industry. While there is still a large number of individual owners, one of the outstanding features of modern industry is corporate ownership, made necessary by the increased capital needed for modern enterprises. The problems and tendencies of large industries will be more fully discussed in a succeeding chapter. Now, just as changed conditions led to a new development of organizations among workers, so they also brought about organizations among employers. There are quite a number of these employers' organizations and some, like the National Association of Manufacturers, are quite powerful. For the most part, they are organized for mutual protection and in some cases they are openly opposed to the labor unions. Industry has, therefore, changed greatly from the old patriarchal days of small enterprises and close, friendly contact between employer and employee to a state where often the worker is totally unknown to his employer except as a *numbered* individual and where labor and capital often stand opposed and fully organized with little sympathy existing between the two groups.

The second half of the nineteenth century brought also a great change in industrial management. Necessarily, the great increase in the size of individual enterprises suggested new and more elaborate methods of executive control. But aside from this, the constant and rapid growth of scientific thought and its wide application to industrial problems have profoundly affected all old ideas of business management and executive control. This phase of our industrial development will also be discussed at length in succeeding chapters.

22. Resultant Effects of Modern Methods.—The resultant effects of the application of modern productive methods have been much debated. Unquestionably they have vastly increased the national wealth and have raised the general standard of living in this country. The growth of new industries and the consequent extension of the field of labor appear to have balanced, so far, the baneful effects due to displacement of workers by new methods. But it cannot be denied that labor has become increasingly dependent upon capital and modern industrial life is surely more complex and more difficult to control than it was 100 years ago. These industrial changes, also, have been greatly intensified by new and more efficient methods of management which will be discussed in later sections of this book. It is advisable, therefore, to defer extended discussion of these resultant effects until these changes in management have been considered; but the student who so desires will find such a discussion in Chaps. IX and X.

23. Corrective Influences.—It is a mistake to assume, as is often done, that practically all industrial reforms have come as the result of the activities of labor unions. The labor unions have never until recently controlled directly a large percentage of industrial workers, but the sympathetic influence of the unions has often been powerful. It is estimated[1] that in 1900 only 4 per cent of all the wage-earners in the United States were members of labor unions. In 1910 this percentage had risen to 7, and it is higher at this time (see Art. 279). Labor unionism has, however, often exerted powerful *sympathetic* influences and it has developed strongly in basic industries and in the transportation callings where it could make its influence felt out of all proportion to the size of its membership.

As might be expected, the dire conditions resulting from the Industrial Revolution brought into life various reactive movements looking to their reform and toward fairer means of distributing the increased wealth that was created by the new methods. Some of these movements are revivals, in modified form, of organizations that had formerly existed and had disappeared because of lack of economic necessity for continued existence. Others, such as Socialism, which have aimed to attack these problems through legislative methods, have not as yet affected industrial organization directly, though exercising great modifying effect indirectly through other channels. These influences bear more directly upon the distribution of wealth than upon the creation of the same so far as this country is concerned. In this connection, the experiment in producing the necessities of life by communistic methods now in progress in Russia is of great interest since apparently the economic efficiency so far developed is markedly below that of other nations organized along other lines.

There are other corrective movements such as factory legislation, welfare work, or, as this movement is now more correctly designated, personnel work, industrial education, and similar agencies that tend constantly to modify industrial methods and conditions and which are of considerable economic importance. Many influences have assisted the growth of these corrective influences and they are hopeful signs of a rise in our national ideals. The economic effects of these influences are discussed elsewhere in this book.

24. The Effects of War.—The effect of war upon manufacturing methods and organization is both interesting and important. The problems of manufacturing small arms for the Northern armies during

[1] BARNET, GEORGE, "Growth of Labor Organizations in the United States," *Quart. Jour. Econ.*, August, 1916.

the Civil War resulted in the firm establishment of the **interchangeable system of manufacturing;** that is, in quantity production of parts so nearly alike in form and dimensions that no hand fitting or adjustment is necessary in assembling them into the complete machine or in replacing a worn or broken part with a new piece. The turret lathe for performing repetitive operations, which was the forerunner of modern automatic machinery, was also a product of those times. These and similar mechanical developments made possible the great industrial expansion of the latter part of the last century, that has already been referred to, and that has been responsible, not only for our present prosperity, but also for our present industrial difficulties through making industry so much more complex.

The World War which closed in 1918 did not develop any new or basic manufacturing principles or machines, but it did teach manufacturers some new lessons in mass production. The immense and successful experiment in producing ships in quantity by the interchangeable system at Hog Island was the largest undertaking of its kind ever attempted, and the marshaling of our industrial facilities for war purposes was an experiment that showed us many weaknesses in our productive methods.

But more important still, the labor problems of the war period brought into being labor adjustments and labor standards that have had far-reaching influences in solving some of the difficult human problems created in part as a result of the industrial methods that were started during the Civil War. The economic status of the industrial worker just prior to the present depression was better in general than it was before the World War. It remains to be seen whether we can restore and retain the comparatively high level of existence that we had reached.

References

BARNET, GEORGE: "Growth of Labor Organizations in the United States."
BROOKS, R. A.: "When Labor Organizes."
LAUCK, W. J., and E. SYDENSTRICKER: "Conditions of Labor in the United States."
WARE, CAROLINE F.: "The Early New England Cotton Manufacture."
WRIGHT, CARROLL D.: "The Industrial Revolution in the United States."

CHAPTER IV

THE GROWTH OF INDUSTRIAL ENTERPRISES

25. Modern Industrial Tendencies.—The new industrial methods have greatly accelerated certain tendencies that had already manifested themselves in the old domestic factories and some of these deserve more than passing notice, as they are affecting not only productive processes but our social organization as well. Perhaps the most important of these influences are those that tend toward:

1. **Growth and increase in size** of industrial enterprises.
2. **Specialization** or the limiting of the field of activity, not only of enterprises but also of men.
3. **Standardization** or the reduction of all lines of product to a limited number of types and sizes and characteristics.
4. **Extreme division of labor,** following aggregation, specialization, and standardization, and requiring special consideration.
5. **More scientific methods in organization and management.**

These tendencies are all closely interlocked with each other, and with modern productive methods. It will be clearer, however, to discuss them separately before summing up their joint action.

26. Principles of Industrial Growth.—One of the most striking features of modern industry is the increase in the size of industrial undertakings. This growth is in two general directions: (1) growth in the size of individual establishments, and (2) growth by the centralization or consolidation of like or unlike establishments under some form of common control. A few years ago, a plant employing 1,000 men was considered a large enterprise. Today factories employing 5,000 men are common, factories employing 10,000 men are not unusual, a few plants have employed as many as 40,000 men within the confines of a single yard, and the Ford plant at River Rouge is reported to employ over 80,000 men when at full capacity. A number of corporations owning several industrial plants in different localities employ even greater numbers of workers. Of course, there is nothing new in the idea of congregated labor itself, since it was employed in building the pyramids. But modern congregated labor involves the use of machinery and the *coordination of effort* in a degree totally unknown to former civilizations. Furthermore, the manner in which modern enterprises grow in size may be different from that of the older enterprises. The older enterprises grew, generally, by simple aggregation of handicraft units, a large factor being an enlarged small factory. The large modern factory may be quite different in design and operation from a small one doing similar work.

Statistics show that the number of corporations as compared with privately owned enterprises and partnerships tends to increase, thus indicating a tendency toward large-scale production and **mass financing** with growth in the size of industrial units; but hasty conclusions should not be drawn from this and the other preceding statements as regards industry in general. It is true that in some industries notable increases in the average size of establishment have occurred; others, again, have remained fairly constant so far as this feature is concerned; while in others, again, there has been a tendency toward a decrease in the average size of establishments.[1] The fact remains, however, that many industrial establishments are even now of vast size and others tend to increase. It is with the characteristics of these large establishments that this chapter is primarily concerned. Similarly, no hasty conclusions should be drawn as regards the centralization of industry which, as will be seen in a later discussion, is a most complex matter concerning which it is difficult to generalize.

Industrial enterprises tend to increase in size in one or all of three ways. The first is by the natural growth of an individual plant or establishment by **accretion** or **aggregation**, as it is usually called. Such a growth may be visualized as *concentric* in character, the plant enlarging around its original nucleus without marked change in character. The second method of growth is by **consolidation**; that is, by combining industrial undertakings of a similar character under one management. Such a growth may be visualized as a *horizontal* growth without marked change in materials, processes, or product. The third method is by **integration**; that is, by extending the control of materials and processes backward toward the sources of raw material; or forward so as to control more effectively the disposal of the finished product; or by extending the control in both directions. Such a growth may be visualized as a *vertical* movement or growth, each succeeding process carrying the product nearer to the market. Obviously, any one or all of these tendencies may be progressing simultaneously so far as any given enterprise is concerned. The economic reasons for these tendencies are of two general kinds: (1) economies that lead to reduced costs, and (2) reduction of competition through wider control of the industrial field concerned.

The Census of the United States divides industrial enterprises into two general classes. The first class includes all **establishments**, so-called. An establishment in this sense is defined as a plant, or group of plants, within an industry and within a locality, which is managed with one set of

[1] The writer is greatly indebted to the masterly treatment of this entire subject in *Census Monograph* 3, by Dr. Willard Thorp, entitled "The Integration of Industrial Operation."

account books. The second class of industrial enterprises are called **central-office groups.**

A central-office group exists when a single central office operates enterprises in more than one locality or in more than one industry or more than one plant within a locality and industry, providing those plants are sufficiently separate entities to keep separate books of account.

These latter industrial combinations are of many and varied forms, presenting all manner of arrangements of horizontal combination and vertical integration. Simple horizontal combination and vertical integration are in fact limiting cases, while in between many combinations and ramifications of these two principles are found. An approximate classification of these combinations is presented later on; but it is believed that the problem of these more complex forms will be clearer after a discussion of aggregation, consolidation, and integration. Aggregation will be discussed first, but before so doing it may be well to define what is meant by *size* and to determine the measures by which increase in size is appraised.

27. Measures of Size.—In this discussion the term "establishment" or "factory" is defined as an industrial enterprise that is managed as a unit; and with the use of one set of account books. In general, also, the buildings employed constitute an organic group. Industrial enterprises that are composed of groups of factories centrally controlled are discussed in succeeding sections. It will be helpful to define and discuss briefly the standards by which the "size" of all industrial enterprises is measured. It will be obvious that these measures are approximate only.

Capital investment is one measure of size that could be used to compare both like and unlike establishments. But accurate data concerning capitalization are difficult to obtain, hence this measure is unreliable. The second measure is **value of product** or **value added by manufacture** for each establishment. This measure has the advantage of making all comparisons in terms of dollars, which is convenient. But this introduces the difficulty of correcting these measures, when comparing different years, to compensate for changes in the value of the dollar. The third measure is the **number of wage-earners per establishment.** The measure is much used and is significant when used to compare establishments of similar character. If applied to establishments of markedly unlike character, however, the results are likely to be misleading. Thus factories where artificial flowers are made are not comparable upon this basis with factories where production is carried on by automatic machines. In the first case, the product is closely proportional to the number of workers, while in the second it will depend more upon the number of machines, which may or may not be in proportion to the number of workers. A fourth measure, the **amount of power used** per establishment, is also an index of the size and growth of manufacturing plants, and data concerning it are collected by the Census of the United States. It is not possible to discuss[1] at any length the advantages and disadvantages of these several measures. The second and third are most frequently used and will be employed here to demonstrate certain characteristics of the growth in size of industrial establishments.

Table 1, taken from the *Biennial Census of Manufactures* for 1929, shows the industries of the United States grouped according to the value of products, etc., from 1914 to 1929. More recent data are not available. In general, the establishments with an output above $20,000 annually tend to increase in number, while those with a capacity below that amount tend to decrease in number. In judging these data it should be remembered that the years 1919 and 1929 were both years of abnormal activity, the first because of unabated war activities, and the second because of the boom period in industry. The distribution of the wage-earners is equally interesting and instructive. Although the smaller factories are by far the most numerous, the great majority of the workers are employed in establishments whose product is over $100,000 in value and over half of them are employed in establishments whose output is valued at over $1,000,000. No data were collected in 1925 or 1929 for establishments with output valued at less than $5,000. Furthermore, 69 per cent out of the total value of the goods produced came from factories whose output was $1,000,000 or over.

The tendency toward large establishments is, therefore, quite noticeable. Data of this kind, however, must be construed as indicating general tendencies only, and an increase in the size of a plant is not necessarily accompanied by a proportional increase in wage-earners and value of products, as can be seen by examining Table 1. A factory may increase in actual size and the value of its output may be greatly increased but, because of the use of improved machinery and processes, the number of workers may be decreased.

Another indication of growth in size is the increase in the number of corporations, to which reference has been made. In 1904 only 23.6 per cent of the manufacturing establishments were incorporated. In 1909 this percentage had risen to 25.9, and in 1929, the last year for which data are available, to 48.3. In 1929 corporations employed 90 per cent of all the workers in industry and produced 92.2 per cent of the value of all manufactured goods (see Art. 71). All data available, therefore, indicate that in many industries at least there is steady growth toward larger industrial units.

[1] For a fuller discussion of this matter see THORP, DR. WILLARD, "The Integration of Industrial Operation."

TABLE 1.—SIZE OF ESTABLISHMENTS BY VALUE OF PRODUCTS—COMBINED STATISTICS FOR ALL INDUSTRIES, FOR THE UNITED STATES: 1914 TO 1929

Class of establishments according to value of products	Establishments		Wage-earners		Value of products	
	Number	Percentage distribution[a]	Average number	Percentage distribution[a]	Amount	Percentage distribution
All classes:						
1929	210,959	.....	8,838,743	.....	$70,434,863,443	
1925	187,390	.....	8,384,261	.....	62,713,713,730	
1923	195,580	.....	8,768,491	.....	60,258,470,607	
1921	249,486	.....	6,978,585	.....	43,563,957,189	
1919	273,804	.....	9,030,771	.....	61,888,634,937	
1914	271,822	.....	7,015,136	.....	24,065,765,817	
Less than $5,000:						
1929	(b)	.....	(b)	.....	(b)	
1925	(b)	.....	(b)	.....	(b)	
1923	(b)	.....	(b)	.....	(b)	
1921	53,931[c]	.....	40,897	.....	136,733,382	
1919	60,173	.....	41,235	.....	151,509,605	
1914	95,354	.....	127,459	.....	228,507,828	
$5,000 and over:						
1929	210,959	100.0	8,838,743	100.0	70,434,863,443	
1925	187,390	100.0	8,384,261	100.0	62,173,713,730	100.0
1923	195,580	100.0	8,768,491	100.0	60,258,470,607	100.0
1921	195,555	100.0	6,937,688	100.0	43,427,223,807	100.0
1919	213,631	100.0	8,989,536	100.0	61,737,125,332	100.0
1914	176,468	100.0	6,887,677	100.0	23,837,257,989	100.0
$5,000 to $20,000:						
1929	69,423	32.9	202,958	2.3	771,417,436	
1925	55,876	29.8	156,373	1.9	628,373,403	1.0
1923	61,881	31.6	189,627	2.2	696,894,346	1.2
1921	70,942	36.3	224,688	3.2	781,520,422	1.8
1919	79,550	37.2	227,792	2.5	864,349,183	1.4
1914	86,431	49.0	423,570	6.1	891,652,694	3.7
$20,000 to $100,000:						
1929	75,225	35.7	693,155	7.8	3,587,697,276	
1925	68,951	36.8	660,309	7.9	3,272,196,872	5.2
1923	72,139	36.9	718,023	8.2	3,414,287,517	5.7
1921	72,011	36.8	745,230	10.7	3,317,984,445	7.6
1919	75,389	35.3	772,947	8.6	3,474,071,749	5.6
1914	56,339	31.9	994,848	14.4	2,530,140,747	10.6
$100,000 to $500,000:						
1929	44,153	20.9	1,672,983	18.9	10,023,771,653	
1925	42,209	22.5	1,675,911	20.0	9,576,090,022	15.3
1923	41,818	21.4	1,718,901	19.6	9,435,841,005	15.7
1921	37,794	19.3	1,627,105	23.5	8,351,582,700	19.2
1919	39,222	18.4	1,710,756	19.0	8,874,896,575	14.4
1914	25,633	14.5	[d]2,996,179	43.5	5,692,172,942	23.9
$500,000 to $1,000,000:						
1929	10,395	4.9	121,547	12.7	7,294,860,945	
1925	9,771	5.2	1,131,439	13.5	6,870,112,293	11.0
1923	9,494	4.9	1,133,471	12.9	6,709,807,524	11.1
1921	7,524	3.8	964,749	13.9	5,257,174,126	12.1
1919	9,130	4.3	1,111,315	12.4	6,411,202,604	10.4
1914	4,279	2.4	(e)	.....	2,994,253,909	12.6
$1,000,000 and over:						
1929	11,763	5.6	5,148,100	58.3	48,751,116,133	
1925	10,583	5.6	4,760,229	56.8	42,366,941,140	67.6
1923	10,248	5.2	5,008,469	57.1	40,001,640,215	66.4
1921	7,284	3.7	3,375,916	48.7	25,718,962,114	59.2
1919	10,340	4.8	5,166,726	57.5	42,112,605,221	68.2
1914	3,786	2.1	2,473,080	35.9	11,729,037,697	49.2

[a] In order to make the percentages for the several years strictly comparable, those for all years have been based on the totals for establishments reporting products valued at $5,000 or more.

[b] No data for establishments with products under $5,000 in value have been tabulated for 1929, 1925, or 1923.

[c] The data for the 53,931 establishments in the "Less than $5,000" class are not included in other tables.

[d] Includes data for "$500,000 to $1,000,000" class.

[e] Included with data for $100,000 to $500,000" class.

AGGREGATION

28. Characteristics of Aggregation.—An industrial enterprise may increase in size simply because of the increase in the size of the product produced. As industry has grown, undertakings have become larger and more complex. The first locomotive was a mere toy compared to modern locomotives; and the building of a 50,000-ton ship or the great bridge over the Hudson River at New York City with a clear span of 3,500 feet involves processes the *size* of which would have appalled the shipwrights and bridge builders 100 years ago. There are certain enterprises, such as gas plants, electric lighting and power plants, water works, and transportation facilities, that must grow in size naturally, to keep pace with population, without reference generally as to whether such growth brings with it any economic gain.

The size of some of the modern **machine tools,** so-called, should be noted, since upon them depends all other construction. The first lathe built about 1800 (see Plate VI) could be carried by one man. Large modern lathes can machine a cylinder 14 feet in diameter, 40 feet long (see Plate VIII); and the largest boring mill in America can machine work up to 60 feet in diameter. Other modern basic tools of this character are equally impressive. More important still, much larger tools can be constructed if necessary, so that if other conditions demand or warrant it, the size of industrial products can be greatly increased. The sizes that locomotives, bridges, steamships, etc., may attain in the future will probably, therefore, be governed *by economic considerations* and not by the limitations in size of our basic tools.

An individual enterprise may also grow by accretion simply by adding to the number of tools of each kind and size, but without marked change in the sizes of the same. Automobile manufacturing plants and textile factories are good examples of enterprises that have grown in size in this manner. Highly specialized, or single-purpose plants can, in general, grow in size only in this way and retain their original characteristics. Such a plant may be enlarged only by paralleling, so to speak, each machine and process with other similar machines, or processes. Continuous-process industries, such as chemical plants, ore-reduction works, etc., can, of course, be enlarged by increasing the size of each unit or process, but this is virtually equivalent to building a new plant. General-purpose plants may grow in size either by adding machines of larger size or by adding to the number of machines of any size. The growth of such general plants is, therefore, complex in character and this type of plant offers the most difficult problem of administration and cost determination.

The economic considerations that follow from these two different methods of aggregation should be noted. If an industrial plant of a general character is expanded by the addition of larger and smaller equipment, or equipment of a different character, there is little change necessary in its general characteristics, but if such a plant is expanded by

Plate VIII.—A modern lathe that will machine work 14 feet in diameter and 35 feet in length. Compare with the Maudslay lathe in Plate VI. (*Courtesy of General Machinery Corporation.*)

adding many tools of the same size and character to each department there is an increased opportunity for the extension of division of labor, transfer of skill, and modern methods of management. Similar results follow, of course, if a specialized plant is expanded in the same manner. In the case of the general-purpose plant, such an expansion may result in a new arrangement of apparatus, new departmentalization, and new methods of management. An expanded plant, therefore, has not necessarily the same economic character that it possessed before expansion, and the costs of production, consequently, may rest upon a different basis. Any comparisons between small plants and large plants doing the same kind of work can be made intelligently only when the exact organization of each plant is known. The larger plant may or may not have an economic advantage over its smaller competitor. Experience and certain theoretical considerations would make it appear that large industrial plants have certain economic advantages and disadvantages, as compared with small plants. While these advantages and disadvantages have been much discussed, there are still apparently some vague ideas concerning these matters. And this is not surprising, for the questions involved are many and complex.

29. Relation of Size to Efficiency.—It is quite frequently assumed that a large industrial unit is more efficient than a smaller one. But while it is often the case that a large unit has an advantage over a small one it is unwise to generalize. The *mechanical efficiency* of a large machine is, in general, greater than that of a smaller one, since the frictional losses are usually less in proportion than in the smaller machine. The radiation losses in a large steam-engine cylinder are less proportionately than in a smaller one, since its external surface is less in proportion to its volume. But in the case of the internal-combustion engine, the larger cylinder is not necessarily more efficient than the smaller one for the reasons that it is more difficult to obtain a perfect mixture of the gases in the larger cylinder and more difficult to obtain adequate ignition of the larger volume. The larger cylinder is more difficult to keep cool as compared with the smaller one, the problem in this respect being entirely different from that of the steam-engine cylinder.

The most efficient size and shape of the common axe and axe handle were long ago determined by experience and any axe markedly smaller or larger than this accepted standard is less efficient. A hand hammer with a handle 12 inches long is highly efficient but a handle 12 feet long is useless. Furthermore, a light hammer is very effective for driving small nails, whereas a very large and heavy hammer would be useless for this purpose, though admirably adapted to drive large spikes. That is to say, efficiency must be measured in terms of the work to be done. A large tool doing large work may not be any more efficient than a small tool doing small work, both being well adapted for the purpose in hand. It is not wise, therefore, to make any generalized statements concerning the relative efficiency of industrial factors of varying sizes.

30. Relation of Size to Unit Cost of Equipment.—Large industrial equipment, in general, costs less **per unit of capacity** than smaller equipment. In a way, this is a corollary of the principle cited in the foregoing, that the capacity of a large industrial unit is often larger in proportion than that of a smaller unit; hence, the amount of material is also proportionately less. The amount of labor necessary to produce a large unit is also quite frequently less proportionately than that required for a smaller one.

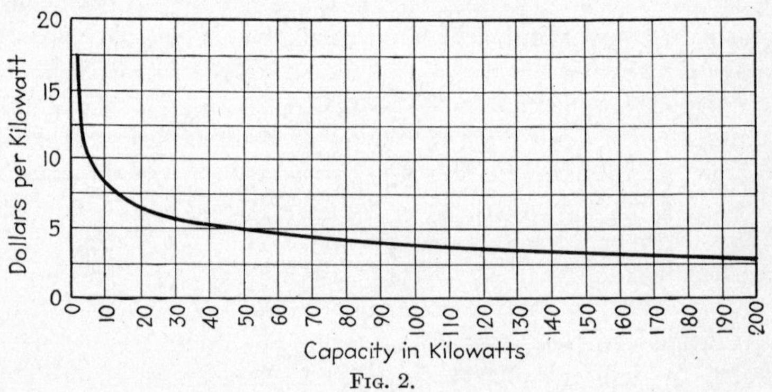

FIG. 2.

Figure 2 shows the commercial cost of a line of electrical transformers running from 1.5- to 200-kilowatt capacity. These transformers are alike in general characteristics and the methods by which they are produced are similar. The demand for small transformers is greater than for the larger sizes and, hence, more of the small sizes are manufactured. But in spite of this manufacturing advantage, the curve of unit costs drops rapidly at first, then more slowly, and finally tends to become asymptotic to a horizontal line. This curve is typical of such graphs.

This general characteristic holds true also for aggregations of industrial units. Figure 3 shows[1] an estimated statement based upon actual data of the investment cost of steam-electric power plants from 10,000 to 170,000 kilowatts. It shows the same type of curve as Fig. 2, the greatest gains in cost occurring in the small sizes. Up to the present, an increase in the capacity of power plants has for the most part been accompanied by increase in size of the component parts such as boilers, turbogenerators, etc. Figure 3 may, therefore, be considered as applying to the discussion in hand.

[1] See "A Superpower System for the Region between Boston and Washington," U. S. Geol. Survey, *Professional Paper* 123, p. 183, 1921.

31. Increase in Size through Duplication of Apparatus.—The foregoing discussion assumes, in general, that increase in size of plant is coordinate with increase in size of the tools and processes of production. But as has been noted in Art. 28, a plant may increase in size by simple multiplication of the tools of production without marked change in the size of the same. Parallel growth of this kind always accompanies an increase in volume of product of limited size and characteristics, as for instance automobiles, typewriters, guns, telephones, etc.

Growth of this character offers several opportunities for economic savings that do not appear with simple growth in size of equipment. (1) It offers an opportunity for more highly specialized arrangement of machinery, since tools and equipment of similar size and character can be departmentalized. This, in turn, may result in more efficient

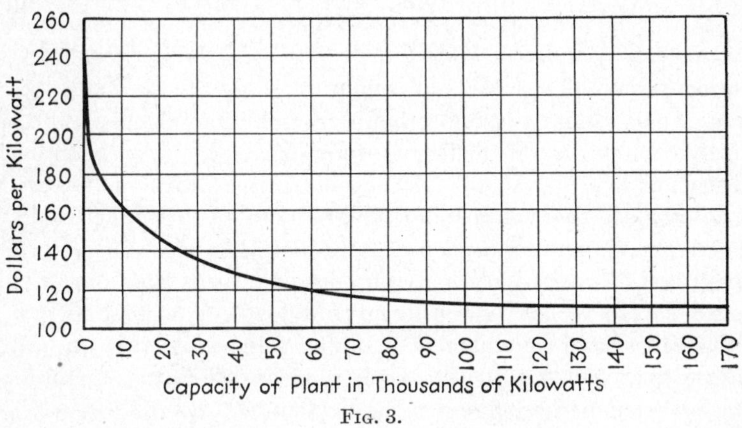

FIG. 3.

use of the equipment, since in general, fewer tools of any given kind are needed when departmentalized than when scattered throughout the plant. (2) Increased quantity of product always stimulates the invention of special equipment and closer specialization of personnel. And (3) increased quantity of product makes possible the application of modern methods of management, which usually are not so applicable to plants of a general character even though the equipment be large. In all probability, it is in plants of this character in which apparatus of small or moderate size is produced that the lowest production cost per dollar of investment and per dollar of wage is attained. The basic financial considerations that underlie the use of improved tools as the quantity to be made increases are discussed at some length in Art. 32.

In plants such as power houses, water works, and similar enterprises, where the product is of the general nature of a *flow* rather than a series of independent units such as automobiles, typewriters, etc., a number of comparatively small machines may be better and more efficient than a few large and more efficient units. This is particularly true where the demand varies considerably and where continuity of service is important. Large units are generally inefficient at low loads or capacities for the basic reason that there are losses, such as frictional losses, that are comparatively fixed regardless of load. If, then, there are marked variations in the load or output it may be, and generally is, more efficient to install a number of productive units so that those in operation are always working at high capacity. The efficiency of such a system will, in general, be higher than if a single unit or a very small number of units carried the load, working a large part of the time at low capacity and low efficiency. Obviously, also, a number of smaller units affords a greater insurance against failure of service than is to be had with a few large units. As an illustration of this reasoning, the Trenton Channel power house of the Detroit Edison Company was originally equipped with six 50,000-kilowatt turbogenerators of the same design. Such a plant has flexibility and the number of spare parts that must be carried on hand to secure continuity of service is at a minimum.

Somewhat similar reasoning holds for manufacturing plants. Such plants, like machines, are inefficient at low capacity because of the residual expenses incident to the life of the enterprise, which do not decrease materially with the volume of the product. A manufacturing plant designed for maximum capacity, but operating most of the time at comparatively low capacity, may give lower returns than one of smaller size and capacity, but operating at full load. And it may be more economical to have a number of manufacturing units that are operated at high capacity or not at all than to concentrate all production in one large plant that will operate for the most part at low efficiency. There are, of course, other reasons why it may be good policy to decentralize a large enterprise as, for instance, labor supply, markets, and transportation or nearness to supplies, but these are economic considerations of another character.

32. Relation of Quantity to Unit Cost.—The most important reason, however, for the growth of individual enterprises is the opportunity that increased size affords for applying transfer of skill and division of labor, for, as will be seen, the economic use of these principles depends upon the volume of work to be performed. Division of labor will be treated separately in a succeeding section and the present discussion will be limited to the *financial basis* of the application of transfer of skill. It is often necessary to apply transfer of skill for other than economic reasons, as for instance, the necessity of securing accuracy. If cylindrical surfaces of great accuracy must be had, a grinding machine is a necessity whether it may or may not reduce production costs. Again, it is often necessary to build expensive drilling fixtures or similar apparatus involving transfer of skill, simply to secure interchangeability of product, though such apparatus may actually increase the production cost. In most cases, however, the financial relations between the cost of *labor-saving* or *time-saving costs* or *methods* must be considered in connection with the probable reduction in cost. These relations may be briefly stated thus: *Will the total savings due to reduced production costs during the lifetime, or the period of use, of the new apparatus or methods more than equal the additional investment?* In computing the production costs such items as interest and depreciation must, of course, be taken into consideration.

These relations may be made clearer by assuming a simple case where interest may be neglected and labor costs and depreciation only considered. Suppose that an independent artisan is performing an operation the labor cost of which is $5, and assume, further, that his overhead expense in the form of interest, rent, etc., is so small as to be negligible. Assume also that by making a special device costing $40 this labor cost can be reduced to $1 for each article. The saving of labor in productive costs would be $4, which would be a reasonable gain in applying such apparatus. Let it be assumed, also, that because of the transient character of the product it is desirable to recover the cost of the special device in the cost of production whether the number produced be small or great. If, then, only 1 operation is performed, the unit cost of the product will be $\frac{40 + 1}{1} = 41$, and if 2 operations are performed the unit cost will be $\frac{40 + (2 \times 1)}{2} = 21$. The corresponding unit cost for 5 operations will be $9 and for 10 operations the unit cost will be $5. That is, there will be no gain in using the new device unless more than 10 operations are performed. For 100 operations the unit cost will be $1.40 and for 500 operations the unit cost will be $1.08, and so on, the unit cost constantly decreasing as the number of operations are increased, until with an infinite number of operations the unit cost will be $1.

Figure 4 shows these relations graphically, the ordinates representing costs in dollars and the abscissas representing the number of operations. The line *AB* represents the cost of the special device or preparation cost, the scale of its vertical ordinates being ten times that shown on the figure. The cost of performing any given number of operations, exclusive of the cost of the special device, is measured by the ordinates between the lines *AB* and *AC*, and the *total* cost of performing any given number of operations is measured by the ordinates between *OM* and *AC*. Thus, it will cost $140 to prepare for and perform 100 operations.

The unit cost is found by dividing this total cost by the number of operations performed, as shown in the foregoing. These unit costs are shown by the curve *DE*. The rapid fall of the first part of this curve should be carefully noted. The greatest decrease in unit costs occurs when two pieces are made instead of one, a constantly decreasing gain per piece being obtained as the number increases until after 500 the preparation costs become almost negligible so far as unit cost is concerned. With increasing numbers the unit cost tends to approach the operation cost as a limit. For basic economic reasons that will be discussed later on, this theoretical limit is probably seldom if ever attained, but the general principle should be kept in mind.

It will be clear, therefore, that the question of whether it will pay to make tools and apply transfer of skill and division of labor depends primarily on the *quantity* to be made. The greater the quantity to be made, the more complete and costly may be the preparation costs. But the more complete the tools, the cheaper becomes the product, and a

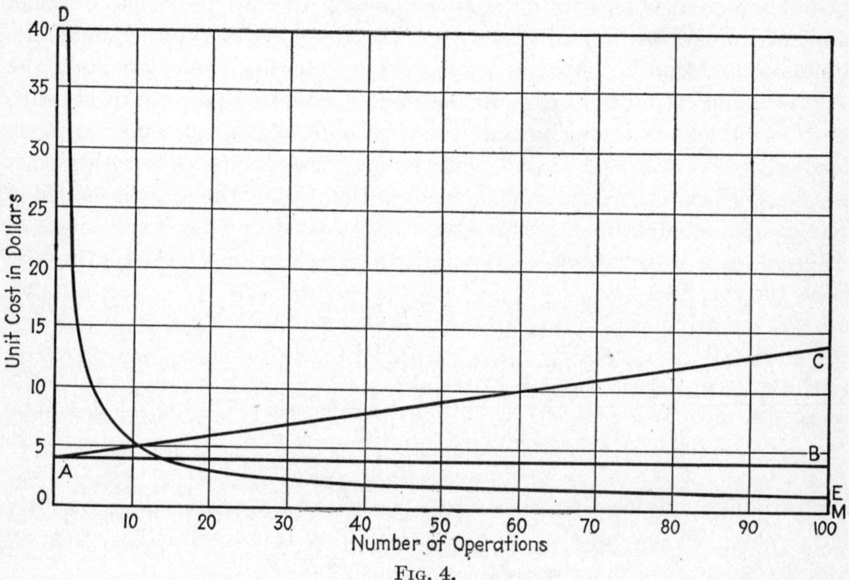

FIG. 4.

decrease in the cost of the product stimulates the demand for it; and this, in turn, increases the number that can be made. Thus is seen apparently an everwidening cycle limited only by the available market and in certain lines, where the product is greatly desired by all and the cost of the material low, as in watches, the limit is practically set only by the population. Where the quantity becomes great, as in typewriters, watches, guns, shoes, etc., the advantages of modern methods can be realized most fully, and much of the machinery employed is of the full automatic type involving also "transfer of intelligence." Such manufacturing is known as **mass production.**

In the example discussed in the foregoing, the actual cost of the new apparatus was included directly in the cost of production in order to show its influence upon the cost. There would also be other manufacturing expenses that should be included in such cost but they would, in general, be fairly constant, and for simplicity have been omitted. The disposition of the cost of improved machinery should be carefully considered, otherwise it may prove to be a source of loss rather than gain. Obviously, in the foregoing example, if the number of operations is to be limited and the new apparatus discarded when these operations are completed, the only safe way is to include the cost of the new apparatus directly in the cost of production, as illustrated in this example. The more special in character the improved apparatus may be, the more care should be taken to include its value directly in the manufacturing costs with which it is concerned.

It is not always convenient to do this, however, as the new machinery or apparatus may be such as to be employed over a long period of time, and other methods must be adopted. In the more usual case, as in the building and equipping of a factory, the preparation costs include the interest, depreciation, and insurance upon the equipment and these, with such items as rent, taxes, superintendence, etc., make up the total preparation costs. If the original investment costs are recovered, such recovery is through depreciation and sinking-fund methods based upon money deducted from sales returns. Now, most of these items such as interest, taxes, etc., are functions of *time;* that is, they *flow* continually with the business and unless disposed of as they arise, they accumulate. Hence, in such a case, care should be taken to insure that, over the period of producing life allotted to the equipment, the *volume* of work that it performs will warrant its installation on the basis of the principle discussed in the foregoing. *It is not sufficient that the new machine or method in question can reduce the labor cost on a single operation. There must be sufficient quantity to insure a return upon the investment.* This principle holds true for new apparatus for time-saving methods, for new departments that may be projected, and for the enterprise as a whole.

This economic principle is, perhaps, the most important one underlying modern mass production, and a failure to recognize it has been responsible for not a few commercial failures. It appears in its simplest form in the purchase of new machines or building of special apparatus, such as jigs, fixtures, etc., where it is assumed that because the new apparatus will reduce the direct labor costs it is necessarily a good investment, while the opposite may be the fact. A particular example may make this matter clearer. Assume that the interest, insurance, depreciation, and other fixed charges upon the *additional* equipment (that is to say the *cost* of this investment) amounts to $50 a day. Assume also that the reduction in variable costs (labor, etc.) by the use of the new equipment is $5 per unit. Obviously, unless an average of 10 units daily is produced, the new apparatus will not pay for itself. And this will hold true for the working life of the apparatus upon which such items as depreciation are based. The writer has witnessed not a few cases where the over-enthusiasm of a salesman and the ignorance of a superintendent concerning such matters resulted in the installation of machinery, the price of which was totally unjustified by the volume of production available. The worst feature of such losses is that they are not obvious, but appear indirectly in the overhead through interest, depreciation, etc.

Exactly the same reasoning applies to labor-saving management, where system, clerks, and administrative mechanisms are installed in order to increase the output. Usually such an increase can be obtained. But care should be taken that this increase is not more than offset by the cost of the new systems. The early days of "scientific management," so-called, afforded many illustrations of this mistake. It is in fact, one of the easiest of errors to fall into.

33. Other Advantages and Disadvantages of Aggregation.—The basic effect of quantity upon unit cost of product as discussed in Art. 32 is, of course, one of the great reasons for increase in size of industrial plants, but there are several others that should be noted in addition to those discussed in the preceding paragraphs. There are general advantages that inherently accrue to congregated labor centrally controlled as against individual effort. The large factory can purchase in large quantities and, hence, more advantageously. As the quantity of supplies purchased increases, the large factory tends continually to manufacture its own supplies from raw material, thus increasing its size and its control over the manufacture of its product. If well managed, the fixed charges (*i.e.*, for management, superintendence, etc.) will be, in general, proportionately less than those of its smaller competitor per unit of product. This is not always true, however. Thus, a manufacturer making a wide range of products may not be able to meet the prices of a small manufacturer who is competing in only one or two lines for which he can furnish an adequate manufacturing equipment at less cost than can his big competitor, and with lower fixed charges.

There are certain economic advantages, however, that are inherent in large-scale production. The labor cost of operating a large locomotive is no greater than that of operating a small one, but the work performed in the two cases may be vastly different. A helmsman can steer the largest liner as easily as, or more easily than, he can a small launch. The labor cost of operating a large tool of any kind is usually less proportionately as compared to the cost of operation of a smaller one. The labor cost of a ton of pig iron decreases as the size of the furnace increases. It does not follow, however, as axiomatic that, the larger the plant, the lower will be the cost of production, because other modifying factors, such as the interest on the investment, overhead charges, etc., enter into all such considerations and frequently in such a manner as to offset in some degree the gains due to large-quantity production.

The prestige and influence of a large factory assist materially in selling its product, largely because of the apparently greater stability and permanency which it suggests. A large organization can afford to hire a better class of men, especially for the higher positions of administration or design. These statements hold true, also, for large stores and other commercial establishments, which, because of wide advertising, can keep themselves before the public. A large enterprise is also in a better position to acquire patents and trade secrets. These advantages were appreciated before the present industrial era by the masters of the handicraft factories, as records clearly show.

Modern industrial methods have not only magnified these natural causes of industrial growth, but have added others. The handicraft system of manufacture was essentially *individual* in its character, congregated labor or factories being incidental and not essential. The very fact that the new machines were *power driven* made it imperative that they be grouped near the prime mover, the number of machines that could be worked depending only on the power available. With the unlimited power provided by the steam engine, the size of the factory and its consequent profits were limited only by the available market. The modern factory system is, therefore, essentially based on *congregated* labor, and the natural tendency of the large and strong to grow larger and stronger at the expense of the smaller and weaker has not, until lately at least, been held in check so far as factories are concerned, though the same tendency has been closely regulated in other human relations. Some critics of the modern factory system have professed to see in the electrical distribution of energy a means of doing away with congregated labor in a large measure and a return to individual effort and workshops in the home as in the "good old days" of handicraft. A very cursory survey of the industrial field will convince any thoughtful persons of the futility of such speculations.

Increase in size, however, is not without its disadvantage. The most widely recognized disadvantage of large establishments and large organizations is the tendency to become unwieldy and, as a consequence, inefficient. There is also a tendency to become inflexible and hence to fall behind in progress both as to equipment and product. Modern methods of organization and management have done much to correct these disadvantages, but in so doing have tended to increase the fixed charges. Further discussion of this point will be deferred until some other characteristics of industrial growth have been examined.

In general it may be stated that up to 1914 industry as a whole showed little tendency toward an increase in size of plant, but since that time there has been a marked growth in the average size of plant in many industries. In others, again, there has been little or no growth. It is apparent that there is no accurate measure of this growth that can be used for general comparisons between industries of varying character. It is true, however, that the number of large-scale establishments is increasing rapidly in some industries and these large plants are of great economic importance without regard to their relative prevalence as concerns different industries.

Furthermore, it should be noted that even in industries that do not lend themselves naturally to quantity production, new methods and processes that involve transfer of skill are being constantly introduced. Even in the simplest callings, handicraft tends to disappear in favor of new and improved tools and methods.

CONSOLIDATION

34. Consolidation.—Consolidation, as has been stated, consists of combining under some single form of management several industrial enterprises of similar character, producing similar products. If these enterprises operate independent accounts, the consolidation is of the class defined in the foregoing as a central-office control and this is also the most common, 76 per cent of all consolidations listed in the Census of 1929 being of this form. Consolidation may be visualized as a *horizontal combination*, that is, it tends to cut *across* the flow of materials and supplies at some stage of their progress from raw material to merchantable product. A good example of consolidation is the Worthington Pump and Machinery Corporation, which is now made up of a number of pump works formerly owned by separate companies and somewhat widely scattered geographically. Railroad repair shops belonging to any given railway system are also good examples of this type of combination.

The economic advantages that accrue from consolidation are quite important. The advantages of centralized purchasing in quantity, of centralized expert services, such as research and engineering, are obvious, as are also the advantages of consolidated advertising. On the productive side there is always the possibility of rearranging the work, where existing plants are consolidated, so as to secure the greatest quantity of any particular product in one place and also of giving each plant the line of work best suited to its equipment and location. By far the greatest advantage, however, is stronger competitive power, since a consolidation can more widely control market prices. There are examples of consolidation where a number of large competing companies have consolidated in the manner described, largely to eliminate destructive competition.

There are other logical reasons for consolidated combinations. Thus, a concern may have surplus capital to invest but lack material and supplies necessary for enlargement and, consequently, may build in some other place where such needs can be satisfied. Or the desire to be near a particular market or the necessity of expanding where labor is to be had may make a new location desirable for an additional plant rather than an enlargement of the old one.

Consolidated plants are quite likely to grow into more complex organizations, and many of them have done so. The principal reason why this is so lies in the fact that whereas a single plant might not require enough of any given supply to warrant manufacturing it, a combination of plants might operate an auxiliary factory for producing this supply with profit. In a similar way the by-product of a single plant might not be sufficient to bother with, whereas the by-product of a consolidated group would be sufficient to warrant a plant for its fabrication. The general tendency of the simple, consolidated combination is toward more complex forms of organization.

INTEGRATION

35. Integration.—Growth of an industrial enterprise by integration is very different from growth by consolidation. In this case, an effort is made to acquire, as far as desired, control of all stages of progress in manufacturing and distributing a line of commodities from the raw material to the customer. Integration may be visualized as a *vertical* movement, the material passing from process to process in direct succession. Integrated industries differ in one important particular from consolidated groups in that normally without integration they would not be competitors in the market, whereas consolidation groups would normally be competitors in the market if not thus bound together. Integration may start from the manufacturer who desires control of supplies and markets; it may start with the merchandiser who wishes better control of the products he is selling; it may emanate from the producer of raw materials who desires an outlet for them; or it may appear as a recognition of the mutuality of interest on the part of all concerned.

Integration, of course, is a relative term, practically all industrial plants being integrated to some degree. In shoemaking, clothing manufacturing, steel and iron production, and in machine work in general, the material passes through a succession of processes from raw material to finished product, each process depending somewhat on the one that preceded it and leading naturally to the one that follows. For example, in machine production the sequence of molding, machining, and assembling is mutually interdependent and closely integrated.

There are, however, certain natural breaks, so to speak, in the production of materials, which naturally give rise to a differentiation in the processes that follow. Thus, pig iron is used in so many ways and in so many different processes that formerly the process of fabricating iron products was conducted almost entirely by plants that possessed no smelting plant but bought pig iron for remelting. In large measure, this is still true. In this way, also, one smelter could serve many fabricating plants, this being also an economic necessity. With the introduction of steel making, integration began to appear and today there are plants, like the Alequippa Works of Jones and Laughlin, for instance, that convert the raw ores into steel billets and from these manufacture tubing, tin plate, wire, and nails of all kinds and sizes.

Again, a textile mill may manufacture certain kinds of cotton cloth which may be used in turn by many other enterprises, each of which produces a different kind of product. Integration as here discussed, therefore, refers to vertical combinations of *industrial establishments* that normally are independent or at least have been so until comparatively recent times. A fully integrated group of establishments contains within itself all the processes necessary to produce the marketable product from the raw materials. The establishments may be collected in one place or they may be widely scattered geographically. The large oil-producing, refining, and marketing companies are excellent examples of highly integrated industries.

Dr. Thorp states that of 4,813 central-office groups that were enumerated in the Census, 903, or 18 per cent, include establishments whose functions are successive and working toward a final product. This form of organization is, therefore, quite common. As will be shown, the large majority of central-office groups, however, are made up of combinations of horizontal consolidation and vertical integration in almost bewildering variety.

Some of the advantages of integration are evident. As explained in Art. 33, the amount of any required material or supplies may be so small that it is good economy to buy from specialists who by manufacturing in quantity for a number of customers can offer good prices. But as an industrial plant grows in size, it not infrequently occurs that the amount of certain supplies needed becomes great enough to warrant their production, thus saving the profit formerly paid to the specialist as well as the intermediate marketing costs, which may be considerable.

By such procedure, also, the needed supplies may be made to conform more closely to the requirements. Not a few large manufacturing industries have been compelled to organize or purchase plants for supplying their needs, solely for the purpose of securing the desired *quality* in certain supplies. It would appear at first sight as though a specialist would be able to give the best service in his own line, but it should be noted that specialization is a function of quantity and if the quantity needed is large enough, the special department within or attached to a plant may be as efficient as, or more so than, the independent specialized enterprise.

Another important reason for integration is the desire on the part of the manufacturer to control the flow of supplies in point of *time* of delivery.

This feature, no doubt, has been one of the most important influences in integration. Where the flow of supplies can be closely regulated, the amount of stores that must be carried in each plant can be reduced to a minimum and the danger of having production slowed up because of lack of supplies greatly reduced. An integrated industry may select new and more advantageous locations for producing its supplies, on the one hand, and it may develop new and better marketing facilities than are existent, on the other—and this has often been done.

Large, integrated industries often have excellent opportunities to develop by-product plants that in themselves may be large enterprises. A striking illustration of this is the packing industry which, while not highly integrated itself, has developed some remarkable by-products. A few years ago, about one-third of a live ox was considered waste material. Today practically the entire animal is worked up into some form of marketable product, these products including glue, buttons, hairpins, printers' ink, and a number of other useful articles.

Integration also has its disadvantages. First, there is the great difficulty of effectively coordinating and controlling a large enterprise made up of dissimilar units. It may be that the cost of coordination will more than offset the gain due to integration. Modern methods of organization and management have made it possible to control large enterprises more effectively than formerly, but nevertheless this danger always exists. Furthermore, it should be noted that when any particular unit in the chain of integrated industries is idle or the demand for its product lessened, there generally is no market for its surplus. A specialist serving a large number of manufacturers has a number of avenues by which he can stimulate the demand for his product. But when the integrated industry is short of work, the entire chain may be idle or nearly so and the owner must carry the residual overhead expense of the entire chain until production is resumed. Highly integrated industries tend also to become inflexible and difficult to adapt to changes in production. Once such an organization is "tuned up" to produce a given product it is difficult and expensive to change over to new models or different products.

36. Combinations of Integration and Consolidation.—It will be obvious that the general economic advantages of large size that accrue to individual plants apply potentially, at least, to combinations of such plants and, in addition, there is the added advantage of holding ruinous competition in check, which perhaps is the greatest reason for large combinations. It should be noted that vertical integration is not necessarily monopolistic in character. Thus, the Ford organization is quite highly integrated, including as it does coal mines, timber lands, power plants, coke ovens, blast furnaces, foundries, rolling mills, glass and paint factories, and other facilities integrated with great plants for producing the final product—automobiles and tractors. But it is far from being a monopolistic organization. Again, the General Motors Corporation consists primarily of a group of automobile factories that have been consolidated under a central office with a certain amount of resulting integration; but, again, it is far from holding a monopoly in the production of automobiles. If all of the establishments in a given field should be consolidated and also highly integrated, however, a monopoly would result that might well be the object of legal inquiry.

These tendencies, however, have already resulted in some remarkably large combinations, as for instance the U. S. Steel Corporation, the several large oil-producing companies, the General Electric Company, the large automobile-manufacturing combinations, and many others. Perhaps the most remarkable example of integration and consolidation was the Stinnes Konzern, which appeared in Germany shortly after the World War. At one time this organization controlled 65 iron mines, 26 coal mines, 26 blast furnaces, 24 rolling mills, 12 different kinds of steel plants, automobile plants, transportation companies, and an amazing array of manufacturing plants of various kinds, including newspapers. The combination was based, therefore, upon a consolidation and integration of iron-working plants, and had not only consolidated others but had spread out over the control of what would appear to be unrelated industries. The collapse of this great combination upon the death of Stinnes, its creator, was as spectacular as its rise and was due apparently to its own unwieldy bulk.

In this regard, also, it should be noted that there may be other reasons for large industrial combinations besides those that grow naturally from the economic laws of production or the desire to secure protection from competition. Two of these may be mentioned. The first is the natural desire on the part of some individual, or group of individuals, to build up a large concern simply for the love or self-satisfaction of so doing. And while such desires may seem vain, they nevertheless are important factors in building up industry and commerce and if properly directed are laudable ambitions. The second, and equally important, reason for great combination lies in the modern method of "promotion," so-called. Even when the advantages of combination are fairly evident, it usually requires the vision and energy of some individual to "sell" the idea to those interested. The promoter may or may not be a member of any of the concerns that are consolidated. He may be a banker or he may be, and often is, a professional promoter who makes a business of consolidating enterprises.

It is the work of the promoter to visualize the possibilities of the proposed combination, to analyze the commercial and financial possibilities of the situation, and then convince all concerned of the economies and other advantages that will accrue from the consolidation. The promoter of course expects to be liberally rewarded for his efforts, and if the combination works out as expected, his reward, which is often given in the form of stock, may be very great. Unfortunately, combinations and integrations do not always work out as expected.

A few years ago the fear that such integrated enterprises as Standard Oil would become oppressive led to the enactment of legislation that at first would appear to check effectually any such growth. While there has been considerable modification of view as concerns large enterprises, regulatory industrial legislation is an integral part of modern law and is likely to remain so. One reason for this modified view lies in the more intelligent administration of large enterprises as compared with that of a quarter of a century ago. The large modern industrial plant of today is not infrequently very advanced in its personnel relations as compared to enterprises as they existed in 1900, and also far ahead of smaller enterprises of the present. Furthermore, the economic advantages that often flow from mass production have been much more fully impressed upon the public consciousness during the last decade. The cheapness of automobiles, radio sets, telephones, and a host of other comforts that have been transformed from luxuries to necessities has done much to make people more tolerant of mass-production enterprises. Another reason for a more tolerant attitude is the increase in the number of people who hold financial interests in industrial enterprises. Nevertheless the curbing of monopolistic tendencies has always been, and often justly, a feature of reform administrations. This matter is more fully discussed in Chap. VII.

37. Economic Limitations of Combinations.—While the potential economic gains of integration and consolidation have been realized quite frequently, such gains are not universal. During the years 1925 to 1935 the average number of failures in this country was 22,040. The Census of the United States of 1900 records 199 corporations and combinations, of which only 60 paid dividends upon common stock; and of 140 such enterprises that had issued preferred stock, only 92 had paid dividends thereon. In a recent stock-market list, it is recorded that out of 927 organizations listed, 307 had paid no dividends. The phenomenon of large corporations and combinations that pay no dividends on common stock over long periods of years is so well known as to merit no discussion and in general it can safely be said that large consolidations and combinations have failed to realize the hoped-for results almost as frequently as they have succeeded. No doubt some of these disappointments have been due to failure to control competition, some to foolish promotion, and more to inefficient management. With the first two of these causes we are not here concerned, but rather with the third cause, and with certain economic reasons that will be discussed.

There are good reasons, therefore, for believing that there are economic limitations to the growth of enterprises that become increasingly effective with size. It will be obvious that the limitations that are inherent in division of labor and transfer of skill apply in combinations as well as in individual enterprises. The law of diminishing returns is ever present, for it appears that all economic gains are always accompanied by corresponding economic losses. The value of the industrial products per worker in this country, in 1900, was about $1,600, while in 1929 (the last census in which such data are available) this ratio had risen to about $7,950. Making due allowance for the changed value of the dollar, this is a great gain in value produced per worker. But the ratio of the value of products to the capital invested has been decreasing steadily for a number of years. In 1850 this ratio was close to 2; in 1860, 1.87; in 1870, 2; in 1880, 1.85; in 1890, 1.44; in 1900, 1.43; in 1919, 1.39; and in 1929 the ratio of the value of products of all corporations to their combined assets was 0.92. This increase in capital cost per unit of product with increased size of plant is to be expected if for no other reason than the law of diminishing returns. It should be noted, also, that this tendency operates without regard to the increased cost of administering larger enterprises.

The tendency of fixed costs, such as interest upon investment, to increase with increased size and efficiency is not always as fully recognized as it should be in the enthusiasm over the reduction of prime cost. Figure 5 shows the operating costs of power plants[1] of 60,000 K.W. and over and the total cost per kilowatt-hour for a period of 13 years. During that time, the size of steam units has increased and, in an effort to secure economies, steam pressure in the Edgar Station of the Boston Edison Company was pushed up to the unprecedented figure of 1,200 pounds per square inch. The curves of Fig. 5 are quite conclusive and without doubt represent conditions that are to be found in many other enterprises of similar and dissimilar character. Curve 5 shows the total cost per kilowatt-hour. It rose rapidly until about 1920–1922 and then, under the influence of larger turbogenerators, higher steam pressures, and more efficient auxiliary apparatus, it fell rapidly until 1925; since then it has shown signs of stabilizing. The cost of operation per kilowatt did not vary markedly throughout the entire period, nor did the unit cost of maintenance. But the fixed charges (Curve 4), which include interest on investment, taxes, insurance, general superintendence, etc., rose steadily and show no sign of decreasing. Obviously, if these tendencies continue, the unit cost of power will first stabilize and then increase. There can be little doubt that the characteristics of manufacturing establishments show many analogous conditions. Anyone who has had experience in managing industrial enterprises is only too well aware of the tendency of fixed charges to grow and the constant fight that must be waged to keep them down. We are in great need of statistical data of this kind from large enterprises that have grown from small

[1] See article by I. I. Moultrop, *Power*, April 24, 1928.

beginnings on a purely competitive basis and without the aid of monopolistic combination.

If the facts were known, it would probably be found that many modern industrial organizations have already passed the point of greatest efficiency and greatest economic returns. The very basis of mass production (see Art. 32) indicates that the advantages of quantity production fall rapidly with increasing numbers, and a plant producing 500,000 units may have practically all of the manufacturing advantages of one producing 1,000,000 units. This is particularly true where standardized

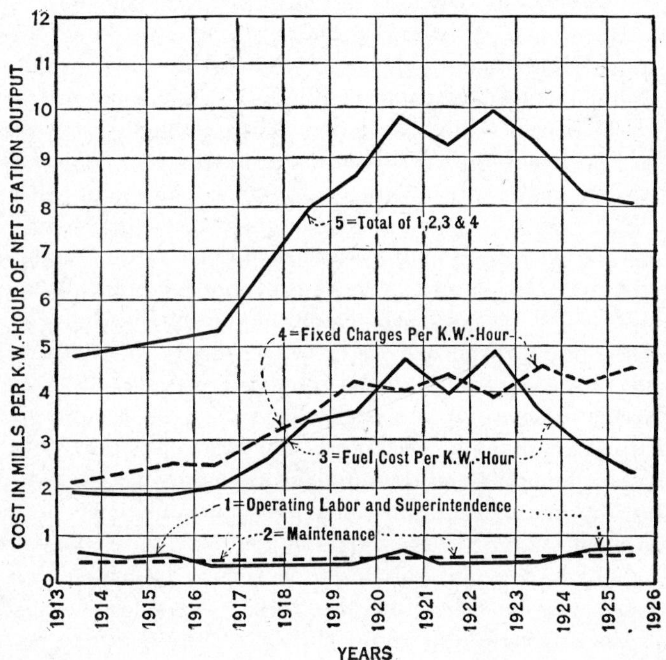

Fig. 5.—Cost of power in central station plants.

machinery is available to all plants. Thus in shoemaking and clothing manufacturing, the best machinery is available to large and small plants alike and any marked advantage must be due to other conditions, natural or developed, as the case may be. Actual data on this point are meager and not very convincing. References are given at the end of this chapter to some articles that present data on a few industries.

In all probability, the plants that can most fully mechanize their operations are most likely to reap the benefits of quantity production and increased size. The use of automatic and semiautomatic machinery and the substitution of mechanical means of handling and transporting material make the problem of production much more definite and controllable. In the highly mechanized plant, the speed of production tends to be governed by the machinery rather than by the workers. A notable illustration of this principle is found in such devices as the "progressive assembly" used in assembling automobile engines and the automobile itself. In such an assembly the product is carried by a traveling chain or carrier past successive workmen or groups of workmen who perform a limited number of operations while the product is passing their stations. The speed of the chain regulates the speed of the worker and the rate of production is almost as definite as that of an automatic machine. In the most extreme case known to the writer, the plant of the A. O. Smith Corporation, the entire plant constitutes, in effect, an automatic machine, the actual workers being largely in the nature of attendants only. The packing industries and many chemical plants exhibit many similar illustrations of highly mechanized production. Of course it should not be overlooked that these highly mechanized plants usually represent large investments and, consequently, have large fixed costs. Their success is more dependent, therefore, upon constant operation than upon the cost of labor.

At the other extreme, a manufacturing plant built up around division of labor with low fixed charges on account of cost of equipment and with a large number of skilled workers cannot avoid high fixed charges on account of the organization necessary to coordinate their efforts. Modern methods of organization have been helpful in extending the possibilities of successful coordination, and the principles of organizing the human element are much better known now than they were 35 years ago. But the fact remains that, as the number of workers increases, the cost of coordination by organization also increases, and unless care is used the increase in fixed charges thus brought about may more than offset the gain in productive costs or, in other words, the law of diminishing returns becomes effective in this direction also.

Lastly, there is a limitation to the size of industrial undertakings because of the limits in the capacity of human beings. Advanced methods of organization can be made helpful to the human element in management, but they can never be made automatic. As industrial enterprises become larger and larger, the demands upon human intelligence and physical endurance become increasingly greater. The spectacle of a large enterprise going to pieces upon the death of its founder and builder, as was the case with the Stinnes combination, is not uncommon, as is also the passing of the control of a large enterprise from the hands of those that have built it up because of their inability to solve successfully the problems of greater size. It is no secret that the greatest problem of large industrial corporations today is not that of obtaining technical skill or constructive ability, but rather the securing of vision, foresight, and managerial ability that can direct the complex activities of large enterprises. It will be obvious that the foregoing discussion of manufacturing plants applies equally to commercial enterprises, such as department stores, mail-order houses, and chain stores.

38. Other Combinations.—Simple consolidation and simple integration are quite common in industry but there are also many combinations of these principles. These combinations are so many and so varied that it is difficult to classify them satisfactorily. The best classification that the writer is aware of is that made by Dr. Thorp, which is given here with some changes in nomenclature.

A. Simple consolidation.
B. Simple integration.
C. Divergent processes:
  (1) Joint product.
  (2) By-products.
  (3) Similar processes.
D. Converging processes:
  (1) Complementary products.
  (2) Auxiliary products.
  (3) Like markets.
E. Unrelated processes.

For a more extended discussion of industrial combination reference is again made to *Census Monograph* 3 of the year 1924 by Dr. Willard Thorp.

The foregoing discussion has been concerned with the *economic* influences that affect the growth in size of industrial plants. The monopolistic tendencies that arise through *concentrated ownership* by holding companies and trusts are discussed briefly in Art. 74.

References

ALFORD, L. P. (Ed.): "Cost and Production Handbook," p. 102.
American Economic Review, Vol. XXI, No. 4.
Harvard Business Review, Vol. XVII, No. 1.
Twentieth Century Fund: "Big Business."
"Recent Economic Changes," Vol. I, pp. 179–206.

CHAPTER V

OTHER INDUSTRIAL TENDENCIES

SPECIALIZATION

39. General.—The growth in the size of industrial plants as discussed in Chap. IV has been accompanied by other tendencies, as noted in Art. 29. One of the most important of these tendencies is **specialization.**

It is human experience that as a man concentrates his efforts, either mental or manual, his skill in his chosen specialty and the quantity of his product increase. This principle has been grasped intuitively by nearly all primitive people and was well developed, for instance, by the ancient Egyptians[1] as illustrated in Plate I. Xenophon, who lived in the fifth century B.C., writing in the "Cyropedia" comments upon this principle as follows.

> In small towns the same man makes a couch, a door, a plough, and a table, and frequently the same person is a builder too, and is very well content if he can thus find customers enough to maintain him; and it is impossible for a man who works at many things to do them all well; but in great cities, because there are numbers that want each particular thing, one art alone suffices for the maintenance of each individual; and frequently indeed not an entire art but one makes shoes for men, another for women; sometimes it happens that one gets a maintenance merely by stitching shoes, another by cutting them out, another by cutting the upper leathers only and another by doing none of these things, but simply putting together the pieces. He, therefore, that is employed in a work of smallest compass must of a necessity do it best.

No clearer statement of the economic gains resulting from the application of the principle of division of labor has ever been made and it is surprising that so little use, comparatively, has been made of it in production processes.

Specialization has been defined as the concentration of effort upon a limited field of endeavor. Thus concentration, in its widest sense, may involve labor, the use of machinery or other facilities of production. In its narrowest sense, where the production of an article is divided up among a number of workers, each worker performing a very limited range of work, the principle is usually defined as "division of labor." Obviously, the underlying principle is the same, regardless of the size or character of the undertaking, but the term "division of labor" has, through long usage, become associated with the individual worker, whereas specialization is

[1] In the Metropolitan Museum, in New York City, there will be found a most interesting and instructive set of models illustrating handicraft callings in ancient Egypt. See also the *Geographic Magazine.*

far-reaching in its effects and influences industrial enterprises or even geographical divisions.

40. Geographical Influences.—Natural resources and climate have always greatly influenced the development of industry geographically. Thus there is copper mining in Montana, lumbering in Washington, cotton growing in the South, fishing in New England, and coffee growing in Brazil. The extent to which industry may develop geographically depends naturally upon facilities for transportation and the proximity of consuming populations. In earlier periods, exchange of goods between distant points was confined largely to very valuable commodities such as spices, drugs, etc. Where water-borne traffic was possible more bulky materials such as sugar, cotton, salt, etc., were exchanged. Modern transportation, however, has brought distant lands much closer commercially, and as a consequence large areas in many countries are devoted to the production of a very limited number of commodities. Cuba specializes in sugar to a large degree, California specializes in fruit, Japan in silk, Germany in cutlery and similar manufactured goods. It would appear that, if transportation costs permit, such specialization would be advantageous to all; but the argument for free trade based upon such an assumption does not meet with universal approval.

Specialization of industry also occurs within geographical areas where natural conditions are the same. The needs of a large population, the habits and racial characteristics of the people, and many other complex conditions may give rise to industries that normally might be expected to develop nearer the natural sources of supply. Thus, the cotton-manufacturing industries of New England, the brass and copper works of Connecticut, and the automobile industry of Detroit have developed partly because of an early start in such enterprises and partly because of an ample supply of skilled labor in combination with other local manufacturing advantages. With increased facilities in transportation and greater mobility on the part of industrial workers, local advantages become increasingly less important. This is so markedly true that the problem of locating any new industry has become one of economic consideration into which many factors must enter. This is true, not only as concerns the location of the industry within a given geographical division, but the exact location within or near a given city may greatly affect the success of the enterprise.

41. Specialization of Manufacturing Establishments.—The advantages of specialization have been quite widely recognized in American industry during the last half century and the tendency to confine the activities of an enterprise to a limited portion of the field may be seen by studying any branch of industry, as for instance the metal-working establishments. Not many years ago, it was common to find single machine shops producing many and varied lines of work. Engines, boilers, mining machinery, and marine work, and in fact almost anything in the line of machine construction were designed and built in the same shop. As the industrial field broadened and competition became keener, manufacturers found that they could produce more cheaply by concentrating on fewer lines of work and obtaining greater quantity of product in these lines, since cost is dependent to a large extent on quantity. This tendency has been greatly hastened by the difficulty of keeping up with the progress of manufacturing in a number of lines, particularly where the industry rests on a scientific basis. Many new industries have sprung up that are very limited in scope, either because they are based on chemical processes, or because, like many of the continuous-process industries, such, for instance, as cement manufacturing and similar undertakings, they are naturally so limited. Thus the manufacturer of automobiles produces no other product. He does not, in fact, as a usual thing manufacture all of the parts of his product, but depends upon other specialists to supply him with springs, bodies, ignition devices, and other accessories. The manufacturer of these accessories again, as a usual procedure, devotes all of his energies to the production of a limited range of such product. This decentralization began when manufacturers found they could buy many things, formerly made in their shops in small quantities, much cheaper than they could manufacture them. Thus, formerly every shop made its own tools and appliances, such as taps and dies, bolts, etc. But other men were quick to see that by manufacturing such supplies in *quantity* they could sell them to other manufacturing plants, that use them in small quantities, much cheaper than the latter could make them. The larger quantity was secured, of course, by supplying many users. The result has been that the factory of today is no longer self-sufficient to its purposes, but depends on many sources, not only for its raw materials, but often, also, for the greater part of its tools and appliances, great and small. It may, in fact, find it advantageous to manufacture certain sizes of a given product and rely on other factories for other sizes, depending upon the quantity of trade it can command. This tendency towards specialization grows constantly, the underlying economic reason being, as before noted, the advantages accruing from division of labor and transfer of skill.

There is a somewhat curious reversal of this general law that sometimes occurs and should be noted. It may occur that an enterprise may not, in the beginning, find it advantageous to operate, say, a foundry, but, because of the limited amount of castings used, can secure them from specialists cheaper than it could make them. As the business grows, however, there may come a time when the quantity of castings is sufficient to warrant the operation of a foundry, thus saving the profit formerly paid to the specialist. Thus, as enterprises grow larger and larger, their ability to manufacture all the accessories of their business increases and they are able to command a wider range of finished product. This is well illustrated in the great electrical manufacturing companies that now manufacture many of their own accessories, such as porcelain, oilcloth, mica board, etc., which were formerly furnished by specialists. There is often a great advantage in being able to manufacture these accessories, aside from the financial saving, in that it affords a better control of the sources of supply, which is not a small matter in these days, when time of delivery is often an important factor. Or it may be that a manufacturer finds it convenient and economical to engage in the manufacture of a product intimately connected with his original line of work. Thus, originally the production of electric generators and of the steam engines that drove them was carried on by two distinct kinds of factories with distinctly different manufacturing background. Today the production of turbogenerators is practically all in the hands of makers of electrical machinery. Other manufacturers have discovered by-products that have been developed into important adjuncts to their principal product. Thus increase in volume of product naturally encourages integration. In general, however, the tendency is toward specialization in manufacturing plants, the old form of establishment which produced a wide range of product being already a thing of the past.

42. Specialization by Callings.—Specialization by callings is the oldest and best known manifestation of this principle. Possibly it had its origin in the diverse work of men and women in primitive families. The degree to which specialization has been affected by occupation has varied greatly with time and place. Thus it is seen (Plate I) that ancient nations had developed very complete occupational division. But in Europe during the Middle Ages, when agriculture was the principal occupation, the trades and other callings were much more rudimentary and closely allied with the agricultural occupations. The separation of agriculture from the mechanic arts and the development of modern industry brought about a great diversity of occupational activity.

Occupational diversity appears to be governed primarily by the *material* to be worked; hence appear workers in wood, stone, iron, leather, etc. Then follows further specialization within each group. Thus wood workers divided into carpenters, cabinet makers, shipwrights, etc. Metal workers divided into smiths, molders, machinists, pipe fitters, etc., while leather workers separated into shoemakers, harness makers, saddlers, glove makers, etc. Similar diversity is seen in the textile and other industries but differentiation in agriculture has not been so marked until comparatively recent years, when specialists in fruit growing, poultry husbandry, grain raising, and so on, made an appearance.

The effect of modern machine processes upon all of these elementary trades and callings should be noted. Not only have they greatly changed and modified many of the old handicraft callings, but many of them have entirely disappeared, as, for instance, the handicraft shoemaker and cabinet maker. On the other hand, new industries are constantly giving rise to new occupations. Some of these, as in the automotive industry, are adaptations of the older trades, but others, such as may be found in electrical construction and in chemical manufacturing, have no counterpart in the original trades. Electric welding, for instance, has nothing in common with welding as practiced by the old blacksmith, and the production of rayon is far removed from the culture of the silkworm. These changes and new developments furthermore are progressive, new callings appearing constantly and older ones passing out of use (see also Chap. I).

It should be noted, also, that these changes and tendencies are not confined to industrial work, but pervade all walks of life. There are many kinds of engineers and lawyers. The medical profession is divided into specialists on the eye, ear, throat, and what not. The work of teaching is highly specialized and specialization is the order of the day in all trades, callings, and professions. The driving power back of this movement is, of course, greater efficiency on the part of the worker and better service to the public. This service may be in the form of lower prices, as in the case of the automobile; or in better, though possibly higher priced, service, as in the case of the surgeon or oculist. As concerns the increased cost of special service in such fields as medicine and surgery, society may be faced with the problem of providing such service as a community matter.[1] The long and costly training necessary today to develop first-class specialists in medicine or surgery tends to place their services almost beyond the reach of most people. The country doctor has almost disappeared, since modern physicians naturally must seek larger communities if they are to earn a fair return upon their costly preparation.

43. Specialization of Men.—As the field of an enterprise narrows, the character of its plant necessarily also narrows, the limit being reached in the form of **continuous** or **single-purpose** industries where practically no flexibility exists in the character of the process, each tool or machine being specially designed for its particular function, and no other. The range of the tools and the work of a specialized shop are hence narrower than those of the old general establishment that now survives mostly in the form of the repair shop. This of itself tends naturally to narrow the field of action of the man employed in the industry, and, in addition, the same influences that are narrowing the field of activity of each enterprise are also at work, internally, narrowing the field of the worker. This is so because greater output can be obtained when men are specialized—the skill and speed in any operation increasing with the specialization. These two influences, specialized machinery and the resultant specialization of

[1] This statement made some years ago in a former edition of this work has already proven to be true. An acrimonious discussion is now progressing between the American Medical Association and a cooperative group who wish the benefits of socialized medicine. Will the same question arise in relation to other professions?

labor, have already produced some very remarkable results. Not so many years ago, the shoemaker measured his customer's foot and made the shoe or boot completely. Today, by means of specialized machinery and labor, the making of a shoe is divided into a great many operations, so that the operator may spend his entire life in sewing one kind of a seam or running a machine for nailing on heels. Shoemaking as a *trade* has disappeared, and its place has been filled by a highly specialized industry.

Certain factories make, as a rule, only a limited class of shoes, and the operations of making them have become most highly specialized, following the specialization of the machinery, and other factory influences tending to extreme division of labor. This tendency exists everywhere, the influence of the new methods being always to narrow the field of the worker and to require more special skill of either hand or mind.

44. Advantages and Disadvantages of Specialization.—The advantages that flow from specialization should be noted. Obviously, the product can be produced more cheaply and better than under the older general methods, and this, in itself, should benefit humanity. It is indeed this basic fact that has given these new methods such a strong hold upon the manufacturing world. With all the disadvantages of the new methods, they have added tremendously to the comfort of living and can be made more effective in this direction if properly controlled. Because of the principle of the extension of the field of labor (Art. 15), countless thousands of men and women are now employed in industries that they formerly could not have entered, and at higher wages than they could ever have obtained at the callings otherwise open to them. Undoubtedly, the advantages offset the disadvantages, but the disadvantages should not be overlooked or forgotten. The greatest of these, perhaps, is the destruction of the old trades and the disappearance of the old, versatile mechanic. This, in itself, would not be so bad if the changed conditions offered an opportunity to those coming after to enter skilled industry easily and advantageously. But the passing of the old methods took away, also, the old apprenticeship systems, leaving little or no provision for preparing men for skilled industry. This, however, while serious, is not beyond remedy. The change was so sudden that manufacturers and educators had not sufficient time, or did not realize the situation, until the mischief was done. Today, however, many influences are at work tending to remedy this deficiency in our industrial system and there is great reason to hope that this need will soon be met. The situation is paralleled in other lines. Thus, the advent of the tramp steamer with its small, specialized crew has practically eliminated the sailing vessel with its large crew of "able-bodied seamen." But no one will deny the economic advantage of the new methods though many may deplore the passing of the picturesque old "wind-jammer."

Extreme specialization may expose a factory or other enterprise to serious financial outlay, if not ruin, because of sudden changes in processes or new inventions. In the earlier history of the New England textile industries, the rapid advance in machinery often put a heavy financial burden on existing factories, thus favoring new manufacturers seeking an entrance into the field. At the present time, the development of the South has placed the New England textile industry at a disadvantage. New mills in the southern states have already caused some New England mills to close down and such idle plants and machinery will necessarily represent a considerable loss, since, in general, they cannot be converted economically to other uses. Continuous processes, particularly those depending upon some chemical reaction for their methods, are always in danger from new and more economical methods, especially if these latter are patentable. A highly specialized plant may often be at a great disadvantage as compared with one less specialized, in periods of depression when certain lines of product may not be in demand while others may be in good demand. In a plant where several commodities are produced, there is more likelihood of having a steadier demand for production. Seasonable fluctuations may also affect the specialized plant in an extreme degree. One of the most extreme cases of this kind is found in the Alaskan salmon canneries, where plant equipment of considerable value must be maintained for use during only a few weeks of the year.

Similar dangers may face the man who is highly specialized. A change of process or a new invention may almost instantly eliminate his calling, and it is becoming increasingly difficult for a man to change from one calling to another of equal remuneration because of the special skill required in each calling. The tendency is always to make the distance between the worker and the tools of production wider and wider, with an increasing need of concerted regulation of industry to compensate for these disadvantages.

45. Limitations of Specialization.—It will be obvious that the principal limitation to specialization is the quantity to be produced. In Art. 32, the relation between the cost of apparatus, the quantity to be produced, and the unit cost of product is fully discussed, but it will be clear that specialization is closely regulated by the extent of the market. An examination of a commodity such as shoes, clothes, nails, bolts, engines, motors, transformers, etc., will show that the quantity consumed varies greatly with the size. Thus, there is no demand for men's shoes *below* a given size. The demand increases as the size increases until a maximum is reached, and then decreases with increasing size until finally there is no demand for shoes *above* a given size. This is characteristic of most commodities which are made in different sizes.[1] Similar variations of demand appear in connection with commodities that vary in other characteristics, as color or quality. The most important problem in organizing a specialized enterprise, therefore, is to select the range of size or color or quality of the product where sufficient quantity is in demand to warrant the special

[1] See *Encyclopedia Britannica*, Curve of Probability.

preparation and equipment. Likewise, the degree of specialization *within* a factory which is manufacturing a complete line of goods will be governed by the quantity demanded in the several sizes or qualities. In factories that produce a complete line of product, as, for instance, engines or transformers, it is necessary, usually, to provide certain special tools for each size of product in order to secure accuracy of product. But beyond that point care should be exercised that any special tools that may be made are warranted by the quantity to be manufactured.

The problem of the extent of the available market is always a difficult one. In some instances, the extent of the market is limited by natural conditions, as is the case with farm crops. There are limits to the number of large engines or locomotives that can be employed. Trade statistics and census reports contain much information upon such limitations. But if the specialized enterprise can produce a product cheaply enough the market may expand tremendously. The automobile, the watch, the radio, and the phonograph are excellent illustrations of this expansion. Specialized machinery lowers costs; lowered costs expand the market; an expanded market permits the development of more highly specialized machinery of production, the limitation of this cycle being set only by the general prosperity of the nation. Ever since the automobile became a marketable product, the market for that commodity has always appeared to be on the verge of "saturation," only to be expanded beyond all expectation. On the other hand, it is obviously safer to build a specialized plant to produce a standard article which is in constant and general demand than to build one to produce novelties or luxuries or one subject to changes in style or fashion to a degree sufficient to render equipment obsolete. While the economics of specialization are well known qualitatively, they cannot be applied mathematically or in a quantitative sense except where the productive processes are dominated by machinery or operations whose time elements can be measured. It is easy, of course, to make fairly accurate computations of the gains to be made by replacing any given set of productive operations with a set of more highly specialized operations if these new operations are to be dominated by machinery.

STANDARDIZATION

46. Economic Basis.—Specialization, as has been noted, is the confining of human activity to a limited field. In industrial work this means the limitation of an enterprise to a portion of the field and to the production of a limited line of products. But even when the line of products is limited, there are usually many *types* that are possible in that line and an infinite number of *sizes* of any one type. Thus, suppose a manufacturer specializes in the manufacture of men's shoes. Here there is no limit to the types that may be produced and no limit to the number of sizes of any type, since no two feet are exactly alike. Again, a manufacturer may specialize on the production of motors between the sizes, say, of ½ and

20 horse power. Here again many types are possible and an infinite number of sizes for each type. But it has been shown that one of the essentials of cheap production is *quantity*, and for a given *total* output the greatest number of each element entering into the product is secured when the numbers of types and sizes are a minimum. By **standardization** is meant the reduction of any one line to fixed **types, sizes,** and **characteristics.** Thus the manufacturer of shoes selects a few types that, in his opinion, will find favor in the market. But each foot is not measured and a shoe of the required type made to these measurements. A limited number of sizes of each type is manufactured, these sizes being selected, by previous experience, so that any average man can find a pair that will fit him. Each size of shoe again may be manufactured in different *colors*, complete standardization of each size not being attempted. The same holds true for the case of electric motors discussed above, and in fact for the entire field of manufactured products. Thus all manufacturers in the United States might agree upon the types and sizes of induction motors to be built. But the exact construction and the electrical characteristics of each type and size might vary with the manufacturer. Each manufacturer, however, would probably standardize the characteristics of his own product. Such extreme standardization usually involves scientific research and the use of basic standards that have been established by scientific organizations, as explained in the succeeding article. Of course small quantities and special machines must always be made for certain conditions; but wherever goods are produced in quantity the above conditions apply. This form of standardization may be called the **method of the average solution.** It is applicable to all manner of goods from watches to locomotives. The basis for its use is, evidently, **economical production.** It is, in a way, an extension of specialization.

Nor does the idea of standardization stop with the consideration of each unit of product by itself. The same standard part may be used for several machines. Thus the same bedplate and frame may do for motors of several capacities; a careful study of several sizes of machines and machines of different kinds may make it possible to use the same part or parts in all of them, thus still further reducing the number of kinds of parts and increasing the quantity of each. The general idea, therefore, is to reduce each line to the smallest number of types and sizes, not only so far as the finished units are concerned, but as far as the idea can be carried down into the details of manufacturing.

The idea of standardization may be extended to other and less material aspects of production. Thus, if it is possible to find out which of several methods, or sequences of methods, will produce best results in doing a given piece of work, the best combination may be recorded and used as a standard **method** of procedure, it being understood that this particular combination is the best, until some better way is devised.

Again, where the element of time is concerned, as in fixing piece rates, a record of performance will enable the manager to establish **standard times of performance** that are valuable not only for setting piece rates, but also for predicting costs. Just as material standards tend to keep up the accuracy of the product, so standard times and methods tend to raise the quantity of product.

47. Interchangeability.—There is another and very important ground for standardization and that is the desirability of having parts **interchangeable.** Standards of exchange have long been in general use, and these have generally been fixed with a view to convenient use rather than on a scientific basis. The units of weight and measure are examples of this form of standard. They may not even be the most logical, or most convenient, but once established they can, in general, be changed only by slow degrees, if at all.

The importance of such standards will depend on the extent of their use. If widely used they may be definitely fixed in character and magnitude for the protection of the public by legal statute, as is the case with weights and measures, thus securing accurate interchangeability of commodities. Again, standards may be adopted in some line of industry for the purpose of securing interchangeability of product, and their importance may, through growth, be of such universal interest that they may become legally fixed. Thus, it is entirely conceivable that our government in the interest of shippers and others might standardize, say, the gage of railway tracks, or it might legalize industrial standards, such as screw threads, so as to secure universal interchangeability. It is presumed, usually, that such standards have been determined with such care and intelligence that they are the best that can be devised for the purpose. This is not always true, however, and, even if true, a standard that is satisfactory today may be far from being so tomorrow. A certain system of gear teeth used in this country was very satisfactory until the problem of the automobile drive made other standards desirable. It is evident that standardization may be of state, national, or even international importance.

Aside from the consideration of standards, as viewed from the standpoint of general use, either by the public or by a special industry, each shop may have its own special problem in standardization. A basic principle in mass production is that every machine element or other manufactured part shall be, as nearly as possible, exactly like every other similar element or part. This is necessary for three reasons. Every manufactured product is, in general, the work, not of one man, but of many men, and is built up on the assembly floor (or corresponding place) from parts made by workmen who may never see the finished product. They may not even know, when doing their share of the work on the particular element on which they are employed, what the finished product may be like; nor, in general, is this information necessary to their work. A modern factory operating on mass production is like a river, the various elements *flowing* like tributaries from the different departments and merging smoothly into the stream of finished product that goes out through the shipping room. Clearly the success of such methods depends on every element being exactly right or **standard** as such requirements are termed.

Furthermore, accuracy of form in every element is important wherever duplicate parts are required. With machinery built by the old hand methods a broken part could be replaced only by sending it to the factory as a model, or sending its exact measurements in some other way. Today all manner of products, from watches to locomotives, are manufactured on the **interchangeable system** and repair parts may be ordered by **number** from the factory with an assurance that they will fit into place with little or no work upon them. And even when the question of duplication is not so important, the very fact that each element must pass through several machines, or tools, requires accuracy and duplication of form. Thus, spare parts are not needed in such products as shoes, and the accuracy of form required need not be so important as in making firearms; yet even in work of this character the fact that each element must pass through more than one machine or process, and the avoidance of accumulated error in the final product, demand duplication and accuracy of form unknown in the old hand processes. The extent to which this form of standardization may be carried will depend, of course, on the quantity to be made. Accurate duplication of parts is dependent on the character and extent of the *tools* employed and these, as has been seen, depend on the quantity to be made. The degree of perfection that has been reached in mass production in America[1] is remarkable, and the method, as before noted, is being applied to all manner of manufactured goods. The modern machine processes of production lend themselves most naturally to this kind of work.

48. Advantages and Disadvantages of Standardization.—The primary advantage of standardization is, of course, reduced cost. Not only is this true of the direct cost of production due to increased quantity, but also because as standardization reduces the required number of elements a corresponding decrease in the tools required naturally follows. The indirect expenses also decrease with standardization. Evidently less engineering talent and less clerical help and superintendence are required to handle a given output consisting of a few types and size than to handle the same output if consisting of many types and sizes. Standardizing the product reduces the variety of stores that need to be carried on hand, thus reducing the investment for a given output. It is evident that much more prompt delivery of product can be made with standardized goods than with those that must be built specially. To the cus-

[1] The interchangeable system was invented in France but was developed in this country by Eli Whitney. See ROE, JOSEPH, "English and American Tool Builders," p. 129.

tomer, therefore, standardization insures prompt delivery, lower prices, and interchangeable parts.

Of even greater importance, perhaps, is the effect that standardization has on the **quality** of the product. Every machine or piece of finished product is, in the first instance, more or less of an experiment, becoming increasingly so as its scientific and mechanical features become more complex. It is clear that the more a given machine is worked upon and the oftener it is built, the more perfect it will be. Standardized product is likely to be more satisfactory than special product for this reason, everything else being equal, and the customer should have very good reason for departing from standard types before doing so.

Standardization tends to concentrate the engineering and manufacturing talent of the factory with a consequent high development of product.

Standardization has, however, some serious disadvantages, and one of the most important is its tendency toward inflexibility, and hence toward impeding progress. Even in the case of standards of universal use this tendency is felt. Thus the metric system of weights and measures possesses many advantages over our present system; but there are so many serious objections to changing our standards that the introduction of the metric units has met with strenuous opposition. In England an antiquated system of money persists because of these same reasons. The standards of today, though representing the best skill and knowledge obtainable, may be inadequate or unsuited to the work of tomorrow. Our most widely used standards, such as standard weights and measures, standard bolts, flanges, gear teeth, not to mention our scientific standards, are objects of constant inquiry and criticism. Once a standard becomes widely used it is very difficult to change it,[1] and no one matter is of greater importance in organizing a manufacturing industry than the consideration of its general standards.

And these same criticisms apply to standardized product of all kinds. Once the types and sizes of a line of product are fixed for mass production everything pertaining to the production is standardized as far as possible. Drawings, patterns, special machinery, and operations are all specially arranged for the work, and these cannot, usually, be changed or adapted to other types except at great financial loss. Special tools and processes are, as a rule, absolutely useless except for the purposes for which they are designed, and changes in type and size almost always mean heavy expenditures for new special appliances. The practical aspects of standardization are more fully discussed in Chap. XVI.

It has been said that America stands in danger of losing her manufacturing supremacy because of the extreme to which mass production

[1] No better example of this can be found than in a people's language. The difficulties experienced in trying to hasten changes in our own spelling that are obviously needed, is some indication of the difficulty the Chinese, for instance, would have in modernizing their written language.

has been pushed in this country. The tendency to resist change or improvement, and to use new ideas and new patents only when compelled to is, no doubt, strong where mass production prevails; and as enterprises become larger, and combinations of interest more common, this tendency may become very detrimental to progress. Serious as these drawbacks may be, they in no manner outweigh the advantages that accrue from mass production, and the tendency is to extend the method in all lines as fast as quantity will permit.

Fear is also expressed that modern methods will standardize life itself to an intolerable degree. As a matter of fact the reverse is true. Manufactured articles such as automobiles, telephones, and other utilities are no doubt highly standardized, but clothing and other personal articles appear in increasingly great variety. The most highly standardized forms of life are found in handicraft nations. Witness for instance the fez of the Arab and the highly standardized garb of the Chinese.

DIVISION OF LABOR

49. General.—In the foregoing discussion, specialization has been defined as the limiting of the activities of an enterprise or of an individual. Thus, a factory specializes in the production of engines and the workers specialize as molders, machinists, pattern makers, etc. More refined specialization of the worker is usually called "division of labor," though this term is often used to denote the general principle underlying all degrees of specialization. A few years ago the shoemaker made the shoe or boot completely, the tailor performed all of the operations in making a coat, and the machinist performed all of the operations in producing a machine part. Today, in all production where parts are produced in any quantity, the process of production is divided into as many parts or steps as the quantity will permit and workers are assigned to perform only the work needed for each step in production. By such a procedure, the production of any part may be reduced to a series of simple operations, each of which can be performed by a specialist in that operation.[1]

> Thus, in the making of a ready-made coat there are 39 distinct operations; in the manufacture of a shoe there are over one hundred; in the slaughtering and packing of cattle about two hundred and thirty; while in the manufacture of a fine watch there are no less than 1,088.

The most effective influence in thus extending division of labor has been the increased use of machinery, particularly semiautomatic machinery. In fact, there are many who contend that modern mass-production methods have carried division of labor too far for the best interests of the worker, but it is difficult to see how the tendency can be checked even though this be true. The very growth of all lines of human knowledge and activity makes it increasingly difficult for one man to retain

[1] BOGART, E. L., and C. E. LANDON, "Modern Industry."

a grasp of any one entire field. He must be content to cultivate a very small portion of it. Men of leisure may still cultivate scholarly habits and acquire broad learning, but in the industrial field and in others such as law, medicine, or teaching, or in fact wherever remunerative service is a factor, the tendency is to require more expert skill or knowledge rather than the older forms of general information. Even then, the total knowledge of the expert may exceed that of the older all-round practitioner, so vast has every field of knowledge become, while his expert knowledge or skill is vastly superior to his predecessor's in the particular branch in which he has been trained. This general tendency to subdivide all kinds of work into simple detail operations that can be performed by men utterly incapable of doing the entire round of operations necessary for the complete product is true of all industrial callings. And a similar subdivision is also taking place in business and the professions.

The most extended use of division of labor is naturally found in the larger industries where production in large quantities is possible. Excellent examples are found in the assembly of complex machinery, such as the automobile, where an "assembly line" is commonly used in connection with what has come to be known as "progressive assembly." An assembly line consists essentially of a bench-like framework 500 or 600 feet long fitted with guiding surfaces along which the automobile progresses during assembly. At the starting end, the frame of the automobile is placed upon the guides and fastened by a carrier to an endless chain that moves along between the guiding surfaces at the rate of 2 or 3 feet per minute. The several parts of the automobile are supplied by carriers to fixed points on the assembly line in the order in which they are to be assembled. At each station are groups of workers whose sole duty it is to assemble the part that is supplied to them in *the time allowed by the speed of the chain.* Thus, a man may do nothing but insert a given bolt and screw it into place. He may be provided with a wrench that automatically regulates the degree of tightness with which the bolt is set up, thus further reducing the mental and physical requirements of the operation so that almost anyone can be taught to do the work in a short time. It should be noted, also, that the time element is controlled by the chain, so that if a man is compelled for any reason whatever to drop out another must take his place no matter how small or detailed the operation may be, otherwise the entire assembly is held up. By the time the machine reaches the end of the line, it is completely assembled and leaves the line under its own power. Similar methods are employed in assembling automobile engines, which are placed in the automobile during its assembly as a self-contained unit. The rate at which both engine and car can be assembled by these methods is surprisingly great compared to the older methods where the same group of men completed the assembly. The reduction in cost is equally great. Illustrations of refined division of labor may be found in any large industry where many detail operations are to be performed, but the example cited above is particularly interesting and important in that the worker is "paced" by the speed of the assembly chain. This feature has been much criticized, but there is no reason to assume that work on one of these assembly lines is any more fatiguing than countless other industrial operations that must be performed in unison with machine operations.

50. Division of Mental Labor.—The term "division of labor" has, from long usage, become associated in the public mind with manual processes. But productive labor is, in general, both *manual* and *mental* and just as there may be division of manual labor so there may be **division of mental labor** or **division of thought.**[1] Modern productive methods tend constantly to separate mental labor from manual labor and then to subdivide each into smaller and smaller parts. The subdivision of manual labor is greatly furthered, as has been seen, by the extended use of tools. Subdivision of mental labor, on the other hand, is hastened by an increase in the amount of knowledge and mental development necessary successfully to perform the work in hand. Thus, the mental labor of designing machinery is performed largely apart from the actual production; and this mental labor has become very closely specialized as the scientific basis of engineering has grown. This process of subdivision is greatly hastened in both manual and mental operations by *increased quantity* since this, of itself, enables the manager to avail himself of the inherent advantages of division of labor already discussed.

The net result of these influences is to subdivide constantly all lines of human endeavor. Thus productive industries are usually divided, primarily, into three branches, namely, **financing, producing, and selling,** the work of the first and the last being purely mental. The productive branch is again divided into **planning** and **building**, as illustrated in the engineering and production departments of manufacturing establishments. This last subdivision should be carefully noted, as it is one of the best examples of a clear-cut division of mental labor of production, so far as design is concerned, from the manual work of actual production. And it is to be carefully noted that the same influences that split factory organization into these fairly well-defined groups are still at work *internally* in all of them. The work of the president of a large works may be entirely mental, while that of some of his assistants may be entirely of a manual character. The chief engineer of a large works does almost no manual labor, while the man who traces drawings does little mental work, and in between these two extremes will be found all gradations of combined mental and manual work. The scope of the department of a works

[1] These basic principles which lie at the bottom of modern factory organization and administration were recognized long ago by Charles Babbage. See "Economy of Manufactures," pp. 169 and 191.

engineer extends all the way from planning a new factory to the actual making of shop tools and fixtures.

All productive processes, mental and manual, were originally performed *in the shop* itself, and in the case of very small shops this is often still the case. As works have grown in magnitude, the continued application of the above principles has taken out of the shop a large part of the planning or mental processes and placed it in separate auxiliary departments. The much-discussed methods of so-called "scientific management" aim, among other things, to carry the process still farther in the actual work of production. They aim to do the **mental labor of production** in a separate **planning department** and to **predict the results** of productive processes in a manner analogous to that in which the engineering department conducts the scientific part of machine design.

51. Advantages and Disadvantages of Division of Labor.—The economic advantages of division of labor may be summarized as follows: First, as has been noted, the constant repetition of any operation develops skill and dexterity which permit the worker to increase both the quality and quantity of his product. It is difficult for any person to do a large variety of operations well and the general practitioner is usually inferior in any field to the specialist therein.

Through division of labor, it is possible to assign tasks or operations requiring varying degrees of skill or strength to workers whose personal characteristics qualify them for the assigned duties. Obviously, a worker will do more and better work when the operations to which he is assigned are congenial and suited to him. This principle is now recognized extensively in all personnel and employment work, "job specifications" being quite commonly furnished the employment officer so that he can select men well adapted to the requirements. Furthermore, the separation of a complex operation into a series of simple operations permits the employment of men of lower degree of skill. A simple task is soon mastered, hence there is great saving in time over the older methods where the mastery of a trade required several years. The simplification of operations also makes possible the extension of the field of labor (see Art. 15), so that workers of a moderate degree of skill may take part in the production of refined product, whereas otherwise they could not so participate. This is particularly true where simple machine operations are involved. An unskilled worker may often be taught to operate a highly developed machine in a surprisingly short time.

Most economical results are obtained when each worker devotes all of his time and energy to one operation. Even though a worker can perform several operations well, there is always a loss of time in changing from one operation to another. And even though he may be familiar with the new operation, it requires some time to bring his production up to maximum. This loss increases in proportion to the number of operations, so that if the number is large enough each operation attempted will appear as a new one though he may have performed it at some time in the past.

Division of labor also leads to new discoveries and inventions. A person who is devoting all of his attention to a limited field is more likely to think out new methods and processes. This, of course, is one of the basic principles of civilization, for through it have come the basic trades, callings, and professions. Even in modern organized research, it is necessary to subdivide the field quite finely and the wise manager will give close attention to the suggestions of his humblest specialized worker. As a corollary, the store of accumulated knowledge is increased with division of labor. In the days of the guilds and apprenticeship systems, the store of knowledge in each trade and calling was transmitted verbally from master to apprentice. Today, this accumulated knowledge has been recorded largely in books and the literature of each specialized calling grows daily.

Division of labor has been strongly criticized because of the narrowing effect it exercises upon the mentality of the worker when he is required to do repetitive work of a very narrow range. There can be no doubt that this danger exists in many industries, but, in the opinion of the writer, this danger has been overestimated. Repetitive work that requires little mental effort is not necessarily deadening to the intellect. In most work of this character, the manual operations become almost automatic upon the part of the worker, leaving his mind more or less free. Thus, cigar makers, whose work is highly repetitive, can perform the necessary operations almost automatically and at the same time listen to readers who are hired for the purpose of providing mental entertainment while they work. It should be remembered, also, that much of the repetitive work is performed by persons whose mental processes are not affected by such work and whose lot in life is certainly better than it would be if they were compelled to earn a living otherwise with their meager mental equipment. This, of course, in no way relieves the industrial manager from the responsibility of making repetitive work as interesting as possible, and in some industries workers are being trained to several repetitive operations so that they may be relieved by change in occupation. Strange as it may seem, workers sometimes are unwilling to be shifted to other operations, especially if there is any danger of a decrease in earnings. Furthermore, shorter hours, education, and the many added diversions of life have greatly modified conditions as they existed when the first severe criticisms were made of repetitive work many years ago.

Extreme division of labor marks the extreme extent of the separation of the worker from the ownership of the tools of industry (see Art. 13). The highly specialized worker is also highly dependent upon the employer. and when he is so unfortunate as to lose his position he may have extreme difficulty in finding another. In common with the specialized factory, he always runs the risk of having his calling obliterated by new processes. In spite of these grave defects, the principle of division of labor is such a powerful economic factor that there is little possibility that its progress will be stayed. A higher standard of life can come only as a result of increased national wealth, toward which division of labor is such a powerful contributor. Enlightened management and intelligent legislation should see to it that this increased wealth is used to make life more attractive to those who produce it. Much has already been done to ameliorate the monotony of factory life through shorter hours, better pay, education, and more satisfying use of leisure time. But much more remains to be done before industry can be said to be upon a satisfactory basis.

52. Limitations to Division of Labor.—It should be noted that there are natural limitations to the extension of division of labor. Thus, there is no logical subdivision of the use of the axe or of the hand saw. On the other hand, the operation of driving nails may be divided logically, since one man may be employed to start the nails in the right place, another to drive them, and a third to "set" the head below the surface so that it can be covered up with putty. The analysis of operations into their smallest logical component parts has received considerable attention recently in connection with *time study*, so called. There is a great similarity between many of the most elementary handicraft operations, and obviously if the time required for each of such elementary operations can be determined it is possible to build up *synthetically* the total time required to perform any piece of work which involves a series of such elementary operations. Quantitative computations as to the economic effects of the use of division of labor are possible where such information is available and considerable work has been done along this line by the late Frank Gilbreth.[1] The available data of this character are meager, however, and accumulate slowly. Where division of labor is extended because of the use of machinery, that is, transfer of skill, quite accurate predictions can be made as to the economic gains, especially if the time element of the machine is the predominating influence.

Division of labor necessarily involves **coordination of effort.** Obviously, where the work of producing a given part is divided up among a number of men, measures must be taken to insure coordinated effort as to both the character of the work and the *time* in which the several operations are to be performed. Thus, the engineering department, through drawings and specifications, directs the character of the work, though a great variety of men may be employed in its execution, while the superintendent and the several foremen direct the actual production so that the parts are produced at the proper time. Such planning and superintendence, however, necessitate expenditures. In a similar manner, if machin-

[1] See "Management's Handbook," p. 873.

ery is introduced to facilitate division of labor, the interest and other items of expenditure connected with it must be considered. These indirect labor and interest expenses constitute a part of what is known as **overhead cost, expense,** or **burden,** which is a necessary concomitant of division of labor. Obviously, also, unless the gain due to the extension of division of labor is greater than the added expense, there is no economic justification for this extension. As will be shown in a later section, the possibility of the gain, due to an extension of division of labor, exceeding the additional expense is dependent upon the quantity to be produced. Failure to recognize this basic fact has caused more than one industrial failure.

53. Limiting Economic Influences.—The foregoing discussion will have made it clear that the economic use of such principles as division of labor, transfer of skill, etc., is governed entirely by the *quantity* to be manufactured. What may be called the law of *increasing productivity* may, therefore, be expressed as follows: *The unit cost can, in general, be decreased as the quantity to be produced increases.*

It should not be inferred, however, that this law holds true indefinitely nor that constant increase in quantity permits of constant decrease in cost. As there is a law of increasing productivity so there is a law of *decreasing productivity* or *diminishing returns,* as it is usually called, which tends to limit its action. Every economic gain is, apparently, accompanied by a corresponding economic loss which tends constantly to neutralize the effect of the economic gain. This principle is well established, but its application to manufacturing problems, unfortunately, is still but poorly understood. Its operation is most readily grasped in relation to land since the limitations of land, in a productive way, can be easily and sensibly appreciated. The application to manufacturing and other industrial problems is thus made easier of comprehension.

Suppose a farmer owns a plot of land that he is cultivating with ordinary hand tools. It will be clear that if he hires a man to help him the two can cultivate the land much more intensively and secure a greater return in the way of products. It will be obvious, also, that he may hire a second man whose labors will still further intensify the cultivation and increase the yield. And a third and a fourth man may be employed advantageously. But all experience indicates that the productive gain will be progressively less *per man* as additional helpers are added. It is clear, also, that there will come a time when the cultivation will be so intense that the labor of an additional man will barely increase the yield sufficiently to pay his salary and beyond that point every additional man is employed at a loss, even though his labors may increase the yield somewhat. There will come, furthermore, a time when the cultivation is so intense that no amount of labor will increase the yield. This example illustrates the law of diminishing productivity *as applied to labor.*

Again, the farmer may decide to add to his capital equipment by improved drainage and by buying more fertilizer and up-to-date machinery. In the beginning, he may, and probably would, succeed in increasing the product of the soil. But, obviously, there is a limit to which he can go in this direction also, as there will come a time when the gain will not offset the expenditure and, finally, there will also come a time when no amount of added capital will increase the yield. This illustrates the law of diminishing returns as *applied to capital.*

Or again, the farmer may elect to buy a large area of land and indulge in large-scale farming in a manner analogous to large-scale manufacturing. This would give him a greater opportunity to use division of labor, and, since he now has large acreage he can advantageously purchase the latest improved machinery. No doubt he can thus decrease the unit cost of production as compared to his smaller acreage, but here again the gain will be decreasingly less as he employs more men and more expensive machinery. For the law of diminishing productivity[1] as applied to both labor and capital will finally assert itself and the time will surely come when additional men or additional machinery will not be justified by the resultant gain.

This principle which is so clear in the case of farming holds equally well for other industrial activities, though it is not always easy to recognize it. Consider, for instance, an office building with elevator service. For a given number of floors and a given quality of service a certain proportion of the floor space must be given up for the elevator shaft. If additional floors are added, the amount of space allotted to the shaft must be enlarged for a given service, and the space available for rental proportionately reduced. Obviously, if the building could be made high enough the entire floor space would have to be devoted to elevator shafts if the service is maintained. As more floors are added, the elevators, of course, may be speeded up, and the amount of shaft space needed can thus be somewhat reduced. This change would be equivalent to the installation of better machinery by the farmer. But here again there are limitations to the speed at which elevators can be operated and eventually the law of diminishing productivity again asserts itself and reduces the income per square foot of floor space as successive floors are added. It is assumed, of course, in this discussion that other factors remain constant. Thus a rise in real-estate values might make the floor space in the building under consideration so much more valuable as to offset the effect of reduced floor space. But even granting that the value of real estate constantly increases, the law would eventually assert itself because of the limits of elevator speed.

[1] This has already been found to be true in the large wheat lands of California and notably in the great experiment conducted in Montana by Wm. Campbell. The success of Soviet Russia with these methods remains to be seen.

Similar limitations will be found to apply to the application of division of labor in manufacturing operations. Thus assume that a given piece of work involves several operations such as planing, milling, turning, drilling, etc. From the preceding discussion it will be clear that these operations can be economically separated as the quantity increases, each operation being assigned to one man or group of men to do nothing else. Thus, a man may be assigned to do nothing except to drill a particular hole in each piece. Again, if the quantity is sufficiently large a drilling fixture or jig may be employed and the work of drilling may be subdivided by having one man put the parts to be drilled into the fixture and take them out again after the operation, another man doing the actual drilling and nothing else. But it would be difficult to subdivide either of these functions no matter how large the quantity may be, or if such a subdivision can be made it would not add to the output. Thus, in general, division of labor can be carried down to certain fundamental operations beyond which it is difficult if not impossible to go, no matter what the quantity may be, and there is always a possibility that the point of greatest economy may be reached before subdivision into lowest fundamentals is reached.

It should be noted, furthermore, that division of labor must always be accompanied by some means of securing coordinated effort. If many men are working independently on many parts of the same machine, not only must all the operations be carefully planned in advance of this performance, but provision must be made to bring all of the parts finally into a coordinate whole. The general principles of mass management will form the basis of a succeeding chapter, but it should be noted here that as division of labor is extended coordinative measures must accompany such extension in the way of engineering and productive planning, clerical supervision, and careful inspection. All of these measures cost money and tend to offset the gain from division of labor. Failure to realize the fact that this cost may more than offset the gain has wrecked not a few beautifully devised theories of management.

The limitations to the use of transfer of skill are similar. As the quantity increases, machinery of greater and greater complexity and value involving transfer of skill may be employed, and in many instances this application can be carried to the point where the machinery is entirely automatic, requiring only the attention of those who can set and adjust the mechanisms. Aside from the limitations imposed by the quantity to be made, there are other economic limitations to the use of this principle that should be noted. In making shoes, for instance, a most remarkable set of machines has been devised for performing almost every detailed operation. Each machine, however, is of the semiautomatic type and requires the attention of an operator. No machine has been attempted, so far as the writer is aware, that will make an entire shoe automatically, and there is reason to believe that even if this were possible such a machine would probably be so complicated and expensive as to be incapable of competing with the semiautomatic machines now in use. Transfer of skill has been carried to a very high development in the production of individual parts, but there appear to be limitations to the extension of this principle no matter what the quantity may be. In other words, the law of diminishing productivity appears also to govern the use of this economic principle. In the manufacture of such machines as typewriters many interesting applications of transfer of skill are employed in the production of the individual parts. But the final assembly and alignment of all parts are performed by hand and probably always will be. It might be possible to make a machine that would automatically assemble the parts, but its economic value is doubtful.

This discussion throws some light, also, on the reasons for the increase in the size of industrial plants, for it will appear from the foregoing that there are economic limitations to the use of division of labor and transfer of skill on which supposedly the growth and competitive power of most large undertakings are assumed to rest. There is reason to believe that many of our large industries have passed the point where any great gain in productive efficiency can be had through further division of labor and the use of labor-saving machinery. This opinion is borne out by the fact that many manufacturing plants of moderate size have existed and competed successfully against very large plants, in many cases being able to undersell their larger competitor and without the protection of patents or trade secrets. In all probability a large factor in the success of these smaller plants is their lower overhead expense as compared with their larger competitors. This reduced expense has been brought about, in many instances, by specialization of greater or less degree, the amount of technical, clerical, and manufacturing supervision being thus reduced to a minimum. At the same time these smaller plants have manufactured in sufficiently large quantities to secure the full benefits of division of labor and transfer of skill that are permissible in the particular product they manufacture.

54. Major and Minor Factors.[1]—A somewhat broader view of the limitations discussed in the preceding may be had by considering the principle of **major** and **minor factors.** In all modern productive processes, more than one factor is usually concerned. Thus, in agriculture, land, labor, fertilizer, and machinery may be employed to produce a crop. Again, a machine tool requires labor, power, repairs, crane service, etc., in order to operate properly. A boiler, in order to produce steam, must be supplied with coal, water, and possibly forced draft by means of a power-

[1] For an extended discussion of this topic see KIMBALL, DEXTER S., "Industrial Economics," pp. 105–123.

driven fan. In railroad work, a great variety of services are required to keep traffic moving, though basically all trains are moved by locomotives.

Now it is common experience that it is possible, in general, to utilize the full capacity of any one factor of production only by having other factors operate at lower capacity or lower efficiency. The term "efficiency" as used here denotes the ratio of actual output or capacity of the productive factor to the total possible output or capacity. Thus, a factor operating at half capacity is said to have an efficiency of 50 per cent. Not infrequently a factor when operating at reduced capacity operates also at reduced *mechanical efficiency;* that is, its output of work for a given amount of supplied energy is less *in proportion* than when operating at higher capacity. Unless otherwise specified, however, the term "efficiency," as used in this section, will refer to relative capacity, or volumetric efficiency which is the sense in which it is used by writers on this topic.

Consider, for instance, the problem of keeping a large number of machines repaired and in operation. If each machine is kept in perfect repair so that its operative efficiency is very high, the repair force must be so large that some of its members will be idle a good portion of the time or, in other words, the efficiency of the repair force will be low. On the other hand, if the repair force is so small that its members are employed efficiently all of the time, some of the machines would have to await repairs at times and their operating efficiency would be below normal. It would be a very difficult, if not impossible, matter to adjust the size of the repair force so that both repair men and productive machinery were operating continuously at high efficiency. A similar argument can be advanced with respect to attendance upon such apparatus as textile machinery, where women are employed to knot up broken threads and to do other services necessary to keep the machines in operation. The higher the efficiency of operation of the productive machinery, the larger must be the force of attendants and the lower its efficiency measured in terms of active time. Again, in domestic housekeeping there are many utilities, such as vacuum cleaners, stoves, sewing machines, etc., which must normally be operated at a low efficiency as regards time of service in order that the efficiency of those operating them may be reasonable.

Consideration of any industrial enterprise will show the general truth of this principle. Such enterprises consist of a number of *major* productive factors which can be operated at reasonably high efficiency, provided other *minor* productive factors are operated at somewhat lower efficiency. Thus, a large manufacturing plant will consist of certain major machines or processes that can be kept at high operating efficiency while such minor factors as superintendence, transportation, crane service, repair forces, etc., are operated at comparatively low efficiency, and it may be good economy in such cases to permit such minor factors to operate at low efficiency, provided, of course, that by so doing some major factors are kept at maximum capacity.

It does not follow, however, as is sometimes assumed, that in a given combination of coordinated productive factors only one can be operated at high efficiency. Thus, it is true that if the farmer tries to till an excess amount of land his efficiency of operation will be high while the return per acre will be low. And, conversely, if he concentrates upon a very small piece of ground he can raise its productive efficiency to a maximum with small effort upon his part. But, obviously, there is some particular piece of land that will absorb all of his energies and at the same time give a high agricultural return. Even in such a case, there would be minor factors, such as agricultural tools, irrigation ditches, etc., that might be operated at low efficiency. So, also, in machine work it is possible to design a machine, such as a turret lathe, that will absorb all of the energies of the operator to keep it operating at high efficiency while such minor coordinated factors as transportation and repairs might still be operating at very low efficiency.

One of the principal reasons for these relations is the variation in the rate of operation of the major factor, since, obviously, every minor factor must be able to care for the maximum demand of the major factor. Thus, the feed pump of a steam boiler must be able to supply the feed water demanded for maximum output of steam and at other times will, therefore, be operating at reduced capacity. If the boiler is always operated at a constant maximum capacity, however, the apparatus for supplying coal, water, and air for forced draft can be built to serve these constant conditions and can be operated at or near maximum capacity, also. In the case of large machine tools that usually operate only a part of the time, minor factors such as power, heat, light, crane service, etc., sufficient for full-capacity operation, must be maintained at all times. Such "stand-by" services not infrequently constitute a large part of the cost of operation of such a large tool. On the other hand, if a great number of large machines are kept in constant operation, as is the case in some large modern plants, such service factors as overhead traveling cranes may operate at high efficiency.

In continuous industries where, as is often the case, every major factor must operate at high efficiency, if at all, the capacities of the minor factors can, in general, be so proportioned as to operate at high efficiency. In the case of large enterprises, where each minor factor serves a number of major factors which operate more or less intermittently, the minor factors may be made to operate at fair efficiency. But in the case of an intermittent industry, such as a ship-building plant, the minor factors must, in general, be of such capacity as will care for the maximum demand and, hence, most of the time must operate below maximum efficiency. These relations are of great importance in the design of industrial enterprises, since the cost of the minor factors of production are of the general nature of overhead or constant cost and, therefore, every effort should be made to keep their maximum capacity as low as possible, consistent with assuring high efficiency on the part of the major factors.

55. Summary.—It will appear, therefore, that the reasons for the growth of industries and the influences that tend to limit that growth are far from simple. If a true analysis could be had of the growth of these large industrial plants and integrated industries, all of these influences would be found to have had a part in accelerating or retarding this growth. It seems fairly certain that some of these great industries could not have been built up under a strictly competitive system, though there are a few very large plants where this appears to have been the case. It is interesting to speculate, also, as to how large these industrial enterprises may become before the limiting factors that have been discussed operate to diminish their productivity so that competitive advantages will cease to exist. It should be remembered also in this connection that state and federal regulations may also affect this issue.

The economic principles and natural tendencies of the industrial field that have been discussed in the preceding articles, namely, transfer of thought and skill, division of labor, aggregation, specialization, and standardization have had, and are still exerting, important and far-reaching influences, not only on industrial methods, as already described, but also upon industrial ownership, industrial organization, and more important still, upon our social and political fabric. *Mass production* has stimulated the growth of *mass ownership* or *mass financing*, giving rise to the vast modern corporations; and has created the need of *mass management* to organize and administer these great enterprises.

The problems of ownership and organization will be discussed in succeeding chapters and it remains to consider here, very briefly, the effect of these tendencies upon the workman.

As before noted the first effect of these influences is always to subdivide labor and to specialize men. This has already resulted in the disintegration of most of the old trades and the substitution in their place of specialized men of many grades, varying from the manager or designer whose work is purely mental, down to the operative of whom little skill and almost no mental effort are required. Each worker, however, is more highly skilled and more productive in the particular operation that he performs than was his many-sided predecessor, the all-round mechanic. This specialization, of itself, is not so deplorable as might appear at first sight. It is not considered deplorable that a doctor specializes on one organ of the human body or even on one disease of that organ; nor that teachers now specialize in a few subjects, rather than trying to cover the whole realm of human knowledge. It is only in the cases where the operations are repeated rapidly, and require little skill or mental effort but great concentration of attention that specialization becomes a menace to the worker.

References

Alford, L. P. (Ed.): "Management's Handbook."
Bogart, E. L., and C. E. Landon: "Modern Industry."
Harriman, W. F.: "Standards and Standardization."
Kimball, D. S.: "Industrial Economics," p. 105.

CHAPTER VI

FORMATION AND MAINTENANCE OF POLICIES

MANAGERIAL POLICIES

56. Introductory.—It was inevitable that the changed industrial methods and tendencies discussed in the preceding chapters should necessitate new views of industrial organization and management. No better index of these changed views can be found than the growth of so-called "*policies*" in all branches of industry. Some of the basic reasons for the growth of policies should be noted. Early American production was largely opportunistic, so to speak. That is, a manufacturer set up in business prepared to meet a wide range of demand since the required quantity of any one product was small. The industrial processes were comparatively few and simple, the tools standard and long-lived and hence obsolescence was not an important factor. Furthermore, the manufacturer expected and with some assurance that trade would come to him with little or no solicitation, in other words he operated in a "seller's market." Some very large manufacturing enterprises were built up on such a foundation during the latter part of the last century, some of them, for instance, producing anything in iron products from coffee mills to fully equipped battleships. The organization of these enterprises was simple, production control in the modern sense was unknown, and policies were directed by men of large practical experience empirically; judgment on all debatable questions being delivered at the time and place where they arose, and not usually as part of any established policy. Profits were more easily obtained in earlier days and these simpler and less costly methods usually sufficed for successful operation.

Many influences have operated to change this picture. The great increase in population, the widening of the market by more efficient transportation, and the increase in national wealth made mass production possible. But this again, as explained in Chap. V, has resulted in standardization and specialization; in larger investments of capital much more liable to obsolescence; in much more intense price competition; and the introduction of scientific methods in all branches of production. These new conditions of vast size and complexity opened up new problems in management. The old individual owner-manager has almost disappeared and in his place has appeared management separated from ownership and management often responsible only to investors who are not competent to judge of the efficiency of management and have no interest outside of dividend returns. Obviously few single individuals are competent to make accurate decisions on all the many problems arising in such a complex field. It has become increasingly necessary, therefore, no matter how talented the leader may be, to establish definite *policies* based upon accurate information that will serve as guides in these complexities. It should be clearly understood that a *policy* is not an inflexible *rule*. It is rather a code of procedure indicating in a general way the best method of conducting any portion of the work in hand. In general, it must be flexible enough to permit adjustments to changing conditions, though it may include inflexible rules. Thus the personnel policy may be very liberal in many respects, but it might include an absolute prohibition of smoking in certain places.

In a broader way the growth of policies is simply another manifestation of the growing necessity of predetermining as far as possible all factors involved in the process of production as opposed to the older idea of casual guidance by those directing the processes. This again is a reflex from the application of scientific methods to productive processes, which started in the last decade of the last century with the measurement of cutting feeds and speeds and has culminated in such controlling devices as the budget, which aims to predetermine the financial operations of every department and every activity.

57. Other Advantages.—In addition to the advantages cited in the foregoing, well-considered policies are valuable in fixing a definite aim and purpose for the enterprise and aid in preventing poorly considered excursions into new ventures—so often the cause of financial trouble. They have a stabilizing effect upon all features of the undertaking which is valuable, not only internally, but tends also to create confidence in the mind of the public as concerns the reputation of the enterprise. A manufacturer who consistently adheres to his established standards of quality and to his established sales policy is much more likely to hold his customers than one who is constantly changing his policies in these regards. Well-established policies are also strong coordinative influences and tend to hold the organization together where much division of labor is used, and where many departments that are not naturally cooperative in character are included in the enterprise. On the other hand, it is obvious that no policy should be so rigorous as to prohibit the possibility of change and growth as industrial conditions change. A periodical review of all policies is a necessity.

58. Character of Policies.—It will be evident that policies may be of widely varying character and importance. What may be of importance in one enterprise may be inconsequential in another, and close classification of industrial policies is impossible. For convenience of discussion, however, they may be divided primarily into *managerial policies* and *administrative policies*, following the generally accepted division of functions in industrial enterprises (see Art. 91, Chap. IX). In either case the policy may have to do with *external* or *internal* matters.

Managerial or general policies are those that would naturally be formulated by the individual owner or the board of managers or directors of a corporation pertaining to the broader problems of the business. Among the external policies that would be so fixed would be those pertaining to methods of financing the project, issuance of stocks and bonds, place and manner of incorporation, etc. Internal policies fixed by this group would include the general scope and character of the business, the amount of capital to be invested, the location of plant and offices, and the type of organization that is to be used. This group would necessarily approve or disapprove of any administrative measures that in any way affected broad, general policies. For illustration, any bonus-payment plan that might materially affect the finances of the enterprise or which might be of interest to the stockholders would require the approval of the management board. A board of directors should, therefore, be composed of men who have had broad experience in the particular field of the work in hand and who have sound ideas and foresight.

Administrative policies are such as will be naturally formulated by the president or general manager, who is responsible to the board of directors, in conference with his chief advisers. In a manufacturing plant these advisers would naturally be such men as the sales manager, the chief engineer, the manufacturing superintendent, and the treasurer. The external policies that this group might fix would be the sales policy, advertising policy, purchasing policy, and the relation of the concern with trade associations and other cooperative movements in their particular field, etc.

The internal policies that will naturally interest the administrative staff are those that govern the detailed organization of the plant, the manufacturing policies as concerns quantities to be produced, the problems of inventory, personnel policies, standardization, additions to and the replacement of equipment, etc. (see Fig. 13).

59. Departmental Policies—Procedure.—Industrial organizations usually consist of a number of departments. If a department is a large one its policy should be carefully considered, and whether large or small the policies of all departments must be in harmony with the general policies both administrative and managerial. In plants producing industrial goods where the work of design, purchasing of materials, and the direction of many productive processes presents problems of constant recurrence the internal policies should be carefully coordinated so as to be accurate, efficient, and intelligent. Such a coordinated set of policies is sometimes referred to as the *procedure* of the production departments, and is discussed more fully in a later section of this work (see Art. 99). In such an organization a production order placed by the manager can follow only one course through the office departments and could not move aimlessly or be pigeonholed as is the case where no such coordinated procedure exists.

60. Creation and Maintenance of Policies.—An example may make this discussion clearer. A few years ago a sales department consisted of a sales manager who usually was resident at the central office and controlled a number of salesmen either traveling out of the main office or located permanently in assigned territory. These men were selected almost solely for their persuasive powers and were given a fairly free hand in developing their sales territory. Much selling is still done in this empirical manner and often quite successfully. Of course, such salesmen must have accurate basic information concerning the product and this with strong personality was considered sufficient, particularly where the units of product were large and the quantity small numerically.

Consider on the other hand the problem of selling the product of a mass-production plant where the sales must be constantly stimulated or *marketed* as the modern method is called. Professor Paul D. Converse enumerates the several functions of marketing as follows.

A. Selling.
   1. Creating demand.
   2. Finding a market.
   3. Advice to buyer as to use of product.
   4. Negotiating price and other terms.
   5. Transfer of title.

B. Transporting (creating place utility).
C. Storing (creating time utility).
D. Standardizing and grading.
E. Assembling.
F. Dividing.
G. Packing.

General business functions involved in marketing:

H. Financing.
I. Risking.
J. Recording (accounting).

Professor Converse further remarks: "The first seven of these functions are typically marketing functions. The last three are general business functions involved in both production and marketing. . . . Recording or accounting has not in the past been generally included as a marketing function. It is, however, involved in many marketing operations. We are coming to realize that cost accounting may be just as important in marketing as in production."

This modern viewpoint presents a more complicated picture than the old simple salesman with his sample case, and this complexity combined with the growing importance of interdepartmental relations calls not only for salesmen of talent, but also for clearly defined sales policies that will embrace and coordinate this complex problem.

In an industrial plant, therefore, the **sales manager** might be so important as to be a vice president. Directly under him there would be a **field sales manager** who would control the district managers, salesmen, etc. He would also have under him an **advertising manager** who would be responsible for all advertising, a **transportation manager** who would supervise all shipping and routing of the product, and a **service manager** who would supervise the work of supplying repair parts and providing the necessary service for quick and reliable repairs. In selling automobiles, typewriters, radios, and other widely used products provision for such service is highly important in its bearing upon sales. In addition to these direct functions there might be a **marketing research bureau** organized directly under the president, but acting in an advisory capacity to the vice president in charge of sales. Such a bureau would be constantly gathering market information, analyzing it, and advising the president and the sales department concerning desirable policies. The official heads of this entire group would naturally constitute a committee on **sales policy** and advise the president accordingly. If, for instance, a new market was to be developed the first step would be a **market survey** by the department of market analysis. This would consist of a careful survey of the territory under consideration as to population, wealth, character of residents, competition, etc., with recommendations concerning the possibilities of sales. Next, a carefully prepared advertising campaign would be conducted to open the way for the salesmen. Lastly, the salesmen would go out with carefully organized material concerning the product, time of delivery, credit policies, etc. Such a sales policy is far removed from the old empirical method in that it is built upon facts so far as they can be obtained. The method of preparation is scientific and not personal or casual. Indeed the viewpoint and procedure of selling have been broadened to the extent that the official in charge of disposing of the product is known as a **market director** rather than as a sales manager.

Consider again the problem of designing the product. All will concede that the engineering department is fully competent to produce a satisfactory design so far as the technical characteristics are concerned. But even here good policy will dictate that before engineering plans are put into production, especially if a large quantity is to be produced, other departments such as sales, production, and finance be called into conference. The salesman may have excellent ideas as to the appearance of the product, the production manager can often make suggestions that will save much money in production, and the financier is always indispensable if large investments in material or credit are involved. Of late the term **product engineering** has come into use to denote and accent the close relation between good design and low production costs. Good policies are, therefore, coordinative in their influences and tend to bring forth the best talent in the organization. The formation and operation of committees such as are suggested in the foregoing are discussed more fully in a later section.

Policies should, of course, be stable. Once a policy has been carefully formulated it should not be changed except for good and sufficient reasons as, for instance, radical changes in the field of business involved. However, as already stated, under no circumstances should policies be so inflexible as to resist all change. Policies are like standards in that they represent the best that can be devised at the time and should be adhered to until good reasons appear for making a change. For these reasons, all policies should be under constant review by the committees or other groups responsible for their formation so as to be sure that they will not become obsolete or ineffective.

Policies, again, like standards, are useless unless they are enforced. They are the best and perhaps the only way in which the management can impress its ideals and ideas upon the rank and file of the employees. For this reason they should be definite and tangible and presented to all concerned in a simple understandable form. The most difficult task in this regard is to get the ideas and ideals of the management clearly before every worker. A most valuable method of doing this is found in a good committee system as described in Art. 105 and Fig. 22. Such a system extended to include large joint conferences of executives and workers can do much to leaven the entire working force with the policies of the management and administration. Smaller committees are valuable in enforcing departmental policies. Printed statements and company periodicals are also effective in promulgating general policies. Policies are not self-perpetuating and labor migrates. Building up company morale and making policies effective are, therefore, a constant process of education.

61. Policies and Personality.—The conclusion should not be drawn from the foregoing that policies established through consultation of a number of persons can in any way take the place of leadership and strong personalities. Policies, like the findings of committees, are advisory in character and useless if not put into active service. There is a tendency in all of the literature of modern management to accent the **mechanisms** of management and to overlook the influence and importance of individual intelligence and leadership. Policies alone are not of much avail, but good policies with strong leadership may be very effective. Furthermore, while committees are very valuable in bringing together the many viewpoints necessary to create good policies, they naturally have not the gift of vision and initiative that are the most marked characteristics of great leaders. No enterprise, industrial or otherwise, prospers without able leadership.

62. Analyzing the Industrial Problem.—The analysis of an industrial problem for the purpose of providing organization policies and procedure, whether it be a new enterprise or one already in existence, will vary naturally with the character of the undertaking. Thus a railroad will differ from a department store or a manufacturing plant, but nevertheless there are some characteristics common to almost all industrial plants. A manufacturing plant perhaps involves more complex problems of policy and procedure than any other, and this work deals largely with this form of undertaking, but the principles and practices herein discussed are capable of broad application. In the analysis of a manufacturing plant and the marketing of its product the procedure outlined in the following nine suggestions may well be given consideration.[1]

1. An analysis should be made of the character and purpose of the product to be sold or the service to be rendered to make sure that this product or service is well suited for the purpose in mind. This naturally involves consultations between the designing, sales, and manufacturing departments.

2. An analysis should be made of the possible markets and the ways and means of disposing of the product as described in Art. 60. Marketing has become such a comprehensive subject as to be beyond the limitations of this book and will not be discussed except as it bears upon other topics.

3. A financial study should be made as to the amount of capital necessary and the best means of obtaining the same. Statistics indicate that lack of capital causes more industrial failures than any other cause. Such a study naturally involves the question of ownership of the enterprise.

4. An economic study should be made of the best location for the plant, taking into account markets, transportation, labor, materials, local conditions, etc.

5. An engineering study should be made to determine the best arrangement of buildings and the equipment best suited to the work. In former years plant and equipment were provided in an empirical manner, often on the sole judgment of the superintendent. Today plant design and equipment are highly refined specialties.

6. The principal *functions* of the business should be determined by analysis and the organization of the venture should, in general, be built up by coordinating these functions rather than around individuals, as is sometimes the case. A well-designed organization is like a well-designed machine whose several parts function together perfectly, good management simply directing the coordinated effort. All functions should be clearly defined as well as their relation to each other. It is axiomatic that authority and responsibility must be properly delegated if best results are to be obtained.

[1] For a brief description of the policies of several successful business leaders, see Converse, Paul D., "Selling Policies," Chap. I.

7. Strong executive control must be provided to hold the several functions together and direct their efforts. As previously stated, leadership and vision are always found in individuals and not in groups.

8. When the several functions have been determined the personnel should be selected to fit into these functions. In the older forms of organization the functions were quite frequently dictated by the personalities at hand, and in small enterprises this still may suffice. But in large complex industrial plants it is imperative that the functions should first be determined and the personnel fitted into the general plan, whence has arisen an entirely new field of endeavor—in fact, it is a new function of management, namely, the personnel department, one principal object of which is to keep the several functions supplied with suitable men.

9. It should be remembered that men *live* one-fourth of their lives under the factory roof. Therefore, the conditions of existence in the plant should be of greatest importance, not only because of humanitarian motives but because good working conditions bring better financial returns. Personnel policies as to both employment and working conditions should receive careful attention.

10. Lastly, the relation of the enterprise to the public, whether this concerns city, state, or nation, should be carefully considered and policies adopted that will make for harmonious contacts. This feature has become so important with large industries that *public relations counseling* has become a specialized calling.

Of these ten items the first two lie outside the scope of this book. The chapters that follow are based upon and are an expansion of the last eight items and discuss policies and procedures that flow from them.

A knowledge of the principal causes of failure of industrial and commercial enterprises should be helpful in considering managerial policies. Such information is found in the reports of Dun and Bradstreet, Inc., and the following table is abstracted from their reports. It will be noted that lack of capital and incompetence are responsible for the major portion of the failures. In fact, the first eight causes listed may be considered as forms of incompetence.

TABLE 2.—CAUSES AND PERCENTAGES OF FAILURES

Causes of Failures	1907	1908	1909	1910	1911	1926	1927	1929	1930	1931
Lack of capital	37.1	34.2	34.5	33.9	31.4	32.7	34.9	37.2	31.6	31.5
Incompetence	22.6	21.6	24.2	26.6	27.0	33.9	34.5	31.4	26.3	21.7
Inexperience	4.9	4.0	4.9	4.4	4.1	5.1	5.2	4.9	5.3	4.8
Unwise granting of credit	2.3	2.0	1.9	1.7	2.0	1.7	1.4	2.1	3.5	1.7
Speculation	0.7	1.0	0.8	1.0	....	0.4	0.3	0.3	1.2	....
Personal extravagance	0.9	1.0	0.9	0.7	....	1.3	0.5	0.5	0.7	0.4
Neglect of business	2.5	2.2	3.0	2.5	2.2	1.5	1.1	0.9	0.9	0.5
Fraudulent disposition of property	10.1	11.5	10.8	11.2	10.6	3.8	3.6	1.7	1.2	0.9
Specific conditions (disaster)	16.3	18.9	15.3	14.4	16.9	15.8	14.8	15.6	22.4	33.9
Failure of others	1.4	1.8	1.2	1.0	....	1.2	1.3	1.5	3.4	2.3
Competition	1.2	1.8	2.5	2.6	2.9	2.6	2.4	3.9	3.5	2.3

CHAPTER VII

INDUSTRIAL OWNERSHIP

63. General.—Industry grows naturally out of the needs of community life and the phenomenon of the independent artisan owning his own equipment and catering to the necessities or luxuries of his neighbors goes back to remote antiquity. Our present economic system is founded largely upon the right of the individual to own property and tools and upon the exchange of services in a manner acceptable to the community concerned. As noted in Art. 10, the separation of industry from agriculture had begun even before the Industrial Revolution, and handicraft factories of considerable size had appeared. Until half a century ago, however, the problems of industrial ownership were not very troublesome. But, as explained in Chap. IV, industrial organizations have steadily increased in size and complexity partly because of the economic gains incident to increased size and partly because the broadening of the industrial field necessitates larger plant and capital to satisfy the demand. Growth, as already noted, almost invariably involves a change in the manner of organization of nearly all kinds of industrial undertakings and may also, though not necessarily, require changes in the form of ownership. A clear understanding of modern methods of ownership is necessary for an appreciation of modern methods of industrial organization. The several forms of ownership are as follows:

1. Individual ownership.
2. Partnership.
3. Corporation.
4. Joint-stock association and other forms intermediate between individual ownership and the corporate form.
5. Holding companies.
6. Trusts.
7. Cooperative ownership.
8. Governmental ownership.

64. Individual Ownership.—This form of ownership is, of course, the oldest and simplest and, in some respects, the most natural. Its characteristics are the same no matter how small or how large the undertaking may be. The individual proprietor is the supreme judge of all matters pertaining to his business, subject only to the general laws of the land and to such special legislation as may affect his particular business. He may hire whom he pleases and delegate such powers as he pleases to his employees. He may also conduct any and all lines of industry that he wishes to. The entire responsibility and authority belong to him personally and the profits or losses are his own. His legal liability, on the other hand, covers all his possessions. The individual owner is not required to be legally registered, thus giving public notice of his business intentions, unless he wishes to operate under an assumed name, in which case he must usually register with some public official, and make a full statement regarding the business which he intends to establish, and state the name of the person responsible for all obligations and liabilities of the enterprise.

65. Partnership.—As enterprises grow large the method of individual ownership may become inadequate. The duties and responsibilities may become too arduous for a single individual, or the proprietor may desire to encourage valuable employees by a share in the profits. He may wish to associate with him men having capital or special skill and knowledge, so that for reasons of finance, personal liking, or commercial gain, a partnership is formed. In these days of large undertakings a partnership is often formed at the beginning of the enterprise for reasons that are obvious.

A partnership, or firm, as it is often called, is, then, a group of men who have joined capital or services for the prosecuting of some enterprise. The exact relations and agreements that may exist between or among them may vary. Thus, one man may contribute capital, another experience or services, and another may contribute prestige, in any way that may be agreeable and satisfactory.

The law in general allows a partnership as much freedom as an individual in transacting business, and a partnership like an individual owner may engage in almost any number of legitimate enterprises without legal restriction.

It is evident, however, that since more than one proprietor is interested in the business it is important that the rights, responsibilities, and obligations of a partnership shall be legally defined; hence there is in all states a considerable amount of legal enactment regulating partnership. The necessity of this regulation is clearer when it is considered that every member of a partnership retains certain personal rights and obligations that are not merged into his rights and obligations as a partner. Thus, in general, the law holds the firm, and each and every member thereof, legally and morally liable for any and all acts of every other member, committed in the name of the firm and within the scope of his authority as a member of the same. Each partner is responsible, financially, for all debts and obligations of the partnership, and judgment may be obtained and collection executed against the private property of the individual partners if the assets of the firm are not sufficient to cover the obligations of the firm. On the other hand, a partner is not responsible for the personal obligations of his copartner incurred outside of the scope of his authority as a member of the firm. If a partner has financial difficulties, for instance, in building himself a residence, or if he should commit a felony in some way not connected with the business of his partnership, the firm is not liable, since these acts were not within the scope of his authority as a member of the firm. In fact, a man might be a partner in several enterprises and would be responsible in such a case for the obligations of each firm only as far as his acts were within his authority as a member of each.

While the law, in general, allows a partnership almost as much freedom as an individual there is one form of partnership that is a little more closely restricted, namely, that which is known as a **limited partnership.** In this form of organization a partner may enter a firm under the condition that his liability or obligation is limited to the amount of his contributed capital. In such a case the firm must file a certificate with the proper official stating who the partners are, the extent of their liability, the place of business, etc., and give such publicity to its organization as may be necessary to protect those doing business with them. Usually the capital of each limited partner must be paid in and there must be one partner whose liability is not limited. This form of partnership is not very common in this country.

CORPORATIONS

66. Nature and Classification.—A corporation is, by nature, an artificial person created or authorized by legal statute for some specific purpose. It can have only such rights and privileges as are conferred upon it by law. These rights, privileges, and obligations vary in different states, depending on the nature of the business and the force of public opinion. A corporation is composed, usually, of a number of persons; but it should be especially noted that these members or stockholders are not the corporation, which has an entity of its own and an existence entirely apart from that of its individual members. Consequently a corporation can carry on business in its own name only. A stockholder in a corporation is usually not liable for his indebtedness beyond the amount of his stock, the corporation differing radically in this respect from a partnership. In former times this was not so, and there are still special cases where the stockholder is liable for more than his holdings but, as a general rule, his liabilities are limited to the value of his stock. A stockholder may do business with the corporation, entering into a contract with it. He may sue it and he may be sued by it. In a corporation any man may sell his stock at will and any man, who can, may buy an interest in the form of stock holdings. In this respect, again, the corporation differs radically from the partnership, in which no member can transfer his share of interest to anyone without the consent of the other members of the firm.

A corporation, as before noted, must be created by law. Individual owners may, as before stated, engage in any legitimate business without public notice, but in order to organize a corporation, a certificate of incorporation must be filed with the proper authorities. This certificate must, in general, reveal:

1. The name of the proposed corporation.
2. The purposes for which it is to be formed.
3. The amount of capital stock and its division into common and preferred stock if there is such.
4. The number of shares of capital stock and the value per share. Maximum and minimum limiting values are sometimes placed by law on the value of shares.
5. The location of the principal business office of the corporation.
6. The number of its directors with the names and addresses of the original directors.
7. The names and addresses of the subscribers to the certificate and the number of shares that each agrees to take. The state will then issue a charter to the organizers, authorizing them to engage in the proposed business. A corporation is not, in general, permitted to engage in a business not fairly within the provisions of its charter, though the charter may be, and in the case of large corporations usually is, very broad and liberal.

Corporations are used for such a wide range of purposes that classification based on the purposes for which they are formed is useless and confusing. Thus corporations may be formed to manage a college or a church, an industrial enterprise, a railway system, a bank, or in fact almost any human activity. The only line of demarcation that is logical or useful divides corporations into:

1. **Public corporations.**
2. **Private corporations.**

Public corporations are those formed by a community for governmental control and are often called **municipal corporations.** In general, all other corporations are classed as private corporations. Corporations formed to operate utilities that serve the public, such as railroads, gas and electric lighting plants, telephones, and telegraph systems, are sometimes called **quasi-public corporations,** but if they are conducted for private gain they are properly classed as private ventures. The services which this class of corporations render make them much more interesting and important to the public, and they are increasingly liable to close regulation by legislation; nevertheless, if conducted for private gain, they are not public corporations. The control by the public of quasi-public corporations is especially important in a service that is a natural monopoly.

67. Corporate Powers.—Subject to the laws of the several states a corporation may make contracts concerning its business, borrow money, buy and sell property, acquire its own stock by gift or legitimate purchase, and make rules and by-laws for the administration of its several functions. The latter power may be vested primarily in the stockholders, but they may delegate their power to the directors whom they elect. In general a corporation cannot donate or lend money or endorse promissory notes that may in any way jeopardize the property of the stockholders, though corporations may extend credit to their customers. In many respects it will be noted that the directors of a corporation, being the custodians of other people's funds, have not the same liberty in employing these funds as has the individual or the partnership that owns its own property outright.

68. Capital and Capital Stock.—**The capitalization or capital stock** of a corporation is the nominal capital authorized by its charter; that is, the number of authorized shares multiplied by their **par** or **face value** as fixed by the charter. These shares of stock are freely transferable and may be bought and sold at the market price like any other commodity. When a person acquires an interest in a corporation he is said to become a **stockholder** and his interest is expressed in shares of stock. The visible evidence of ownership is the **stock certificate** which certifies that the person whose name appears on the certificate owns a specific number of shares. Since these certificates are freely transferable, it follows that the owners of a corporation may be, and often are, a constantly shifting group. Any purchaser of stock may have the certificates that he acquires exchanged for new certificates made out in his name, by presenting the old certificates properly endorsed by the former owner. The corporation recognizes as voters only those whose names are listed on its stock books at the time of voting, and the voting power of a member is measured by the number of his shares. The interest that any stockholder possesses in a corporation by virtue of his possession of stock certificates is an **undivided** interest; that is, he cannot withdraw the value represented by his certificate from the corporation which, as before stated, is an entity that cannot be divided unless the affairs of the concern are closed up and the residual assets after liquidating all liabilities divided, in which case each stockholder would receive his pro rata share.

The entire amount of stock authorized by the charter of a corporation need not necessarily be issued. When stock certificates are issued, and paid for in full, they are designated as **full paid.** If any authorized stock remains unissued it is called **unissued stock.** Evidently such unissued stock has potential value only and cannot be considered at asset. If stock is issued and paid for in full and then by gift or purchase comes again into the possession of the corporation it is called **treasury stock** and is usually treated as an asset.

Stock may be of two kinds, namely, **common** or **preferred.** Common stock is the general or ordinary stock of a corporation which has neither special privilege nor restriction of any kind. Preferred stock is stock having some special preference over other kinds in the matters of dividends or assets of the corporation. Thus a corporation may issue both common and preferred stock, binding itself to pay a definite dividend on the preferred stock before any common stock can receive a dividend. In some states it is provided by law that preferred stock may not receive over a given percentage of the par value in dividends. After the dividends on preferred stock are paid the remaining profits are usually divided equally among the common stock, though sometimes the preferred stock also participates with the common stock in such further distribution of profits.

In recent years a number of states have passed laws permitting the issuance of **no-par stock,** so-called. The real value of a share of common stock is dependent upon the earnings of the corporation and hence this value may vary widely from any par value that may be fixed. Advocates of no-par stock argue that the new practice tends to reduce self-deception and to prevent the sales of stock at a value higher than its real worth. There is probably some logic in this contention, though it is obvious that it may be more difficult to sell stock of an unassigned value and there may be some difficulties in recording the value of no-par stock on the corporate accounts. However, the practice appears to be increasing.

69. Bonds.—The difference between stocks and **bonds** should be carefully noted. When a corporation borrows money the lender may receive a bond as visual evidence of the transaction and he thereby becomes a **bondholder.** Bonds, like stock, may be bought and sold in the market but unlike stock the bond permits its owner no voice in the management of the enterprise. The stockholder is an owner, the bondholder only a creditor. As in the case of any other debt, interest must be paid upon a bond in priority to dividends upon stock of any kind. The interests of bondholders and stockholders, therefore, may be radically opposed. A bondholder will be desirous of keeping the real capital of the company intact since that is his security for payment of his loan. A stockholder is interested in dividends and does not usually care whether they come out of profit or are a part of capital itself, as is sometimes the case where the enterprise is badly managed. These differences of opinion are often important where such matters as appraisal and depreciation are concerned.

Bonds may be classified as

1. Mortgage or secured bonds.
2. Debenture or unsecured bonds.

A mortgage bond is one the payment of which is secured by a mortgage upon some real property of the borrower. It should be noted that a bond and a mortgage are two entirely distinct documents. Mortgage bonds also may be *first, second, third,* etc., mortgage bonds according to priority of claim. If the interest on the bonds is not paid the bondholders may apply for a receivership, taking the control of the property from the directors and selling the property to satisfy the mortgage.

Debenture bonds are mere promises to pay, though often given high-sounding titles, such as "gold debenture" to make them appear attractive. They are often issued in order to secure working capital. Should the corporation default in the payment of the interest upon debenture bonds, the corporation may be sued as in the case of any other debt, but debenture bonds cannot be used as a basis for foreclosing upon the property. Debentures take priority over stock in the payment of returns, but it is obvious that such bonds can be marketed only when the general reputation of the corporation is high and the interest rate offered attractive. The expected lifetime of a bond is fixed at issuance, but it is not uncommon for a corporation to recall a bond issue before maturity at terms advantageous to the bondholders. This may be done by issuing a new series of bonds to replace the issue that is recalled, in which case the new series is known as **refunding bonds.** Sometimes a company may own the bonds of a subsidiary company and *guarantee* their value. Such bonds are called **guaranteed bonds** and obviously their value is dependent upon the financial condition of the holding corporation as far as any guarantee of value is concerned.

70. Capitalization and Assets.—A clear distinction should be made, also, between the *capital stock* of a corporation and the assets or actual property that the stock is presumed to represent. The capital stock, as before noted, is the total amount of the stock authorized by the charter. It is fixed by the charter and may not be changed except by authority of the state. The true value of the property that the corporation possesses may or may not be the same as the capital stock.

In conservative enterprises the capital stock usually corresponds, in the beginning, to the actual value of the assets, that is, for every dollar of stock issued by the corporation it receives a dollar in cash or property. When, however, the enterprise becomes active, the actual value of the assets may be greater or less than the capitalization, depending on the success of the business. In enterprises of a speculative character the capital stock is often intentionally fixed greatly in excess of the value of the real assets, either to sell the stock profitably at a price below its apparent value, or in the hope that the future earnings will justify the capitalization. Such enterprises are said to be **overcapitalized** and the stock is said to be **watered.** The same result occurs when a corporation takes over a property, issuing stock certificates in payment thereof, the face value of which is greatly in excess of the real value of the property taken over. Even in such cases, however, there may be intangible assets such as goodwill, trade-marks, etc., that may justify the overcapitalization so far as earning power is concerned. In fact, in some enterprises, such as magazines and other publications, the greatest asset that they possess is goodwill, or "capitalized earning power," as it has been called, and in the case of a successful publication this may be a very valuable asset, though strictly speaking, an intangible one. There is, nevertheless, a growing tendency to prohibit the watering of stock.

The **net worth** of a business is the difference between its assets and its liabilities. In a corporation the net worth is equal to the par value of the capital stock, plus the surplus or minus the deficit due to trading, at the time under consideration. If there are no liabilities the net worth is the value of all the assets possessed by the corporation. The market value of a share of stock will depend, therefore, on the relation that exists between the net worth, the amount of stock issued, and the earning power of the corporation. If the net worth is greatly in excess of the issued stock, and if the dividends be high, the value of each share of stock is enhanced and it may sell at a price considerably **above par.** If the dividends should fall, without change in the net worth, the market price of the stock would decrease so that even in such a case it might sell **below par.** If the net worth decreases, the stock may fall in value even though the earning capacity remains good; while it is evident that any variation in the earning power will cause a similar variation in the market value of the stock. The effects of these influences are modified, also, by the general reputation and standing of the enterprise and the consequent confidence that the public may have in the success of the venture. It should be noted that the term *net* worth as here used is not synonymous with *actual net value,* since the assets, as before noted, may contain intangible assets which, nevertheless, are often very valuable.

The assets of a concern that are permanent in nature, such as buildings, real estate, machinery, etc., are known as **fixed assets.** Assets that are constantly changing in character and relative amounts, such as cash, accounts and notes receivable, merchandise, etc., are called **quick** or **current assets** or **floating capital** (see Art. 102).

71. Corporate Organization. Directorate.—The actual management of a corporation is vested in a board of directors elected by the stockholders, usually for a term of one year. (Bondholders, it will be noted, have no vote.) The directors elect the officers of the company and appoint all important officials. In some states the law requires that certain specified officers, such as president, secretary, and treasurer, shall be elected or appointed. In large organizations there are usually several vice presidents, each at the head of an important branch of the work, the exact organization varying with the work (see Fig. 13). The powers that may be vested in any one officer will, of course, vary with circumstances. Very often an executive committee composed of a small number of directors that can be called together quickly and easily for consultation with the president or general manager, is given large discretionary powers, but, in general, very important issues are settled by the full board of directors. The question of directorship is hence an important one and often leads to strenuous efforts to obtain control of stock so as to influence the election of these important officers.

72. Advantages and Disadvantages.—The corporate form of organization has several advantages over the simple partnership. Evidently a large number of people can participate in an enterprise by this method and a large amount of capital can be assembled, though no one stockholder may be a large investor. The method, therefore, lends itself readily to enterprises involving large capital outlay. There is an element of *permanency* about a corporation that cannot be attained by a partnership, since the continuity of a corporation is not seriously affected by a change in either the management or the owners. The death of a partner may seriously affect a partnership and the death of a single proprietor may close up the business; but the death, or withdrawal, of any number of stockholders or directors does not necessarily affect the corporation which, as before noted, has an entity of its own. Disputes over the ownership of stock, even in adjusting the estates of the deceased, can have no effect on the corporation. In fact, enterprises that are really individually owned are sometimes incorporated, the owner giving or selling a few shares to friends or relatives so that the business may be organized in such a manner as to insure its continuance after his death. For these reasons there is an increasing tendency to incorporate industrial enterprises. The *Bulletin*[1] *of Manufacturers* of the Thirteenth Census of the United States reports that in 1904, 23.6 per cent of the total number of manufacturing establishments of the country were incorporated; in 1909 the percentage had risen to 25.9. The corresponding percentages of the value of the goods manufactured for the same years is given as 73.7 and 79 per cent of the totals. In 1929 the percentage of corporate ownership had risen to 48.3; corporations employed 90 per cent of the workers and produced 92.2 per cent of the value of all manufactured goods.

On the other hand, the buying of stock in any incorporated enterprise requires care and insight for success. From the foregoing it is clear that assets and capital stock are two very different things and unless a buyer has a good knowledge of the real state of the affairs of the corporation in which he invests, the investment is more or less of a hazard. Again, stockholders who do not agree with the methods of the managing directors have no means of changing those methods if they are a minority of

[1] See *Bulletin of Manufactures* of the Thirteenth Census of the United States, p. 24.

the stockholders. If the majority of the stock is held by a few men they can dominate the policy of the business without regard to the opinions of the minority.

The many and varied issues that have risen in connection with corporations have given rise to a large number of legal enactments known usually as **corporation law.** As enterprises have grown in size and power they have in very many cases not only evaded the limitations of the law, but have been oppressive to other interests. There is an ever-increasing tendency to regulate all forms of corporate ownership much more strictly than in the past, especially where the enterprise is of a quasi-public nature. This legal regulation of corporate organizations is one of the most important and also most difficult problems that faces us today. As has been shown in Chap. IV, the natural tendency of all successful enterprises is to increase in size because of economic considerations. To permit corporations to grow to large size and at the same time to insure the return to the common people of the benefits so derived seems to be no easy task. The federal government through the Securities Exchange Commission regulates the issuing and sale of stock of all corporations doing an interstate business.

73. Joint-stock Association, Etc.—The most manifest disadvantage of individual ownership and partnership is continuity of life of the enterprise when death or withdrawal of a partner occurs. To obviate this and secure the permanence inherent in the corporation and at the same time avoid some of the complexity and disadvantages of incorporation a number of hybrid forms of organization have been devised. One of the best known of these is the **joint-stock association,** which is a partnership with certain peculiar features that bear some resemblance to those of a corporation. Its organization must be authorized by law, and it may assume a corporate name. It may issue stock to its members and this stock is transferable. It is formed, however, by mutual agreement of the members, and no publication of its articles of organization is required. The members, however, are individually liable for all debts and obligations of the association after the property of the association is exhausted. This form of organization is of little utility and is not often used. The name, however, should not be confused with that of *stock corporations*, which are very different in character.

Another device for compromising the advantages and disadvantages of the partnership and the corporation is the **close corporation.** Under this form of organization the shares of stock are all held by a comparatively small group of men, the stock is not on sale publicly, and a partner must give the other members of the corporation an opportunity to purchase his stock before disposing of it to an outsider. A few states have made provision for other modified forms of corporate ownership but since, for the most part, these plans restrict the operations of the corporation to the particular state in which it is formed, they are not of sufficient importance to merit discussion here.

74. Holding Companies—Trusts.—Any industrial enterprise may be owned in any one of the four ways enumerated and any such enterprise could by purchase extend its control over other plants in the direction of either integration or consolidation (see Art. 25) without change in the method of ownership. If, however, a number of industrial organizations should desire to combine in some manner so as to obtain the benefits of concerted action and increased size *and still retain their identity*, a different problem is presented. Many efforts have been made to control markets and prices by concerted efforts running all the way from **informal agreements** between competitors to the more formal combinations of enterprises known as **holding companies** and **trusts.** A. D. Cloud writes[1] of holding companies as follows:

> Holding companies, strictly speaking, are those which are formed to hold stock of other corporations while undertaking no operations themselves. They are purely administrative in function and are permitted in states where corporations are not prohibited from holding stock in other corporations. Rights of ownership are exercised by a duly appointed officer of the holding company. In general they are not permitted too great a diversity in the purposes of the companies whose stocks they own. Thus, where the law requires charter powers to be confined to certain related businesses, the device of the holding company will not be permitted to circumvent the law by diversification of the corporate objects. The holding company has the advantage of permitting corporations in various states to have a central authority of management and a central source of responsibility in the inauguration of policies. A company may be conducting operations and holding the stock of another company. In this case it is generally referred to as the **parent company** with the company whose stock is held as the **subsidiary.**

In the **trust** form of organization *nominal ownership* of the property or properties is placed in the hands of **trustees** who have full power to administer these properties but must pay the *income* to the real owners or beneficiaries. The device is quite frequently resorted to in making wills by men who wish to hold their property intact after death. In this form of ownership the full title and entire control of the properties are placed in the trustees. Each beneficiary or real owner has a claim against the trustees personally so far as his holdings go, but no claim against the trust property, in somewhat the same manner as a stockholder in a corporation. The beneficiaries have no legal redress directly against an outsider in his relations to the trust but must act through the trustees.

In forming such a **business trust** the member corporations or individuals assign their respective investments to a board of directors in trust for the purposes of the business, the agreement usually describing

[1] See ALFORD, L. P. (Ed.), "Management's Handbook," p. 240.

these purposes and naming in detail the duties and responsibilities of the members as well as providing for management of the business and ownership rights and responsibilities of the members. As evidence of ownership, member organizations or individuals have certificates of interest which indicate their respective rights in the income of the property placed in trust. The agreement also provides for the distribution of the property to the original owners upon the dissolution of the trust agreement.

It will be obvious that both holding companies and trusts may be used in integrating and consolidating industries, as described in Arts. 34 and 35, so that, aside from the advantages enumerated in the foregoing, they may be, and are, employed to strengthen the competitive power of the group so bonded together. The trust form of thus bonding a number of enterprises together was first used, and because of the abuse of this competitive power the term has become synonymous with *monopoly* and has been the cause of much *antitrust legislation* so called. The trust form of ownership is less used than formerly, the tendency being to use the holding company for integrating and consolidating large enterprises where this is permitted. Many large holding companies have been formed in this country, particularly in the field of public utilities. Because of their tendency toward monopoly, the federal government has recently enacted rather drastic legislation limiting the scope of holding companies so far as interstate commerce is concerned.

75. Cooperative Ownership.—No discussion of industrial ownership would be complete without brief notice, at least, of cooperative ownership. The term **cooperative** in its present accepted sense refers to a union of individuals "formed for the purpose of obtaining goods, especially the necessaries of life, at rates lower than the market prices by means of cooperative stores or for the prosecution in common of a productive enterprise, the profits being shared in accordance with the amount of capital or labor contributed by each member." It is important to note that these organizations operate within the capitalistic system.

Cooperative ownership as a means of equalizing the inequalities of the present industrial system has been advanced by many able men[1] ever since the inception of the factory system. Robert Owen is credited with giving the movement a great impetus through his socialistic experiments in England, at New Harmony, Indiana, and elsewhere. Cooperative schemes are not new[2] and under simple conditions of living and more uniform requirements of those concerned than can, as a usual thing, be found in the present industrial world, such schemes may be successfully operated. Theoretically, it would seem possible that men could combine their interests and share their profits fairly and amicably; but in the

[1] GIBBINS, H. DE B., "The Industrial History of England."

[2] *Ibid.*

practical working out of such schemes there are many difficulties. In fact, in the present era, those cooperative schemes of large size that may lay claim to any great degree of success have been confined to commercial rather than industrial enterprises or have been operated by people held together by some kind of artificial bond, as for instance some form of common religion that has had a unifying and leveling effect.

If the requirements of the industrial field were uniform and if all men were equally able, mentally and bodily, the case would be different. The needs of the industrial field are many and varied, requiring men of all grades and capacities; and the diverse requirements of the field are equaled only by the differences in the capacities and abilities of men. Even though common ownership in comparatively small undertakings be granted as a possibility, the equal division of profits, so much talked about, is possible only through universal mediocrity or a spirit of self-sacrifice on the part of the more able members of society far greater than has ever been displayed in this era. In this last respect the present generation is somewhat behind some civilizations that have preceded them. Society has, in general, always had to pay for services rendered in proportion to their value, and it is difficult to conceive of the efficient operation of the present industrial methods on the ground of common ownership without such differences in compensation as will most naturally tend to perpetuate the economic and social differences that are now complained of.

76. Governmental Ownership.—Theories concerning governmental ownership cover a wide range of opinion. On the one extreme is the communistic theory that would place, at least, the most important natural resources and productive facilities under governmental ownership. This is the theory that the Russian government has tried to make effective. At this time it cannot be said that this experiment has been attended with much success, nor does it appear that it will eventually be successful. But out of it may come some modified form of governmental ownership that may be a challenge to other nations, many of which are already permeated with socializing ideas. The communistic idea[1] is a very old one but as yet not a single instance of its successful application on a large scale has been seen.

On the other extreme is the theory of governmental *control* of the national resources and facilities of production as illustrated by the dictatorships of Germany and Italy. It is too early as yet fully to appraise these experiments in industrial and agricultural regimentation, but all history[2] indicates that dictatorships are short-lived.

[1] "The Republic" by Plato advances communistic theories and discusses the difficulties of applying them.

[2] *Ibid.*

In this country governmental ownership presents a varied picture. It has long been recognized that municipalities have a logical right to own their utilities, such as lighting plants, water works, street railways, etc. No one questions the right or desirability of having the several states own roads, canals, parks, etc. The federal government owns and operates the post office system, the lighthouse service, many national parks, highways, and waterways. The federal government has also from time to time built public improvements that benefited large areas but which were too large and costly for any private company or state to undertake. The Boulder Dam, the Columbia River dams, and certain large irrigation projects are of this character. And logically the federal government might own and operate the railways and telephone and telegraph lines, since they serve *national* needs; whether it would be economical or expedient for it to do so is debatable. Until very recently, however, the federal government has been very considerate of state rights and has exercised control over industry through regulatory commissions only. The more recent acquisition by the federal government of properties such as the Tennessee Valley dams has brought it into direct competition with private industry. This matter is more fully discussed in Art. 318.

These illustrations are mentioned solely to indicate a definite trend toward governmental ownership that private ownership should recognize. For there is a vast difference between governmental ownership of a limited number of state-wide or nation-wide utilities and governmental ownership of the majority of the national resources and productive facilities. The arguments for and against such ownership are many and embrace a voluminous literature; but it may be noted that all the economic arguments directed against the great size of some existing private enterprises apply with much greater force to governmental ownership (Art. 37). The costly and inefficient bureaucratic and political control of existing state and national functions may well serve as a measure of what must necessarily occur with any large degree of governmental ownership.

Nevertheless, these socializing doctrines have had and will continue to have a profound influence upon our ideas of ownership. They have already resulted in governmental regulation that would have been considered impossible[1] a few years ago, and, if then possible, would have been considered an infringement of personal liberty. No one, whether interested in industry as an owner or as an employee, can afford not to study these tendencies carefully. They come as a direct protest against the social differences resulting from the absolute separation of the worker from the tools of production, and are an effort to restore that lost owner-

[1] Note, for instance, the legal regulation of the price of upper Pullman berths.

ship. **Governmental regulation** even now prevails; how far we in this country may go in **governmental ownership** is a problem not of the next century, but of tomorrow.

References

"Accountant's Handbook," p. 188.
CONYNGTON, THOMAS: "The Modern Corporation."
CROSS, M. C., "Types of Business Enterprise."
GIBBINS, H. DE B.: "The Industrial History of England."
JONES, LLOYD: "The Life of Robert Owen."

CHAPTER VIII

LOCATION, ARRANGEMENT, AND CONSTRUCTION OF INDUSTRIAL PLANTS

PLANT LOCATION

77. Industrial Engineering.—The **location** and **arrangement** of industrial plants have not, in general, received attention commensurate with their economic value. In small shops that supply local demands **equipment** and **management** are no doubt the most important factors in economic production, but as plants have increased in size and markets have become more widespread, the problems of transportation of both raw and finished material and the economic handling of material in process have become increasingly important. Questions regarding power, labor, taxes, and many others that may be comparatively unimportant in the small local factory assume greater proportions when a large undertaking is planned.

The older and still common custom of having the manufacturing superintendent plan and build additions to the plant, or even plan an entire new plant, is no longer productive of best results in large undertakings. The manufacturing expert may be a good judge of the necessary factory tools and appliances, but he is, in most instances, poorly informed regarding the latest economies in power-plant construction or electric lighting and similar correlated problems that have become specialties. The location, construction, equipment, and operation of a large modern industrial plant may require the services of many specialized advisers, and the work of directing such experts is rapidly coming to be recognized as a business in itself and has been named **industrial engineering** (see Art. 89).

78. Location of Plant.—It is well known that industries of different kinds tend to concentrate in different parts of the country. Thus, spinning, weaving, and shoemaking are among the great industries of Massachusetts and Rhode Island. Connecticut has long been a leader in brass goods, and Pennsylvania in carpets. On the other hand, industry may move from place to place. In general, of course, industry will follow population. Thus in this country the center of population has moved west steadily, being located in 1930 near Linton, Greene County, Indiana. The center of manufactures has followed somewhat in the rear. It was last located by the Census of 1920 near Whitehall, Indiana. It must not be assumed, however, that industrial markets necessarily follow population proportionally as these are naturally affected by climate and other natural conditions. In addition to this general movement, entire industries may leave one locality and move to another because of economic conditions. Thus, the New England states are no longer preeminent in certain fields of manufacture that had their origin in that section, economic relations between raw material and markets having given some westerly and southern states such a manufacturing advantage as to cause, in some cases, an almost complete removal of the industry to other localities. On the other hand, some of the older states have held firmly to manufacturing industries for which they possess no raw material, against all the competition of other states possessing not only raw material in abundance, but equal, if not better, facilities for transporting the finished product to market. The jewelry and silverware industry of Rhode Island, and the brass industry of Connecticut are striking examples of this persistence. The geographical trend of manufacturing is, therefore, an important factor in locating an industry and is worthy of careful consideration in locating a new plant or moving an old one.

The factors that govern the location of industries are obviously many and complex. The Twelfth Census of the United States in a most illuminating article (see volume on Manufactures, p. ccx) lists the following as the most important causes that govern plant location:

1. Nearness to materials.
2. Nearness to markets.
3. Water power.
4. A favorable climate.
5. A supply of labor.
6. Capital available for investment in manufactures.
7. The momentum of an early start.

The first two are, of course, fundamental. Without material, manufacturing is impossible and without markets it is useless. They are, also, of prime importance, economically, in localizing industry within a comparatively limited area. Other things being equal, industry naturally locates near the market it serves, since it must necessarily be the result of either a demand from the market or an effort to create such a demand. The location of the supply of raw material has usually, however, a modifying influence, and the result is often a compromise which is also affected greatly by the question of transportation. Clearly, there is no economy in shipping bulky raw material great distances if the larger part of it becomes waste in the process of manufacturing. For this reason industries, such as paper making, that depend on forest products are likely to be found near the forests. Packing houses are placed near stock-raising centers and pottery industries near clay beds. On the other hand, wool grown in the western states can, perhaps, be more economically manufactured at present on the Atlantic seaboard. In the case of copper products the ore is reduced near the mine, since its transportation for any great distance is, in general, prohibitive. The ingot copper obtained in Montana, for instance, may be economically transported to Connecticut, manufactured into many kinds of products, and the small portion of these products used in Montana shipped back to that state for consumption. It is also obvious that the influence of these two items, nearness to markets and nearness to raw materials, grows less as the cost of transportation is reduced. If the transportation charges are small, then one or the other or both of the last two influences, labor and power, may be predominating factors, and both raw material and finished product may be economically transported considerable distances to take advantage of the market. Thus Australia exports vast amounts of raw wool and Egypt exports much raw cotton. It is a rare instance, however, when the influence of any one of these causes fixes definitely the geographical location of an industry. Each case presents combinations of its own that must be carefully considered in making a decision. As will be seen presently, these last two influences, labor and power, also affect the exact location of an industry within the somewhat wide geographical limits fixed by the above general considerations.

In the early days of manufacturing the economic advantages of water power were considerable. New England owes her manufacturing greatness in no small measure to the manufacturing advantages obtained from her abundant waterfalls. Cheap coal and fuel oil have given other localities an equal or greater advantage, temporarily; but these water powers and others in the country are sure to be of increasing strategic importance in the future, and western cities that owe their existence to great waterfalls have, therefore, a reasonable assurance of continued prosperity as the country develops around them.

The effect of climate has also been much modified in many industries by artificial methods. Thus the advantages of a moist climate in spinning, as enjoyed by Fall River and New Bedford, have been nullified by artificial methods whereby the temperature and humidity of weaving and spinning floors are held to a uniformity impossible under natural conditions. The effect of climate upon the producing power of men who must work out of doors is still an important feature. On the Pacific Coast men can work practically all the year round at shipbuilding with great comfort and efficiency as compared with the Atlantic seaboard.

The need of an adequate supply of labor is obvious, but a number of considerations such as the cost of living and the character of the labor available both as to skill and temperament should be taken into account. Thus a silk mill may be located in or near a large town where heavy machinery is manufactured in order to utilize the labor of women and girls who otherwise would not be employed, and manufacturing plants have been known to move to a new location in order to escape labor-union regulations.

As before noted, the economic conditions that lead to the establishing of an industry may change, especially in a new country like America. If these economic changes are great enough, they may so influence industry as to make it migrate long distances. On the other hand, industries often persist and prosper long after the economic balance is apparently greatly against their location. Of the above-named influences that tend to give inertia to established industry, labor supply is, perhaps, the most important. It takes *time* to build up an industrial community, and once built up it is not so easy to transport as it is to transport machinery. Skilled workmen will not, as a rule, leave their native environment without a considerable increase in wages, and even then they easily become discontented and return home if the surroundings are not congenial. There is, therefore, a certain amount of **inertia** that attaches itself to industry when *it has once been successful in a given place.* Many of the early manufacturing enterprises of New England were started in one place or another simply by chance circumstances. The enterprise prospered, others grew up by imitation, or as branches, specialization brought in subsidiary occupations, a large amount of local capital became interested, the whole movement gathering an inertia that often more than compensated for lack of other economic advantages, (see Art. 18). If Samuel Slater had located in Philadelphia instead of Providence the localization of textile manufacturing would have been very different. It is through influences such as these that New England has stubbornly and successfully held the supremacy in certain lines of manufacturing, though the economic advantages leading to their establishment have in great measure passed to other states. In a general way people are likely to feel confidence in an industry that is being started in a locality where similar ventures have been successful, and this adds to the momentum noted above.

It should be noted, therefore, that as any country develops industrially, as transportation becomes more effective and good labor supply more widespread, the intelligent location of manufacturing enterprises must be governed increasingly by strict economic considerations and less by inherited influences. This can be more readily seen by considering the establishment of a new industry in which the inertia of age has not appeared.

79. The Economic Survey.—It will appear from the foregoing that the location of an enterprise that is to serve a wide territory is not a simple matter. It is obvious also that the cost of any commodity to a given consumer consists of three elements, namely the cost of gathering the raw material at some point, the cost of fabricating it, and the cost of delivering the finished product to the customer. *The most advantageous location is that at which the cost of gathering material and fabricating it plus the cost of distributing the finished product to the customers will be a minimum.* The point where manufacturing costs will be a minimum is not necessarily the point at which distribution costs will be the lowest, and therefore there are two distinct problems involved. Thus it might be possible to produce cement at some point where fuel and suitable shale are very cheap and the plant might not be able to compete with less well-situated plants much nearer the market. The first step in such a problem therefore is a market survey as described briefly in Art. 62. This is necessary whether the product is already on the market or whether a market is being sought for a new product. The location and extent of these possible markets upon a map of the territory covered give the basis of transportation and distributing costs from any given point.

In evaluating the most advantageous point for manufacturing, there are certain elements that can be computed. Thus the cost of land, labor, and materials, taxes, heat, light, and power are all items that can be determined for any given location. From any advantageous location so determined the costs of distribution can be computed and comparisons made between several locations. Obviously this is not a problem that can be solved explicitly by formula but is rather one of "cut-and-try" method. But no large plant that is expected to serve a wide territory should be located without such a survey. This is particularly true where there are to be centralized fabrication and decentralized distribution of the finished product, or decentralized assembling of product as conducted by the Ford Motor Company and in other lines of product suitable for "knock-down" transportation.

Such a study will give a sound basis for the primary consideration of plant location. But in addition there may be many other considerations involving judgment rather than mathematics that must be considered. Thus the need of pure water as in some paper mills, the necessity of disposing of large amounts of waste, the problem of smoky chimneys, the attitude of neighboring communities, the attitude of local labor, the necessity of near-by banking facilities and a supply of capital may, one and all, be modifying factors that must be evaluated in considering the bare economic aspects of the case. But it will be clear that an approach to the problem as outlined in the foregoing is much more likely to result in a wise selection than the empirical haphazard methods formerly so much in use.

While the above considerations operate to locate industries within comparatively wide areas, some of them, in connection with other influences, must also be considered in fixing the exact location of the plant within the given area. Among the many considerations that may influence the exact location the following may be noted.

1. Transportation facilities.
2. Initial building requirements and possibility of expansion.
3. Labor supply.
4. Dependence on other industries.
5. Financial considerations.
6. Relative value of community restrictions and aid.
7. Relative value of local markets.

A more coherent idea of the relative value of these several influences may be obtained by considering the relative merits of the three classes of location open to the prospective manufacturer, namely—**city, country,** or **suburban.**

Cities, being natural centers for trunk lines or water transportation, usually offer superior advantages for obtaining raw materials and shipping finished goods. An abundant labor supply is obtainable as compared with other localities. If the plant is small and dependent on other industries as, for instance, repair shops, or some closely articulated industry, the city offers superior advantages, when these other industries are present, as they usually are. It is often easier to finance an undertaking in the city; cities offering better fields for obtaining subscriptions to stock or obtaining special inducements to locate, such as exemption from taxes or even large cash bonuses to assist in starting the enterprise. If the plant is small, and is supplying the local market alone, the city offers market advantages that would not be so important to a larger plant. A plant located in a city enjoys municipal advantages such as good streets, sewers, gas, police protection, fire protection, etc.

As opposed to these advantages, the city location has the disadvantage that land is high priced, and it is very often difficult for large works to secure a site within a city where buildings exactly suited to the purpose desired can be erected without great expense; and if the city is a growing one the taxes in time make the location too expensive. This is one of the reasons why many factories within recent years have been compelled to move to the country or the suburbs. City restrictions regarding smoke and other municipal ordinances governing industry are questions that must be carefully considered. While labor may be abundant in the city the cost of living, and hence the wages paid, are, in general, higher than in the country.

The advantages of a location in the country are not so numerous as those of the city, but they are often of paramount importance. Thus, if water power is obtainable or if a supply of pure water is necessary, as in paper making, a country site may be very desirable. Land is cheap in the country and hence the factory can be built to suit the exact needs of the industry and ample provision made for growth. Taxes are low and restrictive ordinances not likely to hamper the activity of the plant. The larger the plant the less it is dependent on other industries and hence the country site, in general, appeals to the large operator more than to a small one. The local market is, likewise, likely to be of less interest to the large plant. Undesirable neighbors can be more easily avoided in a country location and the danger from fire and other hazards resulting from surrounding industries are also minimized.

On the other hand, the labor supply of the country is usually a troublesome problem. The city offers advantages and amusements to the working classes that cannot be had in the country. An effort is often made to offset these attractions by building model factory villages where employees may acquire homes on easy terms and enjoy the healthful life of the country. The employer that engages in such an enterprise must of course expect to feel a greater responsibility toward his employees than he would in a city where the bond is much looser. But such work as this is worth while, and no doubt the near future will see a great amount of decentralizing of industry from the thickly congested centers in favor of country locations. Just as it is difficult to induce labor to leave the cities, so it is difficult to attract them away from good country industries if the conditions of life are made attractive; and labor troubles are likely to be less in a country location than in a congested city.

The suburbs of many cities offer a compromise between the city and the country and possess many of the benefits of both. Land can be obtained at a price far below that for city property, and bus lines and automobiles have made living in the suburbs cheaper than in the city, and yet made it possible for the suburban dweller to take advantage of the attractions of the city. An examination of any of our large cities will show an immense amount of manufacturing in the suburbs, this location being particularly advantageous for fair-sized plants.

From the above it will appear that the city location, in general, offers greatest attractions to the small plant, the suburbs are best adapted to fair-sized plants, and the country offers by far the greatest attraction and fewest disadvantages to the very large plant, provided an adequate supply of labor can be obtained.

The truth of these observations is borne out by the large number of industrial plants of moderate size that have moved, in recent years, to suburban locations, and the increasing tendency for very large enterprises to seek advantageous locations in the country and there build up industrial villages or even fair-sized towns that will provide the living conditions necessary to make the workers contented. Further reference to the problem of establishing such industrial centers is made in Chap. XXIV.

It is not possible to formulate the requirements of factory locations as regards levelness of the land, character of the soil, etc., since some of these vary widely with the needs of the industry. Some industries, such as ore-concentrating plants, require a steep hillside in order to utilize gravity. Other plants must have a flat plot of ground. One of the most successful plants that the writer knows of is built on solid rock at a considerable expense for excavating; another, equally successful, stands on made ground covering a veritable bog. If all the other economic features of the site are satisfactory these conditions are, in most cases, not so important unless the cost of preparing the site is excessive. Large cities have been built on very poor soil simply because of the strategic importance of the spot or from the accident of original location. Care should be exercised, however, that the factory site chosen is well protected from such occasional accidents as floods. One of the largest manufacturing companies in this country has lost large sums of money by occasional inundation and has spent large sums in making its site safe against periodic occurrence of such disasters, the plant having grown so large that it would be too expensive to move elsewhere.

PLANT ARRANGEMENT

80. Classification of Industries.—Any intelligent discussion of plant organization or equipment must necessarily be based upon an understanding of certain characteristics that industry has developed in its progress from handicraft to some of its more modern forms. Some of these characteristics will now be briefly discussed.

Manufacturing industries are, broadly speaking, of two general classes, namely, **continuous** and **intermittent.** In a continuous process the material flows consecutively through a series of machines or processes that operate as a unit, the amount of material flowing through any set of machines or process being a constant at any time. A continuous process may be either **analytical** or **synthetical;** that is, it may take some natural product and separate it into component parts or change its general form; as, for instance, the industries built on salt products, ore, oil and sugar refineries, saw mills, etc. Or it may take a few natural products and passing them through fixed processes build them up into some other form, as may be seen in paint works and wall-paper factories. In general, such industries deal only with a few raw materials, these passing in at one end of the factory and *flowing*, so to speak, through a number of fixed processes and passing out at the other end in the form of a limited number of finished products and by-products. Chemical plants and automobile factories are generally of this continuous type. The organization that the personnel of such a plant will most naturally take will depend on the character of the industry, but will, in general, be comparatively simple.

Intermittent or interrupted-process industries, on the other hand, may take many kinds of raw material, carry them to any desired stage of completion, store the finished or semifinished parts if necessary, and assemble the various kinds of finished products as the market requires. This finished product may cover a wide range, both as to relative size and character. Shipbuilding plants, agricultural-implement works, and plants manufacturing electrical machinery are excellent examples of interrupted industries which form by far the larger part of organized industry. The above classification is, of course, not clearly defined; in fact, these types of industry represent extreme cases rather than distinct classes. The natural tendency toward specialization tends constantly to limit the range of intermittent processes and this, in any extreme case, might reduce a factory of the intermittent type to one of the continuous type. Thus in many plants such as those building machine tools the work is passed through the shop in large lots periodically, thus obtaining some of the advantages of quantity production. A large number of machine frames or a large number of machine spindles may thus be made on the same shop order and stored in a **finished-stores** department pending the needs of the assembly department. In some such factories assembly is conducted by drawing entirely upon finished stores and not directly upon the machining departments. This method of production is sometimes called the **lot-repetitive** method and obviously, if the lot orders are repeated in rapid frequency, continuous production results. Many plants have continuous, lot-repetitive, and other processes of markedly intermittent character all going on at the same time. Plants of this kind are naturally very complex in character as compared with the continuous type both as to equipment and as to management.

During the recent World War the term "single-purpose plant" was much used to designate a plant that produced one product only as against what may be termed "multipurpose" plants that produce a variety of goods. A single-purpose plant naturally tends to be of the continuous type, while a multipurpose plant may have varying characteristics.

81. Flow of Material.—It will be obvious that the greatest economy in transporting the material through the plant and fabricating it will result when the several machines, departments, and buildings are so arranged with reference to each other that the material is moved along with a minimum amount of traveling and handling so that the factory works smoothly as a whole. The conception of the entire factory as a *machine* through which material is to *flow* is a very helpful one. There are many existing factories where a careful analysis and rearrangement of the plant along the lines suggested would work wonders. Old factories that have grown up from small beginnings are very likely to be organized too much according to *personality*. While personality is valuable in itself, it is not sufficient. A chief engineer may be exceedingly able, but he cannot produce power economically unless his machinery is of the right kind and properly arranged, and the same idea applies equally well to manufacturing.

The ideal sequence or flow is usually obtained in some continuous processes, the building following the sequences naturally or the two being mutually adapted to each other. This is well illustrated in Fig. 6, which shows the cross section of a stamp mill for working gold- and silver-bearing ores, built on a hillside in order to use the force of gravity in carrying the ore through the processes. The building is made to conform closely to the needs of the process, not only as to housing the machinery but as to supporting the shafting, etc. The building is, in fact, one element in a large machine. The ore is delivered from cars to the bin *A*, passing thence through the rough-crushing rolls *B* to the bin *C*. From this bin it passes through the stamps *D*. Water is added during this stamping process and the finely divided product consequently runs easily down to the concentrators *E* where the lighter particles of rock are removed, the ore passing on to the tanks *F*. From here the ore passes into the grinding pans *G*, where it is still further reduced in fineness in contact with mercury, the latter amalgamating with the free gold[1] and silver and forming

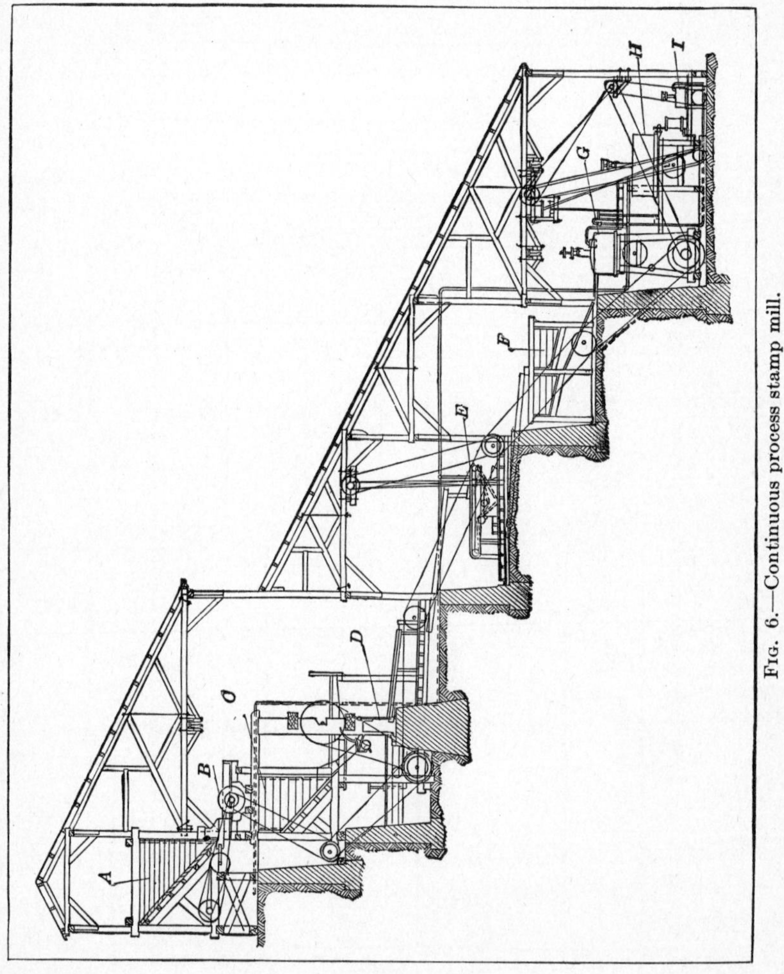

Fig. 6.—Continuous process stamp mill.

an amalgam that is separated from the waste rock by gravity action in the settling and cleanup pans *H* and *I*. The mercury is distilled from the amalgam in a retort placed in an adjoining building, not shown, and the remaining bullion is cast into ingots.

It is obvious that no such sequence or adaptation of building can be secured in the average case of intermittent production, many compromises

[1] Some of the free gold is caught by amalgam-covered plates at the stamp.

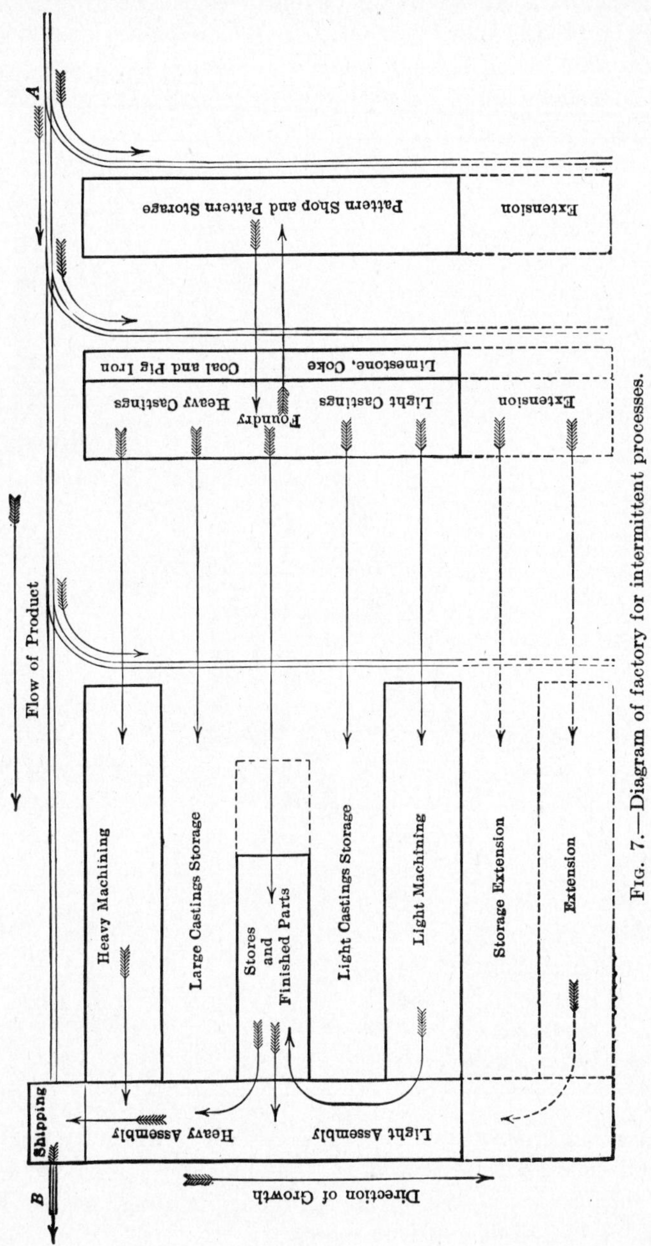

FIG. 7.—Diagram of factory for intermittent processes.

usually being necessary. The general principle, however, should be applied as far as possible, particularly if a well-developed planning and routing department (Chap. XIII) is proposed. This is true, not only of factories housed entirely in one building, but also of large plants occupying many buildings, with the added consideration of proper yard room and perhaps railroad connections. One application of this general principle is shown suggestively in Fig. 7, which may represent any machine works making a line of product, such as steam engines, in many sizes, large and small, and of several varieties. Here the material comes

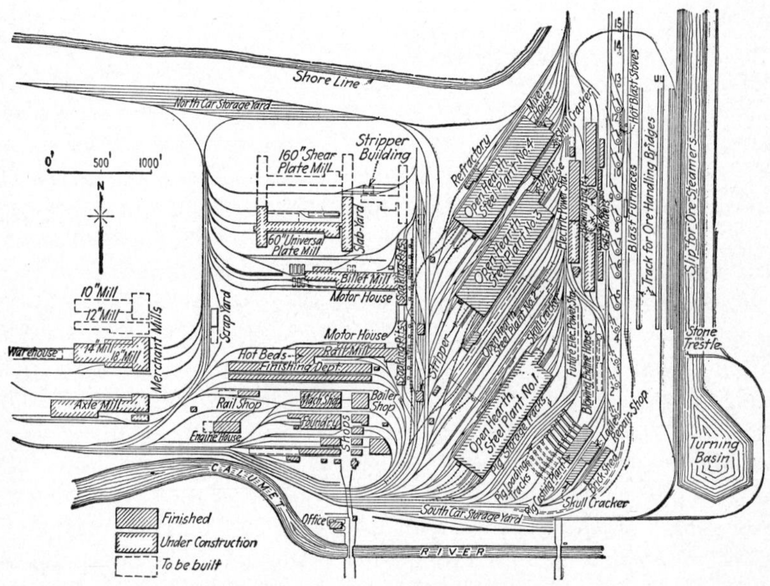

FIG. 8.—Plant of Indiana Steel Company at Gary, Ind.

in at *A* and the finished product goes out at *B*, the general movement being from right to left, and motion in the reverse direction occurring only where storage is necessary; though even this can sometimes be obviated or minimized. In addition to the standard railroad connections shown, the plant would be equipped with an industrial railway for internal transportation and, of course, with cranes and other handling devices.

As plants grow in size these principles may be of increasing importance, particularly if the work approximates a continuous process. Thus, in the Gary plant of the Indiana Steel Company (Fig. 8), the flow of material is from right to left, the general trend of the flow being shown by the railway connections over which the material is transported. Ore is unloaded from steamers in the basin at the right, passes to the blast furnaces, and thence to the open-hearth furnaces where it is converted into steel billets. If these billets are to be made into steel rails they are stored in the soaking pits where they may be kept hot until needed. From the soaking pits the billets are taken to the rail mill where they are worked continuously with one heating into finished rails. In addition to this effort to secure an approximation to continuous flow through the plant considerable thought was bestowed upon securing rapid transportation. It will be noted that the open-hearth furnaces are set at an angle with the blast furnace and finishing mills in order to obtain an arrangement of tracks over which material can be transported at a high rate of speed.[1] In most mass-production plants such as automobile, steel, and chemical works, a close approximation to continuous flow is often secured. In other large plants, on the other hand, these principles cannot be applied to the plant as a whole. Thus, the works of the General Electric Company at Schenectady (see Frontispiece 2) manufacture such a variety of goods, in so many sizes, that flow of material through the plant as a whole is out of the question. In this plant the buildings are placed, for the most part, at right angles to a central avenue, and transportation between shops is effected by a very complete system of electrically operated cars. If a part is to be moved at all on a car it makes little difference whether the destination is in one shop or another, once it is placed on the car.

82. Provision for Extensions.—If the plant under consideration is a new one, care should be taken to provide ample facilities for additions and extensions in such a manner that the equipment may be kept balanced without serious rearrangement. Thus, in Fig. 7, extensions,[2] such as are shown by the dotted lines, can be made without changing the original plan of the works. An ideal building plan is one built on some "unit" system, like a sectional bookcase so that additional units can be added at any time without disturbing the manufacturing system and organization. A little forehanded planning of this kind will often save large sums when additions or extensions are necessary.

Industrial needs vary so widely that it is not possible to lay down fixed rules for the design of a plant that will provide for indefinite extensions without changing existing arrangements. Factory buildings naturally take the form of long and comparatively narrow rectangles. This comes partly from the undesirability of wide roof spans, partly from the desirability of securing good natural lighting, and partly because this form of building often lends itself readily to a flow of work. Factories are therefore for the most part made up of combinations of long rectangular or I-shaped buildings connected or unconnected with each other, depending upon the functions to be performed. If the buildings are multistoried the long rectangular proportions are usually carried to the

[1] Figure 8 shows the original plan of this plant and is used in preference to later plans for this reason.

[2] The original new works of the Allis-Chalmers Company, at Milwaukee, were laid out on a plan similar to Fig. 7. Provision was made for the plant to grow at right angles to the direction of the flow of work.

top of the structure, but if they are single-storied and can therefore be lighted from the roof the rectangles may be placed closely side by side or in any combination that may be desirable. The problem of plant layout therefore is largely one of arranging departments and buildings so as to obtain the most advantageous passage of the material and at the same time provide for future growth. Considering any single combination of rectangles, Mr. Henry T. Noyes, who has written very clearly upon this subject, states:

> The types of buildings possible in selecting an arrangement to meet given conditions are represented by the letters LTUCHFE. In all of these types of buildings, materials and parts in process of construction may travel in two or more directions without reentrant lines on their way toward final assembly. Moreover, different lines of goods can be made in the same wings without interference and brought to a common point for storage and shipment.

It should be noted that all of these forms are made up of rectangular or I sections and that some are limiting forms or modifications of others, as for instance U and E. The plant shown in Fig. 7 consists of I and E sections, while that shown in Fig. 8 is made up largely of I sections. As has been stated, no fixed rules can be laid down for providing for future growth in any of these plans, but there is one idea that is often very helpful: extensions are most conveniently made *at right angles to the direction of flow of work.* Thus, in Fig. 6, the only way of increasing the capacity of the plant is to parallel it with another set of machinery, which clearly is growth in a lateral direction to the flow. In Fig. 7 the same principle is applied and in Fig. 8 it is obvious that the same general plan must be followed unless the capacity of the units is increased by rebuilding. In many factories the question of light is of great importance and this necessarily affects the form of the buildings. Generally speaking, the long sides of such factories face north and south, north light being particularly advantageous for drafting and fine tool work.

83. Adaptation of Building.—The degree to which it is *possible* to adapt a building to the exact needs of an industry will depend upon the *character* of the industry; the *desirability* of adapting a building to conform closely to the needs of any given line of work will depend upon the probable *permanency* of the industry. Most enterprises that start in a small way begin work in rented quarters. Owners of such buildings naturally build them to suit *average* conditions of manufacture and are usually averse to making changes that destroy their flexibility. Anyone acquainted with urban manufacturing has seen many efforts by manufacturers who have acquired such properties to remodel them to suit their needs more closely; and it is common experience that when a manufacturer builds a new plant to replace his old one he naturally makes a strong effort to adapt the new plant closely to the needs of his business.

It is coming to be more fully realized that the factory is not simply a building to house machinery, but is an integral part of the manufacturing equipment and may exert a great influence upon economical production.

Buildings are more easily adapted to fit the needs of continuous processes than to those of any other. This is well illustrated in ore concentrators where the building usually conforms closely to the requirements of the machinery it encloses. Sugar refineries, flour mills, steel-rail mills, and packing houses are examples of continuous industries where buildings often are closely adapted to the needs of the industry, and may often be so closely adapted as to be useless for any other purpose. At the other extreme are many industries that consist principally of assembling operations, little machinery being employed and that of small size, the entire business consisting of small, self-contained production centers. Floor space is the principal requirement and, within limits, the building may be any shape. In some of these industries the density of the workers is almost the only limiting factor, so much so that legal restrictions are in force in many states to regulate the congestion possible in these callings. Between these extremes come all manner of manufacturing processes, each presenting a different combination of needs. The possibility and desirability of adapting the building to suit these needs cannot, in general, be formulated, the best solution usually being a compromise that cannot be arrived at without intimate knowledge of the manufacturing problems presented and the financial condition of the owner.

84. Building Construction.—The machinery that is selected, and its arrangement, will determine the characteristics of the building as to size, strength, and general structure. Experience has reduced the types of factory buildings to a comparatively small number, but a brief discussion of even these few types is beyond the scope of this work. It is evident, however, that buildings of any one type will vary greatly, depending on the character of work they house and the financial condition of the builder. Not even approximate rules can be laid down as to what the structural characteristics of a building must be in order best to solve the problem in hand. The design of factory structures has become the work of specialists and one of these should be consulted in any large undertaking. There are, however, certain general considerations that should be kept in mind in designing any factory building, aside from the consideration of strength and stiffness against vibrations, namely:

1. Fire protection.
2. Good lighting, heating, and ventilating.
3. Sanitary conveniences for employees.
4. Appearance.

Volumes could be, and are, written on each of these items, but the briefest mention must here suffice. It is unnecessary to urge the need of a careful consideration of the danger of fire in planning any building and of considering the danger of a conflagration spreading from one building to another. The modern tendency is toward fireproof structures of steel or concrete or combinations of these materials, though good results may be obtained by the slow-burning timber construction so common in New England mills. Too much care cannot be bestowed upon fire-fighting appliances, such as sprinkler systems, and most of the large manufacturing plants have not only elaborate systems of this kind but keep a completely equipped fire engine and well-drilled fire companies.

It is impossible to overestimate the value of abundant light, heat, and ventilation. These things were looked on, only too often, in former days as luxuries, and the cold, dark, ill-smelling shops so common a few years ago were, in most cases, mistaken efforts in economy. It is true that modern building construction has made the lighting of factories a comparatively easy matter, but it is important that builders keep in mind that light, heat, and ventilation *pay dividends*. Great care was taken in times past that clerks on small salaries were comfortably housed, and they would not have been expected to do good work unless so cared for; while high-priced mechanics were only too often expected to produce good results in spite of all sorts of physical discomfort and inconvenience. There is no difference between the psychology of the office and that of the shop. Workmen can, naturally, produce more and better work in well-warmed, well-lighted, and well-ventilated rooms, and this is in no small measure due to an improved *mental outlook* that necessarily goes with improved physical surroundings. In the case of grinding, buffing, and similar occupations many states have passed stringent laws making proper ventilation of such machinery compulsory.

The question of sanitary conveniences for workmen, facilities for washing and changing their clothes, and similar features of the care of employees other than those mentioned above, will be fully discussed in Chap. XXIV in connection with the subject of welfare work. They will not, therefore, be elaborated at this point.

In planning new buildings or making extensions to old ones it is quite common practice to calculate the new floor space by reference to other plants of the same kind. The floor area per ton of output, the floor area per employee, or the floor area per dollar of output are often taken as standards for determining new floor area. Clearly, such standards should be used with care, especially if they are taken from plants of which the designing engineer has little or no knowledge. Such data are very valuable if their source and limitations are known, but in all cases they should be used with caution. Conditions vary greatly in different plants making the same article. The degree of integration may be vastly different, the equipment either more antique or more modern. New tools, new methods, and new pay systems may make useless any calculations based on old performances. It is much safer, usually, to base all such computations of output on the actual capacities of machinery and processes to be installed, adapting the building to suit the arrangement of the same as far as desirable.

There is a growing sentiment that factory buildings should present as good an appearance as possible. It is true that architectural beauty is difficult to attain in many industrial structures, but many factory buildings are most unnecessarily ugly. Just as a well-designed machine is pleasing to look at, so a well-designed factory building may be just as pleasing, and at a small additional expense. It is to be hoped that decentralization of industry from the large cities may result in more model industrial villages, and that the old factory town with its prison-like factory buildings and bleak and barren-looking tenements will soon be forever a thing of the past.

SELECTION AND ARRANGEMENT OF EQUIPMENT

85. Analysis of the Product.—Assuming that the market survey (Art. 62) has indicated the volume of trade that may be expected, the product can be analyzed and the equipment selected. It will be evident that the analysis of the product will present widely varying aspects depending upon the work to be done. In equipping an intermittent industry such as a shipyard for instance, heavy tools like shearing and punching machinery would be selected for capacity and adaptability rather than for rapid cutting speed, since their operation is quite intermittent and capacity highly essential. The selection of a large boring mill for a shop producing a wide variety of product would also be based upon the maximum size of parts to be machined, its power, and adaptability to the range of work required of it. The selection of the number of such tools in each case will not be based upon a calculated production but rather upon mature judgment and a knowledge of the needs of such plants as illustrated by existing enterprises.

In a simple continuous process fabricating a single commodity, as illustrated in Fig. 6, the character and sequence of the machinery are fixed by the necessities of the case, and the capacity of the entire installation is fixed by the minimum capacity of any given machine or set of machines in the series. In such a case, therefore, the capacity of each unit must be carefully calculated if efficient results are to be attained. Even where the productive processes are not continuous it is often advisable to compute carefully the capacity of all equipment.

In the majority of cases the productive capacity of the machinery needed can be supplied by the manufacturer of the equipment. Thus the capacity of weaving and spinning machinery, of automatic machinery in general, and of metal-working machinery can be obtained from the builders. If, however, it be necessary to make detailed computations for the capacity of metal-working machinery, accurate information as to the most economical speeds, feeds, and depth of cut is available. The methods for acquiring this information are fully discussed in Chap. XIII, and Fig. 27 shows an **instruction card** whereon the details of a machining operation are predicted in advance of the actual work. Computations of this kind may be compared with the known capacity of the equipment to be selected and the *minimum* number of machines thus determined. This minimum must of course be modified by practical considerations such as allowance for breakdowns, time lost in setting up the machines, etc.

In continuous processes complete information of this character is comparatively easy to obtain, since the capacity of each machine or set of machines devoted to any part of the work must bear a definite relation to other machines or groups of machines, or the other factors of the process; and the nature of the process usually dictates the natural sequence of operations, or suggests such handling or conveying devices as may be needed to keep the process continuous. In the other extreme cases, where assembling is the predominating factor, the problem is still easier in some respects, since here sequence is not a factor and the production units are small. But the computation of the output of each worker may be difficult unless data bearing upon this point are available. In intermittent manufacturing, however, this problem is often most difficult and deserves more consideration than is usually accorded to it, not only in securing a *balanced* equipment, but also to obtain any approach to a *flow* of material through the plant with a minimum of transportation expense. Obviously, here, also, no definite rules or methods can be evolved for solving such problems, but there are certain general principles that apply to all plants and which may be worth noting.

86. Machining Time and Handling Time.—As explained more in detail in Chap. XIII, the time expended in fabricating material is divisible generally into **machine time** and **handling time.** Great stress is usually laid upon the first and not enough usually upon the second, which may constitute a large part of the entire time spent. Furthermore, material in transit through the shop is crystallized capital which should, therefore, be kept at a minimum and as active as possible. For these reasons, material should not be permitted to accumulate around machine centers more than is necessary for continuous production, and adequate provision should be made in the design of the plant to transport all material from production center to production center cheaply and quickly.

87. Departmentalization.—There are two general principles by which machinery and apparatus may be grouped, namely by the *processes to be performed* or by the *character of the product.* The principal reason for grouping machines according to the process to be performed is the fact that machines of different size and for different purposes require different surroundings in the way of housing, transportation service, light, heat, power, etc. Furthermore, division of equipment by functions permits of specialized superintendence, which is highly important. Thus, in a textile plant, all weaving would be done in one room which has been specially built and air-conditioned for that purpose, all spinning would be performed in another specially equipped room, and on on. In a machine-building plant such as indicated by Fig. 7, the pattern shop, foundry, and machine shops are located in separate buildings. Furthermore, within these buildings, again, subdivision of function according to size will be noted, namely light and heavy foundry work, light and heavy machine work, and light and heavy assembly, etc. Thus, all lathes up to 24-inch swing might be grouped in one department, all small drilling machines in another, all automatic and semiautomatic lathes in another, and so on. In the majority of industries classification of equipment in this manner is sufficient. Such an arrangement is not uncommon where manufacturing is conducted by the lot-repetitive method and where the assembly floor is fed from the finished-parts store room. The principal advantage of this form of arrangement is that it requires a minimum number of machines for a given output since under it the possibility of keeping all machines in constant operation is at a maximum. As before noted, the superintendence, being specialized, is likely to be more efficient. The principal disadvantage of this method is that the work cannot be made to flow through a plant thus arranged as easily as in the other arrangement; the path of travel is longer and hence more costly.

In the second form of arrangement, each department is equipped with a complete set of tools and equipment necessary for the manufacture of a single product or a number of closely related products. Thus a department manufacturing arc lamps would have a complete installation for its work, the material passing through the machines consecutively somewhat as in Fig. 6. The advantage of such an arrangement is that it eliminates time and labor in moving material and permits it to flow more nearly in straight lines from stores to finished product. In general also less material will be in production at any time than in the other arrangement and in very large plants this may result in a considerable decrease in the material inventory.

The principal disadvantage is that unless the flow of work is fairly constant the idle machine time is excessive. The principle is much used in automobile production and in other plants where quantity warrants its application.

It is not always advisable, however, to make a rigid application of either of these principles, and many departments devoted primarily to one kind of work may often need a few tools of another kind for emergencies and to save time. Thus an assembly floor may need a few drilling machines or lathes near by where quick corrections or adjustments may be made. But in refined continuous manufacturing this form of grouping has been carried out to perfection not only in the production of parts but especially in the assembly of such products as automobiles, refrigerators, etc. In intermittent manufacturing compromises between these two methods may have to be made and a careful consideration of the selective merits of the two systems will often save money in equipment costs and greatly facilitate production.

The term *straight-line production*, so much used in connection with departments where the machines are arranged according to product, should not be taken too seriously. It is true that under old methods of driving machines from line shafts they naturally were arranged in straight lines. This made a very orderly looking layout and partly because of this the practice has continued even when it is not an efficient plan. The introduction of the individual electric motor drive, however, has eliminated the necessity of rigid conformity to straight lines and has left the plant engineer free to arrange the machinery in the most efficient manner he can devise. A careful study of line arrangement will often show that another arrangement will save floor space, shorten the travel of the material, increase production, and lower costs by using labor more efficiently. Figure 9 (in two parts) shows an actual line layout for machining parts weighing 16 pounds.[1] The machines corresponding to the numbers on the diagram are as follows:

1. B. & S. milling machine.
2. Centering machine.
3A. Model R lo-swing lathe.
3B. Model R lo-swing lathe.
4A. Lo-swing lathe.
4B. Lo-swing lathe.
5. Norton grinder.
6. 48-in. hydromatic miller.
7. Cincinnati miller.
8. 50-H Baker drill press.
9. 50-H Baker drill press.
10. 48-in. hydromatic miller.
11. 48-in. hydromatic miller.
12. Baker drill press.
13. 24-in. Cincinnati drill press.
14. Edlund drill press.
15. No. 2 Cincinnati miller.
16. Single-spindle drill press.
17. Whitney hand mill.
18. Whitney hand mill.
19. Whitney hand mill.
20. Taft-Pierce thread miller.
21. Lees Bradner thread miller.
22. Lees Bradner thread miller.
23. Bryant grinder.
24. Bryant grinder.
25. Norton grinder.
26. Norton grinder.
27. Rockford Rigidmill.
28. Taft-Pierce thread miller.
29. Avey drill press.
30. 2-spindle Edlund drill press.
31. Snagging grinder.
32. Wet grinder.
33. Bench.
34. Bench.

T = Hand truck.
C = Chute.

The workmen are indicated by the heavy crosses and parts were moved from place to place on hand trucks marked T on the diagram. The total distance traversed by each part was 200 feet. Figure 10 shows practically

[1] See VAN POPPELEN, F. J., "Motion Study and Plant Layout," *Factory and Industrial Management*, December, 1931.

the same set of machines[1] rearranged after careful study of the operations and measurement of the time of each detailed operation. The machines

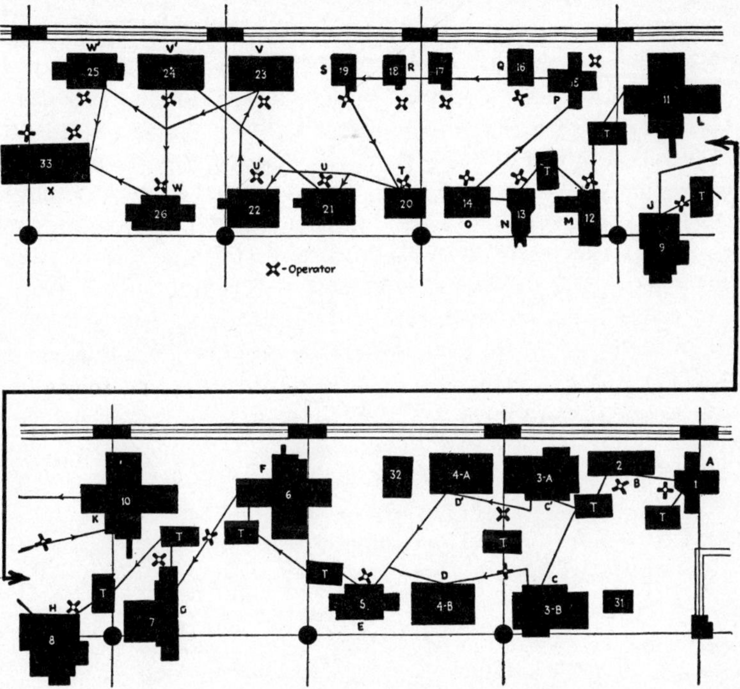

Fig. 9.—Straight-line machine arrangement.

are set closer together so that all hand trucking is eliminated by the use of inclined chutes from machine to machine. The number of men is reduced from 27 to 16, since in the new arrangement more machines can be operated by each man. Floor space has been reduced 40 per cent and the

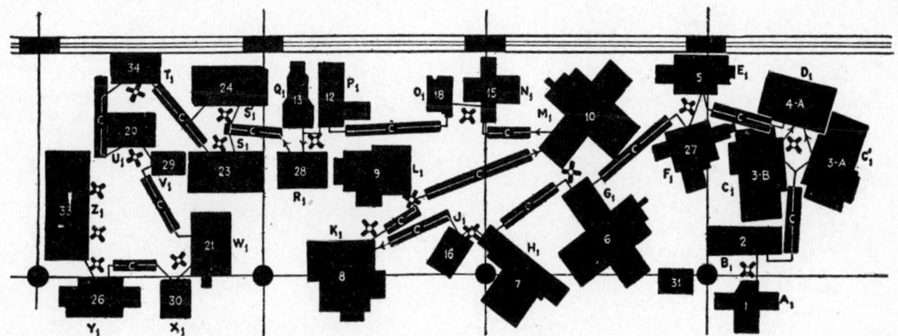

Fig. 10.—Modified arrangement of Fig. 9.

total number of parts passing through the set-up at any one time is substantially reduced, owing to the elimination of storage transfer boxes.

[1] Figure 10 includes some machines not in Fig. 9 and vice versa. The list enumerates all machines in both.

Care should be used to avoid overdoing consolidation of this kind, thus making it so congested as to be either dangerous or overconfining to the workers, as would appear to be the case with the workmen at 3*A*, 3*B*, and 4*A*. Men do not do their best when their freedom is too closely restricted. The general appearance of the layout in Fig. 10 is not so pleasing as that in Fig. 9, and such groups should be surrounded by aisles of liberal width, partly for convenience in transferring material to and from it, and partly to relieve the appearance of overcongestion.

In any manufacturing operation there are three factors, namely the *work*, the *tool*, and the *workman*, any one of which or any combination of which may be fixed or may move. In the usual case the tool and the workman remain in one place and the work progresses. But economy in production may dictate otherwise. Thus, a large boring mill and the man who operates it are naturally stationary, the work progressing to it and moving while it is being machined. But in some forms of heavy machine work it is quite common to fasten the work to a large iron floor plate and operate upon it with portable milling, planing, and boring machines. In this case the work is stationary but tool and worker move from place to place. Again in riveting steel ships and steel buildings the work is stationary while the workman and the tool, which may be a heavy device, move about. In inspecting the work of machine floors it is obvious that if the parts are small and numerous it will be economical to let them flow past stationary inspectors, whereas if the parts are large and scattered, economy would dictate that the inspector and his instruments should move progressively to the work. In assembling a single large engine it is economical to gather all the parts at one place and have a group of skilled assemblymen do the work, moving around as occasion requires. But in assembling automobile engines the work usually moves progressively past *fixed stations*, the worker at each station adding some one part while the work is temporarily stationary. In the final assembly of the automobile the work moves constantly on a carrier while the workers move back and forth over a limited distance carrying their tools with them. No general principle can be laid down for selecting the most economical combination, but obviously the idea is of wide application and should be carefully considered in all shop planning.

When the equipment of each department has been selected, with the above considerations in mind, the internal arrangement of each department can be completed tentatively, at least, due consideration being given to transportation, storage, power, etc. The floor space so determined can be compared with similar departments if such data are obtainable. The most convenient method of arranging manufacturing equipment is to cut out small cardboard patterns of the floor space required for each machine to some convenient scale. These can be moved around at will until a satisfactory arrangement is secured (see Fig. 9).

88. Arrangement of Departments.—In addition to the production departments, an analysis should be made of the administrative and service departments such as stock, stores, engineering department, offices, etc., and careful determination made of the form and size of the floor space required for each. An inventory should be made of the personnel in order to provide proper space for toilets, rest rooms, lunch rooms, and whatever else may be considered necessary for the comfort and care of the working force. Consideration must also be given to the question of power, for if it is to be generated at the plant the location of the power house is an important one as regards the unloading of coal and the disposal of ashes. Finally, a list should be made of all of the departments and activities to be provided for in the fully assembled plant.

This list should now be analyzed and the general features of each department noted before assembling these departments into a general plan. It may be possible to assemble them so as to obtain a free flow of material and still have an inefficient plant. Departments, however efficient in themselves, are not always congenial. Thus the designing room should not be placed near a dirty forge shop or a noisy boiler shop. Grinding and polishing departments should not be near a floor filled with fine machine tools. Heavy machinery should not be placed on upper floors where its vibration would disturb tool makers using precision machinery, and so on. Perhaps some of the operations should be housed in independent buildings, even though that will increase the travel of the product. With these considerations in mind the most suitable type of buildings can be determined upon and the several departments arranged as in Figs. 6, 7, and 8 so as to provide for flow through the combined floors. For this purpose a **flow chart** is sometimes constructed. This consists essentially of an outline drawing showing the several departments in their relation to each other, with the path of the product marked by continuous lines through the system. If the building or buildings are multistory the flow chart can be made in perspective to great advantage. In some instances rough model buildings are constructed so as to show the true relations between departments.

It will be obvious that plant arrangement must usually be an empirical proceeding and that each plant is a different problem. There is, however, a considerable literature on the problem which may be consulted and there are a few suggestions, that may be helpful to the beginner. Thus, having the receiving and shipping facilities constantly in mind one may proceed as follows:

1. Begin with the assembly floor and work backwards making the subassemblies tributary to it.

2. Arrange the machine floors so that their product can flow conveniently to the subassemblies.

3. Heavy material should move over the shortest path. In general, heavy castings and similar material that do not pass through stores can be received and stored at any convenient place (see Fig. 7).

4. Locate general-service departments such as finished-parts stores, tool room, toilets, as centrally as possible so as to minimize travel on part of workman. Sometimes branch stores and tool rooms are essential.

5. Check flow of material through the plant by means of a flow chart and plan transportation facilities accordingly. The problem of safety for employees should also receive careful consideration.

6. Modify and rearrange until the best solution is found that will fit the land available and also shipping and receiving facilities. This work may involve a large amount of labor and thought. Comparison with existing plants is sometimes helpful, but care should be used not to copy the errors as well as the advantages of any such plant. Provision for growth should not be lost sight of in the final arrangement.

7. Prepare complete engineering and architectural plans for construction purposes.

References

ALFORD, L. P.: "Management's Handbook."

ANDERSON, A. G.: "Industrial Engineering and Factory Management."

CORNELL, W. B.: "Industrial Organization and Management."

DIEMER, HUGO: "Factory Organization," Chap. 3.

HOLMES, W. GERALD: "Plant Location."

JONES, E. D.: "The Administration of Industrial Enterprises."

U. S. Department of Commerce: "Location of Manufactures" (1899–1929).

VAN DEVENTER, J. H.: "Machine-shop Management."

CHAPTER IX

PRINCIPLES OF ORGANIZATION

89. Scientific Methods.—As enterprises grow in size the problems of administration and management become increasingly important and require greater consideration. The small grocer can very well be his own porter, clerk, and cashier, and can effectively perform all of these functions. But as his business grows, he begins to deputize the manual side of his business by hiring a porter; and as further development arises he deputizes a part of his mental work by hiring a bookkeeper. This process continues until, if his business is to succeed, he must **organize** it in some definite, systematic manner, reserving to himself **supervisory** duties only. It has been said that the secret of successfully managing a large enterprise is to **organize, deputize,** and **supervise.** No doubt this does express in a rough manner the fundamental laws of successful management, but it may be of advantage to inquire more fully into the details of management.

Management may be broadly defined as the art of applying the economic principles that underlie the control of men and materials in the enterprise under consideration. It makes itself manifest through organization; and since the principles underlying various enterprises vary greatly it is natural that forms of organization must also vary greatly with the character and magnitude of the business considered. Now it would seem reasonable to assume that if the economic laws or philosophy underlying the accomplishment of any undertaking can be discovered and recorded they will form a guide for the management of all similar enterprises. It does not follow, however, that *any* man who knows these economic laws can be a successful administrator. Two men may be given the same equipment of machines and knowledge: one will be successful and the other will fail. The basic facts or laws of any field are *impersonal,* but their execution or administration almost always involves personal qualifications on which success or failure may, and usually does, depend. In other words, there may be a **science** of management and an **art** of management just as there is a science and an art in house building, aviation, agriculture, and other lines of human endeavor. The question as to how far the art of management may be considered to have *scientific* foundation has been the cause of a considerable discussion which may bear further investigation. This naturally leads to an inquiry as to what constitutes a scientific foundation in any activity.

The fundamental laws that underlie any art may be known **qualitatively** or **quantitatively.** Thus, a chemist may know that if a certain acid is added to a given mixture a certain substance will be precipitated. An engineer may know that all beams will deflect when loaded. If, however, the knowledge of the chemist or the engineer does not go beyond these limits, the fundamental laws governing these portions of their respective arts are known qualitatively only. Qualitative knowledge is often expressed **empirically,** that is, in terms that approximately express the true relations that exist between the causes and effects considered. The literature of engineering abounds in such empirical statements.

If, however, the chemist can say that under specified conditions a given weight of a certain acid will precipitate a definite amount of a certain material from the solution under consideration, the law is know **quantitatively** and fully. In a similar way if the engineer can predict that a given weight will deflect a given beam a definite amount, he also knows the law of the deflection of such beams quantitatively.

The principles that underlie any art become known through **experience** and the degree to which they may become known depends largely on the amount of such experience and the efforts made to record and interpret the same. In the early stages of any art such knowledge of the fundamental laws as may exist must exist as part of the personal knowledge of some man or men. And even after these laws are well known quantitatively they are still often preserved by being passed from father to son, or from workman to apprentice, without record of any kind.

Quantitative knowledge, however, involves the **measurement** of cause and effect, and laws are fully known only when such measurements have been made in sufficient number to demonstrate beyond doubt the exact quantitative relations existing between the phenomena considered. And it is only where the laws of an art are fully known both qualitatively and quantitatively that it can be said to rest fully on a scientific basis. Brief reflection will convince anyone that only a very small part of our general knowledge is quantitative in character, the major part of it, that lies outside of pure and applied science, being empirical in character; in fact, much that lies in these fields is not fully known quantitatively.

If, also, the qualitative characteristics and the quantitative measurements of any law are fully known they afford the means of **predicting** with certainty the results of similar operations under the determined laws, and if these characteristics and measurements have been systematically arranged and recorded they become **impersonal** and useful for all men. As the basis of any art becomes more scientifically developed the art becomes less and less dependent on personality; for scientific investigation consists, in part, of separating facts from personal opinion. This point of view is important in attacking any problem, even when the laws involved cannot be fully determined. The **scientific method** which first collects all the data or facts concerning the problem, analyzes them and deduces therefrom logical conclusions, and then applies these conclusions to the prediction of results, is of supreme importance in all kinds of work. Scientific management, so-called, is not a code of rules as much as it is an attitude of mind that aims to replace "I think" with "I know"; and the extent to which this can be accomplished will depend on how far the principles involved can be developed quantitatively.

All branches of human activity have risen above the stage of empiricism and rule of thumb only as they have been able to build upon the accumulated facts of experience and accurate conclusions drawn therefrom. Industrial organization and management are no exception to this rule. Until quite recently industrial management has been largely personal and empirical, rule-of-thumb methods being almost universally used in all matters. The need of more accurate information, especially in administering large enterprises, has led, however, to a more careful examination of the art of management with a view to finding whether any basic principles existed that might serve as a safer guide than the cruder empirical methods; and with the hope that a better understanding and more accurate solution of these problems would come with a fuller understanding of these basic laws.

Such basic laws do exist; and the term **industrial engineer** is becoming synonymous with one skilled in factory design, organization, and operation, who endeavors to rest his conclusions, not on simple empirical information or judgment, but, as far as possible, upon basic proved facts. The *scientific method* that first observes and records the data of the phenomena concerned, then deduces the fundamental laws of the phenomena from these data, and lastly applies these deductions to predict other results, has come to stay in all lines of human activity. Just as the designing engineer endeavors to obtain highest efficiency by eliminating energy losses, so the industrial engineer is a close student of wastes in manufacturing processes. Just as the designing engineer seeks to rest his work on accurate data and scientific facts, so the industrial engineer seeks to observe, record, and formulate the data of industrial operations and industrial management in order that he may accurately predict the results of other operations and arrangements. His field is indeed a wide one, ranging from the collection of statistical data of the industry as a whole, down to the shipping of the factory product, and his sources of knowledge have their roots in engineering, economics, psychology, and other fields of human experience. These relations and conditions apply, in general, to all forms of industry, but apply with special force to industries involving congregated labor, as found in manufacturing plants, and a discussion of the special problems found in organized manufacturing will exemplify those of almost any other form of industry. These general principles apply also to all phases of manufacturing industry, including construction, equipment and operation.

Several titles have been used to denote this new field. It was first called **scientific management** but this name was perhaps, not well chosen and has created some antagonism to the use of these principles, partly because of a lack of knowledge regarding the basic facts and partly because of a well-grounded fear that there is grave danger in extending, to the extreme, some of the methods advocated. At present there is a tendency to apply the name of **industrial engineering** to the more technical aspects of management and the name **administrative engineering** to what may be called the business side of management, in which the engineer has been found useful. Whatever name may be applied to this work it is certain that the *scientific method* of attacking the problems of organization and management is correct, and that it points out the method of intelligently directing the construction and arrangement of factory buildings, the character of methods and processes, the organization of departments, the elimination of wastes, and the increase of efficiency in all phases of industrial administration where data and experience are applicable.

It should be specially noted, however, that scientific data and system can never take the place of personality, as might be inferred from some of the literature on the subject of industrial management. Personality has always been and will always remain the great moving force in human affairs. But personality alone is no longer sufficient where classified knowledge is a factor in the affairs considered. The personality of a Napoleon could never offset modern machine guns and the advanced sanitary methods of guarding the health of troops. The personality of the greatest physicians is often a slight thing compared with the cold science and skill of the modern surgeon. All other things being equal, the advantage rests with the man that possesses the greatest amount of scientific knowledge. This statement has been proved in so many fields, from warfare to housekeeping, that it needs no defense and little explanation. And it is evident that the foregoing discussion applies to all kinds of human activity and gives us a standard by which all such activities may be measured as to their scientific basis.

More than ever, perhaps, the successful manager must be a close student of men and their psychological processes. With the steady rise in intelligence, the increasing complexity of personal relations and the growing tendency of the public to interest itself in industrial matters, the human element in factory management looms up with increasing importance; and no system of management can be successful that does not take this factor into account. Just how far such human relations can be said to be open to scientific methods remains to be seen, though there is no lack, even now, of those who claim that these also can be measured and recorded.

90. Scientific Methods in Management and Organization.—The several economic principles discussed in the foregoing chapters were well understood by industrial managers many years ago and many applications of them were to be found in operation even before the Industrial Revolution. But until very recent times the design, the organization, and the management of industrial enterprises had remained an *empirical art.* The literature on these subjects was very meager; successful industrial leaders, in general, taking their knowledge with them when they departed from this world. About 50 years ago, however, it began to dawn upon industrial leaders that the same analytical or "scientific" methods of attacking problems that had proved so successful in other lines of endeavor were equally applicable to the problems of plant design, organization, and management. A movement started, therefore, looking toward the application of more logical methods in the solution of industrial problems, which must be considered as a whole, in order to understand the more obvious detailed manifestations which have attracted the most attention.

There are several principal reasons for the rise of this movement. (1) There is the vast general increase in the application of the natural sciences in such fields as engineering, medicine, agriculture, and other activities, with results that have distinguished this civilization from any other that has preceded it, and which, in themselves, have stimulated logical thinking in all human activities. (2) There is the great increase in the *size* of industrial enterprises that has already been discussed, and which has necessitated new methods. So long as industry was conducted on a small scale, *personality* and *empirical knowledge* were sufficient to coordinate the efforts of the workers in any group and to obtain good results. But large enterprises not only gave opportunity for a great extension of the use of division of labor and transfer of skill; they also brought into being the necessity of much more highly organized and more complex methods of organization and management. (3) Increasing competition made necessary a more accurate knowledge of the basis of production and distribution. (4) The entrance into the field of manufacturing of many technically trained engineers has been a most potent influence in promoting new methods of industrial management. So long as manufacturing industries were concerned with building such machinery as the old steam engines and boilers, which could be fabricated by the ordinary high-grade mechanic, the engineer's activities were confined largely to the *design* of such apparatus. But industries, particularly such as electrical manufacturing, have developed a highly technical background, not only of design but of manufacture, and it was partly through such necessities that the technical man has found his way into industrial management. Naturally these men have carried with them the analytical methods they learned from the mathematician, the chemist, and the physicist, and it is not too much to say that, in many ways, they have developed a new idea of industrial organization and management. The inception of this movement is inseparably connected with the names of Taylor, Gantt, Emerson, Barth, Gilbreth, and other well-known engineers. The methods these leaders have advanced have spread far beyond the confines of factory walls. The latest indication of the spread of these ideas of logical thinking is the establishment of **graduate schools of business.** This is a clear recognition, or rather claim, that business has a *professional and ethical background that can be taught* and is not merely a matter of shrewd bargaining as has been believed from time immemorial.

Great reforms always gather considerable strength and inertia before they attract the attention of the public in a marked manner, and when they do so attract public attention it is usually in connection with the work of some individual whose name becomes associated, historically, with the movement. This movement toward better management methods is no exception to this general rule, and Frederick W. Taylor stands preeminent as the one man who did the most to further the application of science to management and organization. Taylor was the first to gather together such advanced methods as were in use, in isolated manner, add to them his own brilliant ideas, and weave the whole into a new philosophy of management which became known as **scientific management.** His paper entitled "Shop Management," presented before the American Society of Mechanical Engineers in 1903, created a profound impression and should be ready by every student of industry and sociology. A fuller discussion of the principles and methods which he advocated will be given in Chap. XII.

Mr. Taylor died prematurely in 1915, having devoted the later years of his life solely to the work of advocating his ideas of management. It is possibly a little too early to evaluate fully his work and that of his immediate associates and followers. Like most advocates of reform, they were prone to confuse *mechanisms* with *principles.* Because of this, many of the early attempts to apply the Taylor "system," so-called, ended in financial disaster and the term "efficiency" fell into disrepute from which it has never fully recovered. Few industrial plants have adopted Taylor's methods as a whole. But many of the principles and methods that he advocated have become common practice even in industries quite remote in character from those in which he did his pioneer work, and without doubt much of his philosophy of management will remain, since it rests upon sound economic principles.

But more important, and underlying any and all of these mechanisms of management that may be identified as his work, is the spirit of the man himself as the prophet of more efficient methods. Whether any or all of his specific methods survive, the spirit of inquiry that he set in motion concerning industrial methods, his frank skepticism of the efficiency and desirability of existing methods and processes, even though they bore the imprint of hoary age and the stamp of ancient precedent, will ever remain one of the greatest contributions to the industrial arts. His share in the development of our present industrial system is great indeed and difficult to estimate.

91. Basic Principles.—It has been shown that the following important principles underlie the economic production of manufactured goods:

1. Division of labor, including separation of mental and manual labor.
2. Transfer of skill.
3. Transfer of thought.

It has also been shown that these methods are more effective as the quantity to be made increases, specialization and standardization also being dependent on aggregation or quantity.

It may be stated, therefore, that:

4. The unit cost, in general, decreases as the quantity increases, due regard being had to the law of decreasing productivity (see Art. 53).

It is evident, also, that as enterprises increase in size, as division of labor is more fully applied, and departments multiply, increasing care must be used to **coordinate** the work of men and departments; hence, it may also be stated that:

5. The need of coordinative influences increases with aggregation and division of labor.

And, lastly, it is obvious that any principle gains in effectiveness, if applied systematically on the basis of recorded experience. The above-named principles will, therefore, gain in value if applied in connection with:

6. The systematic use of recorded experience.

Aside from the human factors involved, these may be taken as the most important principles in manufacturing production. The chapters immediately succeeding are for the most part devoted to their application to the problems of organization, and the problems of some of the most important departments resulting therefrom as seen in present-day practice. In later chapters the limitations of these principles, as a scientific basis of the art of management, will be briefly discussed.

92. Management; Organization; Administration; System.—The literature of modern industrial methods is often quite confusing, partly because of faulty nomenclature, and partly because of failure to distinguish between fundamental conceptions. Thus, the word *management* is used to designate a certain field of activity and also to designate those persons who perform the several activities embraced within that field. Similarly, the word *organization* may signify a group of persons or it may denote a certain set of correlated activities of some sort. Again, the terms management, administration, organization, system, etc., are often used indiscriminately, partly because some of them, such as management and administration, are synonymous. It may be well, therefore, to define a few of these terms as they will be used in this book and as they are used to a large extent in this country. In making these definitions reference will be made primarily to the fields of activity that they respectively designate rather than to the personnel that may be engaged in them.

Management embraces all duties and functions that pertain to the initiation of an enterprise, the financing of the same, the establishment of all major policies, the provision of all necessary equipment, the outlining of the general form of organization under which the enterprise is to operate, and the selection of the principal officers. The group of officials in primary control of an enterprise is quite commonly called the **board of managers** and is frequently referred to as "the management." The principal official primarily responsible to the controlling board is commonly referred to as the general manager.

Organization is subsidiary to management. It embraces the duties of designating the departments and personnel that are to carry on the work, defining their functions and specifying the relations that are to exist between departments and individuals. Organization as an activity is in fact a *mechanism* of *management.* A clear distinction should be made, furthermore, between *organization* and *departmentalization.* A department is simply an enlarged individual, that is, it is a group of individuals organized for some specific duty. An enterprise may be well departmentalized, but still be poorly organized. The work of organization embraces not only the relations that are to exist between departments, but also the relations of individuals within each department. For, just as there must be organization of the several departments into a harmonious whole, so there must also be *departmental organization,* which is equally important.

The work of thus organizing an enterprise is usually intrusted to the general manager and his advisers. If the form of organization is simple and obvious this work will consist largely of selecting competent personnel. But the increased size of many modern industrial plants and the growth of the scientific background both in manufacturing processes and in methods of organization have given rise to specialists in organization whose advice may be essential or at least helpful to the manager.

Administration or **direction** includes all functions and activities that are concerned with the actual work of executing or carrying out the objectives for which the enterprise has been financed and organized. It should be noted that those responsible for the management and organization of an enterprise may have provided excellent equipment and a well-departmentalized and organized personnel and the plant may still be unproductive. In this stage it is likely a highly organized army without marching orders. Administration embraces such functions as the issuance of orders concerning the work to be done, seeing that the personnel is fitted for the work and trained to operate efficiently, and caring in general for the everyday routine necessary to insure that men, materials, and equipment are functioning properly toward the desired end.

System is the **mechanism of administration** by which the efforts of all men and departments are *coordinated*. It includes the printed forms and written documents through which all orders and instructions are issued and all records of performances are obtained. It includes all managerial reports and all orders and reports from administrative committees and other coordinative groups. The planning of the system for an enterprise embraces not only the designing of proper blanks and forms but also the specification of the manner in which they are to be used in order that each department shall receive the necessary information and nothing more. Since system is *regulatory* in its effect it must always be applied with care, otherwise it may act as a deterrent to production; or as is sometimes said, there may be too much "red tape." System[1] must nevertheless be frankly recognized as a necessary accompaniment to division of labor.

Again, a clear distinction should be made between **physical arrangement** or **division** of a plant and the **organization** of the same, the first having to do primarily with material and apparatus and the second with the personnel which is to operate it. Management may and often does provide complete physical facilities before a single operating individual is hired. An industrial plant may be divided by product. Thus, facilities for producing generators may be grouped in one building, facilities for producing motors in another, and so on. Or it may be divided by processes, such as pattern making, molding, blacksmithing, machine work, etc. Again, either of these divisions may be subdivided according to products or processes. In the machine shop for producing motors all tools for producing certain motors may be grouped by themselves or again all tools of the same kind and approximate size, such as lathes, planers, etc., may be grouped by themselves, that is, arranged according to the processes performed. And naturally there may be combinations of these arrangements. But whatever the physical characteristics of the

[1] University athletic associations are excellent examples of management and its subsidiary functions. The Athletic Council which "manages" such activities dictates all general policies, selects players, furnishes facilities and equipment, schedules games, etc. The general functional arrangement of the players on athletic teams is fixed by precedent, and the nature of the game to be played, yet the coach must coordinate the efforts of the players into a harmonious organization that is capable of playing the game in a skillful manner. When in action the team is *administered* or *directed* by the field captain with suggestions from the coach, just as a shop foreman may receive suggestions or directions from his superintendent. The field captain, again, directs the team through a well-understood *system* of verbal signals. In some games, such as football, this system may be quite highly developed and known only to the players themselves. For reasons that will be explained later, verbal directions cannot be safely used in industry, all important directions at least being in written or printed form.

plant there remains always the problem of organizing the personnel so as to make it effective as an industrial unit.

It will be obvious that the character and type of organization necessary to secure the desired result will vary widely with the character and size of the enterprise under consideration. Thus, the departmental organization of a plant will depend largely upon its size and the degree to which it is specialized. Increased size naturally brings with it greater subdivision of labor and the consequent need of added coordinative influences. Under the older and simpler systems of production, when small numbers of men were the rule, the relations between master and man were very simple. Each man was competent to perform any and all operations, producing, perhaps, the entire article himself. The instructions, few and simple, were given verbally, and the recording of instructions, in a modern sense, was unnecessary. As the size of industries has grown, as specialization and division of labor have been extended, and as special or scientific knowledge has become more and more necessary, these simple relations have been forcibly expanded and the concerted labors of master and man have been replaced by administrative, planning, and constructive **departments,** to coordinate properly the work of which has become a study in itself.

The tendency toward complexity in organization due to increased size is not so great, however, as that due to the character of the industry and the degree to which it is specialized. Thus, referring to Art. 80, it is evident that the organization of the personnel of an ordinary continuous industry is quite a simple matter as compared to that of an intermittent industry, and the organization of an industrial plant that includes continuous, lot-intermittent, and job-order features is often a most complex structure reviewed from any angle.

While it is possible and desirable to arrange the functions of an enterprise in a logical manner, as discussed in Art. 62, the exact form of organization of any plant sometimes depends, to some extent, on the character and ability of the men available. Able men are always rare and the exact subdivision of authority and responsibility often depends on this factor rather than on the more logical basis of an abstract analysis of the problem. For this reason and the other reasons advanced above, it is not possible to formulate fixed rules for planning industrial organizations.

The primary qualities that men may offer and which may be useful in industrial organizations (aside from such personal characteristics as honesty, integrity, etc.) are:

1. Managerial ability.
2. Organizing ability.
3. Administrative or executive ability.
4. Special technical knowledge.
5. Special skill of some kind.
6. Bodily strength.
7. Combinations of these qualities.

The problem of organization is to select and combine the efforts of men of the proper characteristics so as to produce the desired results. It may be helpful to remember that the problems of organization arise almost entirely out of division of labor.

93. Military or Line Organization.—It is obvious that, where the efforts of large bodies of people are to be directed, **discipline** is an essential feature of the plan of organization whatever it may be. The oldest and most natural form of organization, therefore, is that which is usually called **military** or **line organization,** so called because it was the essential feature of military systems. As used at present the name is a misnomer, as military systems have been subjected to the same modifying influences that have affected industrial and other organizations.

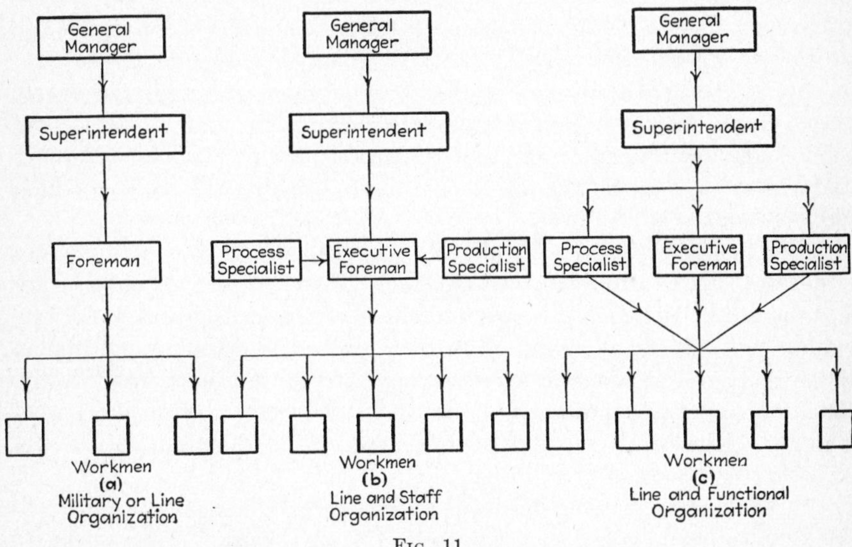

FIG. 11.

Under this system the lines of *direction* and *instruction* are vertical, so to speak, and the growth of such an organization may be illustrated in its simplest form by Fig. 11*a*. Here, as the duties and responsibilities of the general manager grew beyond his physical and mental capacity, he deputized certain of his duties to a superintendent. The latter, in turn, as he became overburdened, engaged foremen to assist him and to administer the several departments, the workman being held responsible only to the foreman immediately above him. If the plant is such as to require physical division, each division under a foreman, as is the case where it is composed of such units as foundry, forge, machine shop, etc., the military plan of organization is such as is shown in diagram in Fig. 12. Obviously the number of such divisions in no way affects the general principles involved. The lines of authority and instruction run directly from manager through the respective foremen to the workers and all men on the same authoritative level are independent of all others similarly situated. A foreman receives neither instruction nor command from another foreman and he can give the same only to those directly under him. The duties delegated by the manager to the superintendent, and from the superintendent to the foreman, or in fact by anyone to another lower down, are of the same general character. Thus the instructions given to each foreman would be of the same character but pertaining to different parts of the work or different lines of product. The proportion of both mental and manual labor is approximately the same for all men on the same level, and such separation of mental and manual work as does exist comes from

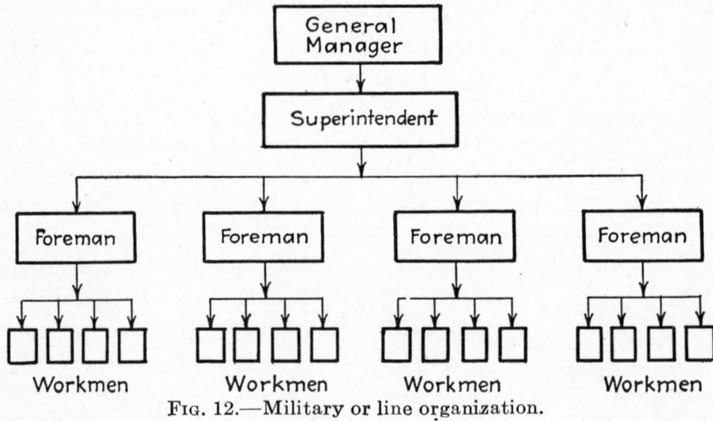

Fig. 12.—Military or line organization.

the natural reservation of mental work pertaining to administration by those higher in authority in delegating surplus duties to those under them. That is, division of mental and manual processes is here incidental rather than the result of logical study. It is assumed that each man on whatsoever authoritative level is fully competent to perform the duties pertaining to his position, no matter how numerous or divergent they may be.

The advantage of this form of organization, so far as discipline is concerned, is manifest. The duties and responsibilities of each man are clearly defined and no misunderstanding need arise as to each man's sphere of activity. It has, however, grave limitations and, because of these, pure military organization is no longer found in undertakings of any size or complexity. As plants grow in magnitude this system tends invariably to load up a few men to the breaking point with a variety of duties, since the number of executives on any one level is limited. It tends also, therefore, to crude methods, since few men can do several things and do them well, particularly if these duties are decidedly different in character. Thus, if the superintendent undertakes, as he formerly did, to be both administrator and chief designer, he is not likely to be a great success in either capacity, as these duties call for characteristics not usually combined in one man. The instructions given to individual workmen regarding the prosecution of the work are necessarily meager, especially if the work is varied, hence reliance must be placed, to a large extent, on the knowledge and skill of the workman. And lastly, this form of organization tends to make the success of the undertaking depend, to a large extent, on the ability of a few strong men, the loss of any one of whom would be very severely felt. The military system has, therefore, seldom existed in a pure form, except where the number of men involved was comparatively small and the scope of the scientific basis of the undertaking narrow, as is sometimes the case in simple continuous processes.

94. Line-and-staff Organization.—So long as industry was composed of small units and was comparatively simple in character, line organization, as has been noted, often sufficed, and indeed some very large plants have been successfully operated with almost pure line organization. However, growth in physical size and in scientific background long ago forced the progressive manager to call to his aid men with special knowledge and special skill. A consideration of any industry today will disclose a large number of such specialists as engineers, chemists, purchasing agents, tool specialists, production experts, etc., and the incorporation of these specialists into industry has raised new problems in organization.

There are two ways in which this problem can be and has been solved. In the first method the specialist is introduced in an *advisory* capacity and without any apparent authority. That is, he has no authority to *direct* the workmen even with regard to his own speciality, all executive orders passing to the workers through some line officer. Thus, in Fig. 11*b*, the superintendent may employ an expert to advise the foreman as to the technical aspects of the shop processes and also an expert on production methods such as cutting speeds, etc.—the foreman, however, actually directing all operations as in pure line organization. In a similar manner, the superintendent might employ a chemist, an engineer, or other specialists to advise him regarding certain phases of the work in which he lacks personal knowledge and experience. Such organization is known as *line and staff* and it will be obvious that the method is one of wide application, as can be seen by an examination of Figs. 13 to 15.

Figure 13, a typical diagram drawn by Professor M. A. Lee, illustrates line and staff in an excellent manner. The diagram is built around a strong central line control which carries all orders and instructions from the top of the diagram to the bottom with precision. Each important administrative officer, however, is buttressed, so to speak, with a strong staff from which he receives specialized advice or even instruction. Thus

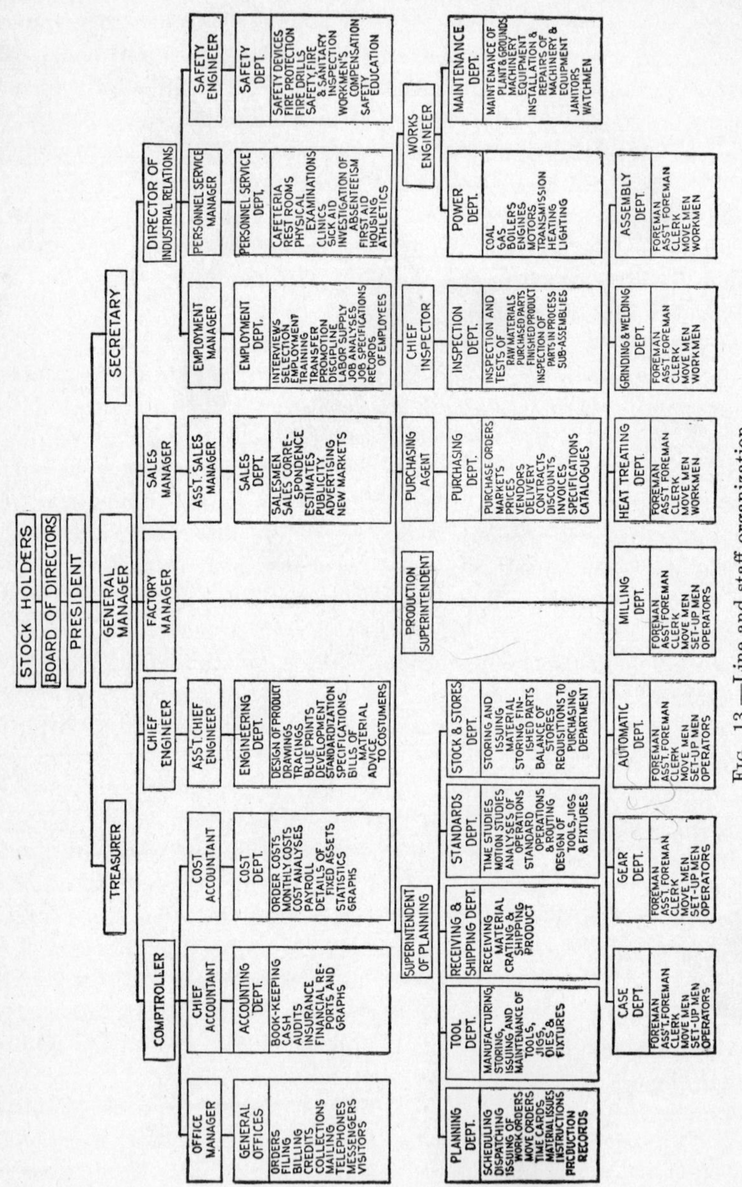

FIG. 13.—Line and staff organization.

the treasurer and secretary are shown as purely advisory to the president. The factory manager receives advice or instruction from the chief engineer and the director of industrial relations. Under the factory manager again are to be found a number of staff officers, with their departments, who advise the production superintendent as to special features of the work. The organization shown under the several staff officers is, in general, of the line type, but clearly any one of these might very well organize his department by line and staff if the size would warrant. In a somewhat broader way a staff department may *parallel* the entire line organization serving on all administrative levels. Thus welfare, medical service, etc., may be concerned with the entire organization. In fact, the term *staff* has been borrowed from military organization, where the *medical staff*, the *ordnance staff*, etc., serve the line on all administrative levels.

A clear understanding should be had of so-called staff departments. In many cases a staff officer may be purely advisory, as is the case of the secretary in Fig. 13. And while it is true that in general no staff officer can issue executive orders to any one in the line organization, nevertheless staff "advice" is often equivalent to a command. Thus in a well-managed manufacturing plant no person in the line would presume to change the plans and specifications of the engineering department or the formula of the chemist. Even if a mistake in these instructions is discovered it would be referred back to the staff department concerned. The advice of the treasurer, even, may have a controlling influence upon manufacturing operations, especially in the case of long-term contracts. But in true line-and-staff organization all actual orders to the working force pass through the line.

95. Functional Organization.—The second method of incorporating special skill and knowledge into the organization is shown diagrammatically in Fig. 11*c*. Here the functionalized specialists are placed upon the same authoritative level as the executive foreman, all three giving advice and instruction to the workers each in his own special field. Such a plan is known as *functional organization*, since the direction of the work is divided by functions rather than by simple authority. The term was first used by Mr. F. W. Taylor, who thus divided the work of production in a metal-working plant and called the specialized foremen *functional foremen*.

It will be clear, also, that this idea is capable of wide extension. Thus, in Fig. 14, the engineer, the chemist, and the superintendent of production are all placed upon the same authoritative level, each one giving his orders and advice directly to each foreman, no one being above the other and each being supreme in his own department except as he is responsible to the general manager. Each foreman receives instruction and advice from three sources and is answerable to each for the portion of his duties that belong in that field of authority.

Suppose, now, that the duties of each foreman are not the same, but that each is charged only with the supervision of certain aspects of each workman's duties and that the instruction that each foreman receives from the three primary sources is somewhat different from his fellow foreman's instructions. Each workman will then be guided by instructions from four separate men, each one of whom will give him expert

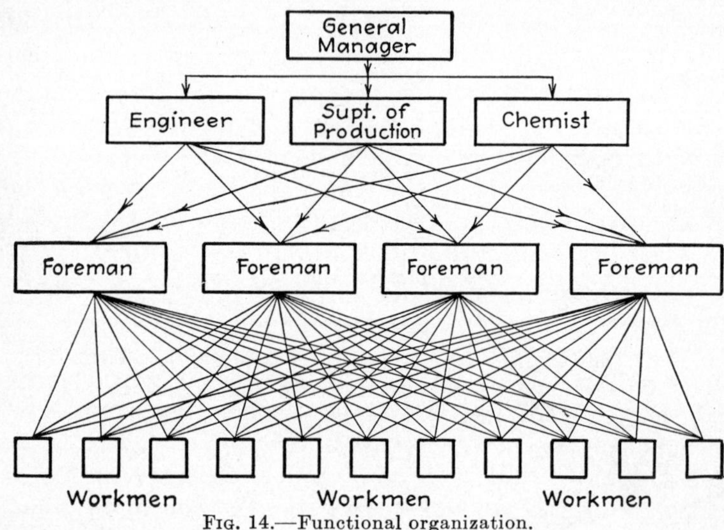

Fig. 14.—Functional organization.

guidance in some phase of the work in hand. Functional organization is a common feature in large enterprises as far as their general management and administration are concerned. The most noteworthy effort to extend functional organization to actual productive processes, that is to the work of foremen and workmen, is that of the late F. W. Taylor referred to earlier and commonly known as "scientific management." A brief description of Mr. Taylor's plan is given in Chap. XII, which should be read at this time.

The advantages of this form of organization are manifest. It conveys specific knowledge and guidance to each workman through experts, and not through foremen partially educated in the several fields. The separation of mental and the manual labor is planned *with reference to the functions to be performed* and not as incidental to other phases of administration. It makes provision also for the fullest use of the principle of division of labor, by keeping the functions that each man is called upon to perform down to a minimum. It tends, therefore, to high functional efficiency in each and every man.

The greatest disadvantage of the system is that it tends to become unstable because of the weakening of disciplinary or line control unless proper means of coordinating the work of men and departments of the same authoritative level are provided. The success of the system, when carried out in large enterprises, rests largely on the ability of the managing authorities to correlate the work of strong personalities and have them work together harmoniously.[1] Since the separation of mental and manual work is a fundamental principle in this type of organization, its application to the lower grades of production has led to considerable criticism on the ground that an extreme extension of the principle makes automatons of the lower grades of workers. This criticism can of course be made of any extreme division of labor, but on the other hand, as noted in Art. 15, it makes possible the employment of workers who otherwise could take no part in productive industry.

96. Summary.—The organization shown in Fig. 15 represents fairly well the extent to which these several principles are used in many progressive industrial plants. The background of the organization is a line formation with considerable staff organization on each administrative level. Under the factory superintendent, however, a certain degree of pure functional organization may be found. Thus, while the order department in Fig. 15 may be wholly responsible for placing all orders and for directing the manner in which work shall pass through the plant, the tool-designing department will usually be charged with the duty of providing all tools and equipment, which in mass production virtually fixes the character and sequence of operations. The inspection department again is usually independent of anyone below the factory superintendent and will, therefore, control the quality of the work and have something to say concerning methods of production. Below the foreman, again, in Fig. 15, the control is purely military or line in character. It will be clear, therefore, that human effort may be effectively organized through:

1. Military or line organization.
2. Line-and-staff organization.
3. Functional organization.
4. Line and functional organization.
5. Line, staff, and functional organization.

There is a general tendency to extend the use of staff officers and departments as industries grow in size, if for no other reason than that many functions that are of minor importance in small plants often assume serious proportions in larger ones. Thus, the human element may be easy to control in a very satisfactory manner in a small plant simply through personal relations between executives and workers. In very large plants, however, this close and often cordial contact may be lost, necessitating special methods of caring for this problem. In Fig. 13, Professor Lee places industrial relations as a major function under the general manager, and the director of this department is a staff officer equal in rank with the other principal staff officers. In this diagram five major functions are recognized under the general manager, four of them

[1] The late Walter C. Kerr once said: "The temperamental question is the greatest one in all management."

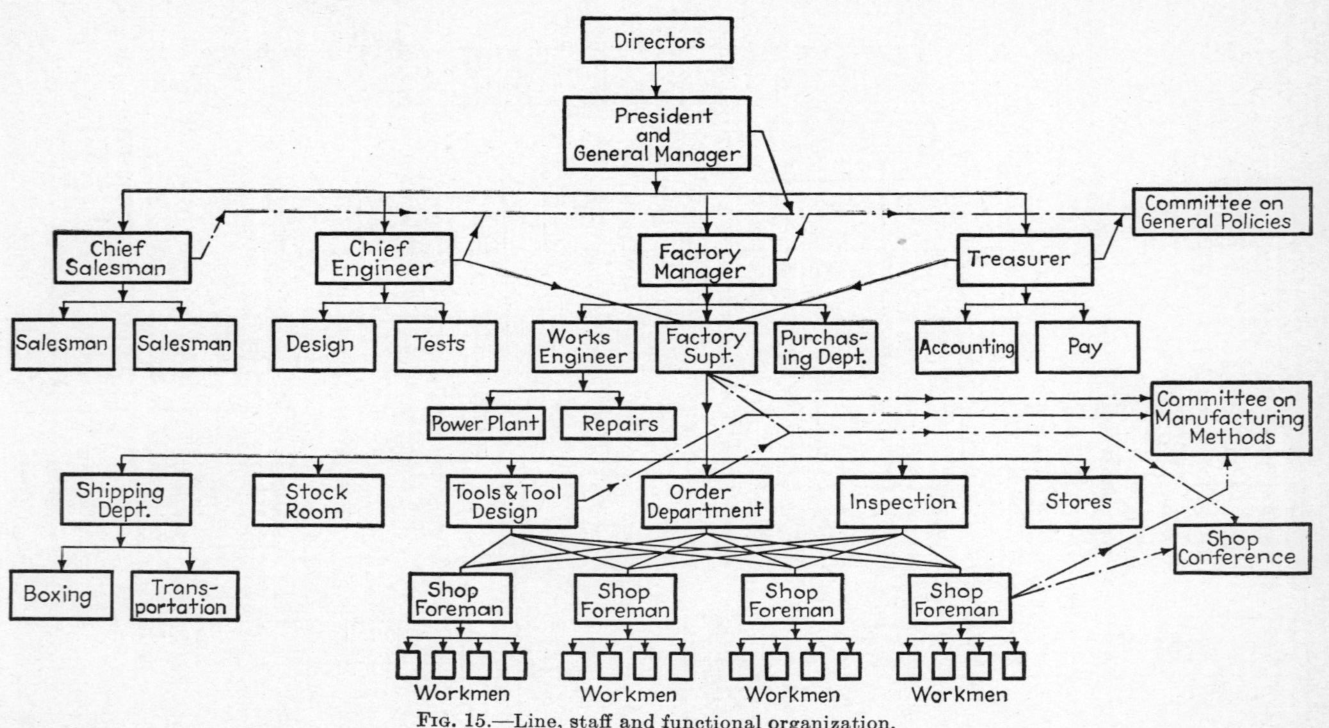

FIG. 15.—Line, staff and functional organization.

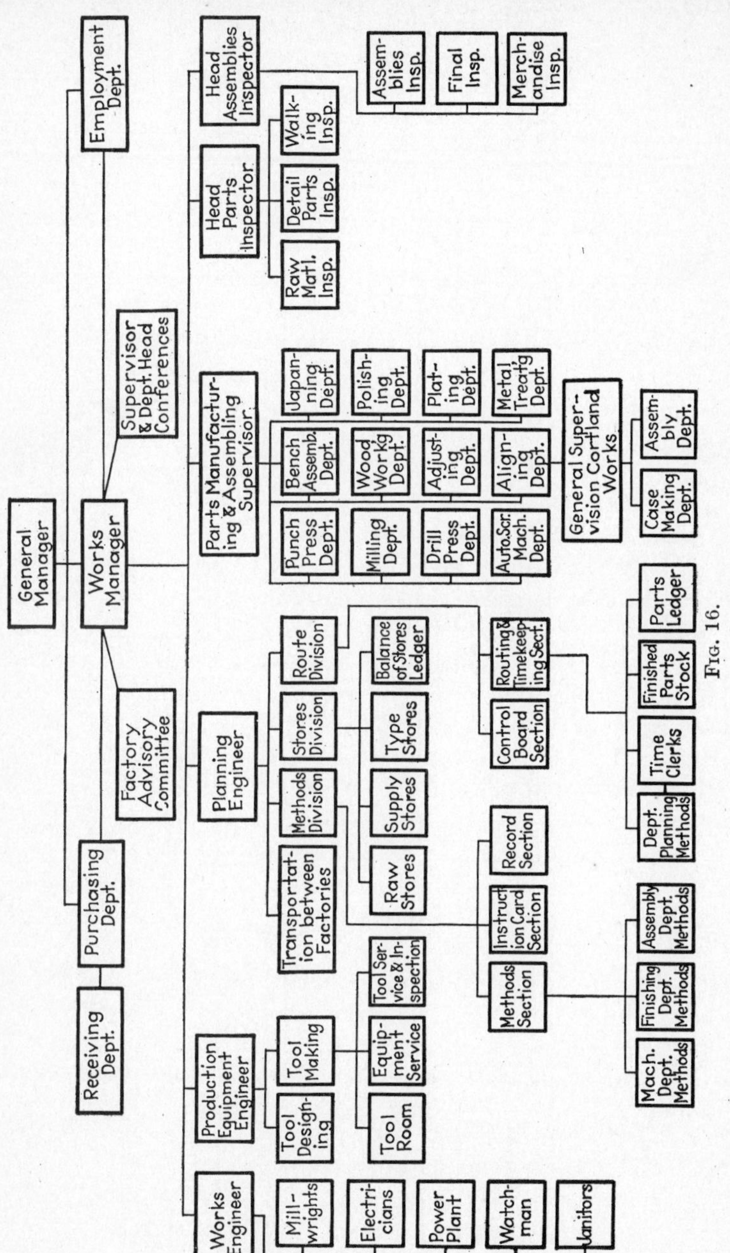
General Manager
Works Manager
Employment Dept.
Supervisor & Dept. Head Conferences
Factory Advisory Committee
Purchasing Dept.
Receiving Dept.
Head Assemblies Inspector
Assem-blies Insp.
Final Insp.
Merch-andise Insp.
Head Parts Inspector
Raw Matl. Insp.
Detail Parts Insp.
Walk-ing Insp.
Parts Manufactur-ing & Assembling Supervisor
Punch Press Dept.
Bench Assemb. Dept.
Japan-ning Dept.
Milling Dept.
Wood Workg Dept.
Polish-ing Dept.
Drill Press Dept.
Adjust-ing Dept.
Plat-ing Dept.
Auto.Scr. Mach. Dept.
Align-ing Dept.
Metal Treatg Dept.
General Super-vision Cortland Works
Case Making Dept.
Assem-bly Dept.
Planning Engineer
Transportat-ion between Factories
Methods Division
Stores Division
Route Division
Raw Stores
Supply Stores
Type Stores
Balance of Stores Ledger
Methods Section
Instruct-ion Card Section
Record Section
Control Board Section
Routing & Timekeep-ing Sect.
Mach. Dept. Methods
Finishing Dept. Methods
Assembly Dept. Methods
Dept. Planning Methods
Time Clerks
Finished Parts Stock
Parts Ledger
Production Equipment Engineer
Tool Design-ing
Tool Making
Tool Room
Equip-ment Service
Tool Ser-vice & In-spection
Works Engineer
Mill-wrights
Electri-cians
Power Plant
Watch-man
Janitors

FIG. 16.

appearing as staff organizations paralleling somewhat the line organizations headed by the factory manager.

Figure 16 shows the manufacturing organization of the Corona Typewriter Company before it was consolidated with the L. C. Smith Company. It is of interest in that it shows a considerable degree of staff organization in what is normally considered to be a plant of moderate size. Six major functions are recognized as necessary for the work of production, namely, works engineering or care of plant equipment; production-equipment engineering or the supplying of manufacturing tools such as jigs and fixtures; planning engineering or the planning and supervising of all productive processes so that all work shall be done in the best manner and at the right time; manufacturing and assembling, that is the actual work of production; inspection of parts as they are manufactured; and, lastly, inspection of the finished product after assembly. Here again five of the six functions are organized as staff activities auxiliary to and serving the principal function under the supervisor of parts manufacture and assembling.

The diagrams shown in Figs. 13, 15, and 16 show for the most part only the authoritative relations of men and departments, but do not show the procedure by which these men and departments are coordinated to work together harmoniously. This problem, so far as the work of production is ordinarily conducted, is discussed fully in Chaps. X and XII. Diagrams such as these, however, are very useful in visualizing the necessary departmentalization of the organization under discussion, fixing the responsibility of the principal officers, and recording these features in permanent form (see also Chap. X).

It will be noted again that in all of these diagrams a considerable degree of division of labor is employed. One of the chief advantages of so dividing the work is the increased ease with which men can be found to fill the several positions. It is not difficult to find a man who can perform well a few functions, but increasingly difficult to find suitable personnel as the number of functions to be performed by each man increases. Furthermore, the loss of a man or two out of a highly functionalized organization is not a serious matter, but was often a calamity under the older forms of organization that frequently were built around the personality and ability of a few strong men. It must be remembered, however, that the amount of subdivision of labor that is justifiable depends upon the size of the plant, the character of the industry, and the ability of the men available to lead the enterprise. It is often difficult to find men with vision, intelligence, and leadership, and while no doubt some form of organization must always be employed, especially for the rank and file of workers, care should be exercised that the administrative methods do not throttle the initiative and enthusiasm of even the lowest subordinate.

Genius does not work well in harness, and men are always more important than machines or methods.

References

CORNELL, W. B.: "Industrial Organization and Management."
EMERSON, HARRINGTON: "The Twelve Principles of Efficiency."
TAYLOR, F. W.: "Shop Management," *Trans. Am. Soc. Mech. Eng.*, Vol. 24.
Trans. Am. Management Assoc.

CHAPTER X

COORDINATION AND EXECUTIVE CONTROL; SYSTEM

97. Coordination.—It is obvious that any plan of organization to be highly effective must be definite; that is, it must define clearly every man's duties and coordinate every man's efforts toward the desired result. The duties of every man and every department should be outlined as clearly as possible and the authority and responsibility of every man definitely fixed. Authority and responsibility are inseparable and are essential to effective service. It is not good policy to keep men in uncertainty as to their position in the organization, and when several men are on the same authoritative level their several fields should be carefully prescribed and their efforts carefully coordinated. This is particularly true when a considerable amount of functional organization is introduced, since this tends, naturally, to weaken the disciplinary effects of line control; and where functional organization is used to any marked degree special care must be used to supply coordinative influences to compensate for this weakness.

While a certain amount of coordination can be accomplished by means of personal influence it is obvious that where large numbers of men are involved, or where preplanning of the work is necessary, written documents must be resorted to. The combination of coordinative mechanisms that may be employed will, of course, vary widely in different enterprises. The particular combination that is in use in any given plant is usually referred to as the **system** of the plant. Of the several mechanisms that are in use to secure coordination of effort and executive control the most important, perhaps, are **organization charts, organization records, standard-procedure instructions, orders and returns, records of performance, administrative reports, and committees.** The use and possibilities of these will be clearer after brief detailed discussion of each.

98. Organization Charts and Records.—The general character and use of organization charts have already been explained in the preceding chapter. Such charts are graphic presentations of the organic functions that compose the enterprise, and of the general *authoritative* relations that exist between departments and individuals in the organization. A well-developed chart, such as Fig. 15, will also show the various activities for which each departmental head is held responsible and over which he has jurisdiction. In general, such charts are of great assistance in planning new organizations or in remodeling old ones.

It is not always possible, however, to show clearly by such charts the full authority and responsibility that devolve upon each executive head, and it is often difficult thus to show where such authority and responsibility overlap. In most organizations, particularly if they are comparatively small in size, the adjustment of such discrepancies and overlapping can be left to the good sense and judgment of those directly concerned, and to the guidance of their superior officers. It may be desirable, however, especially in the case of large enterprises, to put into written form a somewhat more detailed statement of the authority and responsibility of the several executive heads, thus removing all doubt in debatable fields of activity. Such documents may be called **organization records**[1] or **organization instructions,** and they, with the organization chart, form a permanent record of the organization. Whether such instructions are necessary or not it is essential that the duties of all men be made clear and explicit and all necessary adjustments between men made by some superior officer, and not allowed to remain a source of irritation and dispute. The specifying of the duties of the several executive heads has the added advantage of compelling the organizer to think out his plan of organization with the same care that a designer bestows upon the several parts of a machine to insure smooth running.

Usually organization charts are *impersonal* as illustrated by Fig. 13, that is, the names of the several executive heads are not placed upon the chart in connection with the work that they supervise, though this is sometimes done. Organization instructions, however, are usually issued to individuals by name, and such an arrangement permits of a considerable degree of flexibility.

99. Standard Procedure Instructions.—Organization charts and organization records or instructions indicate the several functions that are to be performed, and show, in a general manner, the authoritative relations that are to exist in the enterprise. An organization that has been developed to this degree, however, has potential power only; it is *static*, so to speak. It is comparable to a well-drilled and well-officered regiment where each man fully understands his functions but, lacking *marching orders*, has no idea as to *where* to proceed or *when* to start. A careful distinction should be drawn, therefore, between *organization instructions* and *procedure instructions*. Procedure instructions grow out of the determination of policies as discussed in Arts. 56 and 58, which should be read at this point. Procedure is the logical method of making policies effective.

Professor J. O. McKinsey very clearly illustrates the problem of procedure thus:

It is the primary function of the sales department to secure sales orders. But a sales order is of no value unless it be filled and collection made from the

[1] Parkhurst, F. A., "Applied Scientific Management," pp. 11 and 199.

customer. The sales department must secure the cooperation of other departments before these results are attained. The credit department must approve the credit of the customer; the stores department must deliver the goods to the shipping department; the shipping department must pack the goods and deliver them to the transportation company; the accounting department must invoice the customer and make a record of the amount due; and the collection department must see that the customer pays his account at the date of maturity. If each of these departments is to perform efficiently its part of this task it must know definitely what it is to do as well as the best and quickest way of doing it. If the operation, as a whole, is to be performed effectively, each department must do its part in the proper sequence and must do it in such a manner as to facilitate the operations to be performed by the other departments. These objectives can be achieved best by working out a **standard procedure** for the handling of sales orders and communicating this procedure in written form to all departments concerned. This method provides definite instructions for all departments and tends to prevent conflict of authority and error.

This clear statement of procedure in handling sales orders applies fully to the entire operation of the plant, and good management will insure that the best possible procedure is worked out for the complete cycle of manufacturing and accounting operations from the receipt of the sales order to the collection of the pay from the customer. There are, of course, always several ways by which a given result can be obtained, but if, after careful consideration, it appears that some one procedure is the best, that procedure should be adopted as a **standard procedure** and adhered to until circumstances change, or a better sequence of operations is developed.

In most enterprises, particularly if they are of moderate size, the procedure has been developed empirically and without the aid of written documents. It should be noted that in continuous-process industries the procedure, so far as manufacturing operations are concerned, is fixed usually by the natural sequence of processes. In small intermittent industries the sequence of operations is often obvious and requires no explanations or instructions. In large mass-production industries, and particularly in large enterprises of the intermittent type, the problem of what constitutes the best procedure is often a difficult one. Perhaps the most important attempt to establish standard procedure is found in modern **planning departments** which aim to predict in advance the entire sequence of operations for every piece of product and also the *time* required for each operation. This particular problem in manufacturing procedure is treated fully in a succeeding chapter. It should be noted, however, that the general problem of planning the best procedure for any enterprise is of somewhat wider scope than the planning of the productive operations. It involves the entire sequence of events, sales, financial, accounting, engineering, production, etc. In such cases the procedure should be thought out with great care, and often it is necessary to reduce the main features of the established procedure to written form so that full information can be conveyed to all concerned.

100. Orders and Returns.—It is evident that as the plant grows in size, and organization becomes more complex, the manager loses *personal* touch with both processes and men. In smaller shops and under simpler methods the manager was able to assure himself personally of all the details of the business, to know each man's abilities and hence to use them to the best advantage, retaining his interest in the work on personal grounds. He could settle all disputes and differences personally and the manager's personality played a large part in the administration of the works. This personal method of giving orders and checking up results is obviously no longer possible with modern organizations, even where small numbers of employees are concerned. As the numbers grow large the problem increases in complexity and must be solved by a carefully arranged system of *written* communications. It is a cardinal principle in modern management that all directions and instructions and all reports and returns must be in written form of some kind. This gives *definiteness* to all such matters and, through duplicate copies, records of all transactions can be preserved. It also enables the manager, or others interested, to trace faults and errors and place the responsibility where it rightly belongs.

There are, in general, only two classes of such documents, namely, **orders** and **returns.** Under orders may be classified all instructions and directions issuing from the several departments charged with directing the work, making purchases, etc.; and under returns may be included documents and reports recording the results of operations, accounts of materials, time, supplies, and other data; or, more briefly, orders direct how work shall be done, returns record how it has been performed. For convenience and dispatch, orders and returns are usually made on printed forms so that the amount of information that must be filled in by hand is a minimum. These orders and returns move to and fro along the prearranged lines of communication that have been established by the plan of procedure that has been adopted, whether this procedure has been reduced to written form or not. If the system is adequate each department is fully informed regarding what it should know; confidential information goes only to those for whom it is intended, and the results obtained are much more accurate than can be obtained by any personal direction.

The relative size and the character of the printed form on which orders may be written will, of course, depend on the character of the work and form of organization. It is of little use to try to indicate, even briefly, their general character, as they grow out of the needs of the business.

Figure 17 shows a typical production order issued by the production clerk directing a department to perform certain work. The written order enables the manager and the several heads of departments charged with the direction of the work to issue their directions with a clearness, accuracy, and certainty that cannot be approached by verbal methods. This is very well illustrated in the work of the engineering department. The drawings and specifications issuing therefrom can be, and should be, so made as to make verbal communication almost entirely unnecessary.

CONSOLIDATED MACHINE TOOL CORPORATION
OF AMERICA
COLBURN MACHINE TOOL WORKS
CLEVELAND, OHIO

SOLD TO
ADDRESS
SHIP TO
ADDRESS
VIA
TERMS F.O.B.
RENDER INVOICE IN INVOICED BY

PRODUCTION DEP'T.

SALES ORDER NO.
PRODUCTION ORDER NO.
CUSTOMER'S ORDER NO.
CUSTOMER'S REQ'N NO.
GENERAL OFFICE ORDER NO.
DATE RECEIVED
DATE PROMISED
DATE SHIPPED
CAR NO.

SERIAL NO.	SHIPP'G CHECK	QUANT.	DESCRIPTION	USE DRAWING NO.		USE BILL OF MATERIAL NO.	

FIG. 17.—Production order.

The returns from factory operations and transactions are of necessity numerous and of many kinds. Detail records of all time expended, material used, supplies ordered, progress of work, etc., are usually obtained by a carefully arranged system of cards which are filled out at the place of operation and then returned to the department interested. Thus the engineering data and the records of tests made on the product would go to the engineering department for its information. Inventory records of the stores department might go to the superintendent or to the order department. All cards recording time and material used or indicating progress of work would be returned to the cost department. Figure 18 illustrates a typical time card on which the time of entering and the time of leaving the factory may be filled in on a time recorder, while Fig. 19 shows a job time card giving in detail the time expended on a certain piece of work.

In Fig. 19 the time when the work is started and finished can also be recorded by means of a time recorder. The total amount of time recorded on such cards as Fig. 19 should, of course, correspond to the total recorded on the master card, Fig. 18, for any given period of employment.

These detail returns are, or at least should be, used for three purposes:

1. To record the results of operations.
2. To predict future operations.
3. To serve as the basis of managerial reports.

WEEK ENDING

No.

Name

DAY	MORNING		AFTERNOON				TOTAL
	IN	OUT	IN	OUT	IN	OUT	
SUN.							
MON.							
TUE.							
WED.							
THU.							
FRI.							
SAT.							

TOTAL HRS.			
PIECE HRS.	PIECE		
DAY HRS.	DAY		
RATE PER HR.	TOTAL		

Fig. 18.—Time clock card.

Thus the engineering data from the test floors serve not only to verify the accuracy of the design but furnish information for future designs. The time and material cards returned to the cost department furnish data for finding the cost of the product and also for predicting future costs. These features will be more fully discussed in succeeding chapters.

101. Records of Performance.—A **record** is a statement of experience, an account of what has actually occurred. If it is accurate there is nothing so useful as a guide in predicting future events or in assisting good judgment. It should be noted that any field of endeavor becomes scientific only as it can accumulate **recorded experience.** Management is no exception to this general rule and it becomes more definite and exact, and less personal and empirical, as the results of recorded experience are studied and these results brought to bear upon the problems to be solved. The best examples of the use of recorded experience are to be found in the engineering and other scientific branches of industry where the *prediction of results,* because of the vast amount of recorded experience available, is accurate and sure. The tendency in management, and in business in general, is to proceed along similar lines.

Industrial records are of many kinds and are found among both orders and returns. Thus the drawings and specifications of the engineering

MAN'S NO.	MAN'S NAME		ORDER NO.	
MACH. & CLASS		ASSEMBLY	PART NO.	
QUANTITY ON ORDER	PIECES FINISHED			CLOCK RECORD
OPERATION				
REMARKS				

	PIECES	PROD. LABOR	BURDEN	JOB TIME
This Record				
Forward				
Totals				

FORM C. D. 15

Fig. 19.—Job time card.

department are carefully preserved as records and similarly the reports of engineering tests that are in the nature of returns are preserved with equal care as a basis for future prediction. The greater part of industrial records, however, have their origin in the returns, that is in the time cards, the records of materials issued, and similar documents that are intimately connected with actual production. The information contained in such returns is most usually preserved in *consolidated* form. Thus the time cards may be used primarily for making up the payroll. They may then be passed to the cost department where the information they carry will be recorded as part of the cost of the several pieces of work involved. After this they may be *classified* into general groups and serve as a basis of managerial reports; and finally they can be thrown away since the information they bear is fully recorded in usable form. In a similar manner the many items that flow to the general accounts appear in consolidated form in the ledger, and other consolidated accounts, in connection with the important activities of the enterprise. Sales orders, invoices, purchase and stores requisitions, ledger accounts, etc., are all in the nature of recorded experience and they may be preserved for reference in their original form or in consolidated form, depending upon circumstances. The question of what information should be preserved and the form in which it should be recorded may be made clearer by the discussion of managerial reports that follows. It may be noted in passing that great economies may be effected by correlating the records of the several departments so far as possible. Thus in the example cited above the same set of primary documents is made to serve three different purposes. If the forming of the records of the enterprise is considered as a whole much duplication of effort may be saved and quite frequently the work of one department may be made to serve as a check on the accuracy of the records of other departments using the same data for other purposes.

102. Administrative Reports.—Orders and returns with a well-arranged system of records enable the several departments to do their work properly and to keep account of all that occurs in which they are severally interested. It is difficult, however, for the manager to obtain from departmental records a clear idea of what is occurring unless these records are presented to him in the condensed form of executive **reports.** The written report replaces the old-time manager's personal observations with accurate statistics, and is practically the only way a manager can accurately gage the operation of a large factory and keep a firm grasp upon it. Just as records are consolidated orders or returns, so reports are consolidated records arranged so as to show general tendencies.

The character of the reports that a manager may require depends, of course, on the nature of the industry and the form of organization, and it is not always easy to select the reports that will be of most value. Unless reports are of *use*, unless they tell something bearing on the cost of production, or similar important features, they should be discontinued, as they are a source of waste. Conversely, unless a useful report is used, unless it is the basis of analysis or discussion which throws light on the problems of the business, the data which it presents might as well go into the wastebasket. There are certain reports, that will be discussed for the purpose of illustration, which are applicable to nearly all manufacturing enterprises. In Fig. 13, for instance, the general manager would call upon the comptroller, the chief engineer, the factory manager, the sales manager, and the director of personnel relations for certain reports from each primary department, thus furnishing him with sales, engineering, manufacturing, personnel, and financial reports. These are typical classes of reports, though it may be desirable to have several reports from each department on different phases of its work. Reports may be in the nature of written statements, statistical tables, graphs or charts, geometric figures, or even maps and pictures. The most common forms in industrial management are statistical tables and graphs or charts.

The most important financial reports are the **balance sheet** and the **statement of income and expense,** both of which will be very briefly discussed. Both of these reports have their origin in the general accounts of the organization and are made up by the accounting department[1] at regular periodic intervals. The balance sheet is a statement of the assets, liabilities, and ownership of the enterprise in such a form as to show its financial condition at a specific time. There is no form or arrangement of the balance sheet that is universally accepted as a standard, though considerable effort has been made to establish such a standard. Nor is there any unanimity of opinion among accountants as to the fullness or detail with which the several items of the balance sheet shall be recorded. It may have the form shown in Table 3 and known as the **account form,** or it may be compiled in **statement form** like the income and expense statement of Table 4. It may be a very much abbreviated or **consolidated** document showing only the bare essentials of assets, liabilities, and net worth, or it may be quite detailed as in the standard balance sheet recommended by the Federal Reserve Board.[2] This is to be expected since industries vary widely in character as also do the purposes for which the balance sheet is drawn. There are, however, a number of fundamental characteristics that are common to practically all such documents and Table 3 may be taken as an illustration of an average balance sheet for an industrial enterprise.

On the asset side is shown, first, the **current assets,** that is those assets that vary constantly. Current assets that can be made available for immediate use, such as cash, bonds, and accounts receivable, etc., are known as **quick assets** and are sometimes listed on the balance sheet as a group. Next in order are **fixed assets,** that is, those assets which change very slowly and are in the nature of a permanent investment. Lastly there appear the **intangible assets,** of which patents and goodwill are excellent examples.

On the liability side are first shown the **current liabilities** or those that are constantly changing in value. Just as there are **quick assets** so there are **quick liabilities** or those that may have to be met in the near future. Next in order are **fixed liabilities** or those which do not have to be liquidated in the near future but may stand for a long time or even be renewed when due. The difference between all the assets and all the

[1] Anything approaching a full discussion of these important documents is beyond the scope of this book. The student should, however, inform himself fully concerning them. See Saliers, E. A., "Accountant's Handbook," McKinsey, J. O., "Managerial Accounting," Vol. 1, and Gilman, Stephen, "Analyzing Financial Statements," for fuller discussions.

[2] See "Accountant's Handbook," p. 330.

TABLE 3

ENTERPRISE MANUFACTURING COMPANY

Balance Sheet—December 31, 1932

Assets

Current Assets		
Cash	$ 200,000	
U. S. Government Bonds	600,000	
Accounts Receivable	350,000	
Notes Receivable	180,000	
Inventories		
Raw Materials	$ 200,000	
Goods in Process	240,000	
Finished Goods	440,000	
Total Current Assets	$2,210,000	$2,210,000
Fixed Assets		
Land	$ 200,000	
Buildings	420,000	
Machinery and Equipment	680,000	
Furniture and Fixtures	40,000	
Total Fixed Assets	$1,340,000	$1,340,000
Intangible Assets		
Patents	$ 290,000	
Goodwill	700,000	
Total Intangible Assets	$ 990,000	$ 990,000
Total Assets		$4,540,000

Liabilities

Current Liabilities		
Accounts Payable	$ 340,000	
Notes Payable	360,000	
Taxes Accrued	50,000	
Interest Accrued	60,000	
Wages Accrued	15,000	
Royalties	15,000	
Total Current Liabilities	$ 840,000	$ 840,000
Fixed Liabilities		
Mortgages on Property	$ 400,000	
Other Bonded Debts	200,000	
Total Fixed Liabilities	$ 600,000	$ 600,000
Net Worth		
Common Stock	$2,000,000	
Preferred Stock	500,000	
Surplus	600,000	
Total Net Worth	$3,100,000	$3,100,000
Total Net Worth and Liabilities		$4,540,000

liabilities is known as **net worth.** It consists of the value of the stock and the surplus, and appears on the liability side balancing the assets and liabilities.

The accuracy of such a financial statement will depend, naturally, upon the accuracy of the supporting documents and reports. This is particularly true of the asset side of the balance sheet. Thus the values of the buildings, machinery, and equipment may or may not be the *depreciated* value, that is, the value after allowance has been made for wear and tear. Again, the value of the intangible assets may be largely a matter of opinion. Some very conservative concerns depreciate such items as rapidly as possible, replacing their value with more permanent assets through funds taken from income. Again, there may be liabilities for which a **reserve** should be set up and this reserve carried as an item on the liability side of the balance sheet. Further reference will be made to the interpretation of the balance sheet in the succeeding section.

A **profit and loss statement** is a tabulation of the income and expenses of a particular trading or manufacturing venture for a given period of time. The difference between such income and expense is the net profit or loss incurred for the given period. Quite frequently there are other sources of income and expense not directly connected with the trading or manufacturing activities, but still forming a part of the operations of the enterprise. A combined tabulation of the profit and loss items with other items of expense and income is known as a **statement of income and expense.** As this latter is the broader document it will be briefly discussed. Like the balance sheet, such documents may be compiled in either the statement form or the account form. Table 4, which is compiled in statement form, may be taken as representing good modern practice.

The first item is the gross receipts from sales. From this is deducted all allowances, cost of goods returned, etc., giving the net receipts from sales. Deducting the cost of producing the goods gives the gross profits from sales. Adding to this last item any other income, *due to the trading or manufacturing activities*, gives the gross or total income from manufacturing operations. Deducting from this the operating expenses gives the net operating income or profit, or loss if there be such. The foregoing items are those that are usually found in a profit and loss statement. To the net operating income or profit is added income from other sources not directly connected with the manufacturing operations, and from this sum is subtracted any similar losses or expenses, thus obtaining the net income or profit (loss if there be such) from all sources connected with the enterprise.

The returns that flow into the cost department and other departments under the factory manager may be the basis of many reports; and here again, discretion must be used in selecting those that will be

TABLE 4

CONSOLIDATED MANUFACTURING COMPANY

Statement of Income and Expense for the Year Ended December 31, 1932

Gross Sales		$3,564,850
Deductions from Sales		
Sales Returned	$ 24,460	
Sales Allowances	5,540	
Outward Freight	144,680	
	$174,680	174,680
Net Sales		$3,390,170
Cost of Goods (see schedules)		$2,641,910
Gross Profit on Sales		$ 748,260
Other Income		
Interest on Notes Receivable	$ 5,640	
Interest on Bank Balance	6,430	
Purchases Discount	1,240	
	$ 13,310	13,310
Gross Income from Operations		$ 761,570
Operating Expenses		
Purchasing Expenses	$ 10,460	
Selling Expense	40,270	
Comptrollers Expenses	5,430	
General Office Expense	14,680	
Miscellaneous Expenses	7,890	
	$ 78,730	78,730
Net Operating Income		$ 682,840
Nonoperating Income		
Interest on Bonds Owned	$ 2,680	
Income from Real Estate	2,340	
Sundry Other Profits	5,190	
	$ 10,210	10,210
Net Operating Plus Nonoperating Income		$ 693,050
Nonoperating Expense		
Loss From Temporary Investments	$ 4,320	
Loss on Sale of Real Estate	6,190	
Taxes on Rented Property	570	
Sundry Other Expenses	2,140	
	$ 13,220	13,220
Net Income from All Sources		$ 679,830

most useful. Only a few important ones will be noted. The **weekly labor report** is a classified statement of all expenditures for labor. It enables the manager to see at a glance where the money paid in wages has gone and to check excessive expenditures. Sometimes a statement is made in this report of the total amount of money expended for material and supplies as well as a statement of the value of shipments. This widens the scope of the report and adds to its usefulness. The **special cost report** is a detailed statement of the labor, material, and other expense items which go to make up the cost of a particular piece of apparatus. It is usually compiled for the purpose of making a study of such a piece of apparatus with a view to cutting down the manufacturing expense.

A most useful report is the **progress report.** This may be compiled by the order department, if it is charged with the duty of moving the work through the factory, or it may be a composite report made up from the records or reports of the several foremen. It is of particular value in finding out what contracts and orders are behind schedule time and why this is so. It also furnishes an accurate statement of the volume of unfinished work in the shop.

The **reports from the sales** departments would, of course, show actual sales by territories and a corresponding statement of the expenses incurred in making sales. In addition, the thoughtful salesman can greatly aid the manager by reporting competitive prices, engineering or manufacturing data; in fact, anything that will keep the management informed of what is transpiring in the salesman's territory.

Engineering reports are usually of a technical character and are intended to keep the manager informed on the engineering features of the business. They may also take the form of circulars of information to salesmen.

103. Interpretation of Reports.—Statistical statements can often be made much more effective by combining or contrasting them, and it is often necessary to consider data from different reports to obtain best results. Thus, it may be important to know the value of the output for a given period; but it is, in general, much more important to know the output *per unit of capital invested.* Again, the amount of coal consumed in the power plant per month might be of interest, but the coal *per kilowatt-hour* is a much closer check on the efficiency of the power plant. All statistical data gain in importance, therefore, by *comparison with standards.* Thus, if careful tests or long experience have shown that a given power plant can produce one kilowatt-hour on a certain minimum number of pounds of coal, that minimum number becomes a standard against which all other performances can be judged for efficiency. Reports often furnish excellent data from which to develop such criteria of performance. Thus in the balance sheet the ratio $\frac{\text{current assets}}{\text{current liabilities}}$ is a measure of the borrowing capacity of the enterprise and for any given enterprise there will be a value for this ratio below which it will not be desirable to go. Again, the ratio $\frac{\text{surplus net profits}}{\text{net worth}}$ is a measure of the earning power of the business viewed from the standpoint of the stockholders and for which a minimum desirable value or standard could be set. Many other[1] equally valuable criteria and standards can be developed from well-prepared reports. Ratios that may be used as criteria of efficiency in management will be discussed in a later section.

104. Graphic Reports.—The interpretation of statistical data is often greatly facilitated by expressing them in graphical form,[1] which not only shows more clearly the relative values of any given account, from date to date, but shows the relative values of different sets of data, as well as indicating *tendencies* much more clearly than can be done by tabulated figures. Figure 20 shows a few curves such as might be plotted from the records of a plant employing about 1,200 men and turning out $1,250 worth of product per capita per annum or a total of $1,500,000 per annum at factory cost. The curves shown are hypothetical and do not represent any actual case. They serve, however, to show the general character of such curves. Other curves, of course, may also be plotted if they will assist the analysis. Thus, the curves of material used might be of interest and, if the factory was developing new machinery, the cost of experimental work would certainly be an important account. If the product were diversified it might be desirable to plot separate curves for the several lines of goods manufactured, combining their totals into curve 3. Curve 3 represents the total shop cost of all goods manufactured, while curve 4 shows the total cost of goods including all general and selling expenses. The difference between curves 4 and 5 will be the probable profit for the week considered, but does not indicate what the profits will be on the particular goods shipped during that week. Sometimes it is useful to plot the *average* values of the account considered and again it may be helpful to plot the *accumulated total* up to the time considered, depending on the business and the information needed. The principle is of very wide application and helpful in all cases where large masses of detailed returns must be condensed into a form that will indicate general tendencies at a glance.

One of the most ingenious and useful forms of graphic records is the chart introduced by the late H. L. Gantt and commonly known as the **Gantt chart.** The basic peculiarity of this chart is that it *measures performance against time.* Figure 21 illustrates such a chart[2] which records the actual progress of sales in a certain commercial enterprise. In this figure the spaces between the heavy vertical lines represent one

[1] See ALFORD, L. P. (Ed.), "Cost and Production Handbook," p. 1461.

[2] Published by permission of Wallace Clark.

month; hence the spaces between the light vertical lines represent six days approximately. A horizontal distance, therefore, on such a chart measures elapsed or cumulative time. But a horizontal line can also be made to measure performance, either expected or accomplished, and if such a line is drawn on such a chart as Fig. 21, comparison of expected or accomplished performance within the given time is made very clear.

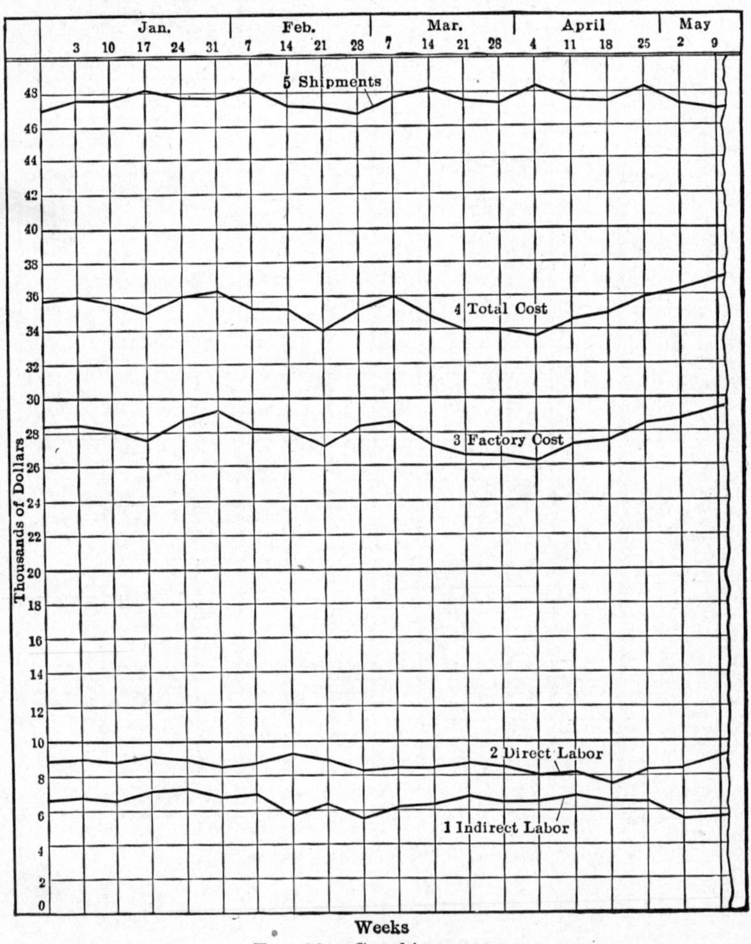

FIG. 20.—Graphic reports.

Thus in Fig. 21 the figures at the left of each monthly space denote the volume of sales that was desired for each line of product. The figures at the right of each space denote the *total* volume of sales desired up to that date. The light horizontal lines indicate the percentage of the monthly quota actually sold. The heavy horizontal lines indicate the percentage of the total required quota sold at any time. Thus the first set of such lines show that the total of all products sold at the end of September just about equals the desired quota. Product *E* is oversold while product *I* is undersold. The letter *z* indicates that no orders were taken during the period so marked. The principle of the Gantt chart is applicable to a wide range of statistical work not only for purposes of managerial control

TOTAL ORDERS - 1923 - BY KINDS OF PRODUCT (Dollars in 1000's)

	%	January	February	March	April	May	June	July	August	September	October	November	December	
Total Orders	100	150	258 408	174 582	252 834	464 1298	328 1626	340 1966	486 2452	640 3092	374 3466	562 4028	472 4500	
Product A	64	86	124 210	118 328	78 3.2 406	392 798	192 990	92 1082	254 1336	438 1774	308 2082	466 2548	332 2880	
Product B	14	2	12 14	4 18	68 86	12 98	60 158	130 288	108 396	146 542	44 586	10 596	34 630	
Product C	3	0 2M	14	0 0.4 14	12 26	0 6.2	26 52	10 62	6 68	4 z 72	0	20 92	44 136	
Product D	5	6	32 38	10 48	42 90	30 120	2 18.1 122	6 128	30 158	4 6.1 162	2 164	34 198	26 224	
Product E	2	18	4 4.9 22	6 8 28	18 2.2 46	6 14.5 52	8 4.6 60	4 4 64	4 4.5 68	8 76	4 80	6 86	4 90	+207
Product F	1	4	6 10	6 16	4 20	4 24	2 26	6 32	2 34	4 38	2 40	2 42	4 46	+8
Product G	2	12	20 32	10 42	8 50	8 58	8 66	4 70	4 74	6 80	2 82	4 86	4 90	
Product H	4	16	40 56	16 72	12 84	6 4.7 90	14 104	14 118	12 130	14 144	6 150	14 164	16 180	+24
Product I	5	6	6 12	4 16	10 26	6 32	16 48	74 122	66 188	16 204	6 210	6 216	8 224	
Miscellaneous	0	3.4	3.6 7	1.8 8.8	3 11.8	2.4 14.2	1.4 15.6	4.2 19.8	1.8 21.6	6.2 27.8				
Outside Work	0	z	6	10.8 16.8	9.8 26.6	0.4 27	0.2 27.2	0.4 27.6	0.2 27.8	3 30.8				

FIG. 21.—A year's sales arranged by products and shown on a Gantt progress chart.

but also to the details of production. It is especially useful where standard performances can be set up.

THE COMMITTEE SYSTEM

105. Committees in General.—Factory problems are nearly always many-sided and hence difficult of solution by any one man, especially where, under staff organization, he is charged with, and capable of, handling only one phase of the work. As before stated, furthermore, when several men are on the same authoritative level there must always be some definite means provided so that they can harmonize their efforts. There is no other way by which these ends can be served comparable to a good committee system. There are several inherent advantages in a good committee. First, it is impersonal in its action, and its verdict, like that of any jury, is usually based on the *facts* presented. The very atmosphere of a committee tends to compel all of its members to lay aside pettiness and personal prejudice and to act in accordance with the merits of the case. The foreman who would, over the telephone, blame a fellow foreman for a delay will hesitate to do so in his presence or in that of his superior officers. The decisions of a committee are, therefore, likely to be more accurate than those of an individual because of the greater accuracy of its basic information. A misstatement on the part of a member is not likely to go unchallenged.

Secondly, committee meetings tend to promote a better understanding between men of the same authoritative level and of different levels. Distrust and jealousy of each other are rapidly eliminated as men know one another better and see the good side of each other's nature. There is something likable in all men if one can succeed in discovering it, and this can be done only by bringing them into close personal contact with common problems to be solved, not by wrangling and fault-finding but by an earnest endeavor to find the very best solution. Thirdly, the committee method tends to awaken interest in the work and to draw out the best efforts of all of its members, and tends generally toward a better *esprit de corps*.

Committees are always of an *advisory* character. They cannot replace strong personality but they can be used effectively to assist a strong executive in finding out what is actually going on in the factory, in deciding what should be done, and in enlisting the goodwill of those under him. The best and most natural basis of committee work is a report on the matter under discussion, and reports are greatly enhanced in value when discussed by an intelligent and representative committee. There may be many kinds of committees and for many purposes, but only a few typical ones will be discussed here. In general, committees should not be too large or too small. If too large they become very unwieldy, and if too small they may not secure a broad representation. A committee of six members is usually large enough.

106. The Committee on General Policies.—Referring to Fig. 15, it is apparent that no one of the four vice presidents would be able, in general, to advise the general manager on the entire manufacturing policy of the works. But if these four men are collected into a **committee on general policies** each of the four important divisions of the works is represented by an expert. The president or general manager would be the natural chairman and such a committee, through him, can direct the manufacturing policy of the plant with great intelligence. The matters that naturally come before this committee are:

1. The general manufacturing policy of the plant, the character and sizes of the articles to be made.

2. The approval of all orders of extraordinary character and the approval of orders for stock, if goods are manufactured for stock. The approval of all extraordinary manufacturing expenditures and recommendations for economies.

The reports that would naturally be laid before it would, therefore, include the balance sheet, profit and loss statement, stock and sales reports, and similar general statements.

107. Committee on Manufacturing Methods.—A committee on **manufacturing methods** would consist, usually, of the superintendent or his representative as chairman, a representative of the tool-making department, and such representatives of the manufacturing departments as may be desirable. This committee would discuss all problems concerning tools for new work or improvements in those existing. The amount of money that it is desirable to spend on tools may often be limited by the committee on policy, and the committee on manufacturing methods must, therefore, have full knowledge of the number of parts to be manufactured and the probability of a repetition of the order. A committee of this character can save or waste a lot of money, and which of these they succeed in doing will depend to a large extent on how closely they consider the effect of the number of parts to be made.

Where it is desired to reduce the cost of manufacture of an existing line the engineer in charge of that line should sit with the committee. The combination of an engineer, a tool maker, a cost-reduction man, and a time-study man provides a powerful method for reducing costs so far as tools and design will permit. The special cost reports, already referred to, are a great aid to such a committee when discussing cost reduction. This committee can also be of great help to the engineering department in standardizing product.

108. The Shop Conference.—The shop conference is usually composed of shop foremen or similar men and a representative of the order department, with the superintendent as chairman. Before this committee come all problems and questions regarding work in progress; in fact, its minutes are sometimes used as a progress report. If a progress report is maintained by the order department it naturally forms a basis of discussion for the committee. All matters pertaining to the operation of the shop may very profitably be discussed by this most important committee and the information gathered from the men actually in touch with the work is of great importance, since it will cover the whole range of shop operation, including labor difficulties.

109. Other Committees.—The committees discussed in the foregoing consist, largely, of the officers of the company, but there are many other forms of committees that may well include some of the humblest workmen as, for instance, the **complaint committee** for adjusting differences, the **suggestion committee,** and **committees on welfare work.** The principle is of very wide application. Whatever the committee may be, its members should be selected with care, its function should be definite, and its meetings usually should be called at regular stated periods. Careful minutes should be kept of its proceedings and careful attention should be

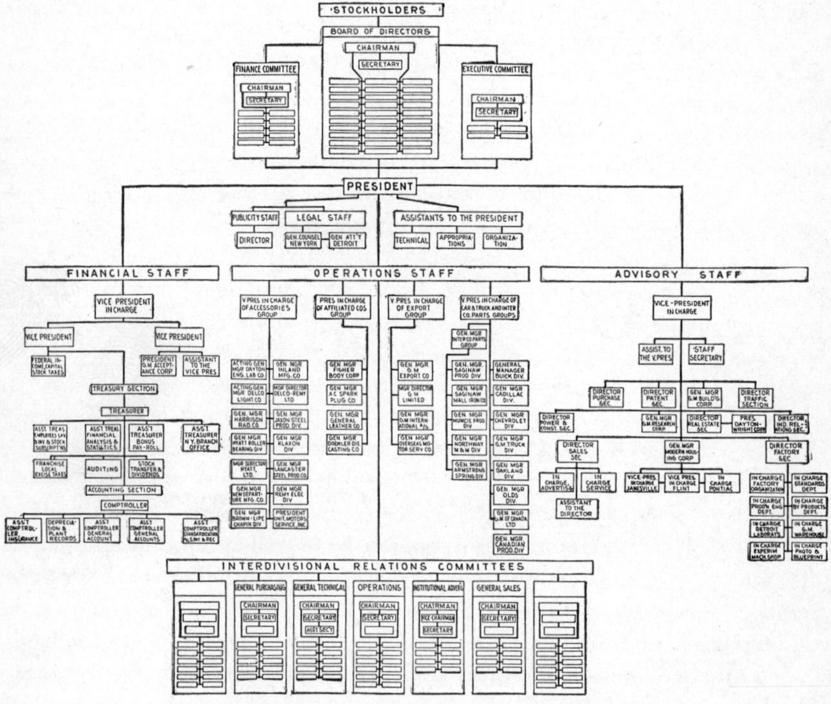

FIG. 22.—Organization of General Motors Corporation.

given to its recommendations. If properly organized and conducted there is no other method that can compare with a committee system for finding out what is needed and how best to accomplish the needed result. As a means of strengthening executive control and at the same time retaining the goodwill of the entire organization it is invaluable. Committees, however, like all other machinery of management, must be used with discretion and intelligence. Obviously, the number and character of the committees necessary or desirable will depend on the size and character of the business. The committee system that will be a perfect success in one plant may be useless in another; and in small plants a committee may be a detriment and a waste of time.

110. Committees as Controlling Mechanisms.—In very large enterprises consisting, perhaps, of a number of plants widely separated geographically, the committee system is a necessity in coordinating the activities of the several groups. A good illustration of such an enterprise is found in the General Motors Corporation, which controls a number of plants that produce automobiles and trucks as well as a number that manufacture automobile accessories. At the time of writing, nearly 200,000 employees are directly engaged in these plants when operating normally. The diagram of the organization is shown in Fig. 22. Four principal committees or staff organizations are employed in coordinating the work of the several divisions. The financial staff is self-explanatory. The operations staff coordinates the work of actual production in the several factories, while the advisory staff coordinates a variety of functions such as patent work, research, etc. The interdivisional relations committee coordinates the work of general purchasing, general sales, general advertising, etc. C. S. Mott, vice president of the corporation,[1] describes the operation of the system as follows:

> Each division operates as an independent unit, the head of which is practically as independent as if he were president of a separate company, but at the same time his work is coordinated by the functioning of certain committees and the advisory staff. Under this arrangement each division enjoys advantages that would be beyond the reach of individual organizations. Among these may be mentioned research facilities which furnish what amounts to an engineering audit on design; forecast and control of budget expenditures; forward commitments with the solid advantages of quantity buying; and a consolidated cash plan which has worked out to the advantage of all concerned.

While such a system of committees may be constituted originally to serve and advise the several divisions they are also very powerful in establishing the general policies of the enterprise and thus they may serve as a check upon unwise action on the part of any component group. Not infrequently general managers are given full power to make expenditures for certain purposes up to a given amount, but are required to submit all proposals for greater expenditures to the advisory committee. In such a capacity the committee becomes an important controlling mechanism. The use of the committee principle thus to control or limit the component groups and to coordinate the several functions is quite common in very large enterprises.

In recent years an extension of the committee system to permit employees to exert a greater influence in the actual administration of the concern has attracted wide attention. These experimental attempts toward a more democratic organization of industry under such names as

[1] *Management and Administration*, May, 1924.

industrial democracy or works councils are more fully discussed in Chap. XXV.

111. Departmental System.—The foregoing is a very brief outline of the more important features of the systematic control and coordination of the departments of an industrial enterprise. Each of these departments, again, will have its own *internal system* of card indexes, filing cases, blank forms, etc. (see also Fig. 13). In the succeeding chapters some of the detail work of several of the departments will be discussed in so far as it bears on general principles of organization, but no effort will be made to discuss departmental systems in detail since, obviously, they vary so widely as to make this of doubtful value, especially as such detail is of peculiar interest to the department specialist only. For such detail the student is referred to the many works on office systems.

References

Bliss, J. H.: "Financial and Operating Ratios."
———: "Management through Accounts."
Brinton, W. G.: "Graphic Methods for Presenting Facts."
Cornell, W. B.: "Industrial Organization and Management," Chap. IX.
Gilman, Stephen: "Analyzing Financial Statements."
———: "Accounting Concepts of Profit."
Jones, E. D.: "The Administration of Industrial Enterprises," Chap. VII.
McKinsey, James O.: "Managerial Accounting."
Smith, W. H.: "Graphic Statistics in Management."

CHAPTER XI

CLASSIFICATION AND IDENTIFICATION

112. Classification.—The orderly administration of every enterprise of any magnitude requires the **classification** and **identification** by some system of nomenclature of its departments, facilities, stores, products, and internal activities. Classification is essentially an orderly enumeration of the facilities and activities of the enterprise, placing like things in groups by themselves and arranging subgroups in each class so that overlapping is avoided. Typical examples of classification are found in the Census of the United States, where industry is carefully classified under 16 principal classes with subsidiary subclasses and groups; and in library work where the books are classified and arranged on the shelves in an orderly manner and according to the subjects of which they treat.

The basic reason for classification is **ease of reference.** The telephone directory, the library catalogue, the index of a book, are examples of the use of classification for this purpose. In a manufacturing plant where constant reference must be made to facilities, materials, accounts, etc., in connection with orders and returns, a classified list of these items is highly desirable. But classification is also a great aid in showing tendencies. Thus the classified expense statement shown in Art. 193 (Chap. XVIII) shows at once just how such money has been spent, and as a consequence enables the manager to fix responsibility and judge efficiency. The forming of adequate records from the returns, and the compiling of condensed administrative reports are greatly aided by a well-arranged system of classification. The application of classification to such activities as tool rooms, store rooms, stock rooms, etc., is obvious and needs no further discussion. In a large enterprise the task of classifying and identifying all of the facilities and activities may be an expensive matter, but, in general, it will pay to do so. A poor system of classification always gives rise to inconvenience, delay, and mistakes. Any extended discussion[1] of classification and identification is beyond the scope of this book and only enough will be inserted to make clear the general principles and applications.

The basis of classification will vary with the enterprise and the objects to be attained. Thus a manufacturer of boilers, engines, pumps, and other apparatus might well classify his product under these headings, since that is the way he wishes his costs to appear. If, however, he is

[1] For an extended discussion see "Management's Handbook," p. 460, and ALFORD L. P., (Ed.), "Cost and Production Handbook," p. 1473.

manufacturing nothing but pumps of a certain type but of many sizes he might classify his product by similar parts. That is, all pump rods would be classed together as would all cylinder heads, all valves, etc. In library work books are usually classified and placed upon the shelves according to the fields of knowledge they discuss. But in the catalogue of the library they are usually classified and indexed not only according to this criterion, but they are also classified and indexed according to the names of authors. The important principle underlying classification is that it should be such as will enable those concerned to find any item quickly and easily, and in industrial work it must also be so arranged as to show results in the form that will be most serviceable for those who are directing the enterprise. The formation of a classified list for an industrial plant should, therefore, be given careful and intelligent consideration.

113. Identification.—The names of the several items on a classified list of facilities, tools, products, materials, etc., in industrial work are usually very cumbersome to refer to, and it is customary, therefore, to attach to such names some designating numeral, letter, or symbol of an abbreviated character that will identify each name apart from all others. Thus, the names of the machines in the classified list shown in Fig. 24 have symbols prefixed to them, and these symbols are used in designating the several machines on all written documents in preference to their trade names. These symbols constitute, virtually, a form of shorthand writing with which all who work in the plant are expected to be familiar.

In continuous-process industries where the work *flows* through the factory, it is not necessary, usually, to mark the product with an identifying number or symbol until after it is produced. Thus automobile engines are marked with an identifying serial number after production. If, however, the product consists of individual parts or of groups of parts to which reference must be made during production, whether for convenience in shop operations, for the purpose of securing cost data, or for future reference in supplying repair parts, some name, number, or other identifying symbol must be attached to the part or lot of parts as the case may be. It will be clear, also, that no two machines or parts should bear the same distinguishing mark, and if many thousands of parts are passing through the plant at one time, as is often the case, it is obvious that the system of identification adopted must be capable of great expansion without danger of repetition.

Constant reference, furthermore, must be made to the several departments of the plant. To write the names of these departments in full would take too long and would be a waste of time. It is customary, therefore, to refer to departments by number or symbol, such numbers or symbols, however, being usually of a different character from those used to designate machine parts. Again, in making up shop orders it is necessary to specify operations or sequence of operations on each part. This may alo involve reference to tools and equipment and in a large plant the tools may be many and diverse including jigs, fixtures, and similar apparatus. The number and character of the operations to be performed may also be many and varied. Again, the materials used may be of many kinds, and since constant reference must be made to them they, also, should be the subject of abbreviated nomenclature. With the rapid and constant growth of modern methods of planning productive operations in advance of actual work, these last items assume great importance in factory administration. The more accurately all machines, operations, and materials are identified, the more accurately and easily can production costs be allocated. A good system of identification is a necessity therefore, for reasons of both convenience and economy.

There are several systems of identification in common use and it should be noted that in a given plant any one or all of these systems may be in use at the same time. Thus it is often convenient to use one system for designating the several departments, and another to designate machines, while still another may be used to identify the parts that are produced. There are four systems of identification in general use, namely:

1. **Alphabetical;** in which each item is designated by a letter or combination of letters.

2. **Numerical,** in which each item is designated by a number or combination of numbers.

3. **Combinations** of numbers and letters, as used on automobile license plates.

4. **Mnemonic,** in which each item is designated by letters or by a combination of letters and numbers suggestive of the classification name of the item.

The late Major Frank Gilbreth has suggested and used **signs,** that are neither numerical nor alphabetical, to designate operations, and these have come into common use in certain work. In some instances pictures of the article are helpful as a means of identification. Thus catalogues of repair parts of complex machines, such as automobiles, frequently show a picture of the part as well as its classification name and identification number in order to facilitate identification by the purchaser. Differentiation by means of **color** is also very effective in some instances.

114. Alphabetical and Numerical Identification.—The use of simple letters or numbers, serially, to identify a comparatively small number of items is so common as to need no discussion, and this applies also to combinations of letters and numbers where the items to be designated are not numerous. In large factories manufacturing a variety of products, these simple methods fail completely and identification must usually rest upon a carefully arranged system of so-called **drawing numbers.** In such a large plant, where many hundreds of drawings are made yearly, accurate identification necessitates a careful consideration of the entire problem of classification and identification through the drawings themselves. Here mnemonic or, in fact, any system of symbols based entirely upon letters is usually inadequate and too cumbersome, and numbers or combinations of numbers are used. Thus, in such a system, the symbol M 3468 might identify the drawing of a steam cylinder, the letter indicating the class of the product, and the number its place in the series. Sometimes, again, all drawings are numbered serially, and an index is kept which shows the serial numbers of the drawings used for each machine. The drawing of any part may be located by looking at the index of the drawings that were so used and finding the serial number of the particular drawing on which the part is to be found. Sometimes, also, an identification system based upon the Dewey decimal system of classification is used, certain blocks of numbers being designated for certain classes of machines or product. Thus all numbers beginning with .012 might identify transformers, and all numbers beginning with .013 might identify oil switches and their parts. In practice the decimal point is usually omitted for convenience and the integers in the number are always preceded by a cipher. The Dewey system has the advantage of unlimited expansibility without repetition; it can be made as comprehensive as may be desired and hence it is well suited to large plants. The system, however, that is best for one shop may not apply to others and each case requires special study in order that the system adopted may be comprehensive without being cumbersome.

In some drawing systems only one part is shown on each sheet so that the drawing number is also the identifying number of the part shown. Where more than one part is shown on one sheet each part may be identified by a **part letter.** Thus in such a system M 3468—A might signify part A on drawing 3468 of class M. This identifies the part beyond question and makes it possible to refer to it with accuracy and also to charge all labor and material entering into its production to the proper cost record. In large enterprises, therefore, where the direction of the production is through drawings, classification and identification of the *product* must originate and be carried on by the engineering department.

In some well-developed systems a **schedule** or **drawing list** is sometimes issued by the engineering department. Such a list as shown in Fig. 23 constitutes a complete inventory of the parts that are to be supplied or manufactured for a given machine, and is also an index to the drawings, lists, and other sources of information necessary for its production. Such schedules, or lists, afford excellent examples of the need and use of identifying symbols. Thus in Fig. 23 the type, size, and class of the machine are given at the top of the list. The names of the several parts are listed with the corresponding drawing number, part number, pattern number, and the number of parts that are required. Reference is also made to the engineering specifications that are to be consulted.

In Fig. 23 the type, class, and general characteristics of the machine are expressed in mnemonic symbols, the drawing numbers are based upon the Dewey decimal system, and the part numbers are alphabetical. The pattern numbers are combinations of numbers and letters.

DRAWING LIST

MACHINE	TYPE	CLASS	VOLTS	DATE
Generator	M.P.R.	10-400-650	2200	10-11-1924

NAME OF PART	DRAWING NO.	PART NO.	PATTERN NO.	NO. OF PARTS	MATERIAL	DATE ADDED	DATE CHANGED
Machine Complete	012						
Machine Outline	0121						
Armature Complete	0122						
” Diagram	0123						
” Frame	0124	a		1	C.I	8-29-20	
” Punching	0125	B			M28		
Base	0034	a		1	CI		
Bearing	0035	B		2	CI		
Brush							
Brush Holder							
” Stand							
” Stand Support							
” Stand Bracket							
” Studs							
” York							
Cable							
” for Field							
” ” Coupling							
Collector	Table	M	Q468	2			
Connection Board	Table	N	R246	1			
Coupling	Table	R	N428	1			
Field Spider	0126	a		1	S.C.	8-24-21	
” Ring	0127	B		1			
Jack Screws	Table	a	S26	2			
Laminated Poles	0128						
Pulley	Table	R	48	1			
Rails							
Shafts and Keys	0346	a		1	MS		8-16-24
Spool Coil	0267	B		1			
Standards and Caps	0436	C		2			
Wrenches							
Armature Shields	0074	B					9-11-23
Sub-base	0346	a					
Modern base frame	0014	C					
List of Castings		01					
Armat. Wind. Spec.	A4684						
Field ” ”	B2678						
Engineering Notice	M46						

FIG. 23.—Drawing list.

In plants where the product is well standardized such lists as shown in Fig. 23 may be printed in outline and the data filled in by hand. Thus the data in that figure that would be so filled in are indicated by script. It will be noted that such a system permits the free and convenient use of any one machine part in the construction of any machine, whether designed originally for it or not, since identification is complete.

115. Mnemonic Symbols.—The best known system of **mnemonic** or **memory-assisting** symbols is found, perhaps, in chemistry, where the elements and their combinations are known universally by such symbols. Thus H, N and O, identify, respectively, hydrogen, nitrogen, and oxygen; while HNO_3 represents nitric acid and indicates also the relative quantities of the constituents. Mnemonic symbols are often convenient for designating departments, accounts, machines, and locations in the plant. Figure 24 shows a partial classified list of machines as used in the Gleason

MACHINE SYMBOLS			
SYMBOL	MACHINE	SYMBOL	MACHINE
G 3 W	3 In. Two Tool Generator	R 9 M	3 Spindle Rougher
G 6 W	6 In. " " "	T 5 Sp	5 In. Spring Vibrating Machine
G 8 W	8 In. " " "	T 4 B	4 In. Bevel Tester
G 11 W	11 In. " " "	T 18 B	18 In. Bevel Tester
G 18 W	18 In. " " "	T 5 R	Rear Axle Tester
G 25 W	25 In. " " "	T 3 Sp	3 In. Spring Weighing Machine
		B 15 B	15 In. Burnishing Machine
G 4 S	4 In. Spiral Generator		
G 8 S	8 In. " "	P 24 U	24 In. Gear Planer
G 15 S	15 In. " "	P 37 U	37 In. " "
G 25 S	25 In. " "	P 54 U	54 In. " "
		P 77 U	77 In. " "
		P 38 W	38 In. Two Tool Gear Planer
R 15 P	15 In. Pinion Rougher		
R 15 G	15 In. Gear Rougher	H 15 M	15 In. Hardening Machine
J 12 R	12 In. Auto Ro. Cutter Grinder	H 25 M	25 In. " "
J 15 P	15 In. Spiral Pinion Grinder		
J 18 W	Generator Tool Grinder	W 8 D	8 In. Mfg. Differential Head
J 4 S	4 In. Cutter Grinder	W 8 G	8 In. Mfg. Gear Head
J 15 S	15 In. Cutter Grinder	W 8 P	8 In. Mfg. Pinion Head
F 15 S	15 In. Spiral Truing Fixture	Z 15 G	Rolling in Machine

Fig. 24.—Machine symbols.

Works and is self-explanatory. Thus R15P represents a 15-*inch pinion rougher;* G4S represents a 4-*inch spiral generator,* and so on. If the departments of a factory are numerous, mnemonic symbols are often very convenient. Thus T.A. might indicate a *transformer assembly* department, and S.M. might identify the *screw machine* department. Similar abbreviations are in common use to designate materials. Thus CI is much used to indicate *cast iron,* and MS to indicate *machinery steel.*

The problem of identifying productive operations is somewhat more complex. If only a few such operations are to be performed, mnemonic symbols are often adequate. Table 5 shows a list of such symbols as used in the Gleason Works to indicate the operations in making a 9-inch cutter head. Here *ML* signifies *mill; DR* signifies *drill; IN* inspect, etc.

In a similar way, in other systems, *TR* may signify *turn; BO* may mean *bore; GR* may mean *grind,* and so on. The problem of identifying departments or operations is, in general, an easy one compared to that of identifying the products and parts of products, particularly in a large plant producing a wide range of work. In factories that make products such as large steam engines, and where a comparatively small number of machines

TABLE 5.—OPERATING SYMBOLS

Nine-inch Spiral Steel Cutter Head

Operations	No.
Mill keyway	15ML
Drill face holes	20DR
CO'bore face holes	25DR
Drill for 7/16-inch tapped holes	30DR
Drill 7/16-inch hole 1/8-inch deep with 1/2-inch drill	35DR
Tap 7/16-inch holes	40DR
Drill and CO'bore for 5/16-inch tapped holes	45DR
Remove threads on back side of head on 5/16-inch holes and chamfer 2 Jackoff screw holes	50DR
Remove threads and tap 5/16-inch holes	55DR
Remove threads on marking screw holes and radius 4 screw holes on front face	60DR
Tap and retap 2 Jackoff screw holes	62DR
Remove threads and tap for marking screw	65DR
Clean out all holes and inspect all tapped holes	80BE
Rough grind both sides	90GR
Mark number of slots	70MK
Mark Gleason Works, Pat. Date, and type of cutter, stocker, or finisher	75MK
Finish grind sides	76GR
Demagnetize	95DE
Grind bore	100GR
Drill pin hole for master wedge	120DR
Retap if necessary	121DR
Dowel and burr	125BE
General inspection	130IN

is to be built at any one time, mnemonic symbols are sometimes used with success. Thus "Osp" was used in such a plant to designate all drawings for an engine built for a certain hospital, and each drawing bore this symbol followed by a serial number which located the drawing in the series. In Fig. 23 the names of the parts in the first column could be given in mnemonic symbols. But such symbols have very definite limitations where the number of items to be identified is very large. They are also troublesome to new men who are not familiar with such shop nomenclature. Whatever system is adopted it should be studied with care before adoption, so as to make sure that it is adapted to the work and also that it is capable of sufficient expansion. It is always a troublesome task to change the system of nomenclature and this can usually be avoided by a little forethought.

References

ALFORD, L. P. (Ed.): "Cost and Production Handbook," p. 1473.
———: "Management's Handbook," pp. 460 and 1514.
Bull., Taylor Society, July, 1916.
PARKHURST, F. A.: "Applied Scientific Management."
"The Dewey Decimal System," *Bull.*, University of Illinois.

CHAPTER XII

THE CONTROL OF PRODUCTION

116. The Necessity for Control.—The coordinative mechanisms discussed in the preceding chapters are general in character and are applicable, therefore, to a wide range of industry. The particular combination of these mechanisms that may best serve the purpose will necessarily vary widely with the characteristics of the enterprise considered; but usually there is little difficulty in selecting such a combination as will insure executive control of the several functions and departments. In certain productive enterprises, however, there is, in addition, a much more difficult problem, namely, that of **controlling production** so that the required product shall be produced in the *best* and *cheapest method;* that it shall be of the *required quality*, and that it shall be produced at the *required time.* Since the work of practically all of the departments of a manufacturing plant, the arrangement of equipment, and the personnel of the plant are influenced to a greater or less degree by this problem it is desirable to discuss it at some length before proceeding with detailed discussions of these other departments and functions. Some typical methods of production control will first be described and the possibilities and limitations of their application to various kinds of enterprises will then be briefly discussed.

In a continuous-process industry (see Art. 80), where the raw material enters one end of the factory and *flows* through it in a steady stream, the problem of production control is obviously very simple since the path or *route* that the material is to follow is fixed by the natural sequence of processes, and the *times* of operations are fixed largely by the capacity of the machines and processes. In an intermittent-process industry of the *special-order* type where products are made only to customer's orders and where repetition of such orders is unusual, the case is very different. Here each succeeding part produced may follow a new path through the shop, the time required for each operation may not be known and, unlike the continuous-process industry, the parts do not move *automatically* from machine to machine but must be so moved as occasion requires. It will be clear that unless some supervision is given to the sequence of parts, congested conditions will arise in the factory, some machines having more work than they can do and some being underloaded, and as a consequence the product will not be produced at the time set for delivery.

There are, as stated in Art. 80, many modifications of these extreme types of enterprises. One of the most common and most important of these is what may be termed the **lot-intermittent** type. In this type of manufacturing, standard products are carried through the factory in *lots* in anticipation of sales. The delivery of product to sales is made from a store of finished products in the stock-room, and the number of machines or other product in each lot and the frequency with which manufacturing orders are placed with the factory are governed by the quantity of product on hand and the probable market demand. If a variety of products is manufactured and if lot-manufacturing orders for each kind of product are infrequent, the conditions approach those of a special-order industry. If, on the other hand, only a few kinds of product are manufactured, and if manufacturing orders for each kind of product come at regular, frequent intervals, the conditions approach those of a continuous industry. In the majority of cases some kind of production control is required in this form of production as in the case of special-order work, and this control is usually attempted through a so-called **planning department.**

117. Development of Planning Departments.—The growth of the planning department is of interest. A few years ago a typical organization of a production[1] department consisted of the superintendent, the several foremen, and a few special officers, such as a storekeeper and timekeeper. The superintendent received the formal order and instructions for the work, gave it a number, letter, or some other distinguishing mark, and sent each foreman an order instructing him how to proceed with his part of the work, trusting to natural cooperation among the foremen to keep the correct sequence of operations so that the finished product would be shipped in time. A record was kept of all time and material expended on the job[2] and the *total* cost of the work recorded, though, in general, detail costs were not obtained.

[1] Properly speaking, the production department embraces all men and departments that have to do with actual production, as distinguished from the other general divisions, sales and finance. Engineering, though a productive process, has become so important in some industries that it is often considered as an independent department, and the name production department limited to that portion of the organization that is controlled by the factory manager. The name is sometimes applied to the factory planning department but this use of the term does not seem to be warranted. The factory planning department is a part of the production department.

The stock room and shipping department strictly speaking are not productive departments but they are so closely identified with production that they are often included in the production department.

A distinction should be made between *stock* and *stores*. Stock refers to finished parts or finished machinery; stores to raw or unworked material.

[2] The writer does not feel that any apology for the use of this term is necessary. True, it is more expressive than elegant, but, like the term "boss," there is no other word that can be used to take its place fully.

As the necessity of more detailed costs became greater, and the science of cost keeping grew, the instructions or **work orders** issued to the workmen were made more and more in detail for each job. As works increased in size it became increasingly difficult for the foreman and others charged with the production to keep the proper sequence of operations on a mental and verbal basis; and when one considers the complexity of the modern shop, and the immense number of small parts passing through even a fair-sized establishment, the performance of some of these superintendents and foremen seems marvelous indeed.

The next step in this development was the establishment of "production departments," so-called, usually directly under the superintendent, which were intended to relieve the foremen and others of the burden of keeping the required sequence of operations. A schedule of performance, more or less complete, was laid out for each production order by the production manager, and an effort was made to meet this schedule by means of "tracers" or "stock chasers" as they are sometimes called. These are clerical assistants to the production manager, usually well informed concerning the shop and the product, who follow the work through the shop correcting and adjusting conditions and removing difficulties. Under certain conditions satisfactory results can be obtained in this manner and not a few of such departments are now in operation.

Obviously much of the work of such simple production departments has to do with relieving difficulties *after they have occurred.* True planning, however, aims to *prevent difficulties from occurring,* and there has been a constant movement, therefore, especially in large enterprises, toward the development of planning departments that can plan productive operations in advance just as the engineering department plans the structural side of the product.

Planning of work may be done in one of two ways, namely, **empirically** or **statistically.** Any man highly experienced in a given line of work can easily plan a desirable sequence of operations for a given piece of work, basing his predictions on his experience and judgment, but there will be definite limitations to the accuracy of his predictions. For instance, if there are several desirable ways of performing the work he will not, in general, be able to say which is the best way, unless he or some other equally competent man has tried them all and recorded his results. Again, he may be able to assign the approximate time necessary to perform the work, or the tools that are most efficient for the purpose; but, in general, unless he possesses *recorded data* bearing on these matters, his empirical estimates are approximate only, and his predictions useful only within the range of his experience. Where recorded data are to be had, however, the basis of prediction is much more sound; and if such data form a record of high-grade performances they are inestimably superior to empirical estimates. The engineering and drafting department is the finest example of the separation of mental and manual processes and the prediction of results on the basis of recorded data. True, a considerable amount of the work of this department is still empirical, and will remain so for many years; yet the progress that has been made is remarkable and foreshadows what may be expected to occur in the planning of manufacturing operations when a sufficient volume of data bearing on capacities of machines, forms of cutting tools, the times required for operations, etc., has been collected.

118. Functional Foremanship.—The first important attempt to solve the problem of production control was that of the late F. W. Taylor[1] in connection with his plan of shop management commonly known as **functional foremanship.** Since this plan has been the basis of practically all such efforts its most important features will be described. Mr. Taylor's typical organization, as here outlined, is particularly adapted to iron-working establishments that machine large pieces, but the principles involved are of almost universal application. Under Mr. Taylor's system the work now ordinarily performed by the foreman under the old methods is divided into several parts or "functions," each performed by a separate **functional foreman** or **functional boss** as he styles him. Care is taken to separate *planning functions* from *executive functions* and all planning is removed, as far as possible, from the shop to the planning department. The latter then performs for the *constructive* side of the industry what the engineering department has long performed for the *designing* side of the work. In fact, the movement to do the planning of all productive processes in advance and in a separate department is analogous to the movement that formed the engineering department. It is in strict accord with the general principles of division of labor and the separation of mental and manual processes.

In his work at the Bethlehem Steel Company, Mr. Taylor found the following subdivision[2] and rearrangement of functions profitable:

In the planning department:

1. The order-of-work or route clerk.
2. The instruction-card clerk.
3. The time and cost clerk.

[1] See TAYLOR, F. W., "Shop Management," *Trans. Am. Soc. Mech. Eng.*, Vol. 24. This classic paper should be read by everyone interested in industrial enterprises. Whether all the methods advocated by Mr. Taylor are desirable or not the fact remains that the principles advanced will increase production if intelligently applied, and the paper no doubt indicates the trend of industrial organization.

[2] Mr. Taylor's analysis of the duties of the average foreman, and his use of this analysis in subdividing the foreman's functions, constitute a masterpiece that will repay reading. See *Trans. Am. Soc. Mech. Eng.*, Vol. 24.

In the shop:

4. The gang boss.
5. The speed boss.
6. The inspector.
7. The repair boss.

And for the entire works:

8. The shop disciplinarian.

The following is a very brief statement of the duties of these several bosses as stated by Mr. Taylor:

The order-of-work or route clerk lays out the route that the piece is to follow through the several shops and the sequence of machines and men

ROUTE SHEET

PART NO. 15-Q-73 — MATERIAL C.R.S.
PART NAME Brake Pawl — PATTERN NO.
DATE ISSUED Feb-15-1925 — FORGING NO.
BAR STOCK ¼″ x ½″ x 1-9/16″ Lg.

NOTE: THIS ORDER OF OPERATIONS MUST BE MAINTAINED. NO CHANGE SHALL BE MADE WITHOUT AUTHORITY FROM THE MANUFACTURING CONTROL DEPARTMENT.

OPR NO.	OPERATION NAME	STANDARD MACHINE	ALTERNATE MACHINE	DEPT.
1	Turn & Cut Off	Gridley		Auto
	Inspect			,,
2	Mill To Length	Mill		Mill
3	Mill 45° Angle	,,		,,
4	Spline Mill Slot	S.Mill		,,
5	File Burrs	Bnch		,,
	Final Inspect. Before Hardening			,,
6	Harden, Reheat, Quench & Wash	.0 1 0		Hard
7	Sand Blast	S.Blast		,,
8	Final Inspection			,,

Fig. 25.—Route sheet.

that are to operate upon it in each shop. He prepares the **route sheet** (Fig. 25), and from it he, or his assistant, makes out the **work or operation orders** (Fig. 26), for each man or machine operating upon it. The work order must give the order number of the job, the number of the instruction card (to be described) or other references which may be needed to identify it. The order-of-work or route clerk is responsible for the sequence of work in the shop, though in some modified applications of Mr. Taylor's system both a route clerk and an order-of-work clerk are used, the first laying out the route and schedule and the second seeing to its operation and enforcement. This division would naturally come about in a large plant, but even then these two men must work in close harmony.

The instruction-card clerk fills out the **instruction card** (Fig. 27), which bears the same relation to the planning department that a drawing does to the drafting room. It gives all the information regarding the

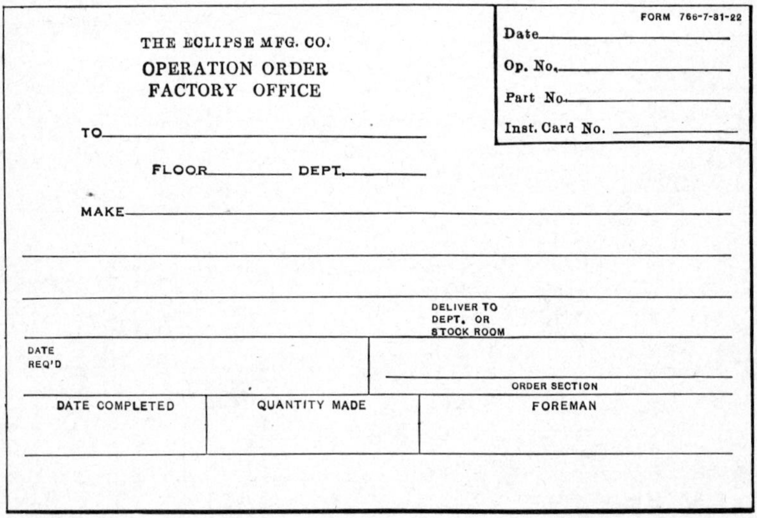

FORM 766-7-31-22

THE ECLIPSE MFG. CO.
OPERATION ORDER
FACTORY OFFICE

Date________
Op. No.________
Part No.________
Inst. Card No.________

TO________

FLOOR________ DEPT.________

MAKE________

DATE REQ'D	DELIVER TO DEPT. OR STOCK ROOM
	ORDER SECTION

DATE COMPLETED	QUANTITY MADE	FOREMAN

Fig. 26.—Work or operation order.

necessary drawings, jigs, fixtures, etc., and gives the exact sequence of detail operations that must be followed by each workman. It may give the number of cuts, the depth of each cut, the speeds and feeds, and the time each cut and operation should take. It may also give full information regarding the piece rate, day rate, or premium on which the work is to be performed. In certain cases it is clear that it might include the information listed on the operation card just described, but usually it is more convenient to use the two cards.

The time and cost clerk prepares for the instruction card the necessary instructions to the workman for the recording of time and cost of all work and for securing from the workman the proper returns for making cost and time records.

The gang boss makes all preparations for getting the work to the workman, collecting the necessary jigs, drawings, etc., and sees that the work is properly set in the machine. He relieves the workman of all preliminary planning as far as placing the piece in working position is concerned.

The work of the speed boss begins after the piece is set in the machine. He sees that the right tools are used and that the feeds and speeds are according to instructions. He also instructs the workman in the best method of doing the work.

The inspector is charged with the duty of seeing that all work is up to standard in workmanship and finish.

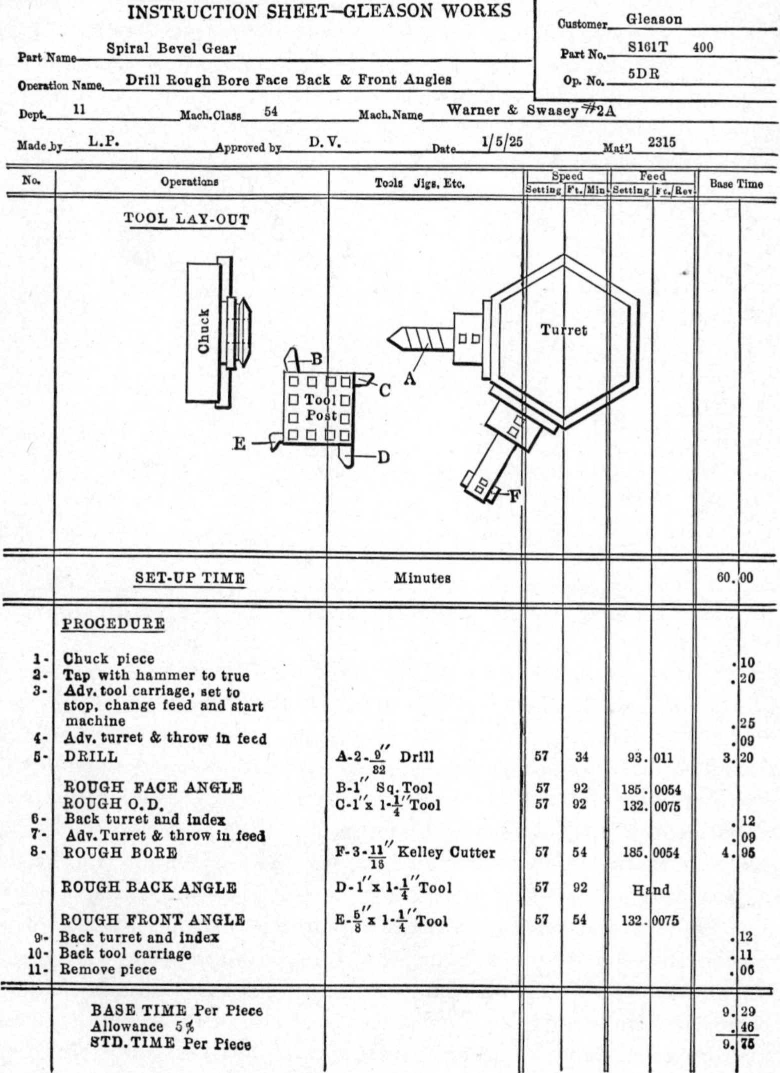

INSTRUCTION SHEET—GLEASON WORKS

Customer Gleason

Part Name Spiral Bevel Gear — Part No. S161T 400

Operation Name Drill Rough Bore Face Back & Front Angles — Op. No. 5DR

Dept. 11 Mach. Class 54 Mach. Name Warner & Swasey #2A

Made by L.P. Approved by D. V. Date 1/5/25 Mat'l 2315

No.	Operations	Tools Jigs, Etc.	Speed Setting	Speed Ft./Min	Feed Setting	Feed Fc./Rev.	Base Time
	TOOL LAY-OUT						
	SET-UP TIME	Minutes					60.00
	PROCEDURE						
1-	Chuck piece						.10
2-	Tap with hammer to true						.20
3-	Adv. tool carriage, set to stop, change feed and start machine						.25
4-	Adv. turret & throw in feed						.09
5-	DRILL	A-2-9/32″ Drill	57	34	93.	011	3.20
	ROUGH FACE ANGLE	B-1″ Sq. Tool	57	92	185.	0054	
	ROUGH O.D.	C-1″x 1-1/4″ Tool	57	92	132.	0075	
6-	Back turret and index						.12
7-	Adv. Turret & throw in feed						.09
8-	ROUGH BORE	F-3-11/16″ Kelley Cutter	57	54	185.	0054	4.95
	ROUGH BACK ANGLE	D-1″x 1-1/4″ Tool	57	92	Hand		
	ROUGH FRONT ANGLE	E-5/8″x 1-1/4″ Tool	57	54	132.	0075	
9-	Back turret and index						.12
10-	Back tool carriage						.11
11-	Remove piece						.06
	BASE TIME Per Piece						9.29
	Allowance 5%						.46
	STD. TIME Per Piece						9.75

Fig. 27.—Instruction card.

The repair boss has charge of all machines, belts, etc., and sees that they are kept in good order and repair.

The shop disciplinarian is responsible for discipline and good order. He is also the peacemaker and assists in adjusting wages. He represents the disciplinary functions formerly executed by the foreman.

Figure 28 illustrates graphically this form of organization. This rearrangement of duties virtually amounts to replacing all line organization below the superintendent of production with functional organization (see Fig. 14). The value of functionalization had, of course, long been recognized and applied as illustrated in the typical organization diagrams, Figs. 13 and 15, where such duties as shipping, purchasing, inspecting, and stores keeping are shown as functional duties. And these diagrams show that the movement toward functionalization of duties had long been operative in the upper part of the organization diagram. Taylor's work, therefore, completed a movement already well under way and

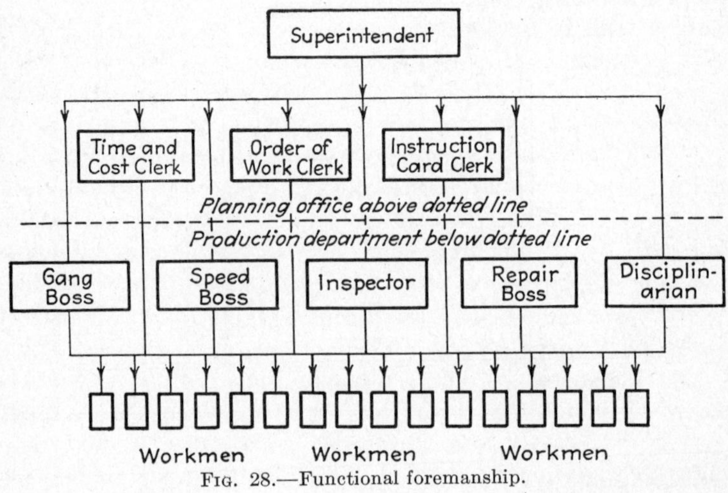

FIG. 28.—Functional foremanship.

carried functionalization to the very bottom of the diagram. It should be noted in passing that functionalized duties, such as engineering, accounting, cost finding, tool making, purchasing, etc., make progress in that direction in proportion to the growth of their scientific background and in accordance with the general law of division of labor. Taylor's plan, therefore, is a perfectly logical extension of a movement that had been gathering force for some time, but which required vision and ability to demonstrate by an actual practical example.

A careful consideration of the foregoing will make clear that there are no new economic principles involved in so-called scientific management, but rather an extension and application of well-known principles. The rearrangement of duties as shown in Fig. 28 is essentially an application of division of labor. The combined duties of the foreman and the workman are separated into component parts and similar parts are then reassembled under functionalized supervisors (see Fig. 14). The workman is relieved of all planning in connection with his work and can, therefore, devote all of his time and energy to actual production. The actual worker is charged only with the responsibility of the *major* factor of production and all *minor* factors are placed in the hands of specialists who guide and assist him exactly in the same way that engineering design was taken from the factory floor and centralized in the engineering department many years ago (see Art. 56). And, as in the case of the engineering department, the functionalizing of these minor factors in an effective manner depends very greatly upon the accuracy of the fundamental data available upon which to base these activities. With accurate data on the cutting of metals and with accurate recorded observations of the time required to do the operations, Taylor was able to predict *where, when,* and *how* the work was to be performed.

Again, it will be obvious that with such a rearrangement of duties and such an extension of division of labor an increase in production might be expected. Such was the case in Taylor's original experiment. It is self-evident that an operator, whether doing hand work or operating a machine, will be able to do much more actual productive work when relieved of all responsibility of transporting material, finding tools and fixtures, planning the sequence of operations, etc. This has been proven too frequently to admit of argument. It does not follow, however, that an increase of production through such means will necessarily be accompanied by lowered costs; in fact, they may be even higher than when the work is performed by simpler methods. There are several reasons why this may be so. First, as noted in Art. 51, any extension of division of labor must be accompanied by some form of coordinative influence to be successful, and Taylor's functional foremanship is no exception to this rule. The particular coordinative measures that have been devised for this purpose are discussed fully in succeeding sections. Functional foremanship with its accompanying coordinative mechanisms is costly and unless the *financial gain* due to increased production exceeds the cost of these refined methods a loss in profit instead of a gain is incurred. In other words, the principle of diminishing returns holds true here as well as elsewhere. A lack of understanding[1] of this important principle was responsible for not a few financial failures among those who first tried to apply Taylor's methods to small or medium-sized plants.

Furthermore, it should be remembered that the major factor in production usually can be operated at high efficiency only if some of the minor factors operate at comparatively low efficiency (Art. 54). The tendency for service departments to be inefficient and the necessity of stimulating them constantly are too well known to merit discussion. Necessarily, this tendency is increased in organizations as refined as that discussed in the foregoing, which again tends to accelerate the

[1] For a very clear discussion of a modification of refined methods of management in recognition of these principles see article by Ralph E. Flanders, *Trans. Am. Soc. Mech. Eng.*, Vol. 46, p. 691.

principle of diminishing returns. Experience has also shown that efforts to stimulate production by these means, to be successful, must be accompanied by some form of financial incentive for the worker. The worker instinctively expects greater pay for greater output and all modern plans of administration recognize this principle. Incentive-wage systems are now very widely used and while they vary widely in their detail methods basically they all rest upon the foregoing principle. Naturally, this principle, while tending to increase production, tends also, if successful, in its operation, to increase the cost of the same, which again accelerates the principle of diminishing returns.

119. Essentials of Planning.—Mr. Taylor's plan of production control has not been widely adopted in the exact form which he used at Bethlehem. Many modified forms of this system are, however, in use, and there is a constant tendency to adopt many of his control mechanisms in various combinations to suit the circumstances. The influence of his work on the problem of planning shop operations in advance of their actual performance has been very great and all modern planning departments are modeled more or less upon his methods.

The planning of industrial operations involves four considerations, namely: *what* work shall be done; *how* the work shall be done; *where* the work shall be done; and, lastly, *when* the work shall be done. The problem of what work shall be done is one for the management and the engineering department to solve. It is assumed, therefore, that the planning department will receive full information from these sources as to the quantity to be produced; the shipping directions, if goods are to be shipped directly from production; the date, if any, on which delivery has been promised; and the necessary engineering specifications and drawings. The planning department will then be required to perform one or all of the following functions depending upon the degree of control desired:

1. **Issuing** all orders that are necessary for production.

2. **Routing** or laying out the sequence of machines, processes, and operations that are the most desirable and efficient.

3. **Scheduling** or assigning to each process and operation the time that should be required for its completion.

4. **Dispatching** or starting all operations and processes at the time set and in the manner in which they have been planned, and insuring that the materials and tools required are at hand when needed.

5. **Collecting** all *returns* and records of performance that are necessary for the work of the several administrative departments or for the production of future performances.

In many instances, the work of the planning department is confined to the first function, but in progressive shops the last four are rapidly becoming important and necessary parts of productive processes. Some remarkable planning departments are now in operation in which the complete schedule of operations is predicted not only as to the manner and place of each operation but also as to the time that is to be consumed. These highly developed planning departments are connected, of course, most frequently with industries involving mass production. The planning department may, and often does, include other functions. A published description of a plant where so-called scientific management has been installed lists the following men as under the planning department: shop engineer, storekeeper, cost clerk, shipping clerk, receiving clerk, and inspector, as well as several others *directly* engaged in planning. In a small concern it is not only feasible but may be good management to include all these activities under one department. It is, however, contrary to the elementary principles of division of labor, which assigns as few duties as possible, to either a man or a department, these duties being of a *similar* character as far as possible. The function of the planning department is the planning and scheduling of the work, and as plants increase in size such dissimilar functions as some of those listed above naturally tend to become independent departments functionalized under the factory manager, or as he is more correctly named in Fig. 13, the **production manager.** They are in reality more highly specialized functions that he formerly was expected to perform himself, and the manner of their formation will depend, to a large extent, on the size of the works and the character of the men obtainable for the several positions. On the other hand, there seems to be no good reason for making the planning department independent of the factory manager (if there be one), thus making the head of the planning department a thorn in the side of the superintendent who is charged with the responsibility for production. The planning department should be in charge of the factory manager and the head of the planning department should be of the character of an assistant superintendent (see Fig. 15). When organized independently, as is sometimes the case, it usually results in much duplicate work and opens up an opportunity for interdepartmental bickering.

120. Issuing Orders.—The degree of detail in which orders are issued to the factory depends largely upon the degree of refinement desired in compiling the costs of production. Production is usually initiated by the general manager sending the factory manager a **production order** which is the authority for the latter to proceed with the work described in the order. If the work authorized by this order is simple in character it may be passed by the factory manager directly to the planning department as a **manufacturing order.** If, however, several machines of different character are authorized by the production order the factory manager may, after consultation with the cost accountant, divide the production order into several manufacturing orders. The planning department again may subdivide each manufacturing order into a large number of **work orders** or **operation orders.** Quite frequently a work order (Fig. 26) is issued for each operation to be performed and all production orders, manufacturing orders, and work orders are identified by number or symbol, as described in Art. 113, so that all instructions issued concerning each part can be clearly understood; and all labor and material used in its production can be accurately charged against it in the cost system, a cost sheet being usually opened for each machine or part so ordered and identified.

When a work order is issued to a workman, instructing him to proceed with a particular operation, it is accompanied by such instruction cards, time cards, engineering data, and all other information as are necessary for the work. The planning department will also issue orders on which material is to be drawn, directing the moving and transportation of material in process (if such a system is used), and for such tools and equipment as may be necessary.

121. Routing.—The demand for a more systematic method of carrying the work through the shop gave rise to the practice of **routing.** Routing may be defined as the selection of paths or routes over which each piece is to travel in being transformed from raw material into finished product. The object of routing is to determine the best and cheapest sequence of operations and to insure that this sequence is followed. It will be noted that routing is automatic in continuous industries, since the plant itself is laid out with a view to passing the product through a fixed, predetermined series of processes. In intermittent industries, however, there is sometimes a very large number of sequences that can be followed though there is usually one series of operations that is best for any given article. The process is analogous to selecting the best railroad route from one place to another.

The economic advantage of routing is based upon division of labor. Someone must do this planning and it demands deliberation and concentration of mind which the busy foreman cannot always bestow upon the problem. Routing constitutes a function that can well be separated from others wherever there is sufficient volume of business to warrant this procedure. Once a good route has been worked out and *recorded*, furthermore, it can be used again for other similar jobs, thus securing the advantages of recorded data that have already been referred to. For this reason routing can often be done to advantage in the drafting room, the route being recorded on the drawings themselves. If routing is done in the drafting room, care should be observed that it is directed by someone who has accurate knowledge of factory conditions and equipment.

The degree of refinement to which routing may be carried will vary with the factory and the product. In some cases it is sufficient to designate the successive departments through which the piece in question is to pass, while, again, it may be advantageous to go farther and designate the particular machine and process that is to be used. Thus Fig. 25 shows a route sheet which lists the several operations to be performed, the department in which each operation is to be performed, and the class of machine tool that is to be used in each case. Figure 27 again lists the sequence of *detail* operations that are to be performed on a piece of product with a certain machine tool. The set-up of the special fixture is shown and the special tool that is to be used for each detail operation is given in the third column. The feed and speed for each tool are given in other columns. It will be obvious that successful routing requires that the route clerk must have great knowledge of the product and of the manufacturing equipment, and he must also have readily available full knowledge of the capacity and characteristics of every machine and process. It will be clear also that the engineering department, if there is one, can be of great aid in intelligent routing.

122. Assembly Routing.—In complex products such as typewriters and automobiles the sequence of operations in assembling is often very important and is, therefore, carefully routed. The importance of an orderly procedure in the assembly of such product will be clear by brief consideration, for instance, of a typewriter or an automobile. Many of these complex constructions consist wholly or in part of an assemblage of **unit assemblies** or **subassemblies,** as they are sometimes called, each one of which is composed of a number of individual parts. Thus the engine of an automobile is assembled in the machine as a *unit* and not built up in place from individual parts. Obviously there is one best way of assembling these units and also of assembling them into the completed product, and this can be accomplished only by careful routing and standardization of assembling procedure. Perhaps the best illustration of such procedure is the **progressive assembly** used in assembling certain automobiles. In such an assembly the frame of the automobile is attached to one end of a traveling chain or carrier about 600 feet long and moving about 5 or 6 feet per minute. Along this chain at fixed intervals workmen or groups of workmen are stationed, each charged with the duty of attaching an individual part or unit assembly in its proper place in the machine, during the time it moves past the station. Thus by the time the frame reaches the other end of the carrier a complete automobile has been assembled upon it. The sequence of assembly operations is presumably the best that can be devised, and the several component parts are routed either directly from production or from stores, so that they arrive at the proper place in the chain of events.[1] The assembly of component parts such as the engine is conducted in a similar manner.

[1] The student will find it instructive to take apart some product such as a Yale lock and arrange an assembly procedure for it, laying out also an assembly bench on which the several parts are placed so as to be most conveniently arranged for the operator.

The problem of routing the material through the plant may have a great influence upon the design of the buildings and the arrangement of the machines. Even in extreme intermittent-process industries, such as a shipbuilding plant, great savings can be made by a logical arrangement of buildings and processes. In such enterprises as automobile, typewriter, rolling-mill, and similar mass-production plants, economical routing in the design of the plant is of greatest importance, and in purely continuous-process plants the arrangement of buildings and processes is almost entirely a problem in routing. This matter is referred to in more detail in Chap. VIII.

123. Scheduling in General.—Routing has been defined as the determination of the proper sequence of a number of operations. Scheduling is defined as the determination of the *time* that should be required to perform each operation and also the time necessary to perform the entire series, as routed, making allowance for all factors concerned. The analogy of the railway may again be helpful. The *route* shows the passenger the path he is to pursue in passing from one point to another. The *schedule* gives him the time elements of his progress in passing from place to place. The problem of routing is, in general, not a difficult one, but the problem of assigning time elements to productive processes with accuracy is often very difficult and sometimes necessitates many refined data. It will be assumed for the present that such data are available and the problem of collecting such data will be discussed in a later section.

Scheduling, like routing, may be of three degrees of refinement, namely:

1. Master scheduling, or the assigning of the dates on which important features of a production are to be completed.

2. Operation scheduling, or the assigning of the *total time* required to do a given piece of work with a given machine or process.

3. Detail-operation scheduling, or the assigning of the time required to do each detail operation of a given job with a given machine or process.

These degrees of refinement may be visualized more clearly by considering the construction of a ship, the contract for which calls for delivery upon a specified date. Beginning at that date and measuring backward a series of dates may be set fixing the latest time on which important features of the work must be completed if the delivery date is to be met. The dates, therefore, for beginning the trial trip; for the completion of the installation of all machinery; for the completion of the construction of the boilers and engines; for the launching of the hull; for the arrival of steel for the boilers and hull, etc., may be set off as a master schedule for the general guidance of all concerned in the schedule of events. It will be clear also that a similar master schedule can be made for each and every large element entering into the construction of the ship. Thus a series of time elements may be laid out for all important parts of the engines so

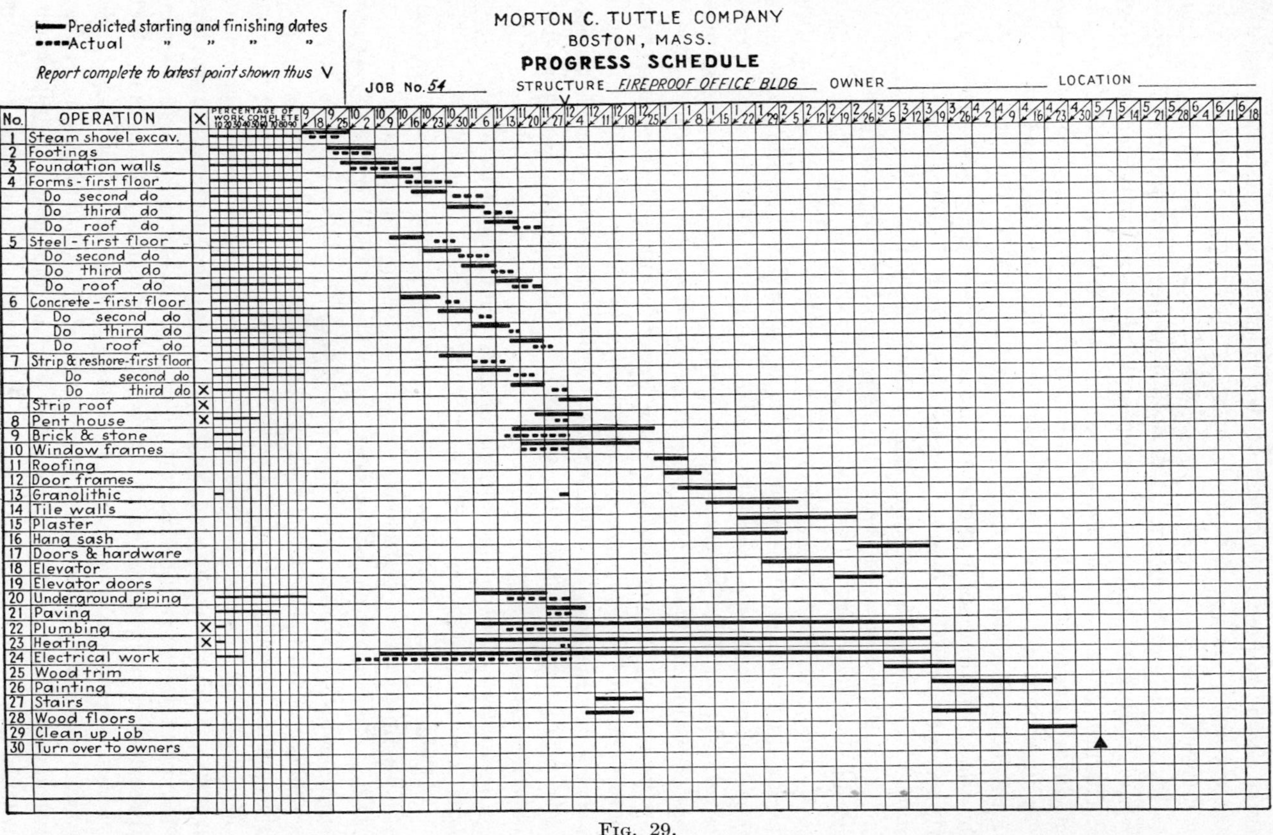
Predicted starting and finishing dates
Actual " " " "
Report complete to latest point shown thus V
MORTON C. TUTTLE COMPANY
BOSTON, MASS.
PROGRESS SCHEDULE
JOB No. 54
STRUCTURE FIREPROOF OFFICE BLDG
OWNER
LOCATION
No.
OPERATION
PERCENTAGE OF WORK COMPLETE
1 Steam shovel excav.
2 Footings
3 Foundation walls
4 Forms - first floor
Do second do
Do third do
Do roof do
5 Steel - first floor
Do second do
Do third do
Do roof do
6 Concrete - first floor
Do second do
Do third do
Do roof do
7 Strip & reshore - first floor
Do second do
Do third do
Strip roof
8 Pent house
9 Brick & stone
10 Window frames
11 Roofing
12 Door frames
13 Granolithic
14 Tile walls
15 Plaster
16 Hang sash
17 Doors & hardware
18 Elevator
19 Elevator doors
20 Underground piping
21 Paving
22 Plumbing
23 Heating
24 Electrical work
25 Wood trim
26 Painting
27 Stairs
28 Wood floors
29 Clean up job
30 Turn over to owners

Fig. 29.

that the base-plate or bed, the columns, cylinders, cranks, etc., shall all arrive at the assembly floor at the proper time, and so that the date of completion of the engine will conform to that set by the controlling master schedule.

Figure 29 shows such a master schedule as actually prepared and used by the Morton C. Tuttle Company[1] in connection with the construction of a building. It is an adaptation of the Gantt chart shown in Fig. 21 in which horizontal distances are used to measure times of performance. The important steps into which the work was analyzed are numbered on the left-hand side from 1 to 30. The time by weeks is indicated along the top of the diagram. As in the case of the ship, a controlling date, May 7, was fixed, on which the building was to be turned over to the owner. The schedule was then marked back from this date, the time for each element being so set that if completed on scheduled time the date of delivery would be met. The heavy horizontal lines indicate the scheduled time, while the heavy broken lines show whether the work is up to schedule, behind schedule, or ahead of schedule. In Column 3 a cross indicates any item that is not up to schedule, and in Column 4 the heavy horizontal lines indicate the percentage of each item that is completed. When this heavy line extends entirely across the column it signifies that this particular item is completed and needs no further attention. The schedule is brought up to date each week by a field engineer and a copy is sent to the main office, thus permitting the manager of construction to make suggestions or modify the schedule. Not the least value of such a schedule is the fact that it records clearly the progress and delays attendant upon the venture, and this is of great value in estimating future undertakings.

Consider next a machine part such as one of the engine cylinders, which is finished by a series of operations such as boring, planing, milling, drilling, etc., similar to the list of operations listed in Fig. 25. Obviously time elements can be assigned to each of these operations which, if they are fulfilled, will insure that the cylinder will be produced at the proper time. This would be **operation scheduling.** Sometimes routing and operation scheduling are both listed upon the same sheet, as illustrated in Fig. 30. Such sheets are sometimes called **planned-operation sheets** but such planning is simple operation scheduling and should be clearly distinguished from detail-operation scheduling, which is to be described.

Detail-operation scheduling is the assigning of time elements to each *detail operation*, as illustrated in Fig. 27, which is usually known as an **instruction sheet** or **instruction card.** This is the extreme of refinement in scheduling and, as will be seen, a considerable amount of data on the characteristics of the machinery of production and of the time required to do basic operations must be available in classified form before such

[1] For a complete description, see *The Architectural Forum*, August, 1929.

refined prediction of time elements is attempted. These required data, and the methods of securing them, are fully discussed in a succeeding section.

124. Master Schedules—Control Boards.—The master schedule is based naturally upon the sales orders or the prospective sales require-

PART NAME Idler Gear — ROUTE SHEET NO. 25
SYMBOL G-3 — CHARGE TO E-183
MATERIAL Nickel-Steel Casting — DATE TO BE STARTED Apr. 14, 1925
NO. WANTED 350 — DUE IN FINISHED STOCK May 6, 1925
SPOILAGE 10 — SCHEDULED BY D. W. Wile

OPR. NO.	NO. OF PIECES	DESCRIPTION	MACH. NO.	MACHINE NAME	DUE AT MACHINE	COMPLETED	REMARKS
1	360	Bore and Face 1st Side	6	J. & L.	Apr. 14	Apr. 16	
		Inspect					
2	356	Broach oil groove	22	Broach	17	17	
3	356	Hand ream bore	—	Bench	18	18	
4	356	Turn O.D. & Face 2nd Side	6	J. & L.	19	21	
		Inspect					
5	354	Block teeth	57	B. & O. Hob	22	25	Delayed to Rush B-53
6	354	Finish cut teeth	47	Sharper	23	30	
		Inspect teeth					
7	354	Point one side	36	Pointer	28	May 1	
8	354	File corners	37	S. Lathe	28	1	
9	354	Roll teeth	39	Lathe	28	1	
		Inspect					
10	354	Harden, Carbonize, Quench,			29		
		Reheat, Draw		Heat			
11	354	Sand-blast, Polish for		Treating			
		Brinell test, Test		Dept.			
		teeth with file				May 4	
12	354	Grind bore	72	Heald	May 2	7	
		Final Inspection			May 5	8	Passed 352
							J.R.W.

FIG. 30.—Planned-operation sheet.

ments. Such schedules can be made up intelligently, therefore, only on a clear understanding of such requirements and the volume of work already in process. General policies and the necessity of keeping all divisions of the plant employed as far as possible will, therefore, enter into its compilation. Usually the making of a master schedule for a single piece of product, however complex it may be in itself, is not a difficult matter, but where many production orders are to be scheduled, more or less simultaneously, the problem may be very difficult. It should be noted that in purely continuous-process industries routing and scheduling are automatically performed by the machinery of production, and the nearer an industry approaches to this type the simpler are the problems of routing and scheduling.

In a plant manufacturing largely on specific sales orders there will be jobs like that of the ship described in the preceding article where there is ample time to meet the delivery date by following the regular procedure laid down. But it may be that one or more of these orders may be coincident as to time in their main features, and unless the master schedule is carefully compiled congested conditions, on the one hand, and idle machines, on the other, are likely to result. Then again, repair jobs, or jobs that for other reasons must be rushed through as quickly as possible, may make it necessary to modify the master schedule so as to prevent congestion and obtain the desired results. It may be also that the plant produces lines of goods for stock in anticipation of sales orders. Orders for such product can be issued at such times as will help to keep the schedule balanced.

The problem of the master schedule in plants that manufacture entirely for stock is not markedly different. More consideration must be given, of course, to market conditions and prospective sales, and questions of general policy are more dominant in compiling the master schedule. This is particularly true where production in anticipation of sales ties up a large amount of capital in materials and labor. The size, sequence, and character of the lots of parts or complete machines that are scheduled for production must be given very careful consideration, especially as the schedules for this type of production must usually be determined months in advance of completion of the product.

A master schedule, therefore, should not be considered as a fixed procedure that admits of no change. Constant minor changes are usually necessary to accommodate new conditions as they arise and sometimes major changes are imperative because of unforeseen troubles. In many cases the master schedule consists simply of a limited number of important dates, the problem of directing the production so that the several parts will be completed at the proper time being left to the superintendent and foreman to work out as best they can. The writer has witnessed some very extensive and important contracts carried through to successful completion in this simple manner. In most advanced modern practice, however, it is not uncommon to chart all important events for all work on the master schedule, thus making some form of **control board.** The Gantt chart is one of the most effective forms of such graphical schedules (Fig. 21). On this chart, as has been noted, horizontal lines represent time and hence a large number of desired events can be scheduled on a comparatively small space and in a form that makes them easy to visualize.

Figure 31 shows a series of operations scheduled on a Gantt chart as actually used by Mr. Wallace Clark, and published with his permission.

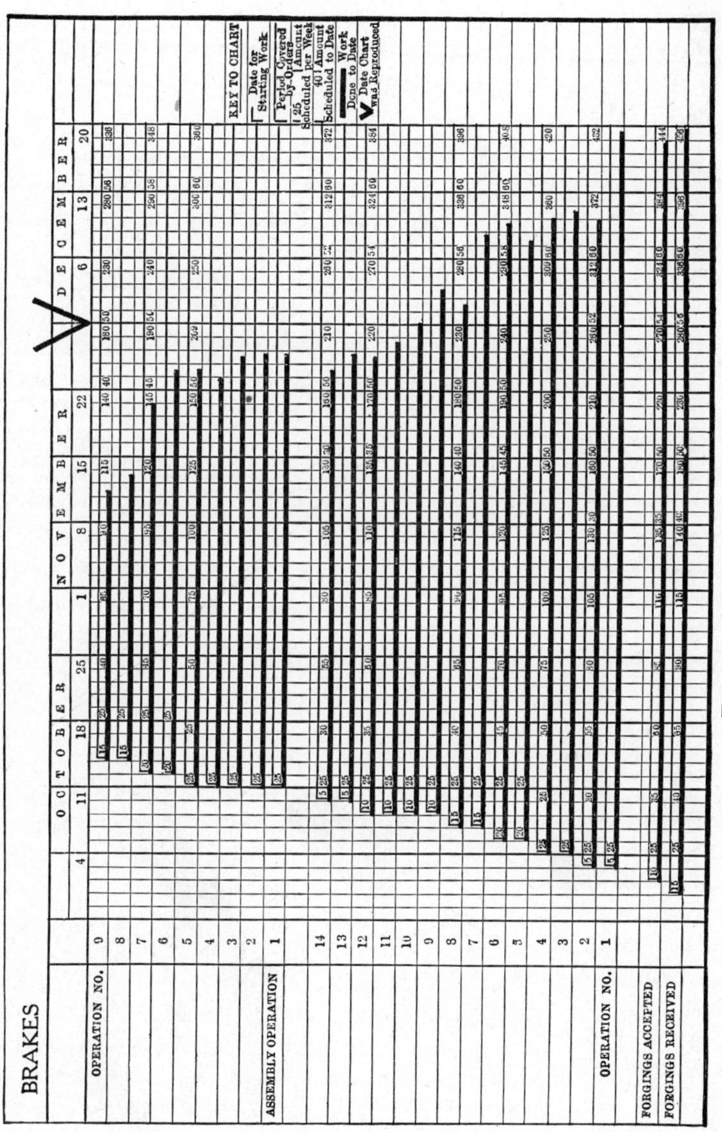

FIG. 31.—Gantt progress chart.

On this chart the date for starting the several operations, the amount scheduled per week, and the total amount scheduled to date are indicated by the key at the right hand of the chart. The heavy black lines indicate the proportion of work actually completed. A similar diagram showing the work ahead for various machines and processes and known as a **machine-load chart** is often very useful in routing and scheduling.

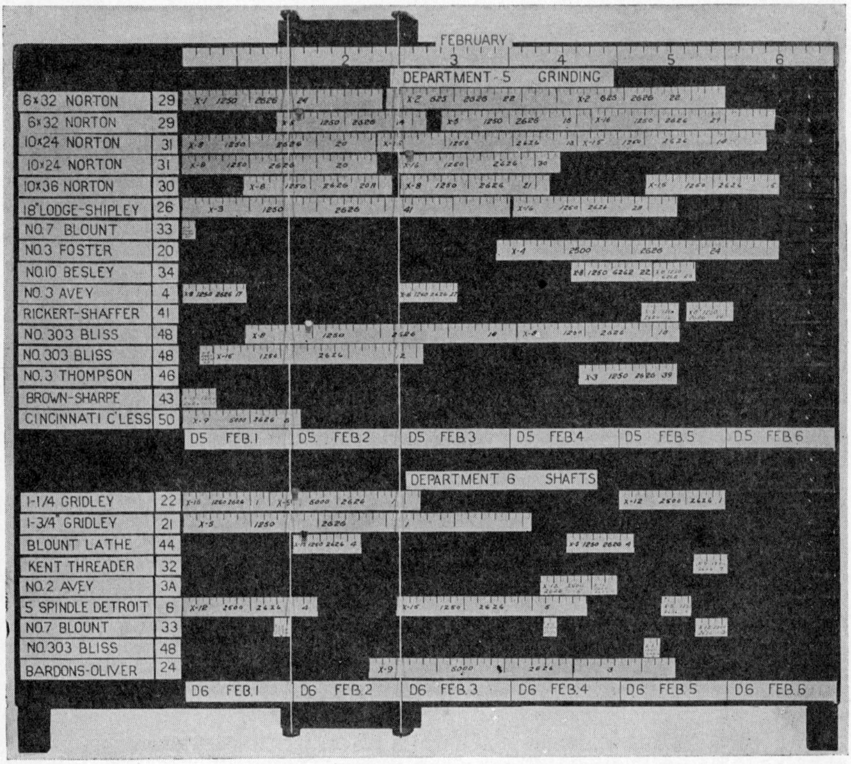

Fig. 32.—Model of control board.

It will be obvious that the idea on which the Gantt chart is based is capable of wide application. The most interesting and most complete application of the principle to control-board methods is that devised by Major George Babcock[1] for the Franklin Motor Company. On this board a great degree of flexibility was obtained by movable markers placed upon the horizontal elements that indicate time. It was, in fact, a *mechanical* Gantt chart.

Figure 32 is a photograph of a miniature model of the production-control board used by the L. C. Smith-Corona Typewriter Company. At the left-hand side are listed vertically, first the machines in Depart-

[1] See Babcock, Major George, "Taylor System in Franklin Management," for a full description of the control board.

ment 5 and below these the machines in Department 6. At the top of the picture, part-way down, between the two lists of machines, and at the bottom of the picture, are identical time scales showing consecutive time by days divided into eight hours each. A traveler, the frame of which is back of the board, carries two white strings set eight hours, or one working day, apart. As shown, they mark the events that are scheduled for February 2 in both departments. Opposite each machine number there is a metal holder shown clearly on the right-hand side, into which can be placed paper strips that indicate the rate at which it is expected the several operations will be performed. These paper strips are laid off into hourly divisions of the same length as those in the calendar strips at the top and bottom of the board. The half hours are indicated by short lines, and every fifth hour is marked by a longer division line to facilitate calculations. Each paper slip also carries a record of the identifying symbol, the number of operations, the manufacturing order number, and the operation number. Thus, opposite the first 10 $\times$ 24 Norton grinder, No. 31, the production slip indicates that at the beginning of the fifth hour on the last working day in January production was started on part No. x-8. The number of parts ordered is 1250, the production order number is 2626 and the number of the required operation is 20. It is expected that this work will be completed by the end of the sixth hour on February 2 and immediately thereafter production is to begin on 1250 pieces of Part x-15 on order No. 2626, the operation in this case to be No. 13. This work is to be completed by the end of the fifth hour on February 4 and is to be succeeded by operation No. 14 on 1250 pieces of part No. x-15 on production order No. 2626, to be completed by the end of the third hour on February 6.

The strings indicate the work that is to be performed on February 2, provided the schedule has been adhered to and all operations are up to schedule. All deviations from schedule are reported by the dispatchers on the machine floors and the board is corrected by sliding the slips forward or backward as may be necessary. Small riders of various colors are clipped over the control slips to indicate variations in schedule caused by such troubles as breakdown of machines, lack of material, etc. Some of these clips may be seen on the picture. The actual control board from which this model was made is long enough to control three months' work, at the end of which time the board is reset from the left end. The hourly division lines are machine printed and the material for the control slips is furnished in rolls, the schedule operator simply cutting off the desired length.

It will be noted that when all of the machines are running, the board opposite the lists of machines will be completely filled with control slips. On the model board a considerable amount of machine idleness is shown and this is a valuable characteristic of such control boards, since they show at a glance the degree of activity in the plant. Again, the total hours of work scheduled for any day is an index of the number of workmen needed at any time and this assists planning in advance for the working force. Thus for February 2 only 62 man hours of work are scheduled for the first group of machines, assuming one man to each machine, whereas the total capacity of the group is 128 man hours on the same assumption. The department is therefore working at less than half capacity. It will be obvious that the general principles illustrated by Fig. 32 are capable of wide variation. A most interesting variation that has been attempted is to schedule only the jobs that fall behind or are delayed from one cause or another. In a plant having, normally, a steady flow of work, there would be a great saving in scheduling only the exceptional jobs that are thus out of line, so to speak. This would be an application of management by exception to which further reference is made elsewhere.

125. Dispatching.—The most important functions in dispatching are:

1. The procurement for the workman of all tools and fixtures necessary for each operation in advance of the time they will be needed.
2. Initiating the work by giving the workman all work orders, instructions, drawings, etc., at the time work should begin.
3. Recording the time of starting and completing each operation.
4. Moving the work after completion to the next operation or process listed upon the route sheet.
5. Tracing the progress of all production and making adjustments in the schedule to accommodate necessary changes.

The work of dispatching may be made clearer by considering the methods in most common use for this work. All of these methods are patterned more or less after Taylor's original plan. An order box containing not less than three compartments is placed near each workman. The first compartment (Fig. 33) holds the work order, instruction card, drawings, etc., for the work in process; the second compartment contains similar instructions, etc., for the next job for which the necessary tools, jigs, and fixtures will be collected by the time work is to begin upon it. The third compartment may be used to hold instructions for future work, the sequence of which has not as yet been determined. In the offices of the planning department is placed a **planning board,** as it is usually named, made up of sets of compartments that are duplicates of those in the shop; each compartment containing instructions and orders that are, in general, duplicates of those in the corresponding compartments at the machine. When any change is made on the planning board by moving instruction material from one compartment to another, a corresponding change is made in the compartments at the machine so that the planning board always shows the exact amount of work before each man or machine. The order-of-work clerk keeps fully informed of

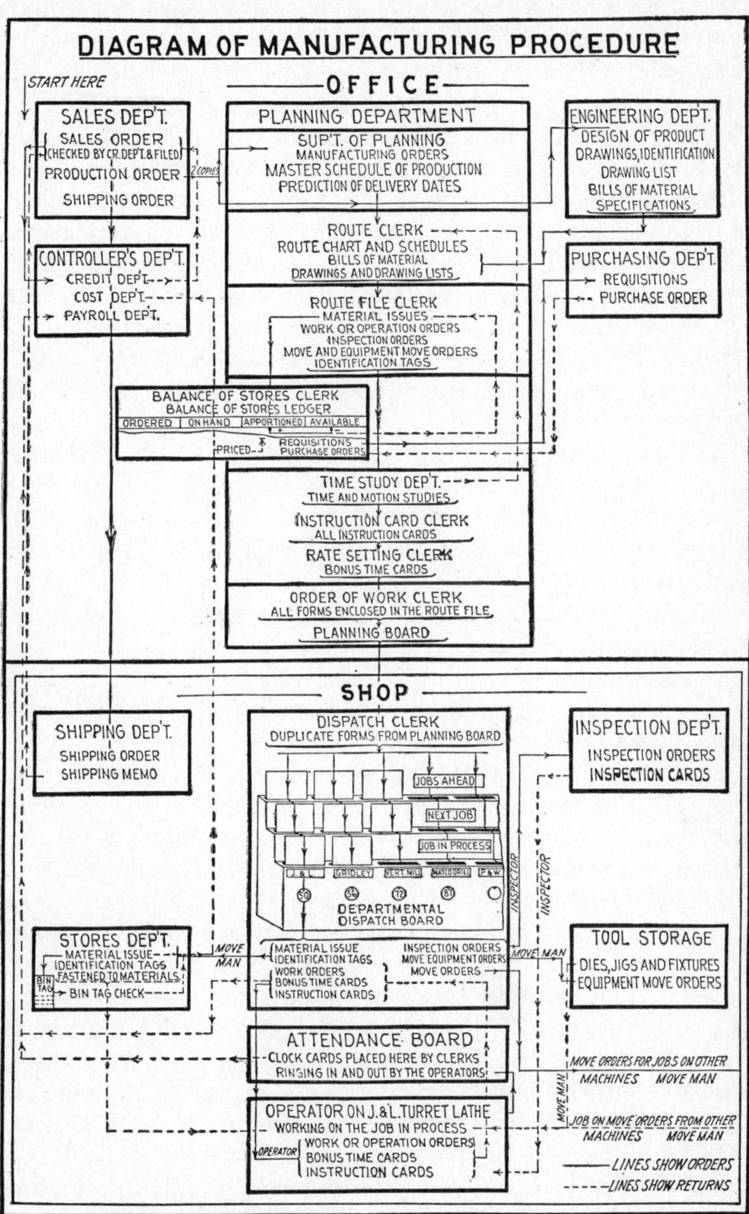

Fig. 33.—Diagram of manufacturing procedure.

the desired dates of delivery, as outlined by the schedule, and of any changes that may be made in these dates. By means of the planning board he can control fully the sequence of operations and make close estimates of the time required to complete work in process, or of new work on which such an estimate is desired.

The moving of all material to and from machines and processes is usually in charge of a centralized transportation service, and the term **move man** working under a **move order** designates the individual who performs this function. Sometimes this service also includes the procurement of tools, fixtures, etc., as in the case of Mr. Taylor's "gang boss," but again there may be a special messenger service for this purpose operated by the dispatch clerk at the departmental board. There must also be a special messenger service for synchronizing the central board and the departmental board, adjusting difficulties, and tracing job orders that may need special attention. The interrelation of these activities and the general procedure of dispatching are discussed in connection with a typical organization in Art. 126.

126. Typical Production-control Procedure.—These several somewhat complex relations may be made clear by considering a typical production-control procedure as shown graphically in Fig. 33, which was devised by Professor John Bangs, of Cornell University, for this special purpose. In this diagram all *office* functions are shown above the heavy horizontal line and all *shop* functions are placed below it. Full lines indicate the paths of orders and instructions moving *downward,* while dotted lines indicate the paths of records and returns moving *upward.* Let it be assumed that a sales order has been received from the sales department. This order will first be approved by the credit department under the controller or corresponding official. If so approved it will pass to the factory manager who will issue such production orders (Fig. 17) as may be necessary. In routine work this is frequently accomplished as indicated in the diagram, the *approved* sales order serving as a production order, copies being sent to the superintendent of the planning department and to the engineering department.

The superintendent of planning will now divide the work called for by the production order into such items as may seem desirable, and will issue a *manufacturing order* (Art. 120) for each item. He will also lay out the master schedule (Art. 123) for the entire work, and fix the important dates of delivery, etc., for each item. All of this information will then be forwarded to the route clerk. The engineering department will prepare or furnish all drawings, drawing lists (Fig. 23), specifications, and bills of material. The drawings and drawing lists will also *identify* each part by number or symbol as explained in Chap. XI. All of these documents will also be forwarded to the route clerk.

The route clerk will now lay out the route sheet (Fig. 25) *for each machine part* or lot of parts to be produced. Or if a combined route and schedule sheet (that is a planned-operation sheet, Fig. 30) is in use he will prepare those sheets, calling upon the time-study department for any information he may need regarding the *total* time required for the several operations, and with due regard to the work already scheduled upon the planning board. He will then forward the route sheets, drawings, specifications, etc., to the route-file clerk.

The route-file clerk will then proceed as follows *for each operation* called for upon the planned-operation sheets: First, if material is to be drawn from stores for the operation he will inquire of the balance-of-

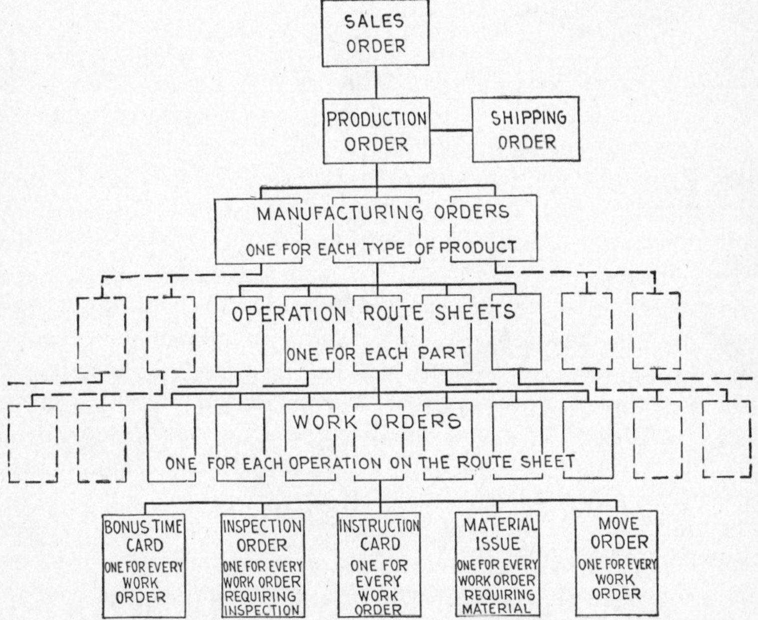

Fig. 34.—Development of Manufacturing Orders.

stores clerk whether the required material is on hand. If it is on hand the balance-of-stores clerk reserves the necessary amount and deducts the material so apportioned from available stores (Fig. 43). If the material required is not on hand, the balance-of-stores clerk will make a requisition upon the purchasing department which will purchase the material and have it on hand when needed; the entire transaction being reported back to the route-file clerk. The route-file clerk will now write all orders for issuing materials from stores or the necessary move order, if the work is to be brought from some other machine. He will make out the necessary orders for procuring tools and equipment, and for the identification tags that are to be attached to the work and move with it; and lastly he will make out the operation orders (Fig. 26), and the instructions to the inspector concerning the times for inspection. For convenience, the operation order, the identification tag, the move order, etc., that pertain to each operation may be placed together in an envelope sometimes called a **job** or **operation envelope,** and these with the route sheets, or planned-operation sheet, the drawings, and other general directions pertaining to the work scheduled may all be placed in a larger envelope or container known as a **route file** and forwarded to the time-study department. Here the instruction-card clerk will furnish an instruction card (Fig. 27) for each operation, if such a card is to be used, and the rate-setting clerk will furnish the proper time card, piece-work or bonus card (Fig. 19), as may be needed, each of these being placed in the operation envelope to which they belong. The relation of these several documents to each other may be more clearly understood by an examination of Fig. 34, which shows these relations completely for a single manufacturing order and which was devised by Professor John Bangs for this purpose.

The order-of-work clerk has charge of the planning board and correlates it with the several departmental dispatch boards. When he receives the route file for a given machine or product he retains the route sheets or planned-operation lists, and he assigns each operation to be performed to the machine or production center for which it has been routed, by removing the duplicate work order and other duplicate documents necessary for complete identification and control of the operation from the operation envelope, and placing them on the planning board, upon the hooks, or in the pockets controlling the particular machine to which the work is assigned. The operation envelope, with its remaining duplicate contents, is placed in corresponding position upon the departmental dispatch board controlling the production center or process to which the work is assigned. He will do this for each operation for which the route file contains operation envelopes, placing them so that the work orders are in the sequence called for by the scheduled time of performance.

Let it be assumed that the first of these machines or processes to which work has been so assigned is a Jones and Lamson turret lathe No. 50, as shown in Fig. 33; and let it be assumed, furthermore, that there is plenty of work ahead of it so that this particular work order and its related instructions in the operation envelope are placed in proper sequence in the upper or **jobs-ahead** pocket of the planning board. In due process of time the envelope will be advanced to the second or **next-job** pocket, corresponding changes, of course, being made upon the departmental dispatch board.

When the work order has been advanced to this position the dispatch clerk takes the material-issue order from the operation envelope, if material is to be drawn from stores, and also the identification tags that are to be fastened to the work bearing the identification numbers, etc., and gives them to the move man. The move man, with this authority, draws the material, tags it, and moves it to the machine. When this is completed he signs the material-issues order and returns it to the stores clerk. The stores clerk, upon the delivery of the material, corrects his bin-tag records and forwards the material-issues order to the balance-of-stores clerk, who corrects his balance-of-stores records, prices the material-issue order, and forwards it to the cost department where it is charged up against the cost of the production order. If no material is to be drawn from stores but is to be moved from some other machine the same procedure applies except that in this case the stores are not involved. The dispatch clerk also issues the equipment orders to the move man, who, with this as authority, procures all special tools and appliances and brings them to the machine in advance of the beginning of operations.

Let it now be assumed that the operator on machine No. 50 has finished the job in process. He takes his operation order, instruction card, time card, etc., to the dispatch station and returns them to the dispatch clerk who stamps the time upon the time card. The dispatch clerk now takes the duplicate documents pertaining to the work just completed from the work-in-process pocket and advances the corresponding documents of the job next in order to that position. He stamps the time upon the time card in this new set and gives it to the workman with the work order, instruction card, etc., for the new operation. The workman then returns to his machine and starts the new operation for which complete preparation has been made. The dispatch clerk also issues the new inspection orders to the inspector. The move man takes the work just completed on machine No. 50 to the next machine listed upon the route, and returns all tools and fixtures to the tool storage. The dispatch clerk returns all work orders, drawings, drawing lists, etc., to the order-of-work clerk who checks the completed operation on the planned-operation list and returns the drawings, instruction cards, etc., to the engineering department. The time cards are sent to the controller's department where they are first checked against the attendance-board record or time-clock record, depending upon which is in use, and then used as a basis for the payroll. They are then forwarded to the cost department where, with the material issues, they form the basis of production costs.

127. Modification and Adaptation.—The foregoing discussion describes a complete plan of production control based on Taylor's methods, and typical of a number of such plans now in actual use. In this discussion an effort has been made to define and describe the principal functions in such a plan and to illustrate the primary documents connected with each function. Thus the moving of material is defined as a separate function under the *move man*, so-called, and the *move order* is the fundamental order connected with that function. It will be obvious. however, that there is an endless number of possible modifications,[1] abbreviations, and adaptations of these general principles, and there are many such in actual use, the particular combination of basic functions used and the method of their combination varying widely with the character of the enterprise and the degree of control desired. In these modifications and adaptations several functions may be performed by one man and his assistants, and in a similar manner the basic documents may be combined. An example of such combination is purposely illustrated in Fig. 30, where both routing and scheduling are listed upon the same sheet. A combination operation order and bonus time card is not unusual.

A not unusual modification is one where routing and scheduling are fairly complete but dispatching is left largely to the foremen with the aid of **follow-up men or tracers,** as they are often called, whose sole duty it is to keep track of the several orders and to assist the foreman in removing any obstacles that may stand in the way of fulfilling the schedule.

There are two methods of organizing such a force of tracers. In the first method every manufacturing order is assigned to some one man and his assistants, who follow the order through production whether there are delays or not. If delays do occur they endeavor to remove the difficulties that delay the schedule through conference with foremen and other officials. In large plants a tracer or group of tracers is usually given charge of a particular class of production, thus specializing their efforts.

The second method is to turn over to the tracers only those jobs that are behind their schedule. The source of information on this point is usually the foreman or the progress report (Art. 102), if such a report is compiled. This method, of course, requires fewer tracers than the first and is, therefore, cheaper, but it is not so thorough. The choice of methods will depend somewhat upon circumstances and upon the degree of refinement in routing and scheduling. If the routing and scheduling are poorly done the tracing must be correspondingly searching if schedules are to be kept. Tracing is greatly facilitated by conferences between the tracing staff and also conferences with the foreman and others charged with the problems of production.

128. Requirements for Production Control.—It should be noted that the degree of refinement possible in production control depends upon the degree of refinement with which route sheets, operation sheets, and instruction cards can be compiled, and upon the degree to which the several departments are organized to fulfill the predicted performances.

[1] A very enlightening discussion of such a modification is given by Ralph E. Flanders in a paper presented before the American Society Mechanical Engineers in December, 1924, entitled "Design Manufacture and Production Control of a Standard Machine."

In general, good production control requires that the following information is available in convenient form and that these specified conditions exist in the plant.

1. Complete detailed drawings and other engineering information.

2. Complete information regarding special tools, such as jigs and fixtures, whether existent or to be provided.

3. Complete information on times and costs of previous performances.

4. Accurate up-to-date information regarding the stores and finished stock that are to be used.

5. Exact knowledge of the progress of the work in process.

6. Complete tabulated data on power, speeds, and feeds of all machines.

7. Complete data, as far as can be obtained, on the most effective forms of cutting tools and the best combinations of speeds, feeds, and depth of cuts for the metal to be machined.

8. Records of the best performances on similar work with best combination of tools, feeds, and speeds.

And to insure the attainment of the performance predicted on the instruction card there must be:

9. Careful instruction of the workmen by the speed boss or some similar person.

10. Careful following up and correction of the shop schedule.

11. Careful inspection of all tools and appliances to make sure they are up to standard conditions.

12. A financial incentive that will enlist the interest of the workman.

Brief reflection will show that similar conditions and requirements apply to other forms of industry, the principles being capable of wide extension.

Of these requirements several are now fairly well met in many modern shops. Thus (1) presupposes a first-class engineering and designing department; (2) a well-developed tool room; (3) a first-class cost system; (4) an accurate continuous-inventory system, all of which have reached a high state of development in many plants. The remaining requirements, however, are in a rudimentary stage in most shops and it may be of advantage to discuss them briefly. Thus (5) presupposes an accurate knowledge of the progress of work such as is obtained only by the dispatching methods discussed in Art. 125. As yet only a limited number of industrial plants have adopted this refined control.

129. Data on Machines (Item 6).—It is evident that before the instruction-card man can intelligently instruct the workman regarding the size of cuts and feeds and speeds to be used, very complete data must be compiled bearing on the cutting power and the speeds and feeds or similar data obtainable with each machine. This information is not available in most shops and must be collected. It is also evident that this would be much simplified if all machines of the same kind were made along standard lines. At present a machine of given nominal size made by any given manufacturer is usually very different in its characteristics from those of rival makers. These new methods will undoubtedly have some effect tending to standardize tools of all kinds.

130. Industrial Data—The Art of Cutting Metal (Item 7).—It would most naturally be supposed that an experienced, skilled workman would know more than anyone else regarding the best shapes of cutting tools and most efficient combinations of feeds and speeds for the work of his particular calling. In simple trades these, or corresponding data, may be easily obtained, but, in general, the information possessed by the mechanic is empirical and based on inherited[1] practice that is never

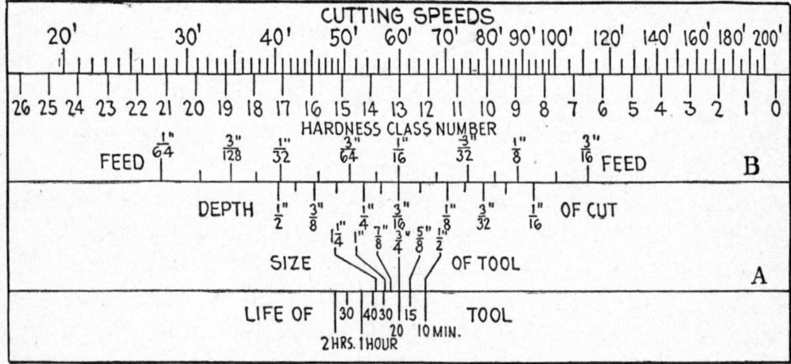

FIG. 35.—Barth slide rule.

questioned by him. All trades and callings abound in practices that are transmitted downward with almost superstitious exactness and with little or no thought as to whether a better way can be found. This is very well instanced in the case of cutting of metals. Here (according to F. W. Taylor) there are 12 principal variables involved and it is evident that no man can carry in his head the best combination for any given case. Actual experience has shown this to be so, and has demonstrated that the best combination of these variables can be found much more accurately by mathematical analysis than by the best empirical knowledge. This problem illustrates the complexity of what may appear to be simple processes.

A considerable amount of general information on this subject has been collected[2] from time to time, but the most comprehensive attempt to solve this problem was that made by F. W. Taylor and recorded in full

[1] One of the best instances of the empirical development of an almost perfect tool is found in the common ax and ax handle. It would have been difficult indeed to analyze this problem and design the modern ax scientifically.

[2] See CARPENTER, C. U., "Profit Making in Shop and Factory Management," pp. 86–91.

in the *Transactions of the American Society of Mechanical Engineers*, Vol. 28, 1907. Mr. Taylor's experimental work and the laws that he deduced therefrom were reduced to mathematical expressions by him and his assistants. The complexity of the problem will be appreciated when it is considered that no less than 12 variables are involved. By means of very ingenious slide rules, however, Carl G. Barth succeeded in making these expressions usable, and with these slide rules the most efficient combinations of speeds and feeds are quickly obtainable. These slide rules are made in several forms and for different machines,[1] and any extended discussion of them is beyond the limits of this book: their general characteristics, however, are clearly shown in Fig. 35. In this slide rule, the parts *A* and *B* are movable and slide endwise relative to the main body of the rule and to each other. The upper scale shows the cutting speeds, and next to it is a scale which indicates the hardness of the material, in this case steel, by a hardness class number. The lower edge of the upper slide carries a scale which indicates the feed in inches. The upper edge of the lower slide carries a scale which indicates the depth of cut in inches, while the lower edge carries a small scale which indicates various sizes of tools. Adjoining this scale upon the fixed part of the rule is another short scale indicating the "cutting life" of the tool. As the rule is set it shows that a ¾-inch tool of standard form will cut well for 20 minutes when the depth of cut is 3/16 inch, and the feed 1/16 inch, on steel of a hardness number of 13 and a speed of 60 feet per minute. If the steel is of No. 10 hardness the cutting speed may be 80 feet per minute, etc.

Tabulated data on cutting feeds and speeds for various machines drawn from Taylor's work and elsewhere, are to be found in Kent's "Mechanical Engineers' Handbook," and also in Mark's "Mechanical Engineers' Handbook." Taylor's work did not cover all kinds of metals and there is still much work to be done in collecting data on the cutting of metals. There is a vast amount of work to be done in other industries before similar data will be common in these other lines of work.

131. Records of Performance (Item 8).—What has been said of the average worker's lack of knowledge of industrial processes is even more true of his lack of exactness as to the time required to do a given piece of work and of the best procedure in doing it. Since this item is of importance and requires a somewhat lengthy discussion it is made the subject of the succeeding chapter.

132. Methods of Insuring Performance (Items 9–12).—It is clear that if the standard performances are based on records somewhat lower even than the best record they will be beyond the attainment of many

[1] In a series of papers in *Industrial Management* beginning September, 1919, Mr. Barth describes in full the development of these slide rules. See also *Trans. Am. Soc. Mech. Eng.*, Vol. 25, p. 49.

of the less skilled workers. It is clear, also, that if the output of the factory is raised to these standards, in general, one of two courses must be pursued. Either the less skilled men must be eliminated and their places filled with better men or they must be *educated* and taught how to raise their performance to the standard. The latter method is, of course, the more humane, and in the long run will be the more effective. H. L. Gantt was the first, the writer believes, to appreciate fully the opportunities of this field, and his work and writings[1] on this phase of shop management form a very valuable addition to the literature of general industrial education.

It is also self-evident that if the planning department is to predict performances that can be successfully executed, all machines and tools must be in the first-class condition that the planner must presume them to be. For this reason the inspection, care, and repair of all productive apparatus should, if possible, be under one man whose business it is to see to these matters and nothing else. Such a man can earn his salary even in a comparatively small shop. Under such a system matters such as breaking of belts are, in large measure, obviated by preinspection and repair, and the same principle applies to apparatus in general.

And last, and by no means least, if the worker is to raise his output to a standard higher than he has been accustomed to he must receive extra compensation for his extra effort. Otherwise he will not make the effort. It has been noted previously (Art. 20) that the worker is usually skeptical regarding the effect of increased output. It is useless to point out to him that increased output will tend to help him because of the ultimate good flowing from abundant production. The reasoning is usually beyond him; and the only incentive that will move him is an immediate gain. All efforts to increase production by the methods described in the foregoing paragraphs usually are, and in fact must be, operated in connection with some method of rewarding labor that gives increased compensation for increased effort. The various methods of rewarding labor are more fully discussed in Chap. XXI.

133. Collecting and Recording of Data.—The last function of the planning department listed in Art. 119 is the collection of returns and records of performance. The planning department does not, of course, collect all the returns. It does, however, record all times of beginning and completing work and all details of time expended upon direct production, which form one of the factors in production costs. All progress reports, and all reports as to idle equipment and spoiled work, are compiled in this department. If special studies of productive operations, such as time study and motion study, are attempted they are usually conducted by the planning department, since the records so obtained are for its use.

[1] See GANTT, H. L., "Work, Wages, and Profits."

134. Limitations.—The foregoing is a very brief account of the more important tendencies in the planning of factory operations. It should be noted that functional foremanship and similar methods are in no way connected with any particular form of wage system, nor do the methods discussed in this chapter, taken singly or collectively, constitute a complete philosophy or scheme of management that will be best for all cases. The combination and arrangement that will be best to use will, necessarily, vary with the conditions; and what may be good for one place would not apply at all in another. These methods, however, are excellent illustrations of the separation of mental and manual processes, and the use of division of labor and transfer of skill. The strong coordinative influences necessary for such forms of organization are found in the instruction card and route card, and the incentive of extra compensation for extra effort. Some very complete applications of these methods have been made in this country though, as yet, few complete accounts of such applications have appeared.

It should be noted, also, that these methods are, for the most part, refined extensions of old principles. Some of them are efforts to apply the scientific method to the measurement of human effort and aim to do for the field of management what engineering research has already done for the designing department. How far they can be considered to be scientific is a debated question. Mr. Taylor and many of his followers maintain that these methods can be considered very scientific. Others as strongly insist that the personal equation enters into these methods so greatly as to make accurate and scientific results impossible. Clearly these methods do touch the human side of industry very closely. Mr. Gilbreth said that they are closely connected with experience, skill, contentment, training, habit, fatigue, and other personal matters. A résumé of these debated points of view can be made more intelligently after a consideration of other industrial problems, and will, therefore, be deferred to a later chapter (see Chap. XXVI).

Objection is often made, particularly by managers of the older type, to the introduction of any such system as described in this and the preceding chapter on the ground that it adds to the cost of production. This may often seem to be true as most of the men employed in planning and carrying the work through the shop do not work *directly* upon the product. There is no doubt, furthermore, that a useless and costly system is sometimes installed where the conditions do not warrant, and in such cases the cost of the product is necessarily raised. There is no virtue in system of any kind unless it is installed intelligently and with a clear idea of the results it is desired to obtain.

Usually there is no difficulty in deciding how far it is economical to go in providing system to collect valuable information, as in cost systems, or in a system for facilitating the transmission and use of information that will hasten operations, and thereby increase the efficiency of productive processes already existing; but it is not always easy to decide such questions when they involve the separation of productive processes into mental and manual constituents. Functional foremanship, for instance, is based on a somewhat different reasoning from that underlying a cost system. A cost system is valuable no matter how large or small the shop may be, although its characteristics might vary with the size of the shop. But all extensions of the principle of division of labor that involve separation of mental and manual processes and transfer of skill necessarily involve a reduction in the amount of time and labor *actually* spent upon the work and an increase in the amount of planning or *indirect* labor expended upon it. Whether such a rearrangement of duties will result in netting a greater output and reduced cost will depend on the quantity to be made and the character of the work; and it is very easy to oversystematize unless these conditions are fully understood.

This statement is fully borne out by the number of industrial plants that have introduced quite complete systems of production control and have afterward either abandoned these systems or have greatly modified them, retaining only those features that were of real economic value. It cannot be disputed, however, that these principles do result in increased output and decreased cost when properly applied; and the manager that does not use them so far as the limitations of his case will allow, simply because he does not believe in system of any kind, is blinding himself to his opportunities.

135. Management by Exceptions.—The procedure described in Art. 126 is fairly typical of the majority of administrative mechanisms. In general they aim to visualize and control all details of the work in hand and therein lies the danger of oversystematization and possible loss therefrom. The thoughtful manager will therefore seek logical limits for his procedure. One of the most effective methods of limiting managerial system is by the so-called **principle of exceptions,** by which the manager concentrates his attention "solely upon those executive matters which vary from routine plan or standard."[1] This idea runs like a thread throughout the entire field of organization, particularly wherever standards of any kind have been set, deviations from which can be noted and reported. Thus it is not necessary to report to the general manager all of the details of the operation of the power plant so long as its performance is up to standard, while it is highly important to report the occasional deviation of performance from the standard. If the costs of all products are not greater than the standard costs that have been set, it is clearly a waste of the manager's time to go over all of the cost details. But when costs exceed the expectations the principle of exception would naturally be applied through a special cost report as discussed in Art. 102.

[1] See ALFORD, L. P., "Laws of Management," *Trans. Am. Soc. Mech. Eng.*, Vol. 48.

And so in scheduling work through the plant it may not be necessary to lay out the progress of every shop order as in Fig. 30, but it may be sufficient to post only those orders that are behind their schedule or are irregular. Thus in manufacturing which approaches continuous production or where the production orders are comparatively few in number and where the execution of each requires a considerable period of time, it may be necessary only to schedule those that fall behind through one cause or another. Mr. C. D. Hart of the Western Electric Company has thus successfully used the exception principle in manufacturing telephone cables, employing a modified Gantt chart somewhat like that shown in Fig. 21.

The principle is of broad application and the thoughtful administrator will give it careful consideration in organizing his procedure. As Mr. F. W. Taylor so truthfully remarked when discussing this principle:

> Under it [the exception principle] the manager should receive only condensed, summarized, and invariably comparative reports, covering, however, all of the elements entering into the management, and even these summaries should all be carefully gone over by an assistant before they reach the manager and have all of the exceptions to past averages or to the standards pointed out, both the especially good and especially bad exceptions, thus giving him in a few minutes a full view of progress that is being made or the reverse and leaving him free to consider the broad lines of policy and to study the character and fitness of important men under him.

References

Alford, L. P. (Ed.): "Cost and Production Handbook," p. 227.
———: "Management's Handbook."
Anderson, A. G.: "Industrial Engineering and Factory Management."
Babcock, Major George D.: "Taylor System in Franklin Management."
Cornell, W. C.: "Industrial Organization and Management."
Knoeppel, C. E.: "Graphic Production Control."
Parkhurst, F. A.: "Applied Methods of Scientific Management."
Taylor, F. W.: "Shop Management," *Trans. Am. Soc. Mech. Eng.*, Vol. 24.
Van Deventer, J. H.: "Machine Shop Management."

CHAPTER XIII

OPERATION STANDARDIZATION—TIME AND MOTION STUDIES

136. General.—It was shown in the preceding chapter that the degree of refinement in production control depends upon the degree of refinement in routing, scheduling, and dispatching; and the degree of refinement to which these can be carried depends largely upon the possession of such industrial data as are necessary to prepare such documents as the instruction card shown in Fig. 27. This chapter deals with the methods of finding such data and with the conditions that must exist at the **production center** or place where work is performed, whether this be a machine, a bench, or simply a floor space, in order that the predicted performance may be carried out as intended by the instruction card or similar documents. The object to be attained is that each operation shall be done in the best manner, that is, by the best possible procedure, and that it shall be done in the shortest reasonable time. If such procedure can be established, and if such reasonable times of performance can be fixed, the entire operation can be standardized, and *if all conditions of performance are kept at the same degree of efficiency* the operation can be repeated indefinitely with uniform results. The study of industrial operations for this purpose is called **operation analysis** and the principal methods used in this work are **time study** and **motion study.** Time study may be defined primarily as the art of observing and recording the time required to do each detailed element of an industrial operation, though, as will be seen, it has a somewhat broader significance. Motion study may be defined as the study of the movements, whether of a machine or an operator, in performing an operation for the purpose of eliminating useless motions and of arranging the sequence of useful motions in the most efficient order. It is in effect a refined form of routing and may be closely connected with the routing of work through the plant. Motion study and time study are not necessarily closely connected, but usually this is the case. Time study should be preceded by a careful examination of methods, both personal and mechanical, and time study is of course the logical method of measuring the effect of changed methods, since time is the measure of the efficiency of industrial operations. In general, motion study precedes time study, and logically the combined process should be called "motion and time study." However, usage and ease of expression have made the sequence "time and motion study" most common. It should be remembered that the object of time study and motion study is to establish standardized performances.

137. Operation Standardization.—It will be obvious that standard performances, however carefully prepared, cannot be realized unless all the conditions under which the operation is performed are also standardized and do not vary materially. A lathe cannot be expected to make the same performance with a slack belt as with one in prime condition, nor can the worker produce good results if he is surrounded by adverse conditions. Operation analysis, therefore, to be intelligent, must consider the operation, the workman, the production center, and its surrounding conditions. In general the following steps must be taken in making such a study:

1. Investigation and standardization of the production center and its surrounding conditions.
2. Investigation of the elements of the process to insure that no unnecessary movements are made and that the best sequence of the elements is followed.
3. Making time studies of the details of the operation.
4. Analyzing time studies and establishing standard performances through the instruction card.
5. Developing a routine procedure that will insure the accomplishment of the performance, and also insure the permanence of all necessary standard conditions.
6. Determining the financial incentive necessary to interest the workman in the project.

Of these topics all but the sixth will be discussed in this chapter. This item is so closely connected with wage systems that its discussion will be deferred to the chapter which deals with that subject.

THE PRELIMINARY INVESTIGATION

138. Reasons for Preliminary Investigation.—There are several reasons why a preliminary survey is essential before making time and motion studies. The first is the psychological aspect of this work. The success of any innovation in any industry depends to a large extent upon the degree to which it is possible to enlist the sympathy and confidence of the foremen and workmen concerned. In the early days of these new methods a great mischief was done to the movement by time-study men endeavoring to make observations secretly and without explaining to the workman under observation what he was trying to do. The reaction of workmen in general, and of labor unions in particular, to modern management methods is discussed at some length in a succeeding section. But it should be noted in connection with time study and motion study that it is useless if not dangerous to the harmony of the plant to undertake any time studies without a full understanding upon the part of all concerned as to the objects of such studies and the extent to which all will be benefited thereby. Confidence on the part of the workmen in the objects to be attained is most essential. The analyst who undertakes to make time studies must, therefore, be not only expert at this work but he must also be a diplomat of high order.

The second reason for a preliminary survey is to familiarize the analyst or investigator with the tools, methods, and operations that are in process, and their relations to each other. If a good routing system is in operation the relation of the several processes will be satisfactory, but in many cases rearrangement of the sequence of processes may be necessary for best results. The surroundings of each production center should also be studied so as to remove any conditions adverse to production. A record should also be made of production under the existing conditions for the purpose of comparison with production under new conditions.

The third reason for the preliminary survey is to gather data on each machine concerning its feeds, speeds, cutting capacity, etc. As indicated in Art. 129, the problem of predicting performances would be simplified if all machines of a given capacity had similar characteristics; that is, for example, if all 36-inch lathes had the same lead screw, ratio of back gears, feeds, etc. In some cases a certain amount of standardization of this kind can be accomplished, but in most instances the variation is so great as to require a large amount of work in collecting these data. Data must also be collected on the **handling time** of all machines, that is, the time required by the operator to set, change, and otherwise operate the machine; also on **material handling time** or the time required to transport material and place it in the several machines. If well-developed scheduling methods are in use, many of these data will have been collected.

It should be noted that the amount and character of these data that will be needed will depend upon the kind of time studies that are to be made. If time studies are to be made upon product that is in constant process of fabrication, as in mass production, for the simple purpose of standardizing methods and times of performance, a minimum of such data is necessary. But if the object of the time study is to develop a set of data that will make it possible to build up an instruction card *synthetically* for a product that *has not as yet been produced* very complete data on men, methods, and machines are necessary. Instruction cards built up by the first method may be called **observed instruction cards,** while those that are built up from data obtained from the time study of elementary operations on other products may be called **synthetic** or **compiled instruction cards.** In any case some of the data collected will necessarily be applicable only to the production center to which it pertains, while other data may be basic and applicable to a wide range of similar operations.

139. Motion Study.—With the survey of the conditions surrounding the production center disposed of, there remains a preliminary investigation of the operation itself to see that it is performed in the best possible manner, that the sequence of detailed operations is correct, and that they are efficiently performed. This may involve an examination of the methods and movements of the operator or **motion study,** as it is usually called. Since this form of study is usually involved more or less with time study it will be discussed at some length at this point.

It has been shown that it is highly economical to plan the sequence of operations in a broad way by the routing methods that have been described. The same arguments apply to the details of any operation such as are listed on the instruction card in Fig. 27. It has been customary until recently to assume that the skilled workman is the best judge of such a sequence. While this is probably true in simple cases, experience has shown that even here systematic analysis will often prove to be superior to empirical knowledge.[1] It has long been recognized that a workman can do most work when his equipment and surroundings are *convenient.* Builders of machine tools have long appreciated and applied these general principles in the design of tools, and manufacturers interested in such work as the assembly of small machines made up of many parts have for many years paid close attention to the proper division of work and the arrangement of parts to be assembled so as to require as little effort and motion as possible on the part of the workman. These efforts, however, have in general, been confined to the best examples of mass production and have not been recognized as fully as might be supposed.

The work of the late Frank B. Gilbreth[2] has very ably called attention to the fact that great gains may be made by systematic **motion study** in all lines of work and particularly in the simpler trades where one would not suppose such possibilities existed. Mr. Gilbreth's most striking study of this problem was in connection with the ancient trade of bricklaying. From time immemorial masons have worked from a scaffolding that was raised only when the workman could no longer easily reach the top of the wall which he was laying. It was then raised to such a height that he must bend his back constantly or work on his knees until the wall grew high enough to relieve him of such awkward positions. From time immemorial, also, the mason's helper has dumped unsorted brick and mortar of varying consistency upon the scaffolding at the mason's feet so that the mason had to stoop to get both brick and mortar. It has been customary, furthermore, for the mason to select the brick as he worked, rejecting those that were unfit, and to turn the selected brick over in

[1] The student can easily demonstrate this by trying to arrange the *best* sequence of movements in assembling some small but complex mechanism, as suggested in the footnote to Art. 120.

[2] GILBRETH, FRANK B., "Motion Study."

his hand when there was a choice as to which side should face upward.

One of Mr. Gilbreth's first improvements was a scaffolding that can be raised quickly, a short distance at a time, so as to be kept near the level for most easy working on the part of the mason. To this was added a shelf-like attachment on which the brick and mortar could be placed in a convenient position for the workman. The bricks were carefully sorted on the ground by cheap labor and placed in packets of 24 each, carefully arranged with the right side up so that no sorting was necessary on the part of the mason. The mortar was carefully standardized and improved forms of both mortar box and trowels made it easier for the mason to secure mortar while following with his eye the hand that held the brick. A careful study was made of the sequence in which the bricks should be laid for various types of wall and also of the motions made by the mason in laying up these several types. It was quickly discovered that many of the motions made by the workers were useless and resulted only in fatigue and wasted effort. On the basis of these observations standardized methods were worked out which enabled the workmen to lay three times as many bricks as formerly and with less fatigue. The results are all the more interesting since they were obtained in a strictly handicraft industry. The work of Mr. Gilbreth and others has proved beyond doubt that motion study opens up great opportunities for time saving and has accented the belief that even the skilled worker who has learned his trade in the usual empirical manner is often inefficient and wastes much of his energy in useless motions, though the final result of his labor may be all that is desired.

In many cases the motions of the workman are too rapid and complex[1] to be segregated from connecting motions and timed by the human eye with the aid of the stop-watch. Mr. Gilbreth very ingeniously used a moving-picture camera in connection with a clock of special design, which he called a microchronometer, to investigate such rapid motions. This clock which has a dial about 30 inches in diameter is placed near the workman who is to be studied. The clock has a hand which makes 20 revolutions each minute. The dial is divided into 100 parts so that each division of the dial represents $\frac{1}{2000}$ of a minute as the hand moves over it, hence the name **micromotion** as applied to this procedure. When the film is exposed a permanent record is obtained of the smallest movement accompanied by a record of the time required to perform each movement,

[1] The reader may gain some idea of the complexity of ordinary hand work by studying the motion of his fingers and thumb in buttoning his coat. Note that the procedure of performing this operation is entirely different when done with the left hand from that when it is performed with the right. The effect of motion upon the efficiency of operation is beautifully illustrated in rowing with a sliding seat. In such rowing the speed of the boat is as much dependent upon the *manner* of operation as upon the *power* applied.

however rapid. These pictures can then be studied at leisure and any unnecessary movements can be detected. Some very interesting results have been obtained in this manner. Mr. Gilbreth also made some interesting motion studies by attaching a small electric light to the hand of the operator and connecting it with a source of light by small flexible wiring. The light in the vicinity of the worker is then lowered and a photograph is taken of the operator's movements by an ordinary camera, the path of the light appearing as a continuous line upon the plate. From this diagram deductions can be drawn as to the efficiency of the worker's effort. It will be noted that these photographic methods yield both time and motion records of extreme refinement. The films can also be run through a projector so that the process can be examined at leisure upon the screen and the wasteful motions noted. In the majority of cases visual observation and timing with a stop-watch are sufficiently accurate to enable a skilled observer to separate the work into its elements, eliminate the useless motions, and rearrange the sequence of elementary operations into the most efficient cycle. An elementary example illustrating such procedure is given in Art. 141.

140. Principles of Efficient Motion.—If, however, very refined time and motion study is attempted, the theories of efficient motion as developed by Dr. Lillian Gilbreth and the late Frank Gilbreth must be studied and mastered. Only the briefest mention can be given them here. The Gilbreths state that there are 17 fundamental motions and that every operation consists of a combination of some of these elements which they have named "therbligs" (Gilbreth spelt backward). These elementary motions are:

1. Search.
2. Find.
3. Select.
4. Grasp.
5. Position.
6. Assemble.
7. Use.
8. Disassemble.
9. Inspect.
10. Transport loaded.
11. Preposition.
12. Release load.
13. Transport empty.
16. Wait (unavoidable delay).
15. Wait (avoidable delay).
16. Rest (for overcoming fatigue).
17. Plan.

The Gilbreths have also devised mnemonic symbols for these elements for use in charting motion studies. And they have also developed 16 rules for the most efficient execution of hand motions. For a more extended discussion see "Cost and Production Handbook," page 515.

It is obvious that all motions should be easy and natural. As noted elsewhere, machine designers long ago appreciated the importance of this requirement. In the case of operators seated at a bench there is a maximum and minimum efficient range of both right and left hand, not only in the horizontal plane of the bench but also in the vertical direction. That is to say, both hands can easily sweep out a maximum and minimum curved surface within which all parts to be reached for should be placed for best results.

141. Process Charts.—Motion study is greatly facilitated by the use of charts which show the relation of the several elements to each other. Such charts are of three kinds or rather of three degrees of refinement. First is the **flow sheet,** which is discussed in Chap. VIII and which is a diagram of the flow of work through the entire plant. It gives an accurate *geographical* picture of the entire process (see Figs. 6 to 9), and is indispensable in planning industrial plants. Next in order of refinement is the **process chart,** which shows diagrammatically the sequence and relation of the elements of a process. It may or may not show the geographical relations of the several elements, but always shows the sequence. Such charts are very useful in showing the relation and sequence of elements in machine operation where both the movements of the operator and the work of the machine can be charted and analyzed. In such diagrams symbols are sometimes used to denote elements of the process. The Gilbreths have developed a set of 41 such symbols in which a small circle denotes an operation, a small square denotes an inspection, a triangle denotes storage, and so on. The writer is somewhat skeptical of such refinement, especially as it is almost always necessary to write the name of the element near the symbol. For more elaborate illustration see "Management's Handbook," page 802.[1]

A still more refined application of this principle is the **operation chart,** which is particularly useful in diagraming small assembly work involving both hands. Thus the data shown in Fig. 37 can be shown diagrammatically by arranging the elements performed by both hands along two parallel vertical lines, the elements being represented by symbols (circles, squares, etc.), and the time elements represented by the distances between symbols. Such a diagram helps to visualize the entire operation and assists in eliminating useless motions. It will be obvious that the time elements may be recorded on any of these diagrams.

Example.—A simple example may make the application of motion study somewhat clearer. Figures 37 and 38 show two studies made in the Department of Industrial Engineering at Cornell University by Professor Dexter S. Kimball, Jr., on the assembly of an electrical plug such as is used to connect up an electric iron for laundry purposes. Figure 36*A* shows the assembled plug. Figure 36*B* shows the detail parts assembled in one-half of the outer shell with the other half, 36*C*, removed. Figures 36*D* show the spring clips which engage with the terminals on the iron before they are placed in Fig. 36*B*. Figures 36*E* show the small screws and nuts that hold the two half-covers together. The spring-like part shown in Figs. 36*A* and *B* is a wire guard for inclosing the extension cord as it passes into the plug to engage with the spring clips. No cord is included in the assembly. The only tool used in the assembly was a small screw driver.

An experienced worker was directed to assemble a terminal, using his natural motions and his own sequence of operations. His performance was recorded with

[1] See also "Cost and Production Handbook," p. 532.

a micromotion camera and his elementary motions and the corresponding unit times are recorded in Fig. 37. An examination of this figure shows that in the elements performed by the left hand a total of 0.184 minute was employed in holding the pieces, 0.037 minute in waiting and 0.012 in returning the empty hand. In the case of the right hand, 0.114 minute was expended in holding and 0.034 minute in waiting. This makes a grand total of 0.381 minute out of a total of 0.990 minute of idle time.

Again, a comparison of the movements of the two hands shows much lack of symmetry. The left hand grasps two clips while the right hand grasps a spring guard, the left hand grasps a nut while the right hand grasps a screw, and so on. In this experiment also the parts to be assembled were placed in trays before the

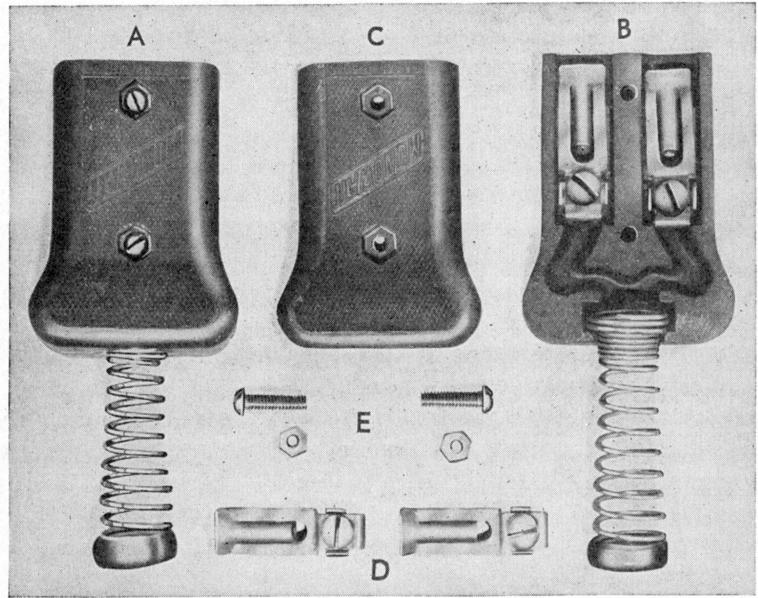

Fig. 36.

worker with little thought as to convenience or sequence of assembly. A visual examination showed much wasted travel of the hands and some unnecessary effort in reaching for the parts.

To correct these defects a small assembly table was constructed with a groove or depression extending across it from left to right of such dimensions that the shells can be pushed from either side toward the center, guided by the sides of the groove. A stop in the middle of the table locates the assembled plug as it is pushed inward. The half-shells are exactly alike and are recessed on the outside with two small depressions that accommodate either the nut or the head of the small binding screws. Two sets of parts were arranged symmetrically, one on each side of the operator in trays so placed as to be convenient and in best sequence. The operator then proceeds as follows and as indicated in Fig. 38. A half-shell is grasped with each hand and placed in the groove against the locating stop. Each hand then reaches for a clip and places it in the half-shell and in a similar way each hand builds up the complete assembly in symmetry with the other. In order to facilitate the work still further, the nuts which engage the binding screws are fed down four supply chutes from behind the groove so that they automatically center under the recesses in the shell. Pressure

Clock reading	Elapsed time	Left-hand movements	Clock reading	Elapsed time	Right-hand movements
620	. . .	Discard assembled plug	620	. . .	Drop screw driver
632	012	Return hand	632	012	Grasp 2 shells
669	037	Wait	669	037	Place 2 shells
685	016	Arrange shells	685	016	Arrange shells
716	031	Grasp 2 clips	716	031	Grasp spring guard
764	048	Place 2 clips	730	014	Place spring guard
		Place 2 clips	764	034	Wait
786	022	Grasp one nut	786	022	Grasp screw
809	023	Place one nut	809	023	Hold
834	025	Assemble shells	834	025	Hold
846	012	Raise assembled plug	846	012	Hold
878	032	Hold	878	032	Place screw
938	060	Hold	938	060	Set-up screw
951	013	Drop assembly	951	013	Grasp screw
973	022	Grasp nut	973	022	Hold
996	023	Place nut	996	023	Hold
008	012	Raise assembly	008	012	Hold
040	032	Hold	040	032	Place screw
100	060	Hold	100	060	Set-up screw
115	015	Discard assembled plug	115	015	Drop screw driver
		Total time for one plug		495	

Fig. 37.—Motion study of electric-plug assembly. All readings in thousandths of a minute.

from a foot lever operates small plungers that force the nuts up into the recesses. The screw driver, which is of the spiral-drive type, is suspended in balance directly over the center of the table and the operator drops the small screws into the assembled plug, presses the foot lever, and sets up the screws with the screw driver. The last operation is to discard the assembled plugs, one on each side. In actually operating

Clock reading	Elapsed time	Left-hand movements	Clock reading	Elapsed time	Right-hand movements
400	...	Discard assembled plug	400	...	Discard assembled plug
420	020	Grasp half shell	420	020	Grasp half shell
432	012	Place half shell	432	012	Place half shell
457	025	Grasp 2 clips	457	025	Grasp 2 clips
505	048	Place clips	505	048	Place clips
525	020	Grasp spring guard	525	020	Grasp spring guard
537	012	Place spring guard	537	012	Place spring guard
557	020	Grasp top half shell	557	020	Grasp top half shell
567	010	Place top half shell	567	010	Place top half shell
608	041	Grasp 2 screws	608	041	Grasp 2 screws
661	053	Place screws	661	053	Place screws
684	023	Grasp screw driver	684	023	Grasp screw driver
739	055	Set up 4 screws	739	055	Set up 4 screws
752	013	Grasp assembled plug	752	013	Grasp assembled plug
770	018	Discard assembled plug	770	018	Discard assembled plug
		Total time for two plugs		370	
		Total time for one plug		185	

Fig. 38.—Motion study of electric-plug assembly. All readings in thousandths of a minute.

this cycle three assemblies are worked upon by each hand, the outside shells being used to push the others inward against the stop, thus minimizing the distance which the hand must move from the trays to the table. The time elements for this new cycle are shown in Fig. 38, and it will be noted that the time for the complete assembly is about 38 per cent of the original experiment. The clock readings are in decimals of a minute.

MAKING TIME STUDIES

142. Time Study.—What has been said of the average workman's lack of knowledge of industrial processes is even more true of his lack of exactness in estimating the time required to do a given piece of work. This, after all, is to be expected, and a few attempts on the part of the reader to estimate the time required by him to do customary performances will quickly show how elusive the time element is and how difficult it is to estimate time accurately by any empirical methods. A good cost system, therefore, may give fairly accurate data regarding costs, but its records are not necessarily the best that can be made with a given equipment. In times past piece rates, and estimates in general, have usually been made by judgment either on the part of the foreman or of the rate setter, if one was employed. Occasionally trial performances were made to find a satisfactory basis. The inaccuracy of the first-named method of setting rates and the troubles arising therefrom will be more fully discussed in connection with a discussion of systems of rewarding labor. Such methods could, of course, still be used as a basis of creating the instruction card, but Mr. Taylor has pointed out[1] a much more accurate method of finding what length of time should be required for any job with given equipment and conditions. In this method careful measurement is made of the time required to do the several detail parts of a given operation. This detailed subdivision is often made quite minute so that the observation must be made with a stop-watch or micromotion camera. This work has become known as time study.

There was, of course, nothing new in the idea itself. Time studies had been made many years before and it had long been customary for superintendents to obtain such data for the purpose of fixing piece rates. These older attempts, however, were confined largely to finding the *total* time required to do a given piece of work and the data obtained were useful only for the particular job in question or for one very similar to it. Mr. Taylor endeavored to make observations of the most minute details of the operations studied, even to such small details as the time required to stop and to start a machine. His contention, which seems warranted, was that many detail operations are common to many jobs and that if these could be observed with accuracy these observations or **unit times** could be used to build up *synthetically* accurate time estimates on new work on which time studies had not been made. Taken in connection with full information concerning cutting tools and machines, the plan seems perfectly feasible and many interesting data have already been obtained along these lines. In fact, the synthetic prediction of the time required for industrial operations is now common practice.

[1] *Trans. Am. Soc. Mech. Eng.*, Vol. 24, p. 1423.

143. Methods and Apparatus for Time Study.—Time study in the modern sense, therefore, consists in finding the time required to perform each elementary detail of an operation, whether these details be mental or manual. The basic idea, of course, is to determine the proper time for performing the operations and it may involve many observations of the same detail operation as performed by skilled workmen. Special methods must be employed for such work, as the time element may be very small, and the observations are valueless unless taken with accuracy. It should be noted that accurate observations of this kind are similar to those required in scientific laboratories, and both natural aptitude and experience are required on the part of the observer for accurate results.

The first step in making time studies is to divide the operation into its elements as shown in Fig. 27. It is here assumed that the detail elements of the operation have been arranged in their most logical and efficient sequence. Then the time required to perform each element is observed and recorded, sufficient observations being made to insure the recording of fair or average values and to permit the detection of occasional errors in observation. There are two methods in use for making and recording these observations. The first is that due to Gilbreth and known as the **micromotion method,** which was described in Art. 139 in connection with motion study. This method is obviously very exact since it records everything connected with the operation, except sound, and reduces the element of human judgment to a minimum. The record made is a permanent one that can be used for study and comparison better perhaps than any other form of record. But the equipment is elaborate and costly, particularly where a motion-study laboratory is set up, as is sometimes necessary. It is also more distracting to the workers than other methods. Where, nevertheless, the quantity of work will warrant it, as in large mass-production plants, this method can be made of great value.

The other and simpler way of making time studies is the **stop-watch method,** so called because the unit times are measured on some form of stop-watch.

A convenient apparatus for making time observations is formed by mounting a stop-watch on the upper right-hand corner of a board large enough to hold the record sheet and in such a manner that the watch can be operated by the thumb of the left hand of the observer, as shown in Fig. 39. This also places the watch near the line of vision, thus obviating excessive movement of the eye. The observer holds the board with his left hand and his left arm, leaving his right arm and hand free to record the observations. A blank form ruled in a convenient manner is an essential to success, and this blank form should make provision for recording full data concerning the operation, the operator, and other information necessary for a full understanding of the procedure.

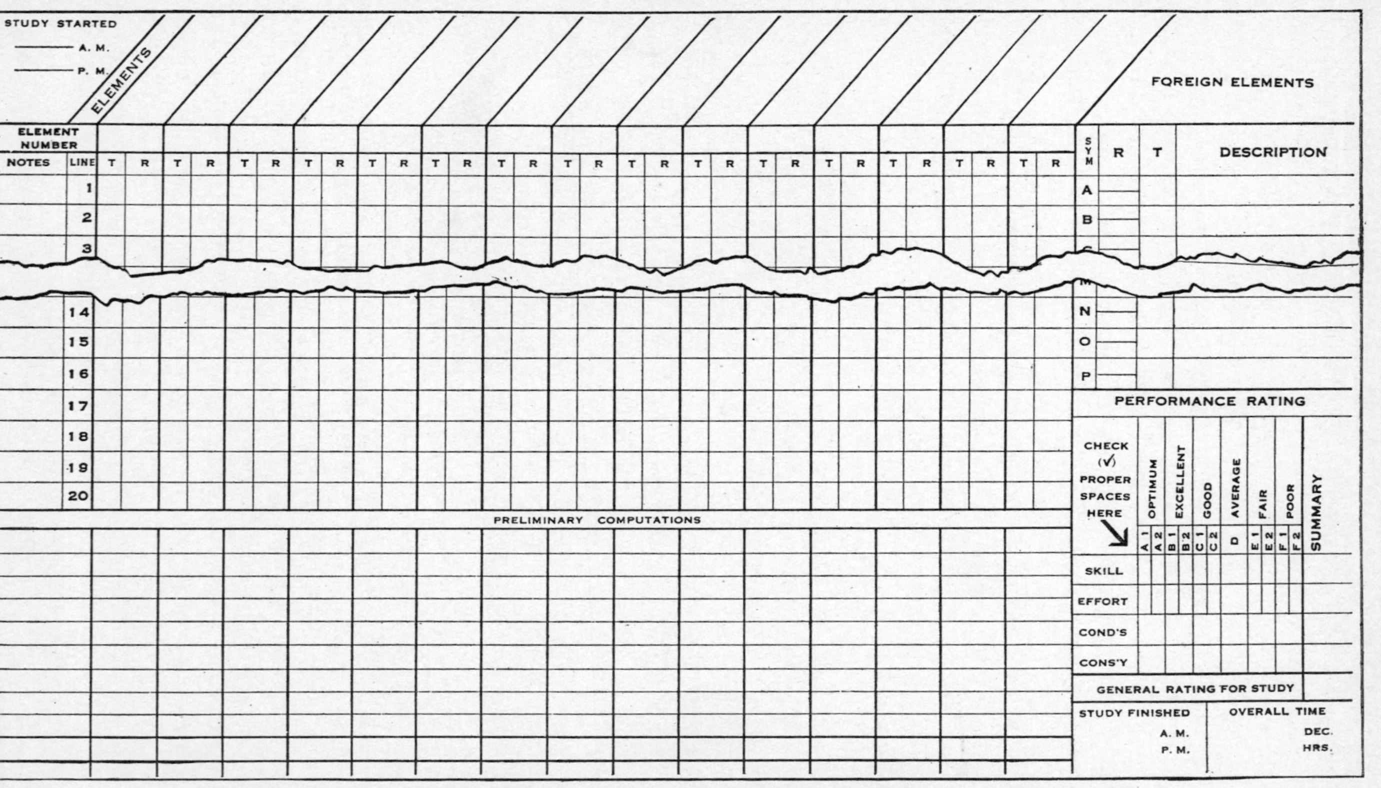

FIG. 38*a*.—Time study sheet as used by Professor H. H. Rothrock at University of Pittsburgh.

Care should be taken, also, that the conditions under which the study is made are conducive to good results. It should be remembered that the object of making time studies is to be able to predict performances later on. It is not easy to duplicate a given performance unless the conditions are as favorable as when the recorded performance was made. It will be clear that if the best method of doing an operation or a series of operations can be determined and the proper time for doing each operation can also be determined, standards of performance can be set up; provided, of course, that the conditions under which the work is performed are also standardized. Figure 38*a* illustrates a form for recording time-study observations.

It is natural to wish to make time studies of first-class men, as from them the lowest records will be obtained. It should be remembered, however, that it is not fair to use the records of first-class operators to set rates, if such rates will exclude all but the very best workmen from earning a premium, and still more unfair to use rates thus determined for eliminating all but the very best workers from participation in industry. It will be obvious, furthermore, that accurate time-study records cannot be made without the full confidence of the workman who is observed. In fact, none of these advanced methods can be successfully operated without a complete understanding with the working force. Stealthy and underhand methods are sure to end in trouble.

Fig. 39.—Time-study board used for instruction purposes in the College of Engineering, Cornell University, for continuous readings. For "snap-back" work the watch is placed under the thumb of the observer to the left of the gripping space.

144. Stop-watch Observations.—The ordinary stop-watches are not suitable for time-study work and a number of watches with specially graduated dials have been produced for this purpose. A common form of dial is one divided into hundredths, around which a single indicating hand moves once in a minute, thus indicating hundredths of a minute. The hand can be stopped at any point by pressing upon the top of the stem. A second pressure on the stem returns the hand to zero. Another stop-watch has a dial similarly graduated but the indicating hand can be "snapped" back to the zero position by a single pressure on the stem, and it instantly begins to record time again. The first type is much used in making **continuous observations,** which will be considered first. Some time-study men prefer a dial divided into 100 spaces, each representing

Observer's Name..........Morss	Machine No..............59v	Date...........2-21-1914
Workman's Name......Turner	Piece No......... ..19398-25	Differential Gear Section

Detailed operations	1	2	3	4	5	6	7	8	Average	Minimum time
1. Carry gears from pile to bench	....	....	....	....	....	0.09	8.41			
2. Pick up differential, land in vise and tighten	....	....	....	....	....	0.16	0.17			
	0.15	0.16	0.17	0.12	0.16	0.25	8.58	0.16	0.156	0.13
3. File corners off cap screws	0.43	0.57	0.78	0.58	0.62	0.62	0.65	0.71	0.620	0.50
	0.58	0.73	0.95	0.70	0.78	0.87	9.23	0.87		
4. Loosen vise, turn differential, tighten vise	0.07	0.11	0.04	0.27	0.07	0.10	0.11	0.11	0.0875	0.07
	0.65	0.84	0.99	0.97	0.85	0.97	9.34	0.98		
5. File cap screws	0.53	0.65	0.74	0.18	0.55	0.57	0.43	0.35	0.523	0.41
	1.18	1.49	1.73	1.15	1.40	1.54	9.77	1.33		
6. Loosen vise, turn differential, tighten vise	0.07	0.08	0.07	0.08	0.09	0.11	0.07	0.08	0.0813	0.07
	1.25	1.57	1.80	1.23	1.49	1.65	9.84	1.41		
7. File cap screws	0.28	0.28	0.41	0.35	0.51	0.60	0.21	0.44	0.385	0.30
	1.53	1.85	2.21	1.58	2.00	2.25	10.05	1.85		
8. Open vise	0.06	0.08	0.08	0.10	0.09	0.12	0.07	0.08	0.085	0.07
	1.59	1.93	2.29	1.68	2.09	2.37	10.12	1.93		
9. Turn differential, 90 degrees, tighten vise	0.11	0.09	0.07	0.08	0.14	0.11	0.05	0.11	0.095	0.08
	1.70	2.02	2.36	1.76	2.23	2.48	10.17	2.04		
10. Wipe grease off differential, burr edge of flange	2.88	2.43	1.76	1.44	1.29	1.56	1.76	1.53	2.60	1.29
	4.58	4.45	4.12	3.20	3.52	4.04	11.93	3.57		
11. Pick up gear, wipe off grease	0.70	0.48	0.49	2.08	1.48	1.74	1.39	2.02	0.524	0.48
	5.28	4.93	4.61	5.28	5.00	5.78	13.32	5 59		
12. Land gear on differential	0.07	0.12	0.13	0.14	0.23	0.10	0.10	0.08	0.105	0.08
	5.35	5.05	4.74	5.42	5.23	5.88	13.42	5.67		
13. Align holes in gear and differential	0.46	0.71	1.31	0.45	0.43	0.20	0.55	0.37	0.558	0.45
	5.81	5.76	6.05	5.87	5.66	6.08	13.97	6.04		
14. Assemble first 5/16-inch cap screw	0.38	0.13	0.25	0.23	0.22	0.17	0.22	0.77	0.264	0.22
	6.19	5.89	6.30	6.10	5.88	6.25	14.19	6.81		
15. Assemble second 5/16-inch cap screw	0.33	0.23	0.23	0.20	0.22	0.31	0.33	0.54	0.296	0.22
	6.52	6.12	6.53	6.30	6.10	6.56	14.52	7.35		
16. Tighten nuts with wrench	1.09	0.63	1.05	0.88	0.98	1.02	0.69	0.82	0.895	0.72
	7.61	6.75	7.58	7.18	7.08	7.58	15.21	8.17		
17. Loosen vise, turn piece end for end	0.16	0.11	0.02	0.08	0.10	0.08	0.12	0.10	0.0963	0.08
	7.77	6.86	7.60	7.26	7.18	7.66	15.33	8.27		
18. Tighten vise	0.07	0.03	0.04	0.03	0.03	0.03	0.03	0.03	0.0363	0.03
	7.84	6.89	7.64	7.29	7.21	7.69	15.36	8.30		
19. Align rivet holes with drift	1.46	1.11	1.42	0.45	0.60	0.20	1.73	0.26	1.03	0.83
	9.30	8.00	9.06	7.74	7.81	7.89	17.09	8.56		
20. Loosen vise	0.03	0.03	0.04	0.03	0.03	0.02	0.03	0.03	0.03	0.03
	9.33	8.03	9.10	7.77	7.84	7.91	17.12	8.59		
21. Land assembly in box	0.10	0.12	0.20	0.12	0.12	0.11	0.12	0.11	0.125	0.10
	9.43	8.15	9.30	7.89	7.96	8.02	17.24	8.70		
22. Return to bench	0.13	0.17	0.10	0.11	0.11	0.18	0.09	0.12	0.126	0.10
	9.56	8.32	9.40	8.00	8.07	8.20	17.33	8.82	8.69	

FIG. 40.—Continuous time-study observations.

0.0001 hour, one revolution of the hand thus representing 0.01 hour. The advantage of such a dial is that the readings are in fractions of an hour, which is the most common unit of time used in setting wages, with which time study is intimately connected.

Where the time elements are short and hence succeed each other rapidly, some observers prefer to let the watch run continuously, noting the *total elapsed* time at the end of each time element. The stop-watch readings when recorded will then give the elapsed time for the entire series and the differences between successive readings will give the time consumed for the several detail operations.

Figure 40 illustrates such a series of actual observations as reported by Major George D. Babcock. The lower numbers opposite the names of the operations are the **continuous observations** and give the elapsed time from the beginning of the series. The difference between any continuous observation and the continuous observation immediately preceding it is the actual time for the operation concerned and is recorded between the two continuous observations. These differences are sometimes called the **individual times.** The average of the individual times and also the minimum individual time for each operation are shown at the right. The average total time is also recorded.

Some observers, however, prefer to use the direct or "snap-back" method, using the second type of watch described in the foregoing and returning the recording hand to zero at the end of each time element, thus obtaining direct observations and obviating all subtraction, as in Fig. 40. Accurate work was not possible with this method, using the first watches of this type that were developed, because they were sluggish and did not pick up quickly from the zero position. With the best type of such watches and with time elements not too small, skilled observers can obtain excellent results with this **repetitive method,** as it is sometimes called. These snap-back watches can also be stopped at any point and started again without returning the hand to the zero position, so that the time due to accidental delays may be taken out rapidly. These are the methods most in use, though others have been advocated. If the time elements are extremely short it may be necessary to measure the combined unit times of several successive operations thus securing enough of these combinations to compute mathematically the several individual unit times.[1]

Considerable effort has also been made to develop a mechanical recording machine which would permit the observer to keep his eyes constantly upon the work, recording the times by simply pushing a button. So far no fully successful machine of this kind has been produced

[1] For a more extended discussion of this method the reader is referred to Mr. Taylor's paper, "Shop Management," in *Trans. Am. Soc. Mech. Eng.*, Vol. 24.

but it appears to be a need that should and probably will, be filled. If the operations that are being observed require a considerable time to perform, a few observations may be sufficient and the errors in observation will, normally, be a small percentage of the observed time. If, however, the time element is very small many observations may be necessary to secure accurate results.

ANALYZING TIME STUDIES

145. Interpretation of Data.—An examination of any observed time-study sheet such as Fig. 40 will show that in any set of observations made from any operation there will be marked differences in the recorded values. Obviously some of them will be abnormally high and a few may be abnormally low. The abnormally high readings are usually due to some unforeseen delay or to inattention on the part of the operator, while those that are abnormally low are due, usually, to an error in reading on the part of the observer. In this respect these data are very much like experimental data. All abnormal values should first be discarded and stricken from the sheet, as is done with experimental data, and, as is the case with experimental data, this calls for judgment on the part of the investigator. No definite percentages can be set as a guide in eliminating abnormal values. The data shown in Fig. 40 were recorded by skilled observers, and represent a preliminary study to be used as a basis of obtaining better results through standardized conditions. The variations in the unit times of the several operations are not markedly greater, however, than is usually found in time-study work. It will be clear that it is a most difficult matter to measure human motions of short duration with great accuracy, and equally clear that a worker will not always do a given operation in exactly the same time, and different workmen, again, will require markedly different periods of time for the same operation. The question naturally arises as to how these observations shall be interpreted if they are to serve as a basis for fixing rates of pay for similar operations. Several methods may be used. Some time-study men use the minimum observed time and make an allowance which varies from 25 to 75 per cent of the observed time to provide for unavoidable delays and the personal requirements of the worker. Another method is to take the average time, as computed in Fig. 40, as a basis.

Another method is to take the **modal time** or the observation which occurs most frequently as a basis. This procedure will be logical only where there is a large number of observations. Skilled observers of tabulated data of any kind can frequently "scan" such data and thus select the desired mean almost as accurately as it can be computed from the data. Thus in the sixth line from the bottom of Fig. 40 the observation 0.03 occurs six times out of the eight observations. It happens also to be the average time for the series.

There are other and more refined methods of selecting these **base times** but such refinements are of doubtful value in view of the source and character of the basic data. In the opinion of the writer the efforts of some advocates of these new methods to invest them with an appearance of great exactness has done more harm than good to the progress of logical methods. This feature of time study should be carefully noted because it indicates that, as yet, a certain element of good judgment must be used in interpreting time studies if the results are to be used in setting piece rates and predicting performances. This in no way detracts from the value of time study, but the exaggerated idea held by many respecting the exactness of these methods is hardly justifiable. Where the work is so connected with machine operations that the machine governs the time element to a large degree, it may be possible to make exact observations that can be repeated quite accurately. Where the human element predominates such exactness is hardly to be expected. For this reason some time-study men make a sharp distinction between the time of machine operations and those in which hand work predominates. It is evident that the degree of perfection to which the study of unit times may be profitably carried depends largely upon the kind of work and the amount of repetition that is involved, but in any case it is also evident that this method of approaching the problem is an advance over empirical methods and any rate setter will profit even by its limited use.

146. Time-study Allowances; Leveling.—The foregoing remarks are amply borne out by the fact that after the most careful study has been made of time-study observations certain **allowances** must be made to provide for uncertainties. The reasons for these allowances should be noted. As stated in Art. 143 it is natural to make such studies on first-class men as only from the observations made on such men can good records be obtained. But to set rates based upon such records, unmodified, will, as has been noted, exclude all but the very best men from earning a bonus if it does not eliminate all but the best men from the plant—a proceeding that would be manifestly unfair. Time observations, therefore, that represent a very high performance must be modified to be within the capacity of any good worker. If the rates are fairly set the average worker should be able to make good wages and the exceptional worker should be able to make high wages. A **variation allowance** must, therefore, be added to the selected base time.

Again, it should be remembered that records covering a comparatively short period of time, with the operator who is being observed working at high speed, do not apply to longer periods of time in which the element of fatigue appears. The phenomenon of fatigue is discussed more fully in a later section and at this time only its relation to time study will be noted. It will be evident that a fair task is one that the average man can perform for a long period of years without injury to his health and happiness. An allowance must, therefore, be made for this factor.

With the most careful preparation and supervision some delays are sure to occur. These delays may be due to minor difficulties with the machine, or **machine delays,** or they may be due to minor interruptions to the worker that throw him momentarily "out of swing" with his work or **personal delays.** These must also be considered in fixing the time rate. Provision must also be made for **personal needs**—washing, etc. This allowance should be the same for all men working under the same conditions, but obviously it will vary considerably with conditions. Men working out of doors in a hot sun will obviously need more time for personal needs, wiping perspiration, getting drinks, etc., than they will if working in a cool well-appointed factory. In factory work this allowance need not exceed 3 per cent of the total time.

The simplest, and a very common, method of making these allowances is to add a flat percentage to the total cycle time, as illustrated in Fig. 27, where 5 per cent is thus added. Such a flat rate can be used logically on a range of operations only where the character of the work and the conditions of operation are similar and where experience has shown such a factor to be reasonably applicable. Where character of work and conditions vary, as they do in most instances, it is more logical to consider each operation separately, assigning a percentage to each that can be varied with conditions. Clearly the elements of delay in the case of a bench worker differ from those of a machine hand, and the percentages that are used should be selected with the conditions in mind.

Consider first the relation of the base time as determined by the methods of Art. 144, and the actual time in which an operator of average skill and energy working at an average rate under the existing conditions can accomplish the task. A number of methods have been suggested for determining a modifying factor for this purpose. Of these only two will be discussed.

In the first and simplest method the time-study man while making his observations estimates the skill, effort, and general attitude of the operator. From this he estimates a percentage factor which he applies to the base time in order to determine the standard time at which a good average man can do the work. If the observed worker is such a man this percentage would be unity. There are variations in the manner in which this percentage factor is computed, but all are based upon observation and judgment. Obviously the value of a factor so determined will depend entirely upon the experience and accuracy of judgment of the observer and is likely to be subject to variations as between different observers. In the hands of an experienced observer it will produce satisfactory results.

The most systematic method for determining such a factor is that proposed by Messrs. Lowry, Maynard, and Stegemerten,[1] who designate this factor as a **leveling factor.** According to these experienced time-study men the value of this factor varies with skill, effort, conditions under which the work is done, and the consistency with which the operator works.

TABLE 6.—PERFORMANCE RATING TABLE

Skill			Effort		
+0.15 +0.13	*A*1 *A*2	Superskill	+0.13 +0.12	*A*1 *A*2	Killing
+0.11 +0.08	*B*1 *B*2	Excellent	+0.10 +0.08	*B*1 *B*2	Excellent
+0.06 +0.03	*C*1 *C*2	Good	+0.05 +0.02	*C*1 *C*2	Good
0.00	*D*	Average	0.00	*D*	Average
−0.05 −0.10	*E*1 *E*2	Fair	−0.04 −0.08	*E*1 *E*2	Fair
−0.16 −0.22	*F*1 *F*2	Poor	−0.12 −0.17	*F*1 *F*2	Poor
Conditions			**Consistency**		
+0.06	*A*	Ideal	+0.04	*A*	Perfect
+0.04	*B*	Excellent	+0.03	*B*	Excellent
+0.02	*C*	Good	+0.01	*C*	Good
0.00	*D*	Average	0.00	*D*	Average
−0.03	*E*	Fair	−0.02	*E*	Fair
−0.07	*F*	Poor	−0.04	*F*	Poor

On the basis of logical reasoning (which cannot be stated here for lack of space), verified by many practical applications, they have compiled the performance rating table (Table 6), which is printed, in their practice, on the right-hand lower corner of the observation sheet, the decimal equivalents being omitted. As the observer makes his record he checks on this table his estimate of all four factors which the worker appears to possess. Thus, suppose he checks skill as B1, effort as C2, conditions as B, and consistency as E. Then the leveling factor is the sum of the corresponding decimals (or 0.11 + 0.02 + 0.04

[1] See LOWRY, MAYNARD, and STEGEMERTEN, "Time and Motion Study," p. 144.

− 0.02 = 0.15) plus unity or 1.15. If all conditions are average the leveling factor will of course be unity, or the base time is also the standard time. The base time as determined in Art. 144 is multiplied by this factor, thus computing the standard time in which an average worker should be able to perform the task.

147. Personal Allowances—Fatigue.—An allowance must also be made for personal needs and this is usually provided for by adding a fixed percentage to the standard time. Experience indicates that this factor varies from 2 to 5 per cent of the standard time, depending upon the person and conditions. Four per cent is usually an ample allowance.

The problem of fatigue is quite different. Under the old and still much-used methods, the common idea was to keep a man as busy as possible during the entire working period for which he had engaged. It now appears that he will do more and better work if given periodic rests.

All are familiar with the phenomenon of fatigue. In beginning work there is a period during which effort is not only easy but agreeable, and the rate of production increases. Then follows a period during which conditions are uniform, succeeded in turn by a decline in interest and pleasure in production, straining begins to be felt, and finally, if the effort is continued, pain appears. During this last period the worker must put forth his will power to continue at the task, "working on his nerve," as is said; and at last, if the effort is continued, it becomes unbearable and complete exhaustion takes place.

Physical or mental effort of any kind results in the breaking down of tissues, which creates certain toxic poisons in the blood, giving rise thereby to the phenomena described. If the effort is slow the system reacts fast enough to dispose of these waste products as fast as they are formed, but it cannot perform this cleansing action against great and continued effort. Recovery from moderate fatigue is rapid, but the recovery from great effort is slow and as the worker gets older it is less and less complete. It is a well-known fact that violent exertion on the part of old people is dangerous. Fatigue within the "elastic limit," however, is wholesome for anyone and good health cannot be maintained without some bodily effort.

It should be remembered also that change of work is relative rest and under the old methods, where the worker performed several different tasks daily, recovery from one task took place to a certain extent while performing another. Under such conditions the rest obtained during the hours when he was not employed was sufficient for his recovery. Thus farm laborers work long hours daily during a large part of the year, yet the short periods of daily rest, supplemented by the Sabbath rest, seem amply sufficient for physical recovery.

Under modern industrial conditions, however, where men are compelled to work at one machine or, worse still, where the work is of a repetitive character involving little or no change of mental or bodily exertion, common experience indicates that the rest periods should be more frequent and more definite than under the old conditions of general work. The effect of monotonous labor has long been a matter of study and psychologists have demonstrated fully the harmful effects of such labor, if carried to an extreme. Efforts have been made, also, to relieve the monotony of repetitive labor by introducing other distracting influences. Thus, in cigar making, paid readers have been employed with success to relieve the monotony of this repetitive occupation. There can be little doubt but that the practice of "soldiering," or pretending to work while really accomplishing nothing, has been fostered to a large extent by lack of proper and definite rest periods. Aside, therefore, from all humane considerations of the matter, this subject is one of considerable economic importance.

There are few or no data as yet that can be used as a guide in fixing rest periods. Experimental psychologists have done considerable experimental work, but so far their results have been expressed in very general statements. It is well known also, that fatigue is a function of the speed of performance, for a man exhausts himself much more by doing a given task quickly than by doing it slowly. This follows naturally, of course, from the general theory of fatigue that has been discussed. These relations are not simple ones, however, and an immense amount of experimental work in actual productive processes must be performed before there will be sufficient data to enable the prediction of the correct proportion of work and rest in a new performance.

Advocates of scientific management, so-called, have made some interesting and convincing experiments on a fairly large scale and have demonstrated that production is greatly increased by the introduction of definite rest periods. F. W. Taylor has observed that a first-class laborer handling pig iron, each pig weighing 92 pounds, could be under load only 43 per cent of the day and must be entirely free from load 57 per cent of the day. He stated, furthermore, that as the load is made lighter the percentage of the day under which the man can carry the load can be increased. Thus, if the workman is carrying a load of 46 pounds he can be under the load 58 per cent of the day, and if the load is made light enough he can carry it practically all day long. Other experimenters have found similar results and the general principles of the economy of fixed rest periods seem to be well established. It will take some time, however, to obtain sufficient data to formulate practical rules for the guidance of industrial workers in general.

Nor is fatigue a function of bodily exertion alone. Jobs that require little or no bodily effort but very close attention and concentration may be even more fatiguing than others that involve considerable muscular effort. Mental work is often as fatiguing as bodily effort.

The matter is, therefore, one that should engage the attention of every manager, and there are many industries where it would be economical, no doubt, to establish more frequent rest periods than those now in vogue, even though such periods are fixed empirically.[1] The general theory of fatigue, furthermore, indicates that a careful study of the worker's surroundings and implements may often greatly increase his output by decreasing the fatigue caused by distracting influences or wasted efforts. Thus noisy surroundings, accident hazzards, inadequate illumination or ventilation, and dissatisfaction with working conditions may be almost as conducive to fatigue as the actual work itself. In addition outside influences such as home conditions, lack of balanced diet, inability to sleep, and other circumstances largely beyond the control of the employer may greatly reduce the markers' resistance to fatigue.

Obviously the allowance that must be made for fatigue will vary widely with the worker and the character of the work. It is possible, however, to make fatigue studies for any given conditions. Messrs. Lowry, Maynard, and Stegemerten cite the following example of an actual study of this kind which is instructive. The base time of a certain worker making die castings was observed to be 0.00875 hour. During a working day of 8¾ hours he produced 682 castings. His time was observed to be divided as follows:

		Per Cent
Actual production time	Making castings	70.4
Setting-up time	Oiling die	4.4
Setting-up time	Filling machine with metal	6.4
Unavoidable delay	Repairing machine	11.3
Personal needs	Drinking, etc	3.5
Setting-up time	Preparing to start, cleaning up	4.0
		100.00

Then the actual production time $= 8.75 \times 0.704 = 6.16$ hours. If the operator had worked at the base rate of one casting in 0.00875 hour, he should have produced $\frac{6.16}{0.00875} = 704$ castings. But his actual production was only 682. Hence the percentage of loss due to fatigue was $\frac{704 - 682}{682} = 3.2$ per cent.

148. Merrick and Barth's Method.—Some very constructive work toward determining these allowances on a rational basis is that of Dwight V. Merrick with the assistance of Carl G. Barth, both of whom have had long experience in this work. Mr. Merrick in his time-study observations makes a clear distinction between **preparation time** and the time *actually* spent in production. Preparation time includes all time spent in transportation of material in connection with the operation. Thus Items 1 and 22 of Fig. 40 are preparation movements. It would also include the

[1] For a more extended discussion see "Management's Handbook," pp. 820 and 877 and "Cost and Production Handbook," L. P. Alford, (Ed), p. 537.

periodic grinding and adjusting of cutting tools that are to operate during a number of operative cycles. A careful distinction should be made, however, between preparation that is directly connected with the operation and for which the operator is responsible, and preparation such as setting up semiautomatic machines or similar apparatus that is to perform many operations before being reset and with which setting the operator has nothing to do. The time consumed in such preparation work is often considered a general charge and carried to the costs without appearing upon the instruction card. Much of the work of the move man is of this character of preparation work.

Merrick, as the result of a very large number of studies covering a wide range of work in the machine industries, concludes that the allowance for variation and fatigue varies with the proportion of handling time to the total cycle time. Carl G. Barth has very ingeniously expressed these relations as shown by Merrick's observations in the following formula:[1]

$$T = t\left[1.2 + \frac{0.495 - 0.00326C}{\sqrt{0.376 - 0.0000216C^2 + t}}\right]$$

where t = the selected handling time, or base time.
C = the percentage that t is of the cycle time.
T = the augmented handling time, that is t plus the allowance.

Mr. Barth points out that the theoretical basis of this equation is very meager and that these data are drawn largely from machine industries, and hence their use in other fields may be of doubtful value. The basic assumption on which the formula rests, however appears to be reasonable, and in the absence of anything better it is helpful. Mr. Barth has also very cleverly expressed this equation in graphic form as shown in Fig. 41, to which further reference will be made. For variations and interferences in preparation time, Merrick adds 25 per cent of the preparation time. For unavoidable machine delays he recommends the following:

	Percentage
Power-driven power feed	5
Power-driven hand feed	20

For personal needs he adds 2½ per cent to the total cycle time.

A numerical example may make this method and the use of the chart clearer. Assume that the preparation time is 0.5 minute and that the cycle time exclusive of preparation time is 1.8, of which 0.9 is handling time and 0.9 machine time, so that C = 0.50. On the diagram (Fig. 41), there is a scale on each side giving values of t, corresponding values being connected by diagonal lines. A series of lines parallel to the scales give values of C, and the outer scales, which are duplicates, give the required values of T. If a straightedge is laid so that its edge passes through the intersection of a diagonal with a line representing the values of C so as to

[1] See Merrick, D. W., "Time Studies," p. 64, and also *Management and Administration*, February, 1925.

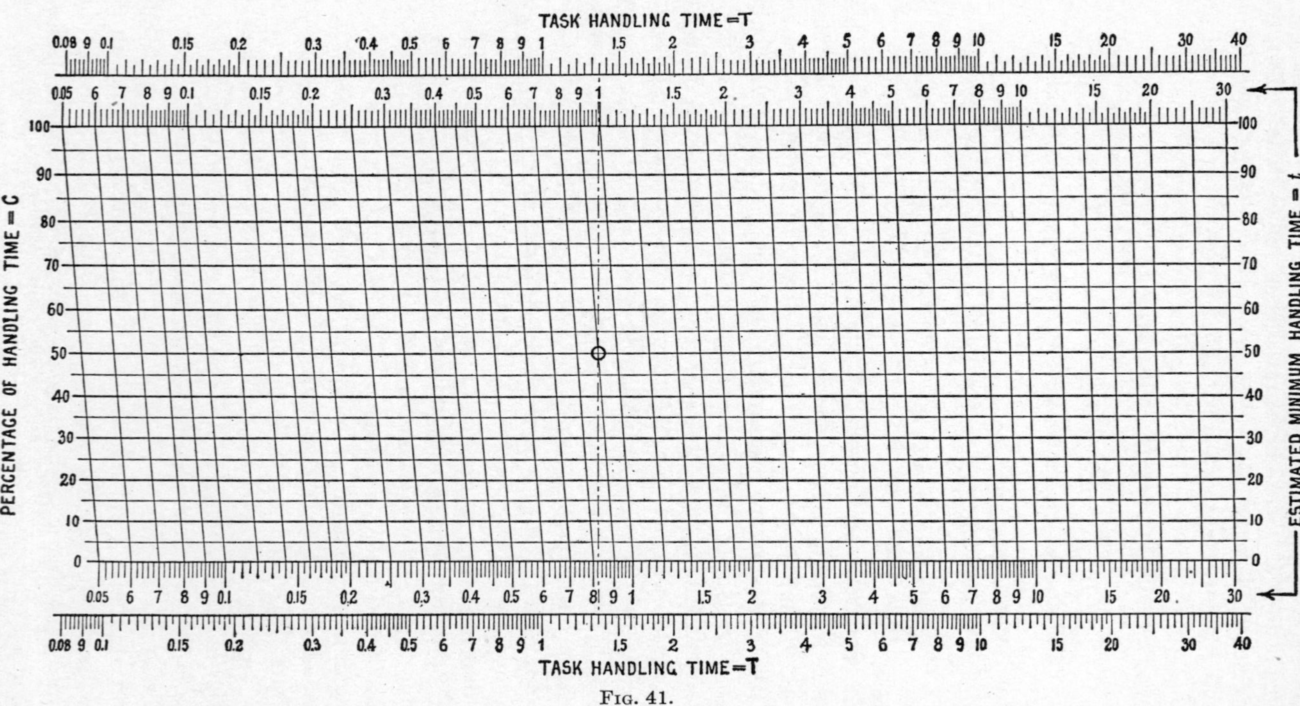
TASK HANDLING TIME = T
ESTIMATED MINIMUM HANDLING TIME = t
PERCENTAGE OF HANDLING TIME = C

Fig. 41.

give equal readings upon the outer scales, these readings will be the required values of T for the simultaneous values indicated by the intersecting lines. Thus for the values assumed above the intersection of the diagonal line representing 0.9 with that representing a value of $C = 0.50$ is indicated by the small circle and a straightedge through this point gives equal readings upon the outer scale of $T = 1.35$. Hence

The augmented handling time		= 1.35 minutes
The augmented machine time	= 0.9 × 1.05	= 0.945 minute
The augmented preparation time	= 0.5 × 1.25	= 0.625 minute
Total cycle time		= 2.920 minutes
Allowance for personal needs 2.92 × 0.025		= 0.073 minute
Total time for operation		= 2.993 minutes
Or in round numbers		= 3.0 minutes

149. Synthetic or Compiled Cycle Time.—The foregoing discussion has been directed largely to the problem of making *observed* time studies on work in process, for the primary purpose of setting reasonable tasks and rates. Most of the literature of this subject deals with this phase of time study. One of the greatest needs, however, is to be able to build up **synthetic time allowances** in advance of production as noted in Art. 138. In fact that is what Taylor started out, primarily, to accomplish through *unit times.* Much work has been done with observed times, but comparatively little has been accomplished in making synthetic instruction cards. One reason, perhaps, for this is the fact that the information necessary for making synthetic time predictions is usually extensive and it must be quite accurate to be effective. It should be noted in this regard that while observed-time studies may give quite accurate data on the motions of the operator himself they do not necessarily give accurate data on machine times and performances if it is left entirely to the worker to set the speeds and feeds. Workmen, in general, are not well informed as to the maximum capacities of tools and processes and, in general, do not work them up to their full possibilities. If best results are to be obtained, therefore, the capacities of all machines must be determined with accuracy. In the case of the machining of metals there is a considerable quantity of data, as noted in Art. 130, and where such data are not already available they must be secured by experimental methods.

It may be helpful to describe briefly an actual accomplishment in making synthetic time allowances in the Gleason Works in connection with the hobbing of plain spur gears on Barber-Coleman hobbing machines. In this case the data on the maximum allowable feeds and speeds of gear hobs were not available originally and they were, therefore, carefully determined by experiment, some hobs being driven to destruction in order to find their limitations.

The data that were collected and tabulated for the purpose of making these synthetic allowances were as follows:

1. Drawings giving full particulars as to dimensions of gears.

2. Tabulated data on number of cuts to be made and method of making the same.

3. Tabulated data as to time required to set up the machine.

4. Tabulated data as to the number of gears that are to be hobbed at any one setting.

5. Tabulated data on outside diameter of hobs.

6. Tabulated data on cutting feeds and speeds of hobs.

7. Tabulated, allowed, overtravel of table.

8. A formula giving cutting time in terms of feed, speed, and characteristics of the hob.

9. Tabulated handling time based on time studies.

With reference to (9) the formula developed was:

$$\text{Cutting time in minutes} = \frac{N \times L}{F \times S \times H},$$

where N = number of teeth in hob.
L = total length of cut.
F = feed in inches per revolution.
S = speed (revolutions per minute).
H = lead of hob (single or double).

The time studies for handling time were carefully made, no less than 40 detail operations being observed. An allowance of 5 per cent on the cycle time is used to provide for delays, etc.

Example.—Required the time for hobbing plain spur gears of 10 diametral pitch, 60 teeth, 1-inch face. Referring to itemized list of data above:

From (1) diametral pitch = 10, N = 60, width of face = 1 inch.

From (2) number cuts = 2, roughing hob No. 24A, finishing hob No. 24B.

From (3) set-up time = 50.00 minutes.

From (4) three blanks to be cut at one time.

From (5) outside diameter hob 24A = 2.69; outside diameter hob 24B = 2.756.

From (6) roughing speed 110 revolutions per minute; 0.060-inch feed. Finishing 161 revolutions per minute, 0.045 feed.

From (7) allowed overtravel, roughing 0.74 inch; finishing 0.125 inch.

From (8) (see formula for cutting times above):

$$\text{Roughing time} = \frac{60 \times 3.74}{110 \times 0.06 \times 2} = 17.0 \text{ minutes}$$

$$\text{Finishing time} = \frac{60 \times 3.125}{161 \times 0.045 \times 1} = 25.8 \text{ minutes}$$

Total machine time = 42.8 minutes

From (9) handling time = 5.06

Machine time plus handling time = 47.86 minutes

Allowance for delays, etc. = 47.86 × 0.05 = 2.39

Total cycle time = 50.25 minutes

$$\text{Total cycle time per gear} = \frac{50.25}{3} = 16.75 \text{ minutes}$$

Compiled instruction cards are built up on such data and have proved very satisfactory. The flat allowance of 5 per cent is used for simplicity, all men being on day work. It is obvious that the more refined methods described in the foregoing could be applied if desired.

A great amount of criticism has been made of all of these methods of making allowances, the general tenor of such criticisms being that they are in the nature of guesses and hence vitiate any claim that time study is even *rational* not to mention *scientific*. It is true, as has been stated, that extravagant claims have been made for these methods and a great deal of guessing has been indulged in. It is true also that much harm has been done to this field of work by ignorant and overenthusiastic "efficiency" men, and it is little wonder that many manufacturers look askance at all of these new methods. But it is only a short time since psychology was held in doubtful regard and practical men long doubted scientific methods of design because designers used "factors of safety" to allow for uncertainties. These are still used even in refined design but scientific design is accepted as logical. So with these new and less tangible fields it will take some time to develop methods as accurate as are in daily use in other fields. Yet progress will be made, and even now at the *lowest* estimate that can be made of the *best* work in time study it is vastly superior as a basis of setting rates to the old empirical methods so familiar to all who know anything of factory management 30 years ago.

INTRODUCING STANDARD PERFORMANCES AND ROUTINE PROCEDURE

150. Interesting the Worker.—Time-study data are usually collected for record in tabulated form or in the form of graphs. Occasionally they can be expressed as formulas, as illustrated by Mr. Barth's work in the last section. Mr. Taylor developed a formula for the time required to move earth, and formulas have also been constructed for the time required to lay brick. The usual method of placing the standard performances that are derived from these data before the workman is through the instruction card and similar documents. For several reasons, however, it is not always easy to secure the cooperation of the workers in putting standardized operations into effect, especially as they usually call for a higher production. One of the strongest objections has come from labor unionism, and this is briefly discussed elsewhere. The worker, furthermore, cannot, as a rule, be induced to increase his output unless he is to benefit thereby; hence comes the necessity of financial incentives that must invariably accompany these new methods and which are fully described in Chap. XXI. Aside from these considerations workers are always afraid of new methods they do not understand, and for this reason the methods must be explained fully and clearly before being put into effect. Quite frequently explanations are not sufficient and the worker must be actually taught correct methods before he can earn the desired bonus. The work of the late H. L. Gantt[1] in this regard is noteworthy, and a real contribution to management. Under the plan of functional foremanship as advocated by Taylor this teaching devolves upon the speed boss.

Lastly, the worker wishes assurance that the improved conditions thus held out to him will be permanent, since he has deep-seated suspicion of new methods, as is fully explained elsewhere. Some companies have met this difficulty by issuing written guarantees of good faith. While these may be helpful the best guarantee of good faith in such agreements is a reputation for fair dealing and these new methods have a much better chance of succeeding in plants that enjoy such a reputation.

151. Perpetuating the Standards.—It should be noted that highly developed methods such as are described in this and in the preceding chapter are not naturally self-perpetuating and must be constantly stimulated. Standard *performances* are possible only under standard *conditions.* Both the procedure (Art. 136) and the physical plant itself must, therefore, be kept up to standard. It will be noted, also, that the task of working such highly developed methods into the *routine* of the plant is no easy one and only to be attempted by skilled men who also have wide knowledge of the human factors involved. Perhaps more failures of such systems have come from lack of the latter than from lack of technical skill.

References

ALFORD, L. P. (Ed.): "Cost and Production Handbook," p. 515.
———: "Management's Handbook," p. 799.
BARNES, R. M.: "Industrial Engineering and Management."
GILBRETH, FRANK B.: "Applied Motion Study."
———: "Fatigue-study."
LICHTNER, W. O.: "Time Study and Job Analysis."
LOWRY, MAYNARD, and STEGEMERTEN: "Time and Motion Study."
MERRICK, D. V.: "Time Studies for Rate Setting."
REED, H. K.: "Making and Using Time Studies." A series beginning March, 1924, in *Industrial Management.*

[1] GANTT, H. L., "Work, Wages, and Profits."

CHAPTER XIV

PURCHASING

152. Purchasing and Storing.—It will appear from Chap. XIII that one of the important problems in the control of production is that of having the required material on hand when needed. Under ideal conditions material would arrive from the sources whence it is purchased just when it is needed and in the desired quantity. Such ideal conditions can rarely be realized and usually a considerable amount of raw material must be carried in stores, the store room acting as a reservoir to equalize the variations between the plant and the sources of supply. It is the primary function of the purchasing department to make all purchases of material and supplies as required and it is the primary function of the storekeeping department to guard and care for all purchased materials and to insure that they are issued only on the proper authority and in the correct amounts. Purchasing and storekeeping are, therefore, closely connected. Included in these functions also are the **receiving** of purchased goods and their **inspection** before acceptance. In comparatively small enterprises all four of these functions are usually conducted as one department under one head. In large plants purchasing is an independent function and receiving and inspecting are usually combined with storekeeping. In very large enterprises receiving and inspecting are sometimes organized as an independent function.

153. Organization of Purchasing Department.—The position that the function of purchasing may occupy in the plant organization depends upon the size of the plant and upon the degree to which general policies enter into its operation. In small plants it is not uncommon to find purchasing under the supervision of the treasurer, stores, of course, being under the direction of the shop superintendent. In plants of moderate size the purchasing agent is usually responsible to the factory manager as shown in Fig. 13. In very large enterprises, consisting of several plants that are separated geographically, and in which general policies are important, there is usually a general or central purchasing organization to direct policies and to make such contracts as affect all of the plants, with a local purchasing agent at each plant to care for routine matters as shown in Fig. 42. The best arrangement will, therefore, depend somewhat upon circumstances, but in any case responsibility for all purchases should be centralized, and purchasing by several persons or departments should never be tolerated as it always leads to loose, extravagant ideas and methods, higher purchase prices, and needless waste. The oppor-

tunity for dishonesty is also much increased. A good purchasing agent is always a valuable man and as the size and complexity of a business increase, his value rises. It is axiomatic that he must possess the business training and natural commercial instinct that will make him a keen student of market conditions and a judge of values. It is equally important that he be able to systematize his department so that it runs smoothly in connection with the other departments, *serving* them quickly and well. If, in addition, he is well informed on the technical and practical side of the industry his efficiency will be increased manyfold. For these reasons a man promoted from the shop or engineering department will, all other things being equal, make a better purchasing agent than one promoted from the clerical force of the office. Purchasing, however, involves a knowledge of business methods and forms, of which shop men and engineers are, unfortunately, seldom well informed; hence, purchasing agents are usually recruited from the clerical force.

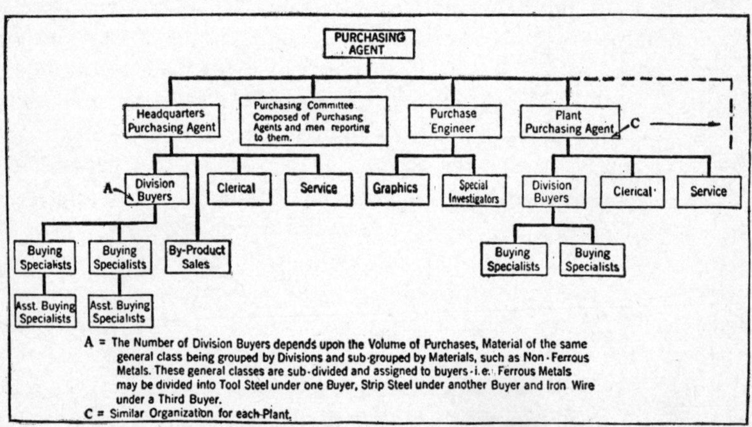

FIG. 42.—Organization chart of large purchasing department with centralized and local buying, stores and inspection under separate heads.

The internal organization of a purchasing department will vary with the size of the enterprise. In the small plant a purchasing agent with an assistant or two may suffice, while in the large enterprise the department must be large and consequently organized with care. Figure 42 shows an organization suggested by P. M. Marshall[1] for a large enterprise with several branches that are separated geographically. It is assumed in this plan that the volume of business, both at the central purchasing division and at each departmental division, is large enough to permit of specialization. In each division, therefore, the work of purchasing is functionalized under three sections, namely, **buying, clerical,** and **service.** The buying section does all the purchasing, this work again being separated into classes and a specialist assigned to each class. The clerical section

[1] ALFORD, L. P. (Ed.), "Management's Handbook," p. 490.

performs all clerical work and keeps all records. The service section follows up all orders, conducts relations with other departments, and makes all necessary adjustments. Such a highly developed department is, of course, necessary and possible only in very large organizations such as shown in Fig. 22.

154. Sources of Supply.—A primary function of the purchasing department is to keep fully informed concerning sources of supply of all materials. Viewed broadly, all industrial effort is concerned with the transforming of natural resources into useful forms and the transportation of the same to the places where they are needed. As each increment of labor is bestowed upon the material, as it passes through the process, it rises in value. Thus, coal is mined in one place, iron ore in another. Both are transported to some convenient place, arriving there worth a few cents per hundred pounds. By means of the coal the iron is here transformed into pig iron worth perhaps 1 cent per pound. This pig iron may be transformed in the same plant into steel rails worth 1¼ cents per pound, or it may be again transported to some engine works and made into steam engines worth 20 cents per pound. Or it may be shipped to a crucible steel works and made into crucible steel bars worth 16 cents per pound and these steel bars may be transformed elsewhere into watch-springs worth many dollars per pound. This is true, in a general sense, of all the products of industry; material values being, in the main, accumulated labor values, the value of the original material in its natural state often being a negligible part of the market value.

In some cases the transformation of the raw product into useful form is accomplished in one plant. Thus, table salt, kerosene, and similar commodities may each be made in a single reduction works and placed directly upon the market. In most cases, however, this is not so, most market products being the result of several distinct stages of manufacture, each stage separated widely by character and geographical distance. This is so from the nature of the case and from the complexity of modern manufacturing. The man that smelts pig iron would not be expected to produce, also, all the finished products into which it enters; in fact, he may be compelled to supply a widely diversified field of industry in order to secure the quantity necessary to manufacture pig iron economically. These general conditions apply to all those that in turn transform pig iron into other forms, and equally again to those that in turn use these other forms for other purposes.

What, then, appears to one manufacturer as *finished product* appears to some other manufacturer as *raw material*, and the extent to which any manufacturer may depend upon other branches of industry varies widely. In very few instances is he entirely independent of other lines of industry. It is a fundamental requirement, therefore, that the purchasing department have full and accurate knowledge of the material requirements of the plant and of the sources of supply of these requirements. This latter information is obtained from personal knowledge, from records of transactions already consummated, and from trade catalogues, "buyers' guides," and other publications containing such information in condensed form. A well-organized purchasing department will have this information carefully classified and indexed so as to make it readily available.

As explained in Art. 192, the materials that enter into any given finished product are, in general, of two kinds: direct and indirect; and even though a manufacturer may control the direct material from its natural sources to the market, he must, in most instances, depend on other people for much of his indirect supplies and his tools of production. If, however, the required quantity of any material, direct or indirect, becomes great enough, it may pay the manufacturer to extend his control of that particular material a little further back toward the natural sources. Thus, a growing concern may not have enough demand for castings to operate a foundry, but as the business increases it may pay to build one, even though no reduction in price is so obtained, in order to control the supply of castings and thus facilitate deliveries. If the quantity increases so that foundry work can be prosecuted as economically as in the foundries from which castings were formerly purchased, the profit formerly paid these foundries is thereby saved. The electrical manufacturing companies in this country depended originally on other sources for their porcelain and mica products, and small companies still do so. As the quantities incident to great growth have appeared, some of the larger electrical works have put up their own porcelain works and have installed presses for making mica products. Some have even put in wire-drawing plants, not so much with a view, perhaps, of obtaining lower priced wire, as for convenience and better control of deliveries. The importance, therefore, of the control of the several streams of material coming into an industrial plant will depend on their relative bearing on questions of economy of manufacture or convenience as affecting delivery of finished goods. It may be highly important to control a large stream for financial reasons. It may be no less important to control a very small one because of its effect on deliveries. The lack of a small detail will hold up the delivery of a machine as effectually as will a larger one; and thus control of the sources of supply may vary from the simple case where all materials are fully controlled, to the other extreme where nothing but *assembling* is carried on, the finished parts coming from many factories ready to be assembled. The first extreme is rare but many cases of the latter are to be found.

155. Purchase Requisitions.—The demand for materials grows naturally out of the needs of the business and cannot, therefore, originate with the purchasing agent. In a shop devoted to general repairs, the requisitions for materials would, most naturally, originate with the foremen in charge of work since they will know better than anyone what is wanted. In a shop building new work to order only, such as an engine works, these material requisitions for direct material would originate in the engineering department, though they should pass through the storekeeper's hands before going to the purchasing agent in order to check off material on hand. In a shop manufacturing standardized articles, as knives, watches, etc., the material requisition would naturally originate in the stores department, which is the reservoir that feeds the factory, and here also would originate, always, the requisitions for all indirect and expense material. In a shop doing all three of these classes of production, therefore, material requisitions might originate from several sources; and just as it is necessary to centralize the authority and responsibility of the purchases based on these material requisitions, so it is absolutely necessary to fix definitely the authority and responsibility of originating these requisitions. In a factory that is well managed this power is limited to responsible men, and the requisitions in many cases must be countersigned by some higher official as a check on irregularities. Where production is fully controlled, as described in Chap. XII, the planning department will, as a matter of routine, issue such information concerning the material needed as will be necessary both for the stores department and for the purchasing department in obtaining the proper material at the proper time. The purchase requisition should specify accurately the character and amount of the material needed, the time when it is required, the place where it is to be delivered, the purpose for which it is to be used, and any other information needed to identify it fully with its purpose. The requisition should be signed by the person responsible for its issuance so that any necessary adjustments may be taken up with him.

156. Routine of Purchasing.—A full discussion of the problems of purchasing and of the printed forms and documents used in purchasing is beyond the scope of this work. Only those features that are of general interest will be noted. If the items called for by the purchase requisition are not important the buyer to whom it is referred may place a **purchase order** with some reliable vendor with whom a regular business is conducted. If, however, the amounts involved are large he may ask for quotations from a number of vendors. On the basis of the bids received he will place the order to best advantage. It is in this connection that good department records are of great importance for it is not sufficient that the bidder's price be right but the buyer must be assured of his reliability in the matter of meeting delivery dates, quality of material furnished, etc., and past experience may show that the lowest bidder is not desirable from these viewpoints.

The purchase order will necessarily vary widely in form depending upon the business but, in general, it should include all information necessary to make misunderstandings impossible. It should bear an identifying number, the date of issue, the name of the vendor to whom it is sent, a full description of the article desired and the quantity thereof, the date of delivery at the plant, shipping directions, prices and terms of payment, and the name of the company making the purchase, with the signature of the purchasing agent. Quite frequently the purchase order has an **acknowledgment** form attached to the purchase order which the vendor signs, detaches, and mails to the purchasing agent as an acknowledgment that the order has been received. The buyer usually sends a duplicate copy of the purchase order to the receiving and inspecting departments and sometimes to the requisitioner of the material as a check on accuracy.

Skillful purchasing involves five principal features, namely:

1. **Price.**
2. **Quality.**
3. **Quantity.**
4. **Time of delivery.**
5. **Verification of goods purchased.**

1. For a given quality and quantity of material the securing of low prices becomes a commercial matter depending on a knowledge of the sources of supply, transportation facilities, market conditions, discounts, and similar considerations that apply to all purchasing. Price, however, is not always the only factor that must be considered, for, as will be seen, an effort to obtain low purchase prices may result in high manufacturing costs, though it is fundamental that, other things being equal, the lowest possible prices should be obtained.

2. It is obvious that the judgment of the purchasing agent as regards the quality of materials required increases with his knowledge of the trades and processes for which he buys. In the buying of many indirect or expense materials such as oil, waste, stationery, etc., it is customary in many plants to trust to the judgment of the purchasing agent. In fact, this is true in many cases of much of the direct material. But as an industry grows more complex and the scientific knowledge on which it is based becomes more important, the purchasing agent must depend more on the expert in each line for instructions as to the quality of material required. In electrical construction, for instance, the quality of many materials is of highest importance and the characteristics must be carefully specified to the purchasing agent. Many large companies keep well-equipped experimental laboratories for determining the best qualities of material; foundries now buy their iron by chemical specification; and careful managers specify the character of their supplies, such as coal and oil. Best results will, therefore, be obtained when the special buying ability of the purchasing agent is reinforced by the expert knowledge of the specialist who knows the characteristics desirable in the material under consideration. Where necessary, therefore, the purchase requisition

should be accompanied by complete specifications and the purchasing agent should be guided strictly by these in making purchases. Any other method will be found to be wasteful. Standards of quality, etc., are discussed in Chap. XVII.

3. The temptation to buy large quantities of material is always strong for two reasons: (1) lower prices are obtained as the quantity to be purchased increases, and (2) a large stock on hand insures prompt service to the shop and consequent quick deliveries. But here again the judgment of the purchasing agent should be reinforced by expert knowledge and advice. There is no money in ordering several years' supply of any one article, storing it, and thus tying up considerable capital and losing the interest thereon simply for a small saving in price. The quantity ordered, therefore, should have a reasonable relation to the prospective output of the factory. Mr. Frank Parrish, Supervisor of Inventories of the United States Steel Corporation, is quoted[1] as estimating inventory carrying charges for average warehouse stocks as 25 per cent per annum, divided as follows:

Storage facilities	0.25
Insurance	0.25
Taxes	0.50
Transportation	0.50
Handling and distribution	2.50
Depreciation	5.00
Interest	6.00
Obsolesence	10.00
	25.00

Furthermore, before placing orders for large quantities of stock, particularly special stock, careful inquiry should be made as to prospective changes in design that may render such stock obsolete; an occurrence only too frequent in an industry that is in a state of development. In large works a great purchasing advantage can be obtained by standardizing, as far as possible, articles of a similar character used by different departments, thus decreasing the variety and increasing the number of each kind purchased. This principle should be observed from office lead pencils to the largest common supplies and tools purchased.

4. The time element is a most important one in purchasing. It is essential that all material for a job arrive so as to be fabricated in time to avoid delay in assembling the completed product. Yet a contract might be taken for machines involving the use of tons of copper, say, and requiring a year for completion, the copper not being needed till near the end of the construction. Evidently the purchasing agent, working in connection with a good planning department, can save considerable money by means of well-arranged schedules of delivery. The same thing can be

[1] See "Cost and Production Handbook," p. 357.

accomplished for material used constantly, such as coal, by making long-term contracts but with periodic deliveries and payments. In other cases, again, the purchasing agent is often justified in paying a high price for a quick delivery if it will save great delay in the factory or secure a remunerative contract because of early shipment.

5. The verification of purchased goods is usually conducted by the receiving department which is, in general, a branch of the stores department and is, therefore, discussed among the problems of that department (see Art. 159).

157. Market Purchasing.—The routine methods of purchasing, described in the foregoing, are those in general use where it is the purpose simply to satisfy the manufacturing needs at the proper time and at the best prices of the existing market. There are many cases, however, where it is possible to satisfy these needs without strict reference to the requirements of the manufacturing program and, by taking every advantage of market conditions present and future, make great savings in purchasing. Such a procedure is called **market purchasing.** There are three sources of information[1] from which prices may be forecast: (1) the many published statements of price movements; (2) special advices furnished by private statistical bureaus for remuneration; and (3) whatever statistical data the purchasing department may gather from its own experiences. A competent purchasing agent should be able by a careful study of such statistics to forecast the trend of market prices and thus make advantageous purchasing contracts. If, for instance, such studies show prices to be low but with an upward tendency, contracts for material at the low price and extending some time into the future will be advantageous. Again, if prices are high with a tendency downward, close buying will be advisable.

Statistical data presumably reflect changes due to supply and demand. There are, however, other factors that may exert a large influence upon the policy of purchasing. Labor troubles, congested conditions in transportation facilities, and many other movements in the industrial field all tend to affect prices. Furthermore, market movements in fields other than the one in which the purchasing agent is directly interested must be kept in mind. Thus, market movements in basic industries such as steel and copper, the amount of unfilled orders, and the stocks of material on hand in these industries are indicative of future prices in other lines. Unemployment and import and export statistics may also be of service in evaluating future market prices.

In some industries where the manufacturing processes do not change materially, where the cost of production is small compared with the cost of the material, and where large quantities of some basic commodity are

[1] Alford, L. P. (Ed.), "Management's Handbook," p. 505, and "Cost and Production Handbook," p. 356.

used, purchasing is often conducted without much reference to immediate factory needs. Thus in the textile industries and in some of those industries that use large quantities of copper, where the cost of the raw material is a large part of the total cost, it is often good purchasing policy to buy large quantities when the market price is low without any reference to the immediate manufacturing program. Such purchasing is known as **speculative purchasing.** Obviously such purchasing cannot be successfully carried on without a comprehensive knowledge of all market conditions, and while, no doubt, there are industries in which it has a proper place, it should be avoided so far as ordinary manufacturing is concerned. Such methods tie up large amounts of money and in many forms of production are likely to upset the manufacturing program and to leave large quantities of unusable material on hand due to changes in design or policy.

158. Purchasing Contracts.—In ordinary commercial purchasing the purchase order and a written acceptance are considered all that is necessary, it being assumed that the mutual interests of purchaser and vendor are sufficient to insure good faith on both sides. Usually this is true, though when business declines suddenly the practice of canceling orders is all too common. In very large and important undertakings dependence is not placed upon the purchase order and its acceptance but a written **contract** is drawn up binding both parties to the fulfillment of their share of the transaction. Thus the federal government contracts for practically all materials, supplies, and services rendered to it by those doing business with it. In important contracts the bidder is required to deposit with his bid a certified check for a specified amount as a guarantee of good faith and performance. This practice is not uncommon in private practice where the work is of considerable magnitude.

Many enterprises that use large quantities of basic materials such as pig iron, coal, coke, etc., have found it very desirable to contract for the entire supply of such commodities for a considerable period of time. Usually the schedule of deliveries of the commodity is worked out to fit into the manufacturing program and incorporated into the contract. The advantages of such an arrangement are that the purchaser obtains reasonable assurance of a supply of material during the contract period; he is protected against excessive price fluctuations; and, in general, he is able to secure low prices because of the large quantities contracted for. The vendor also enjoys corresponding advantages that are obvious. Frequently it is not possible to fix a flat price for long-term contracts and in such cases the price may be fixed with reference to lowest market quotations or by quotations in some selected periodical.

These contracts are of many kinds varying widely with the circumstances. It should be noted, however, that these contracts may not be broken by either party with impunity and they should, therefore, be drawn with care so that they are fair and binding and include all necessary stipulations. In important cases, especially where the contract fixes penalties for non-performance, it is advisable to have legal advice before signing the contract.

References

ALFORD, L. P. (Ed.): "Cost and Production Handbook," p. 341.
———: "Management's Handbook," p. 487.
BOFEE, L. F. and E. T. GUSHEE: "Scientific Purchasing."
HARRIMAN, N. F.: "Principles of Scientific Purchasing."
TUCKER, J. I.: "Contracts in Engineering."
VAN DEVENTER, J. H.: "Planning Production for Profit," p. 89.

CHAPTER XV

STORES AND STOCK

159. Functions of Stores and Stock.—Under ideal manufacturing conditions the raw materials would be used as fast as they arrive at the factory, passing directly through it; and the finished product would be shipped to customers as fast as it was turned out. Such conditions are almost impossible to attain, though they may be approached in some of the simple continuous industries. In most manufacturing industries the raw materials are used in varying amounts at varying times, and sales are likewise intermittent and varied. For these reasons, and also because purchasing and transportation are facilitated by quantity, provision must be made for storing such quantities of raw material as will insure prompt service for these varying demands. Where sales are varying and product must be made in advance of sales, similar provision must be made for caring for finished product, in order to insure prompt delivery to customers. In shops that make product to order only, as a shipbuilding company, this last feature would not be important.

Unworked material is usually known as **stores** and the space where it is housed is known as the **store room.** The store room is, in effect, a reservoir between the incoming materials and supplies and the factory proper, equalizing the varying supply and demand. Finished product ready for shipment is usually called **stock** and the place where it is stored is called a **stock room.** The stock room is in effect a reservoir between the factory and the selling department equalizing the varying demand of the customers and the varying output of the shop. In small factories the store room and stock room may be one, and under the control of the same official, but there is a distinct difference in their functions, and as plants grow in size separation becomes almost inevitable.

In order to obtain the advantages of manufacturing a large number of pieces of one kind it is often necessary to finish large numbers of parts of machines or other products and store them, drawing them out for final assembly in completed products as the business of the factory requires. In fact, in some factories carrying on semicontinuous manufacturing, the quantities are so large that it is necessary to store them between successive operations, especially if the materials involved are valuable. In many cases, also, the same part is used in several different kinds or sizes of product that come through the factory at different times, and repairs and supply parts always demand a stock of standard finished parts on hand. The store room may, therefore, also act as a reservoir to equalize inequalities in the manufacturing processes of the factory by storing so-called **finished parts** and in some cases a special section of the store room called the **finished-parts store room** is set aside especially for this purpose. A distinction is sometimes made between finished parts made by the factory and those purchased. Thus bolts, screws, or any other element that is purchased and used directly in the product are, strictly speaking, finished parts and are sometimes called **purchased finished parts** to distinguish them from **manufactured finished parts.** The distinction is, however, somewhat academic and not of practical importance, provided the cost of each article is accurately determined. The store room may be said, therefore, to care for three classes of material:

1. **Stores,** or raw material that is to be fabricated into product, consisting largely, therefore, of direct material.
2. **Supplies,** or indirect material, such as oil, waste, etc.
3. **Finished parts,** or product, fabricated, but not fully assembled.

The stock room in its fully developed form will care only for finished product, that is, fully fabricated and ready to be shipped. In large organizations this department comes, naturally, under the shipping clerk. In such cases the stock room may carry many finished parts for convenience in supplying repair parts. In smaller concerns the stock room, store room, shipping and receiving rooms may be under one man and in one room. But as factories grow in size these different functions should be separated in the interests of efficiency. These relations are shown graphically in Fig. 45.

160. Store-room Organization.—The store room is usually organized under the superintendent of planning (see Fig. 13) and the chief stores clerk is responsible to him. It will be obvious that since the stores constitute a *service* function the exact manner of this organization will depend upon the size of the plant. In plants of moderate size a single store room centrally situated will serve all needs, but in a very large plant with many buildings housing diverse activities it is frequently economical to establish branch store rooms throughout the plant at convenient locations. And in large enterprises with factories separated geographically it is obvious economy to have store rooms at each plant even though the purchasing may be centralized. The personnel of a large store-room system such as this would not be unlike that shown in Fig. 42 for the organization of purchasing departments.

161. Store-room Methods.—The necessity and the advantages of a well-organized store room are not always fully recognized. Managers who would look with horror upon a financial system that would permit the easy extraction of small sums of money from the office safe, often look complacently upon store-room methods that permit the unauthorized withdrawal of valuable material from the stores, wastes due to excess material drawn, and losses due to valuable material unaccounted for, out of all proportion to their care of the cash in the office till. Managers who would look most carefully into the tying up of money in securities permit the investment of large sums in raw material with little thought as to the relative amount invested, the possibility of how long it may remain so tied up, or the depreciation it may suffer while so invested. Yet material represents value as truly as the money in the office safe, though this is not always appreciated. Any saving in material is as effective as a saving on the payroll. Money tied up in material is *crystallized* capital and while in this form is inactive. Clearly, the amount so invested should be carefully scrutinized and its total kept as low as proper service of the factory will allow (see also Art. 156).

The principal business of the store room is to anticipate the needs of the factory in the most effective and economical manner possible. In order to accomplish this it must fulfill the following functions perfectly:

1. Issue requisitions on the purchasing department for the most economical amount of the right kind of material for delivery at the most advantageous time.
2. Check all material received as to quality and quantity.
3. Store all material in a safe and convenient manner.
4. Issue materials and supplies in the exact amounts needed and at the exact time required.
5. Maintain exact records of all receipts and issues and of all balances on hand.

The work of the stores department is, therefore, closely connected with that of the purchasing department, on the one hand, and with the shop and cost system on the other. In small concerns the store room and purchasing department are often included in one department.

Item 1.—As noted in Art. 155, the origin of requisitions will vary with the character of the industry but usually all requisitions originating outside the store room should be passed upon by the storekeeper so as to insure the use of material on hand before ordering more. For this reason all requisitions are drawn on the store room in some organizations, the store room alone requisitioning the purchasing department.

The problem presented in obtaining material for repair work or for special work done on order is comparatively simple, since the quantity and quality are here fairly definite in character, the question of *time*, however, being often of great importance. If the work is of great magnitude and is to extend over a considerable period of time a careful planning, by either the engineering department or the planning department, of the time schedule on which materials should be delivered is almost essential to prevent premature and over-investment of funds. In the case of repairs, on the other hand, quickness of delivery is usually an essential.

The problem of anticipating the needs of a large factory that is manufacturing standardized products of several kinds and many sizes is a more difficult problem, including as it does the consideration of the quantity of raw material that should be carried in all stages of fabrication from raw material to finished product. An adequate discussion of this problem, which is one of the most important in all manufacturing, is beyond the scope of this book; but a brief outline may be of interest and assistance (see Art. 164). Among the leading considerations that must be given weight in deciding what stock of goods shall be carried in the several stages of production the following may be noted:

1. The demand for the particular part or combination of parts.

2. The saving that may be effected by manufacturing in quantity.

3. The interest on the capital tied up in material in process of manufacture, and in facilities for storing and caring for it.

4. The time required to obtain raw material and to assemble it into completed product from various stages of fabrication.

5. The probability of change of design and consequent depreciation of raw material, finished parts, or completed product.

To make the interrelation of these considerations clearer consider a hypothetical problem of manufacturing a complete line of alternating-current transformers. The demand for the smaller sizes of transformers or, say, up to 100 kilowatts, is large though varying, very quick deliveries are essential, the voltages are moderate, and the design will be assumed to be fairly stable. These small sizes would be in continuous manufacture, or they would, at least, be passed through the factory in large lots, finished completely, and put in stock. To facilitate delivery some stock of these sizes would also be carried in branch sales offices. Complete sets of special winding machines and other labor-saving devices would be developed so as to take advantage of quantity in reducing shop costs. Anticipation of the demand for raw material in this case is comparatively simple, care being necessary only to see that the supply of any material does not get so low before ordering that production is held up; and care exercised, on the other hand, that the amount ordered is not so excessive as to tie up too much capital or to run the risk of any of it becoming obsolete through changes in design. This case represents in a general way the problem of continuous processes of all kinds.

Now, in general, the demand for a given class of product lessens as the size of the unit increases. Transformers from 100- to, say, 250-kilowatt capacity would probably not be in such demand as the smaller sizes and would not be carried in branch-office stocks.

The demand may also vary with the season.[1] The yearly demand, nevertheless, is such that they can be economically put through the shop

[1] Seasonable products are often difficult problems. They must, as a rule, be made during the season when they are not wanted so as to anticipate the market, and production comes to a standstill during the season of demand. Manufacturers usually try to equalize these demands by making articles that are complementary; as, for instance, fan motors may be manufactured during the winter for the summer

in large lots, the size of these lots and the proper times for authorizing their production requiring careful consideration to keep the investment as low as is consistent with prompt delivery. A good equipment of special tools might also be warranted for these sizes, though they may not be in continual use.

Transformers of, say, 500-kilowatt capacity may present a very different problem. Here the demand may be so small that it may not be advisable to put large lots through to completion and stock, because the interest on the money so tied up would more than equal the saving made by production in quantity. Yet the time required to manufacture these larger sizes may be prohibitive from the standpoint of the salesman and, therefore, it may be good policy to make up and stock some of the parts that require the longest time to produce. Thus the copper coils may be wound and insulated and carried as finished parts, thus also providing spare parts for repairs. A limited amount of sheet steel for building up the laminated cores might also be carried among the finished parts. The cast-iron casings or any steel or malleable-iron castings that require time to obtain might be carried in the raw-material supplies, labor being expended only on such parts as would greatly facilitate delivery when orders to assemble these sizes were received. The outfit of special tools for these sizes would also be very limited and carefully considered.

In the case of still larger sizes not even finished parts of any kind would be justifiable and only such raw materials as require a considerable time to obtain would be carried. Thus, certain special sizes of copper strip might be justified, though usually special material of any kind should be avoided, if possible, since, if rendered obsolete for any reason, it depreciates very rapidly, and is, in general, useless for other purposes. No special tools might be justified for these larger sizes because of the small quantity demanded.

In still larger sizes and perhaps for higher voltages it may be that not even raw materials should be carried. The more difficult engineering problems involved, the possibility of changes in design, the varying requirements to be met in the field, would perhaps make all anticipation of materials hazardous and out of the question. The problem has passed from the extreme case of the continuous industry to the other extreme where the product must be made to order and material ordered as needed and not anticipated.

The relative sizes assumed above are, of course, hypothetical but entirely possible. The principles involved are, however, universal. The question of the quantity and form in which material shall be carried is not a simple one, nor one that can, in the general case, be decided by

---

trade and arc lamps during the summer for the winter trade. Other lines of industry do not permit this principle because of limitations in the equipment.

any one man. The storekeeper can easily handle the extreme cases. In the cases that approach continuous production it is simply a matter of considering the stock bins as hoppers feeding the factory. Minimum limits can be set to each bin, or other storage, that will serve as a warning to order more material. Maximum limits may be set based on the sales demands that will prevent over-investment. In the other extreme where work is done to order, the problem is specific as to quality and quantity and the important element is the time relation. But between these extremes the combinations are complex and an intelligent solution can be reached only by the joint efforts of the storekeeper, the salesman, the engineer, the financier, and the tool maker (see also Art. 107).

Item 2.—When the vendor ships goods to the purchaser he mails the purchaser an **invoice** or list of the goods. This invoice is sent to the **receiving department** which is usually a part of the stores department, and when the goods are received they are checked against the invoice and purchase order in order to insure fulfillment of the purchase order *before* sending the purchased material to the stores or to fabrication. This checking at the receipt of the material includes the quantity and quality of the shipment, the price, terms, and freight charges. Any discrepancies are referred to the purchasing department for adjustment. In many lines of work a visual checking is sufficient, but again it may be necessary to inspect the material as to chemical or mechanical characteristics, in which case an **inspection department** fitted with laboratory apparatus may be a necessity. This form of inspection of material as it is received is discussed along with the general problem of inspection in Art. 183.

Item 3.—It is axiomatic that all materials should be stored in places where they will be safe against deterioration or pilfering. They should also be stored in a convenient and systematic manner and so that they can be delivered quickly to the shop. In large works branch store rooms are a necessity, for reasons of both convenience and economy. If the stores are extensive a book, plan, or written record of some kind showing the location of stores is imperative to guard against the delay and confusion arising from the loss of experienced employees who carry such matters in their heads. The same remarks apply to pattern and other storage problems. A carefully planned systematic way of storing tools, patterns, and materials of all kinds is an important feature of good management. A well-developed stores system also necessitates a system of identifying nomenclature[1] so that the location of all material is easily found. The physical arrangement of store rooms and the methods of placing material in bins,[2] racks, etc., will depend upon the character of the plant, and a discussion of these matters is beyond the limits of this treatise.

[1] See Chap. XI.

[2] See *Bull.*, Taylor Society, August, 1919.

Item 4.—In former times, when shops and factories were small, materials and supplies were stored on open shelves and each workman helped himself to what was wanted. The custom still prevails in small plants, particularly where the stores are such as are of no personal value to the workmen, or where they consist of indirect material and form a very small part of the material cost. There are, no doubt, many cases where it would cost more to employ a storekeeper than he could save by his watchfulness; but in most cases it pays to put all stores under a good storekeeper, give him needed facilities to keep the stores properly, and then hold him responsible for wastes and losses, so far as the stores are concerned.

It is common experience that workmen cannot, in general, be trusted to draw either direct or indirect material from stores without great waste, both as to the quantity drawn and as to its economical use. Furthermore, loose methods of issuing materials are always likely to lead to dishonesty and pilfering. The first method of checking these difficulties was to put the responsibility on the foreman. Under this system each foreman is furnished with an order book and no article can be issued from the store room except on the authority of the foreman's order which describes the material required, the amount needed, and the order number to which it is to be charged. Indirect material is ordered in the same way; in many cases the foreman also notes the order number to which the expense material is to be charged, this number usually being the order number on which the workman is, at that time, employed. The unfairness of such a method of distributing expense material is obvious. The orders issued by the foremen are taken up by the storekeeper and are his authority for the issuance of the material and also the basis of material costs.

The advantages of such a system are its simplicity, flexibility, and quickness. No delays are experienced in getting the material from the stores to the factory floor. It responds instantly to emergencies, either in production or in the shop repairs. There are many places where it is adequate, particularly where the force of men is small, the foreman intelligent, and the stores of no value to the workman personally, and where the number of orders issued daily is small and the accounting consequently easy.

As departments become larger, on the other hand, it is not good economy to use a busy foreman for this purpose. His time is more valuable for other purposes, and he will not do it well if he pays the attention he should to the more important problems of production. He may, of course, be given clerical help; but this, again, is a palliative only, as the system falls down for other reasons. It is explained in Art. 190 that as shops grow in size the problem of cost keeping becomes more and more important and, in most instances, when the problem of drawing material becomes too great for the foreman, it is high time to consider better methods of cost keeping.

This leads naturally to the **preplanning** of work and the use of the **production order** (Fig. 17). Under these modern methods full bills of material are prepared either in the engineering department, the planning department if there is one, or by someone in the office of the superintendent. These bills of material give full information[1] regarding the quality and quantity of the material and the order number to which it is to be charged. They are made in multiple, one copy going to the foreman with the drawings and other directions for the work and constituting his authority to draw the material. One goes to the storekeeper and constitutes his authority for issuing the material specified, serving also as the basis of costs (see Art. 192).

The accuracy of the method is manifest. If properly operated it prevents unnecessary drawing of direct material, fixes responsibility and authority definitely, and in such a manner that errors or irregularities can be instantly attributed to those responsible. Most important of all, it permits of more accurate costs than are attainable under the older methods.

The method is not flexible, however, and emergencies must be cared for by modifications of the plan. Small jobs would cost too much if passed through a system of this kind. It does not take account of expense material and supplies. For these reasons it is customary to give some foreman, or other official, power to issue emergency requisitions to care for these special conditions. Thus, in an emergency repair job brought into the shop on Saturday afternoon, or an imperative repair job on the shop power house on Sunday, when the machinery of the planning department is not running, this official would issue the requisitions, subject to the approval of the proper authorities when the office and store room open up again. Emergency methods must always be provided, in any well-organized system, to prevent inflexibility destroying its usefulness. It is the fear of this inflexibility that often leads superintendents and foremen charged with the duties of production to oppose new systems that savor of "red tape" because, while they may cure certain evils, they may do so at the cost of convenience and flexibility. This particular defect in all systems deserves careful consideration in installing them and it is in making modifications of this kind that the manager shows his true ability in organizing.

Expense materials and supplies such as oil and waste cannot, of course, be handled on production orders. They may be issued on the foreman's order, but in no case should the foreman assign the order number to which

[1] It is, of course, difficult to specify with great exactness all material required for some classes of work. The corrections necessary, however, need not be great except in very complex work.

BALANCE OF SUNDRY STORES

DESCRIPTION ½" × 4½" HEXAGONAL BOLTS.

ORDER IN QUANTITIES OF 4000
WHEN AVAILABLE SHOWS 1000
LOCATION IN STORES D-10

SYMBOL X25
DRAWING NO. LD50

INSTRUCTIONS FOR POSTING: (A) WHEN MATERIALS ARE ORDERED, ADD THE QUANTITY TO COLUMNS 1 AND 4. (B) WHEN MATERIALS ARE RECEIVED, SUBTRACT THE QUANTITY FROM COLUMN 1 AND ADD QUANTITY TO COLUMN 2. (C) WHEN MATERIALS ARE APPORTIONED SUBTRACT QUANTITY FROM COLUMN 4 AND ADD QUANTITY APPORTIONED TO COLUMN 3. (D) WHEN MATERIALS ARE ISSUED, SUBTRACT QUANTITY FROM COLUMNS 2 AND 3. (E) WHEN MATERIALS ARE RECEIVED, ON CREDITS, ADD TO COLUMNS 2 AND 4. **NOTE**—IN ALL CASES BRING DOWN AT ONCE BALANCE IN EACH COLUMN AFFECTED.

1—ORDERED BUT NOT YET DELIVERED			2—ON HAND IN THE STOREROOM						3—APPORTIONED TO AN ORDER BUT NOT YET ISSUED FROM STOREROOM				4 AVAILABLE THAT IS ON ORDER AND ON HAND		
DATE ORDERED	PURCHASE ORDER	QUANTITY	DATE REC'D	QUANTITY	DATE ISSUED	ISSUED TO ORDER NUMBERS	TOTAL COST	COST PER UNIT	DATE APP. OR ISSUED	QUANTITY	APPORTIONED TO ORDER NUMBER	DATE DUE IN STORES	DATE	QUANTITY	REMARKS
			2/11	1500			$35 00	.0233					2/11	1500	
									2/12	600	C.D. 760			600	
														900	
2/12	I.E. 258	4000												4000	
				600	2/15	C.D. 760	21 00	.0233	2/15	600				4900	
				900						0			2/16	75	RET'D on C.D. 760
			2/16	75										4975	
				975											
	I.E. 258	4000	2/17	4000											
		0		4975			115 92	.0233							

NOTE: THE ENTRIES ARE PURPOSELY SEPARATED SOMEWHAT VERTICALLY TO ENABLE THE STUDENT TO READ THE BALANCE ON ANY DATE MORE READILY

FIG. 43.—Balance-of-stores ledger sheet.

they are to be charged unless classified standing order numbers have been provided for this purpose (see Art. 184). Standard supplies, such as oil and waste, are often given out at assigned times only, and in definite quantity, to each man. Extra quantities may be drawn at other times by special order only.

Item 5.—It is obvious that if the stores department is to anticipate the needs of the factory it must keep a fairly accurate record of all material and supplies. If a planning department exists this need is accentuated, since skillful planning cannot be carried on without accurate record of materials on hand. The extent and detail necessary in such records will, of course, vary greatly with the business. In the case of continuous processes, or of manufacturing approaching a continuous process, where the material for the most part moves from the store room directly through the factory without interruption, the store-room bins and racks may be considered as reservoirs in which the material should never fall below or rise above certain economical limits that have been fixed by the considerations already discussed.

Several methods are available for making intelligent use of such maximum and minimum limits. The simplest is that which may be called **observation of limits.** Usually only two limits are set, the maximum and the minimum, though sometimes a lower or **danger** limit is set for the purpose of indicating that orders for a fresh supply of material must be rushed. To keep account of the material a printed form is attached to each bin or rack, and as material is withdrawn the storekeeper deducts the amount taken away, thus keeping a continuous record of what is left. When the amount falls to the lower limit an order is placed that will bring the amount up again to the maximum.

162. Balance-of-stores Ledger.—In more highly developed systems of production, as described in Chap. XII, the stores records are kept by a head storekeeper or his clerical assistant on a card system or in a loose-leaf ledger ruled especially for this purpose, as illustrated in Fig. 43, and known as a **balance-of-stores ledger.** As noted in Chap. XII (Art. 121), the complete control of production and the accurate prediction of the schedule of productive processes depend to a certain degree on the control of materials. The required information concerning material is recorded on these ledger sheets in the following manner. Each ledger sheet records the transactions in one part or item only.

Referring to Fig. 43 it will be seen that there are four main vertical divisions, namely, **1—Ordered; 2—On Hand; 3—Apportioned;** and **4—Available.** If entries are properly made the sum of divisions 1 and 2, that is the amounts **ordered** and **on hand,** will always equal the sum of divisions 3 and 4, that is the amounts **apportioned** and **available,** and the distribution of all stores recorded upon the sheet may be seen at a glance. To illustrate the procedure let it be assumed that on February 11 there were on hand 1,500, ½- by 4½-inch bolts. Being **on hand** they were also **available,** and entries to this effect were made in these columns. The balance of stores shown by the four division columns was then 0 + 1,500 = 0 + 1,500.

On February 12, 600 bolts were apportioned to production order 760. The entries made were as follows: 600 was added to the Apportioned

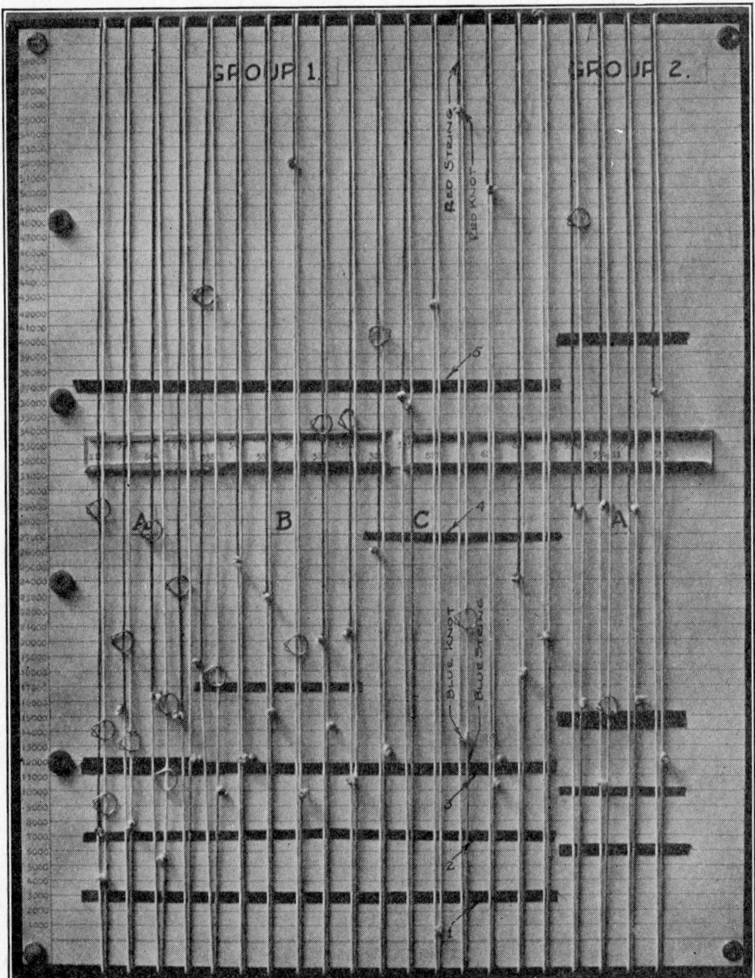

Fig. 44.—Visual balance of stores of Corona Typewriter Co.

column and 600 subtracted from the Available column and the balance was 0 + 1,500 = 600 + 900. This transaction, however, brought the available amount below the minimum allowable quantity as shown at the top of the sheet, consequently an order was placed for 4,000 bolts, which is also the predetermined quantity to be ordered. Ordered material is considered as available, due allowance being made for time of deliveries, hence 4,000 is added to both Column 1 and Column 4, making the balance 4,000 + 1,500 = 600 + 4,900.

On February 15, the material issue of production order 760 to which 600 bolts had been apportioned was presented by the move man to the stores, and these bolts were issued and this amount subtracted from both Column 2, On Hand, and Column 3, Apportioned. The balance then was 4,000 + 900 = 0 + 4,900.

On February 16, 75 bolts were returned to stores, it having been found that the material issue of production order 760 was that much in excess of actual requirements. This number was, therefore, added to both Column 2 and Column 4 and the balance then stood 4,000 + 975 = 0 + 4,975. On February 17, the 4,000 bolts that were ordered on February 12 were received. This number was, therefore, deducted from Column 1 and added to Column 2. The balance on that date was, therefore, 0 + 4,975 = 0 + 4,975. In Column 2 provision is also made for pricing the bolts both for unit cost and also for total cost. This serves as a memorandum of the value of the inventory and also provides the information for evaluating the material issue for the benefit of the cost department. From time to time the actual quantity on hand is checked by actual count against the quantity recorded on the ledger. This is indicated by drawing a vertical line as shown in Column 2 down to the date at which this checking was performed.

163. Visual Balance of Stores.—In industries that manufacture a standardized product, where the variety of stores is not very great and the quantities fairly large, a visual balance[1] of stores may be operated to advantage. Figure 44 shows a miniature model[2] of such a device in successful operation at the plant of the L. C. Smith-Corona Typewriter Company. The actual board is about 15 feet long and 6 feet high. Through a series of corresponding notches at the top and bottom of the board, pairs of strings are carried completely around the board so that they can be moved at will. The right-hand string of each pair is made up of two parts, one white and one blue, knotted together, the knot serving as an indicator. The left-hand string of each pair is made up, also, of two parts, one white and one red, knotted together in a similar fashion, the knot serving again as an indicator. These knots will be referred to as the *blue knot* and the *red knot*, respectively. Each pair of strings indicates for one part as follows:

1. The amount of raw material on hand.
2. The amount of finished or partly finished parts in process.

[1] See also LORD, C. B., "Visualized Management Control," *Management and Administration*, September, 1903.

[2] Since this was written this control board has been improved but the basic principles as here described remain unchanged.

3. The point where raw material should be ordered.
4. The point where new manufacturing orders should be issued.
5. The amount of raw material on order.
6. The total inventory of finished parts, parts in process, and raw material in stores for any given machine part.

To illustrate the method of operation consider the pair of strings on which the blue knot and red knot are indicated. The horizontal markers 1, 2, 3, 4, and 5 are made of colored ribbons and are placed on the board at the desired level as indicated by the scale at the extreme left. The lower ribbon indicates the danger limit for finished parts and is so placed that if, when the blue knot falls to that level, a new manufacturing order for finished parts is placed with the factory, these parts would be available by the time the blue knot reaches zero. It is not advisable, however, to work so closely to the limit and, therefore, ribbon 2 is placed somewhat above ribbon 1 and indicates the minimum limit to which the supply of finished parts should be permitted to fall before placing a new manufacturing order. The distance between ribbons 1 and 2 represents a cushion or reserve to provide for emergencies and should never be too large, as this increases the inventory value, which should be kept as low as possible, compatible with safety in production.

A certain amount of time must be allowed to the planning department for issuing manufacturing orders, bills of material, etc. This time is represented by the distance between ribbons 2 and 3. There should also be a limit to the number of parts on hand and this limit is set by ribbon 4. The distance between ribbons 4 and 2, therefore, measures on the scale the size or number of the lot to be made on new manufacturing orders.

The height of the red knot measures the total inventory of finished stores, parts in process, and raw material, all in terms of numbers of finished parts. The distance between the red knot and the blue knot, therefore, measures the amount of raw material on hand. The ordering point for new material is indicated by ribbon 5 and is set as far above ribbon 2 as will permit the stores and purchasing departments to obtain new material by the time it is needed. By means of auxiliary clips attached to the strings and colored marker buttons shown at the left it is possible to visualize all the conditions shown on the balance-of-stores sheet (Fig. 43). Space will not permit, however, of a more extended discussion of this board but it will be obvious that the principle is capable of wide application.

164. The Control of the Inventory.—As noted in Art. 161, materials in stores, in process of fabrication, and in the form of finished stock are, for the time, crystallized capital and not infrequently represent a large part of the capital investment. While it is essential, therefore, that the material needs of the enterprise be adequately provided for, it is equally important that this form of capital investment be kept at a minimum value. Under older and cruder methods of management this value was known, with any degree of certainty, but once a year when a **visual inventory** was taken of the entire plant; in fact, this method still prevails in many plants. In taking such an inventory all assets are evaluated and all material measured, weighed, or counted, and priced according to the judgment of those taking the inventory, with a view of finding the current value of the business. Usually this means a total suspension of work for several days and it always makes a serious interruption of the work, though it does give a good picture of the state of the business.

It will be clear, however, that if stores have been issued only upon proper orders and if the balance-of-stores ledger is accurately kept it will be a **continuous inventory** of all material in stores. And since the cost of all material is also placed upon these ledger sheets they also record the *cost value* of all material in stores. Whether this value or the *present market* value, or a *depreciated* value (see Chap. XIX) shall be placed upon such an inventory is a matter of judgment upon the part of the management. It is customary where a continuous inventory of this kind is kept to check the actual amount in each bin or rack against the stores ledger, whenever an order is placed for additional material, so that verification of the stores ledger is in constant progress. Many managers are not satisfied, however, with such a clerical inventory, and, while using it for ordinary accounting purposes, insist upon a periodic visual inventory. An analogy is found in banking where book values are always verified by periodic counting of all assets on hand.

As will be shown later in Chap. XVIII, the **cost ledger** shows at all times the values of all material in process of fabrication. Finished product or stock is recorded in a **stock ledger** not unlike the stores ledger. The value of all fixed assets such as land, buildings, machinery, etc., are recorded in a **plant ledger** (see Fig. 51). These several ledgers, therefore, if accurately kept, constitute a complete continuous inventory of the physical assets of the enterprise. The relation of stores, material in process, stock, and the three corresponding ledgers in their relation to the main ledger are shown graphically in Fig. 45, where production is visualized as a *flow* from left to right of the diagram. The stores act as a reservoir between the market for supplies and the factory; the stock room acts in a similar capacity between the factory and the market for sales. The stores ledger registers the level of the value of the stores, the cost ledger registers the accumulated values of materials in process, and the stock ledger indicates the value of the finished product on hand (see also Art. 190).

It is obvious that the methods, blanks, forms, etc., that may be used advantageously in store-room and stock-room work will vary widely with the business and conditions, as indeed they necessarily must in all business organizations. The methods suggested in the preceding paragraphs have been included more to explain the problems met in handling material than to advocate them as the best for all cases. They are, however, in successful use in many places.

While it is essential that the necessary stores shall be on hand when needed it is just as essential that no more stores shall be carried than is necessary. The maximum and minimum quantities of all materials should, therefore, be determined with care. In many cases these limits can be set only by experience and careful observation and such observation will often result in a great reduction of inventory.

A number of efforts have been made to determine mathematically the most economical number of pieces that should be produced at one time, taking into account probable sales, cost of setting up the machinery of production, interest upon the investment in stores, etc. Professor Ralph C. Davis[1] has developed a very complete and fairly simple solution of the problem as follows:

Let Q = the most economical number of pieces to be manufactured.
A = total cost of preparation for manufacturing, setting up, etc.
M = rate of manufacturing expressed in pieces per year.
S = rate of consumption by sales per year.
C' = unit cost per piece.
I = current rate of interest.
R_1 = quantity of material necessary to manufacture the lot of parts.
R = quantity of material in stores when order for new material should be placed.
R_2 = reserve material held in stores for emergency purposes.
$F = \frac{R}{R_1}$ for convenience.

It should be noted that, in general, $R_2 = R - R_1$. If, however, no reserve is considered necessary, $R = R_1$ and ordering would begin when the material on hand was just sufficient to manufacture a lot of parts. If, however, material can be obtained quickly and if the withdrawal of material is gradual so that ordering and receiving of new material may proceed coincident with the manufacturing of the same, R may be less than R_1, and R_2 is then a negative quantity. The value of F, furthermore, will be greater or less than unity depending upon whether R is greater or less than R_1.

Then according to the demonstration of Professor Davis:

$$Q = \sqrt{\frac{A}{K}}$$

where K is a constant whose value for different values of F is as follows:

[1] See Davis, R. C., "The Principles of Factory Organization and Management," p. 259.

F	K	F	K
0.25	$\left(\frac{M - 0.5S}{2MS}\right)C'I$	1.25	$\left(\frac{M^2 + 1.5MS + 0.5S^2}{2M^2S}\right)C'I$
0.50	$\frac{C'I}{2S}$	1.50	$\left(\frac{(M + S)^2}{2M^2S}\right)C'I$
0.75	$\left(\frac{M + 0.5S}{2MS}\right)C'I$	2.00	$\left[\frac{(M + S)(M + 2S)}{2M^2S}\right]C'I$
1.00	$\left(\frac{M + S}{2MS}\right)C'I$	3.00	$\left[\frac{(M + S)(M + 4S)}{2M^2S}\right]C'I$

To illustrate the use of the equation, assume that the rate of sales $S = 30,000$ per year and that where the machinery of production is set up parts can be manufactured at a rate per year of $M = 150,000$. Let $C' = \$20$; $I = 0.06$; $A = \$1,000$; and assume that conditions are such that no reserve is needed, hence $R = R_1$ and $F = 1.0$

Then

$$K = \left(\frac{M + S}{2MS}\right)C'I = \left(\frac{150,000 + 30,000}{2 \times 150,000 \times 30,000}\right)20 \times 0.6 = 0.000024$$

Hence

$$Q = \sqrt{\frac{A}{K}} = \sqrt{\frac{1,000}{0.000024}} = 6,455 \text{ pieces.}$$

This would be about 4 months' supply and it would require about 2 weeks to produce the lot of goods.

This discussion indicates that for lowest unit cost the quantity to be manufactured varies as the square root of the preparation costs. This appears to be corroborated by other similar discussions. The effect of preparation costs upon unit costs as discussed in Art. 31 and as illustrated in Fig. 4 should be noted. It will be seen that this influence is very great when the number produced is small, decreases rapidly as the number is increased, and becomes negligible when the number produced is very large. It should be noted also in this regard that in solving the Davis equation the unit cost is assumed from preceding records. If this cost has been obtained from manufactured quantities not markedly different from the value of Q, the solution may be considered satisfactory. If, however, this cost has been obtained from much larger quantities than Q and particularly if Q should be a moderately small quantity, a rise in manufacturing costs might result if the quantity represented by Q was put into production. In other words, the quantities must be such as to be well away from that portion of the curve (Fig. 4) where the rate of change of curvature is very great.

The Davis equation is simple and easy of application and considering that all such expressions rest partly, at least, upon certain assumptions, such as the rate of interest, the unit cost of production, and the yearly rate of sales, it is probably sufficiently accurate for most cases. Professor F. R. Raymond has developed fully the theory of economical lot sizes in his book "Quantity and Economy in Manufacture," and the reader is referred to this volume for a very exhaustive treatment[1] of the subject. A discussion of the Raymond formula and of other simpler equations by Younger, Camp, Lehoczky, and Norton will be found in Alford (Ed.), L. P., "Cost and Production Management," p. 236.

165. Economical Use of Material.—The material wasted around a factory may be a serious source of loss, particularly if the material has high intrinsic value as in the case of copper and brass. These wastes may be due to several causes. It is not always possible to specify exactly just how much of a certain material is needed for a job and, if a liberal amount is drawn, that left over after the completion of the job is seldom returned to the store room, but collects on and under benches, and in out-of-the-way corners. In certain kinds of work, as in punch-press processes, the material left after the punched parts are removed is often as great as or greater than the parts themselves; and, if the material is valuable, care should be taken to recover it. In all cases systematic and constant effort should be made to collect and store all scrap so as to recover as much value as possible, and also to keep the shop or factory clean.

In nearly every store room will be found old material for which there is no apparent use. This comes usually from two sources. The first is overordering of material for special jobs. Special material is always a hazardous investment and care should be taken that no more is ordered than will give the minimum margin of safety. The second most important cause is a change in design. The engineering department can save a great amount of money by carefully considering the question of material. The standardization of parts, and the use of the same part as often as possible, keep down the value of the inventory; and great care should be taken that no change in design is made that will leave raw material, finished parts, or completed machines in danger of obsolescence. Obsolete material, raw or worked, depreciates very rapidly, completed machines often being worth less than the original cost of the materials of which they are composed. Before scrapping such material, however, a report should be sent to the manager, approved by all parties concerned, giving the inventory value, scrap value, and loss, with the reasons and responsibility for such loss clearly determined.

The wasteful use of indirect materials and supplies is another source of great loss, especially in large plants. As before noted, it is a difficult problem to specify accurately, and supervise intelligently, the drawing of expense material from the stores. A cost-keeping system, however, that furnishes accurate records of all expense material is a powerful means of regulating these expenditures. The purchasing of expense material best

[1] See also *Factory and Industrial Management*, July, 1930.

suited to the needs of the plant and their economical handling and use are a fruitful field of study for the works engineer, and his labor will be greatly expedited by well-kept records of performance in all branches of the business from office to power house (see Art. 101).

References

ALFORD, L. P. (Ed.): "Cost and Production Handbook," p. 445.

———: "Management's Handbook," pp. 543 and 1090.

CARTMELL, M.: "Stores and Materials Control."

DAVIS, R. C.: "The Principles of Industrial Organization and Management," Chap. XVII.

JONES, E. D.: "The Administration of Industrial Enterprises," Chap. XVI.

LANDSBURG, R. H.: "Industrial Management," Chap. XXXIV.

VAN DEVENTER, J. H.: "Machine-shop Management."

———: "Planning Production for Profit."

CHAPTER XVI

STANDARDS AND STANDARDIZATION

166. Wastes Due to Variety.—One of the most important sources of industrial waste is the great variety in which many articles are manufactured. As explained in Art. 32, the unit cost of any article can, in general, be decreased as the quantity to be produced is increased. For a given total production of any article, therefore, the greater the variety in which it is produced the smaller must be the number of each variety and consequently the higher will be the unit cost. This principle is well known to most manufacturers, but there are often other considerations which lead them to produce a given line of goods in such a variety of patterns and sizes as greatly to reduce, if not entirely eliminate, all profits.

These considerations may be on the part of the manufacturer or on the part of the purchasing public. On the side of the manufacturer is the natural desire to have something different from his competitors in order to put forward real or imaginary superiorities in his product. There is, therefore, a natural tendency to bring out new and "improved" models while possibly continuing to manufacture the old lines. There is also the very natural desire to produce a line of goods to satisfy the varying purchasing powers of customers. Thus the manufacturer of phonographs would naturally produce instruments of varying quality and price if he expected to interest customers of varying wealth. This tendency on the part of the manufacturer has been greatly increased by the attitude of the modern aggressive salesman in constantly demanding new and more attractive models and sometimes by overprogressive designers and engineers who insist on producing new models that may have engineering advantages so small as not to warrant their introduction.

On the part of the purchasing public there is always a demand for certain products having individuality. Thus many people wish to have special writing paper, pocket knives of distinctive design, furniture made to suit their peculiar ideas, automobiles unlike their neighbors, etc. And in wearing apparel there are always the demands of changing styles to be met. The desire on the part of producers to meet these changing conditions has brought about such a complexity as to give rise to a well-defined movement not only to check this tendency, where possible, but also to eliminate some of the existing wastes due to this tendency. The basis of this movement is **simplification and standardization.**

167. Simplification and Standardization.—The economic principles that underlie standardization with its advantages and disadvantages are quite fully discussed in Chap. V. It was there stated that industrial standardization may be introduced for any one or a combination of four purposes, namely:

1. To reduce a given line of product to fixed *types, sizes,* and *characteristics.*
2. To establish *interchangeability* of manufactured parts and products.
3. To establish standards of *excellence* and *quality* in *materials.*
4. To establish standards of *performance* of men and machines.

Thus, many years ago engineers agreed that the best types of heads and nuts for bolts were hexagonal or square. They also agreed upon certain fixed diameters for the bodies of all bolts up to certain sizes. Later they agreed fairly well upon the number of threads that should be cut upon each size of bolt and upon the dimensions of the heads and the nuts. The length of bolts necessarily has not been standardized except as regards small sizes and short lengths. Later the Society of Automotive Engineers prescribed very closely the chemical constituency of all steels to be used in automobile bolts, thereby almost completely defining the types, sizes, and characteristics of all such bolts. Prior to the World War, however, commercial standardization of this character had been confined largely to the efforts of the larger engineering and scientific organizations.

After the United States entered the war the Conservation Division of the War Industries Board began an active campaign to reduce excess varieties of all manner of manufactured product in order to release labor, capital, material, and equipment for war purposes. The remarkable degree to which this board succeeded in eliminating excess types and sizes should be studied[1] to be appreciated fully. This work is now being continued with considerable success by the Division of Simplified Practice of the United States Department of Commerce. The general method of attacking such a problem is to study it thoroughly and then call together representatives of manufacturers, distributors, and users of the article under consideration, and endeavor to get them to agree to the elimination of certain types and sizes. Thus, in this manner 60 out of 66 varieties and sizes of paving brick have been eliminated and many similar reductions have been made in other lines of product.

The term **simplification** has been used to denote this movement to eliminate excess types and sizes, and the statement has been made by some writers that simplification is entirely independent of standardization. This statement cannot be very well defended. Thus consider the history of standardized bolts, to which reference has been made. When all other shapes of nuts and heads, except square and hexagonal shapes, had been eliminated, surely these remaining shapes became the standard shapes for these items. In a similar way when all other body sizes, except

[1] See ALFORD, L. P. (Ed.), "Cost and Production Handbook," p. 303.

those now universally used, were eliminated, surely also these selected body sizes became standard for this purpose. Consider again, the matter of paving brick. When the 60 types and sizes had been eliminated the remaining 6 most certainly became standards to which manufacturers were supposed to work. Simplification, so called, is just as much the selection of standards from a large variety as it is a process of eliminating all but these chosen standards. Simplification in fact, as thus defined, is simply standardization *in a limited number of particulars*.

Nor can a distinction be made on the ground that true standardizations must be based upon scientific study. It is true that excess types and sizes can often be eliminated with little scientific research, but it is always dangerous to generalize. Thus, elimination of excess types and sizes of alarm clocks would not require much scientific investigation, but the selection of a chime of bells is a strictly scientific matter that cannot be solved in an off-hand or empirical manner. And yet the object to be attained is the same in each case; namely, to find the smallest number of units within the required range that will most successfully answer the requirements. There is, however, some justification for the use of the term simplification in the appeal that it may make to an industry at large, whereas the more formal term, standardization, might not be well received.

168. Standardizing Organizations.—Modern standardization work may be conveniently divided into four fields, namely; **international, national,** that pertaining to a **particular industry,** and that pertaining to an **individual plant.** Standards of international interest would naturally be basic in character. Thus the ohm, the volt, the minute, the meter, etc., are international in importance. The standard gage for railways may also be of similar character between adjoining countries.

In the United States, reliance is placed, to a large extent, upon the United States Bureau of Standards for the development and definition of basic scientific standards. Industrial and engineering standards, however, have been developed largely by the many engineering and technical organizations. Thus the Boiler Code of the American Society of Mechanical Engineers has become the standard for all boiler construction in this country and is a legal requirement in many states. In order to prevent excessive overlapping and to secure fullest cooperation, the 40 most important technical societies and federal government departments are united into the American Standards Association, through representation. While the actual work of standardization remains, as it should, within the group to which it rightly belongs, the American Standards Association furnishes a means of discussion and comparison. This is no doubt the most powerful standardizing organization in existence and in all probability it will eventually exercise a great influence on international standardization.

Standardization within an industry is well illustrated by the work of the component members of the American Standards Association. Thus the American Society of Mechanical Engineers has published many engineering standards and a number of safety codes for the construction of elevators, etc. Another notable illustration of standardization within the industry is the work of the Society of Automotive Engineers, whose standardization committee has fully standardized many automotive parts not only as to form and dimensions but also as to chemical composition. Although these several agencies have done much to establish standard practices in the industries, as yet only a comparatively small part of the work possible has been accomplished.

Every industrial enterprise may, therefore, be influenced in its operation by international[1] and national standards and by standards that have been established by the industry of which it is a component part. But in addition most large engineering and manufacturing plants have standards that apply to their own peculiar activities. As has been fully explained in Arts. 47 and 48, such standardization within the plant itself may be for economic reasons or it may be necessary for purposes of interchangeability of parts. The most important standardizing agencies within a plant are usually the engineering department, if one exists, and the production department, or whatever corresponds thereto in the organization. A more detailed discussion of the several forms of standardization may make the entire matter somewhat clearer.

169. Standards of Form and Size.—It will probably be some time before the movement toward simplification of the types and sizes of manufactured product will make itself felt in all industries, and the problem of the selection of the best form and size of product will long be before most manufacturers. One reason for this is the fact that this phase of standardization is not capable of mathematical solution but must always remain more or less empirical. Thus a manufacturer elects to manufacture engines of definite sizes and capacities or he elects to make shoes in certain widths and lengths, basing his deductions upon the law of averages and expecting to produce the sizes of product that are in greatest demand.

It is obvious, however, that standards of this kind are more or less arbitrary and that there is considerable latitude in their choice. Thus there is no special virtue in the standard of length that has been adopted and named "one foot." It might well be a little longer or shorter and be equally serviceable. The standard dimensions for collars, coats, shoes, and a multitude of manufactured articles have all been fixed by more or less arbitrary methods. They represent an approximate solution of an industrial demand between certain indefinite limits of that demand;

[1] For a full discussion of national and international standardizing organizations see N. F. Harriman, "Standards and Standardization."

and the field covered by one standard size laps over that covered by the standard size both above and below it. The fixing of standards of exchange or of interchangeability is, therefore, a somewhat arbitrary matter, while the skillful fixing of standards of form and size for manufacturing purposes requires an intimate knowledge of that part of the industrial field which is to be covered.

An interesting effort to apply rational methods to these problems is found in the theory of **preferred numbers,** so-called. According to the reasoning on which the theory of preferred numbers is based, the human mind naturally accepts a *geometrical* progression as against an *arithmetical* progression in fixing a series of graded sizes. It is pointed out that our standard bolt sizes, pipe sizes, etc., if plotted as ordinates against serial numbers as abscissas, all lie along curves that are roughly parabolic in outline and the argument is advanced, with some justification, that it would be better frankly to accept this basic theory and lay out all such series in true geometric progression. This matter has been given considerable consideration abroad and both French[1] and German authorities have developed such series which have been adopted to some extent by industry in these respective countries. Whether such systems will come into extended use in this country is somewhat problematical.

170. Standards of Excellence.—It often occurs that there are certain combinations of form, size, quality, conditions, or other circumstances that are the best that can be selected for a certain purpose. Thus many makers of boilers may all produce a standardized boiler of a certain nominal capacity. The form and shape of the boiler built by each shop may vary widely but all may conform to certain standards set by state or national laws. The efficiency of these boilers in burning coal and in transforming the heat into steam may also vary considerably and the performance of the boiler which shows the highest efficiency may be selected as a standard of excellence for all boilers of that size. A certain piece of work may be performed in several ways, but there may be one sequence of operations that produces better results than any other. Such a sequence may be adopted as a standard method. Experience may show that an operator will accomplish more and better work with a given tool and this tool may be adopted as a standard for that process. A rapid workman may do a certain piece of work in a given time and this time may be used as a standard for judging other records of performance. In the textile industries, it is found that the best work can be done only when the temperature and humidity of the rooms are kept at certain points. These conditions when once determined may be adopted as the standard conditions under which the work is to be done. Many other

[1] See ALFORD, L. P. (Ed.), "Management's Handbook," pp. 127 and 1015. See also HIRSHFELD, C. F., and C. H. BERRY, "Size Standardization by Preferred Numbers," *Trans. Am. Soc. Mech. Eng.*, Vol. 44.

illustrations of this kind might be quoted, though the advantages of standards of this kind are not so widely appreciated as might be supposed.

It should be noted that an article that has been standardized in form or size may be built to several *standards of excellence.* It may not be necessary or desirable, furthermore, that the highest standard of excellence be attained in all cases. Thus it may be desirable to make shoes of a given model and size in several grades of quality. If only the highest grades of phonographs were manufactured a very small number of people could enjoy them. It may be necessary to build an article of highest quality for one service while the same article so far as form and size are concerned, but of inferior quality, would be equally serviceable for some other purpose. It is usually important, however, that all articles of a given form and size should be fully up to the standards of excellence that have been established for its manufacture, whether these standards be high or low. A few illustrations of the applications of standards to various industrial activities may make their use clearer.

171. Engineering and Production Standards.—The engineering department must necessarily determine largely the types and sizes of product that are standardized for production, and must fix the dimensions and forms of all parts of standardized machines. This department is expected to determine the standards of *size* and *form* necessary for interchangeability if that is desired and to fix all limiting dimensions to that end.

The idea of interchangeable manufacture originated in France, but the first successful application of the principle and its most extended development are generally credited to this country. In fact, the method of production based upon this principle was long known in Europe as the "American system." Priority in the use of this method is usually given to Eli Whitney,[1] the inventor of the cotton gin, who, in 1798, began the manufacture of muskets for the United States government on the interchangeable system. Without doubt, it has been the most important factor in American manufacturing methods.

It is important to understand the accuracy demanded in modern interchangeable manufacturing and the consequent accuracy necessary in the basic gages and manufacturing machinery. In the production of such products as typewriters, adding machines, sewing machines, guns, automobiles, etc., the parts must be produced so accurately that no hand fitting is necessary or permissible in assemblying the completed product. All parts are, therefore, manufactured to predetermined limits of accuracy and in some cases these limits are unbelievably fine. Thus, in the production of certain automobiles it is claimed that more than 5,000 machine operations are performed in which the deviation from the required measurement is not permitted to exceed one 0.001 inch, more

[1] See Roe, J. W., "English and American Tool Builders," p. 129.

than 1,200 operations are held to a deviation not to exceed one-half of 0.001 inch and in more than 300 operations the deviation from standard is not permitted to exceed one-quarter of 0.001 inch. No doubt other manufacturers of high-grade apparatus can show similar results.

The ability to produce such results depends upon the possession of basic reference gages of extreme accuracy and upon machining methods by which this accuracy can be transferred to the product in simple and inexpensive manner. The highest refinement in basic reference gages for manufacturing is found in modern **block gages,** so called. A full set of Johannson gages consists of 81 steel blocks about 1 inch long, 3/8 inch wide, and varying in thickness from 0.1001 inch to 4 inches. They are made in three grades of accuracy. In the highest grade the error in thickness and parallelism does not exceed 0.000002 inch. The corresponding guaranteed errors for the other sets are 0.000004 inch and 0.000008 inch. Special sets of such gages have been made that are even more accurate

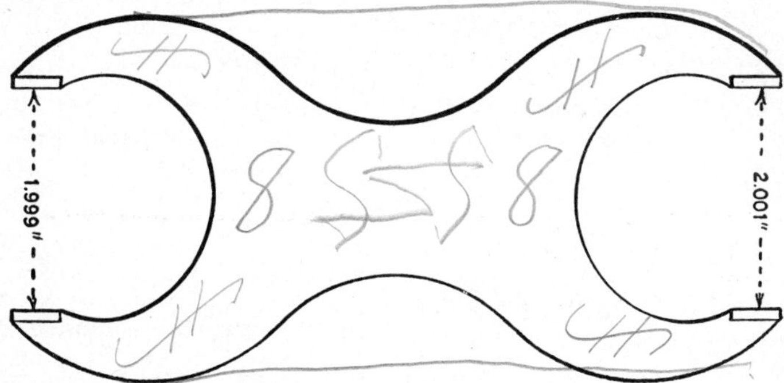

FIG. 45.—Limit gauge.

than this and it is reported that Johansson, the originator of block gages, has produced a set of blocks that are accurate to 0.000001 inch. All dimensions are as indicated at a fixed temperature of 65°F.

There are a number of ways by which extreme accuracy is obtained in producing machine parts but, no doubt, the grinding machine is the most accurate and will be used as an illustration. In grinding a circular section, such as the bearing of an automobile crankshaft, the shaft is rotated *on fixed centers* while the grinding wheel traverses the bearing lengthwise removing the surplus metal, thus producing a section of extreme accuracy so far as *form* is concerned. The diameter may be gaged by a skilled mechanic with a micrometer caliper but in quantity production, where it is desired to use semiskilled labor, the **limit gage** is employed. Figure 45 shows such a gage. Suppose it is desired to grind the bearing in hand to 2 inches with a "tolerance" not to exceed 0.001 inch. That is, the bearing is not to be larger than 2.001 nor smaller than 1.999 inches. One jaw of the limit gage is then ground and gaged by the standard blocks to the maximum dimension and the other to the minimum dimension, the standard gage block being used only for this purpose and never for actual manufacturing. The grinding machine, from its very nature, can reduce the diameter of the bearing by exceedingly small increments, much smaller than can be removed by a cutting tool. It is easily possible, therefore, to grind down the bearing until the large jaw will just pass over it, but the small jaw will not do so. Obviously, when this is the case, the bearing is smaller than the largest dimension but larger than the smaller limit and, therefore, within the desired limits.

Most important, also, is the fact that this operation can be performed by a semiskilled man. It is an excellent illustration, again, of transfer of skill and gives a good idea of the manner in which most refined processes are performed by moderate or even low-degree manual and mental skill. It will be obvious that methods of this kind are expensive and are applicable economically only where large quantities are to be produced, or where interchangeability is imperative for other reasons. M. F. Harriman states:

> The production and inspection of Springfield Army rifles require the use of 1,263 gages and a machine gun about 2,200 gages. The Ordinance Department of the Army has under its charge in the various arsenals more than 500,000 gages, the replacement value of which is about $30,000,000.

In spite of the great accuracy of modern machine methods, there is always some difficulty in keeping productive machinery in such accurate repair and adjustment that the work is always up to the desired standards. All parts made by mass production methods must, therefore, be carefully inspected as they are produced, and the machines kept in constant adjustment. Inspection is, therefore, a concomitant of quantity production and constitutes a productive function of itself.

The engineering department should also carefully standardize its own work. Thus, all drawings should be made on sheets of standard size; all engineering instructions should be issued on standard forms; standard methods of lettering and bills of material should be adopted, and a system of standard nomenclature for all drawings and manufactured parts should be worked out. Such standard methods lead not only to clearness but to efficient methods.

More important still, the engineering department must specify the *quality* of the product and often should share in the responsibility of maintaining that quality through the supervision of some of the features of inspection. The selection of standards of quality, however, cannot always be left to the discretion of the engineering department. A good engineer and a good designer naturally wish to make only the very best product. Manufacturing, however, is a commercial undertaking and standards of excellence must often be fixed with reference to market conditions. The sales manager and the general manager in consultation with the chief engineer are more likely, therefore, to arrive at a wiser conclusion regarding the quality of the product than will any of them if undertaking this problem alone (Art. 106).

For similar reasons the engineering department cannot be trusted implicitly in the matter of changing standardized lines of product. If the engineering department is a live organization it will naturally wish to put new designs upon the market. Such a procedure may be very costly if it means the discarding of many valuable special tools that have been made for the line of product that is to be displaced, and especially if they have not paid for themselves in actual production. Engineering changes in standardized product should, therefore, be carefully considered before being put into effect. This particular phase of mass production is a difficult one especially in an industry that is growing and changing. How far, for instance, can a manufacturer of automobiles change his product yearly in order to keep up with engineering progress and popular fancies without going bankrupt by scrapping special tools? Problems of this kind require the most careful attention on the part of the administrator and they are not solely engineering problems, but rather pertain to general policies.

172. Standard Materials.—The necessity of standard specifications as a basis of purchasing has already been noted in the chapter on purchasing. The advantages and economy arising from standardization of materials have not, however, been widely appreciated. In many cases the decision as to quality of the material to be used is left entirely to the storekeeper or to the foreman. In small shops or in shops doing repair work the judgment of such men may often be sufficient. Yet, obviously, better product and lower costs should result from an effort to have the proper material used in every part. This does not mean that the best of material should be used everywhere, but it does mean that when a certain material of a certain quality has been selected for a given purpose care should be taken that this quality is adhered to.

Much money can often be saved by reducing the number of the sizes and shapes of material, and standardization of material reduces the danger of having special material left on hand to depreciate and to tie up capital. All of these advantages are of equal importance in the matter of supplies. These should be bought only after careful consideration of the purpose for which they are intended.

173. Standardization of Quantity.—Great economies can often be effected by carefully prescribing the **amount** of material that is to be used. In repair work the economical use of material usually becomes a matter of personal vigilance, but wherever work is to be repeated the quantities should be worked out with care, and standard bills of material made which will serve both as a basis of purchasing and also as a basis on which material can be drawn from stores. Whether these bills of material are made in the engineering department or by the production clerk they should be filed so as to be available for future work.

Standardization of the amount of supplies used is also a source of great economy. In large plants such supplies as waste for cleaning machinery, oil, brooms, etc., can be issued on a budget system, each man receiving periodically what he needs according to his duties. It is an easy matter also to standardize the coal that should be burned in the power house for a given amount of power generated, or to establish standards for the use of gas, chemicals, or other materials that may be used in industrial processes (see Art. 103). If these standard amounts are exceeded some good reason should be forthcoming for the excess.

174. Standard Methods and Performances.—The advantages of standard methods and standard performances have been discussed in connection with the work of the planning department (see Chap. XII). It should be noted, however, that time study and motion study are effective only when they serve as a basis for standards of operation, and their application is not confined to shop processes; they are applicable over a wide range of activities. The accuracy of these methods and the expediency of their application are discussed in Chap. XII.

175. Standard Tools.—While American manufacturers have been the strongest advocates of standardized product they have been very backward in standardizing the tools in their own shops. This is particularly true of the iron-working industries. It is common to see in the same shop a group of lathes all of the same nominal size and capacity, but made by different makers, and markedly different in construction. One will have a lead-screw with 6 threads to the inch, one will have 4 threads to the inch, and still another will have 5 threads to the inch. One will have change gears with the number of teeth based on a multiple of 10, while its neighbor's gears will be based upon a multiple of 12. Competition and a rapidly growing art have brought about these variations.

While such variations in machines of the same size may be of no importance in shops doing general and repair work they become a serious disadvantage when work is planned in advance. Thus it will be clear that in making an instruction card (Fig. 27) a great saving of time and expense can be made if all machines of the same nominal size have the same characteristics. It will not be surprising if the demand for standardization of this kind results in manufacturers adopting some standard characteristics for similar product.

These general principles hold true, also, for small apparatus such as cutting tools. There is no reason why there should be an infinite variety of metal-cutting tools. Several standard sets have been evolved and special grinding machines are now in the market that will grind these tools to standard shape and size. There are many lines of work where these standardized tools can be used to great advantage.

Nor is the application of this principle confined to the tools usually furnished by the employer. It will pay any employer to examine carefully the hand tools that are the property of the workman. In many cases it will pay the employer to replace the worker's personal tools with standard tools at the employer's expense. The same argument holds for personal equipment as goggles, shoes, etc., where the work is dangerous to life and limb. Not only will better work be accomplished where the equipment is adequate, but a saving will be effected through fewer disablements.

176. Standard Conditions.—A most important feature in the attainment of standard performances is the maintaining of standard **conditions.** The example of the textile mill that has been referred to where the air must be kept at standard temperature and humidity for best work illustrates this point very well. The principle holds for all industry. An automatic machine which is impersonal cannot make a standard performance unless it is in as good condition as when the standard was first established. If the driving belt is slack, or if the tools are dull, it is not reasonable to expect the same results as when these factors are up to standard conditions. These relations are even more marked wherever the human element is involved, since men are more sensitive to their surroundings than are machines. A workman cannot make fine measurements with cold fingers be he ever so ambitious, and all are aware of the difficulty of performing wonted tasks in strange surroundings.

The truth of these statements is proved by an examination of any set of costs covering the production of successive lots of product, all presumably made by men of the same degree of skill and upon machines of the same kind and size. The variation in such costs is well known, though the reasons for such variation are not always easy to ascertain. Allowing even for the variation in personal effort under ordinary conditions, as prevailing in most shops, careful attention to the conditions under which men work, the character of their equipment, and similar factors would do much to eliminate some of the wider variations in costs.

177. Permanence of Standards.—It was noted in Art. 49 that standardization tends to crystallize methods and processes and thus retard progress, and for that reason standards should be chosen with care. The standardization of machine tools suggested in a preceding section might tend to retard progress in that field, though there might be compensating gains. A clear distinction should be drawn, however, between standards of such universal use as our standards of weights and measures, and those standards that are peculiar to a particular industry or factory. Standard designs, standard methods, standard tools, and standard conditions as here understood are simply the best methods, tools, conditions, etc., that can be devised at the time for accomplishing a given task and are subject to change whenever better ways and means can be found.

Standard methods, furthermore, do not infer that the highest degree of excellence is sought. It may be just as important to develop standard methods for a cheap machine as for one of the same design but of higher quality. The conditions in a manufacturing establishment are somewhat different from those in industry in general. The special tools that tend to prevent progress wear out and must be renewed and sequence of processes can be changed at will. There is usually ample opportunity for making changes in standardized product without great loss through discarding special equipment. There is nothing inherent in the principles of shop standards that prevents a reasonable degree of progress. The highest degree of excellence in fact is frequently found in highly standardized products, such as electrical apparatus, where long experience in production, coupled with steadily rising standards both in design and in shop methods, have produced machines that are nearly perfect for their purpose.

178. Effect of Standards.—The statements made by some writers, therefore, that standards exercise an injurious effect upon the quality of a product, are based upon a misconception of manufacturing methods. The claim is also advanced that nothing but the very best of any product should be produced. The writer would take direct issue with this view. Modern society has need of many grades of product. It is better that all men should have certain books, for instance, though they are cheaply bound, than that only a few people should have elegantly bound volumes of the same. Those who have the money to pay for special highly finished articles have had no trouble as yet in having their wants satisfied. There will always be a market for the highest hand skill as in painting and carving. What standards really do is to insist on a definite form, quality, or performance, as the case may be, in accordance with the standards selected. They thus tend to raise the average quality to the maximum demanded by the standards set. This effect is common knowledge with all men who have had experience in mass production under modern methods.

It is often objected that standardization by retarding the use of new patents and improvements robs the consumer of the benefits of these innovations. It should be remembered, however, that if a manufacturer is compelled to discard valuable machinery in order to manufacture an improved product before this machinery has paid for itself, the loss must be paid by someone and in all probability by the consumer. For this reason it may be good policy to move slowly in such matters. When the wonderful facilities and implements are considered such as telephones, typewriters, phonographs, bicycles, automobiles, etc., that modern standardized production has made possible, there would seem to be little to worry about so far as retardation of development is concerned. There can be little doubt that the economic advantages of standardization greatly outweigh these objections.

179. Standardization and Individuality.—There is fairly well-established agreement as to the necessity for and value of standardization for articles of strict utility. No one objects to standardized plows, hoes, telephone receivers, Pullman cars, automobiles, paving brick, etc. There are misgivings, however, in some circles lest this principle be carried so far as to affect our artistic life. No thoughtful man wishes to see standardized houses even in factory towns and for the same reason there is reasonable objection to extreme standardization or simplification (see Art. 171) of such articles as windows, doors, building brick, house furniture, etc. The architect does not object to the standardized electrical conduit, socket, and lamp, but he may wish to set the lamp in an artistic bracket of his own design. Similar conditions can be quoted from other callings.

This would no doubt present a difficult problem if it were not for the immense quantities in which all manner of products are produced. Thus strict standardization of cloth for exterior garments would reduce this product to two varieties, one for men and one for women, as practiced widely in some oriental countries. So vast is the required amount of cloth goods, however, that it is possible to have a very great variety and at the same time manufacture a large amount of each pattern. The same holds true of shoes, hats, etc. What is sought is *reasonable* simplification and the elimination of the *excess* varieties that reduce the quantities of each kind of product of uneconomical amounts. There is little danger that standardization will make such progress as to affect the fine arts, and in the meantime there are other movements in modern industry that make decidedly for the production of goods of finer appearance than were possible under handicraft. The effect of standardization upon the worker has already been discussed in Art. 29 and will be referred to again in a succeeding section.

References

ALFORD, L. P. (Ed.): "Cost and Production Handbook," p. 303.

———: "Management's Handbook," pp. 700 and 989.

HARRIMAN, N. F.: "Standards and Standardization."

Publications of American Standards Association and of the leading national engineering societies.

Publications of the U. S. Department of Commerce.

Best way of doing job.

CHAPTER XVII

ATTAINMENT OF STANDARDS—INSPECTION

180. Relation of Inspection to Standards.—It is not difficult to set up standards but it is often exceedingly difficult to realize them fully, because absolute accuracy is almost unattainable in practice. Even with the best of tools and with careful and skilled workmen, exact duplication of form and size is not an easy matter. In practice, therefore, theoretical standards must often be replaced by practical standards which will indicate how far the product may vary from the theoretical standards and yet be satisfactory. The variation from the theoretical standard that may be permissible will differ greatly with the character of the work. In rough work considerable latitude may be permissible in quality, workmanship, and finish. In such work as the manufacturing of military rifles, where a high degree of perfection as to interchangeability is imperative, the dimensional variation that is allowable in the several parts is exceedingly small and satisfactory results not easy to obtain without great care. The experience of many American rifle and munition makers during the World War has furnished ample proof of this statement.

Inspection, then, is the art of comparing materials, product, or performances with established standards. There can be no intelligent inspection without definite standards. In any such items that are to be inspected some will fall outside of a liberal allowance of variation from the standards, some will be well within the limits of error, and others will be very close to the limits. Inspection is the art of selecting from these three classes of product those that will be satisfactory for the work in hand. If the allowable limit of variation from the standard is small this may be a delicate operation. It should be noted that inspection is not always a purely mechanical operation, but often involves good judgment on the part of the inspector. Good inspection requires keen judgment and knowledge of the work in hand, combined with good common sense, particularly where the limits are exceedingly small, as in mass production of fine products.

181. Working Standards.—Theoretical standards in the form of engineering drawings and specifications and all such similar documents are intended to define the exact *form* and *quality* of materials. As before noted, it is usually difficult to secure absolute attainment of these theoretical standards. Furthermore, it is usually not necessary to secure absolute adherence to theoretical standards, and wise management will always prescribe the variation from the theoretical standard that is permissible. Thus if a shaft is to be theoretically 2 inches in diameter a *tolerance* of 2/1,000 above and below that size may be permitted before rejection of the piece. Again, the Boiler Code of the American Society of Mechanical Engineers[1] prescribes that the tensile strength of boiler-plate steel shall be not less than 55,000 pounds per square inch and not greater than 65,000 pounds per square inch, and fixes maximum limits for the sulphur and manganese contents. The American Society for Testing Materials has provided working standards for a wide range of materials.

Sometimes working standards cannot be put into writing with any degree of accuracy, and recourse must be had to *samples*. Thus colors and finishes cannot be described accurately but can be prescribed by samples. Again, in chemical work it is often possible to secure product that is practically 100 per cent pure and fully up to the standard specification. The problem, therefore, of the closeness with which working standards should conform to the theoretical standards will vary widely with the work and the industry. Intelligent inspection cannot be conducted without a clear conception of these limitations. If the limits are too close much work may be wasted. If they are too great poor work may result.

182. Reasons and Basis for Inspection.—As factories increase in size the problem of the careful inspection of all materials becomes one of increasing importance. In a small shop the purchase of material is usually conducted by a skilled man who *sees* what is purchased, and if by chance a lot of poor material is purchased, the financial loss is not great. In large plants, where purchasing is specialized and conducted by specifications, it is of greatest importance that all purchased material be carefully examined before putting it into production, because here the loss may be very great. For the same reason it is also imperative that great care be used to insure accurate workmanship where the quantities are great. In small plants it was, and still is, the practice to use the final assembly of the product as a check against poor workmanship and the final running test as a criterion of the fitness of the materials. Obviously, no such chances can be taken in mass production. There is furthermore, always grave danger that, under modern intensive methods of production, where workmen are pressed by one cause or another to increase the output, the quality of the product will be lowered. This is common experience; any speeding up of productive processes must be safeguarded by careful checks upon the quality of the workmanship. A good inspection system will, therefore, check all material as to quality, quantity, and workmanship, from the time it arrives at the store room till it is placed in the finished stock room; the detail with which this is accomplished, and the methods adopted for so doing, necessarily vary greatly with the industry and plant.

[1] The Bulletin of the Committee on Limits and Tolerances of the American Society of Mechanical Engineers should also be consulted.

The requirements on which material is inspected may be based upon one or all of the following characteristics:

1. Quantitative, *i.e.*, as to quantity or number of pieces.
2. Qualitative, *i.e.*, as to physical or chemical properties.
3. Dimensional, *i.e.*, as to accuracy of form or finish.
4. Salability, *i.e.*, as to fitness of the finished product for the purposes for which it is intended.

In general, it is not convenient or desirable to have all inspection done in one department or by one body of men, and in most large plants it is divided into three distinct divisions, though the work of these divisions may overlap at times. Raw material is usually inspected by the stores department under the jurisdiction of the storekeeper; dimensional and other manufacturing inspection is usually conducted by the shop inspectors, who are directly under the superintendent; while the final inspection of the finished product may be under another head. In engineering works, and manufacturing based on scientific principles, the final inspection and tests of performance are usually under the direction of the engineering or designing department.

183. Inspection of Purchases.—The skill and prudence of the best of purchasing agents may be largely nullified unless all material received is carefully verified as to both quality and quantity. Many large works have a **receiving department,** which is usually part of the stores department, and under the control of the head storekeeper. Here all purchased materials are counted and inspected and all articles not up to the specifications on which they were purchased are rejected. This inspection may include visual examination as to quantity and quality or it may extend to chemical and mechanical tests, if necessary, to determine whether the materials are up to the standard paid for. In large works, manufacturing interchangeable apparatus, the careful inspection of such articles as taps and dies, machine screws, and similar supplies is not only absolutely essential for the sake of interchangeability, but is a source of great financial saving. If possible, it is also advantageous to be able to identify materials that develop defects in process of fabrication, so as to make such just claims on those furnishing them as may seem desirable.

184. Inspection during Manufacture.—Inspection during the process of manufacture should be organized with the following considerations in mind.

1. To prevent unnecessary hand work on the assembly floor.
2. To inspect mass-production operations in the beginning and often enough thereafter to prevent any great amount of material being spoiled.
3. To prevent further work on parts already spoiled.
4. To see that no parts are lost in transfer from process to process and that all are accounted for.
5. To pay only for good work.

6. To find and locate imperfections in machines and processes and lack of skill on the part of the workman.

7. To guard against the natural tendency of intensive production to cause a lowering of the standards of accuracy.

Under the older and cruder methods machine parts were made as accurately as the tools available would allow, and the discrepancies adjusted with the file or other hand tool at assembly. Today, with the demand that exists for interchangeable parts, such hand work cannot be tolerated, and with modern machine tools and measuring appliances it is not necessary, provided all parts are carefully inspected when made. It is, furthermore, more economical, where there is any considerable quantity, to spend a little more to insure accuracy in detail parts, thereby saving the annoying, and often very expensive, corrections so often experienced in assembling. It should be noted that the accuracy of component parts will depend largely on the accuracy of the tools furnished the workman. Not only the machine tools but all standards and gages must be kept up to exactness if accuracy of product is to be maintained.

It is almost axiomatic that the first parts in mass production should be very carefully examined, and inspection made often enough to insure that machines and men are working up to the standards. Constant vigilance is needed where the parts are numerous to prevent large quantities of spoiled work. When any defective work is discovered it should be set aside at once and no more labor expended upon it until it is definitely settled that it can be used.

Every workman should account for all work turned over to him; and if the inspection shows that any has been spoiled the matter should be settled then and there. Each workman should be held strictly accountable for the accuracy of his product; but in judging of these matters great care should be exercised that the blame is not placed on the workman when, perhaps, it is not his fault but the fault of defective gages or standards or, worse still, faulty verbal instructions. Even though the workman is not penalized by deducting from his pay the value of the spoiled work, a systematic record of such occurrences is not only valuable as a guide for future reference but has a salutary effect upon the workman. Furthermore, every effort should be made to remedy at once the cause of the defective work, whether that entails correction in machinery or instruction to the worker. Very often the latter is not an easy matter to accomplish, but it is often better to try to help his weakness, and thus prevent a recurrence of the difficulty, than to be satisfied with reprimanding or discharging him, to repeat the same performance with a new man.

Above all things, the inspection system should be a bulwark against the lowering of *quality* in order to obtain *quantity*. As before noted, this is a natural tendency under intensive methods. Before any speeding up is tried careful consideration should be given to the matter of inspection, and proper provision made in the way of gages and means of applying them. Unless this is done haste will most assuredly make waste. Inspection, on the other hand, will not cause a diminution in product if proper facilities are provided. To try to hasten the output of a lathe that is turning very accurate bearings, would thus be, in general, an open question, so far as the resulting accuracy is concerned. But the installation of a grinding machine in connection with the lathe would not only increase the production, but would make possible an accuracy not attainable at any rate of production by means of the lathe alone. Accuracy and output cannot be considered apart from the tools needed to produce them.

185. Organization of Inspection Department.—From the foregoing it is almost obvious that an inspection system that will accomplish these results must, in most cases, be organized apart from the manufacturing proper, if it is to serve as an effectual check upon wastes and bad work. Usually, therefore, the **chief inspector** is put directly under the superintendent or principal officer in charge of production and reports directly to him (see Fig. 13). Like all of these modern functionalized activities such as engineering, purchasing, planning, etc., the size of the inspecting force and the manner of its organization will vary widely with circumstances. In plants producing large machinery of comparatively few pieces a small inspecting force is sufficient, while in large mass-production work such as rifle works and automobile factories the inspection force must be large and very carefully organized. The fundamental principles of organization already discussed apply here as elsewhere (see Fig. 42).

Inspection is a *judicial* function and requires a somewhat different temperament from that usually found in a good, aggressive foreman. The inspector must be a man of firmness and decision, yet eminently fair in his judgment. His business should be to detect errors and defects and not to cure the troubles from which they arise, though his suggestions and recommendations may be very valuable and should be obtained. His authority regarding his own work should, however, be unquestioned, and for these reasons it requires a man of ability to make a successful inspector.

186. Methods of Inspection.—The method of conducting the inspection of material as it moves through the shop, and the detail into which it is necessary or remunerative to go, will, of course, vary greatly with the requirements of the industry. The detail and accuracy necessary in producing firearms or watches would be, of a necessity, much greater than in manufacturing pipe fittings. This is a matter of judgment and cannot be fixed by rule.

Leaving out of consideration the several inspection methods that depend in some measure on the foreman, or some other member of the manufacturing force, there are two principal methods of conducting inspection, namely, by **traveling inspectors** or by **centralized inspection.**

In the first, the inspector spends all his time on the shop or factory floor, moving from place to place as necessary, checking up the initial parts as they come from the machines, and checking up the finished lots both as to quality and quantity as they leave or arrive at each process. In large works an inspector may be assigned to each department and special benches and platforms may be provided for his convenience in checking over the various parts. His approval or disapproval of the work is indicated on the tag that accompanies the work.

In the centralized method of inspection, central inspection rooms are provided and all work is returned to the proper room after each operation. Here the inspectors work free from any influence of the shop. This method is an advantageous one where the parts are small and the limits of accuracy close, as in instrument work. If, however, the work is large and the parts heavy it is obviously unworkable and the extent to which one or the other, or a combination of both, should be employed is a managerial problem often requiring very good judgment. In general, if the parts are small, and the work of transferring them is not great, centralized inspection will be cheaper and more accurate; while, on the other hand, it may not be so effective in forestalling bad work as the traveling inspector system, for reasons that are obvious.

187. Performance and Assembly Tests.—In practically all industries a final examination is made of the finished product before shipment or storage. In some classes of manufacturing, as, for instance, in making steam engines or electrical machinery, these final inspections and tests may cover not only the verification of refined scientific theory, but may include physical tests of the apparatus as well. As before noted, such final tests and inspections are usually made under the supervision of the engineering department since usually an engineer is alone competent to perform this work intelligently, and because the engineering department is responsible for the performance of the apparatus.

The requirements of the final test are often set by the purchaser, and he, or his representative, may be present at the test, taking such information or data as he requires to satisfy himself as to the characteristics of the product. Sometimes this authority is delegated by the purchaser to some insurance company. Thus, builders of boilers will furnish a paid-up policy in certain insurance companies for a limited period of time. Such a policy guarantees that the boiler has been built and inspected under the supervision of this particular insurance company, which in this manner becomes responsible for the constructive features of the boiler. The United States government and other governments always have a corps of inspectors detailed to inspect and test all apparatus going into the construction of navy vessels when built by private contractors. Care should be exercised in taking contracts, that the conditions of performance and test are not so severe as to be unattainable, or attainable only at an expense that would make profit doubtful.

188. Inspection in General.—It should be noted that inspection in a general sense has a much wider significance than indicated even by the foregoing discussion. The general principles underlying it grow naturally out of the modern tendencies toward aggregation and specialization discussed in Chap. IV. Under older and simpler methods the workman on day wage naturally took sufficient time to insure his accuracy, and the foreman or erection boss had sufficient time to check the work. Under high-speed production and greatly increased number of parts these methods will no longer suffice. The foreman has neither time nor, in general, the information necessary to inspect the product properly. Division of labor must necessarily be resorted to as the complexity of production increases.

Mistakes, furthermore, are much more costly as the number of parts becomes greater and as the design of the product becomes more scientific and complex. Careful inspection of all work, from that of the engineering department down to the shipping department, may be justified. The careful examination of the scientific basis on which machines are designed and the inspection of all drawings before sending them into production becomes a matter of great importance as the number of parts to be made becomes greater. The principle is universally applicable, but the extent to which it is desirable or remunerative to apply it is a matter of managerial judgment. If the limitations are intelligently decided, there is, as a rule, no difficulty in devising the necessary methods and appliances for a proper execution of the principle.

Inspection presupposes *preplanning* and definite *standards.* No inspector can be efficient unless he knows exactly the requirements of the part concerned and has the necessary tools and gages to test its accuracy. It is a functionalized duty that goes naturally with well-organized and well-equipped establishments. The need of accurate gages and measuring devices and the importance of keeping them properly adjusted is obvious.

References

Alford, L. P. (Ed.): "Cost and Production Handbook," p. 277.

———: "Management's Handbook," p. 709.

Carpenter, C. U.: "Inspection as a Factor in Cheap Production," *Eng. Mag.*, July, 1904.

Harriman, N. F.: "Principles of Scientific Purchasing."

Van Deventer, J. H.: "Machine-shop Management."

Webb, A. D. Jr.: "Relation of Inspection to Money-making Shop Management," *Eng. Mag.*, February, 1907.

CHAPTER XVIII

PRINCIPLES OF COST FINDING

189. Need of Accurate Costs.—Modern manufacturing is, usually, a complex process, particularly where articles of varying size or character are made in the same works. It is not sufficient to know that the factory is paying, as a whole, especially when competition is strong in special lines. It is comparatively easy to determine whether the plant is, as a whole, paying dividends, but without the aid of a good cost system it is impossible to form any idea regarding the profitableness of any single line of product. With a good cost system the manager can keep himself informed regarding shop operations *as they progress* and can often avert losses and difficulties, instead of waiting until the work is finished, when remedy will come too late. The absolute need of statistical data and condensed reports has already been touched upon. Without a good cost system these are not obtainable and the manager is without one of the most powerful aids in administration. If work is to be planned in advance and if correct estimates are required, whether as a basis of securing new work or of insuring that productive costs shall not exceed market possibilities, a cost system is indispensable. This last feature is a most important one and grows more so daily. The custom of estimating costs in advance of production and then insuring that these costs are not exceeded in production, or finding out only why they cannot be met, is coming more and more into use as the practice of planning work in advance becomes more common.

The necessity of accurate costs is of prime importance to an industry as a whole. The manufacturer who underbids his competitors on the basis of faulty cost keeping not only works his own ruin but that of his competitors who are bidding on a sound basis. This form of competition is the very worst and should be most feared. It is no satisfaction to the manager whose costs are correct to know that the successful bidder is on the way to bankruptcy, so long as others, no better informed regarding costs, are constantly coming into the field. On a certain boiler installation that came under the writer's observation the bids on the boilers ranged from $11.50 to $16 per horse power, the bids on one item of piping ranged from $5,244 to $7,539, and on another item of piping from $1,200 to $4,493. The specifications for this work had been drawn with great care and permitted the use of certain apparatus and material only; and, making all due allowance for the lowest bids being as close to the margin of the specifications as possible, the only reasonable explanation of the wide range of the tenders is the lack of knowledge of the costs of production. The necessity of wide publicity of correct principles of cost keeping is obvious, and the successful manager who once offered to send his expert cost man to teach correct cost-finding principles to any competitor was a foresighted individual.

190. Relation of Cost Finding to Accounting.—The relation between **cost finding** and **accounting** should be carefully noted. Cost finding can be and frequently is conducted without reference to the accounting system of the plant. In fact, the first modern cost systems grew up with little relation to the general accounts. These relations may be better visualized by considering Fig. 46, which presents ordinary productive processes as a *flow* of material and labor from left to right of the diagram. The value of *all* material flowing into the plant is measured by the invoices. The value of *all* labor flowing into the plant is measured by the

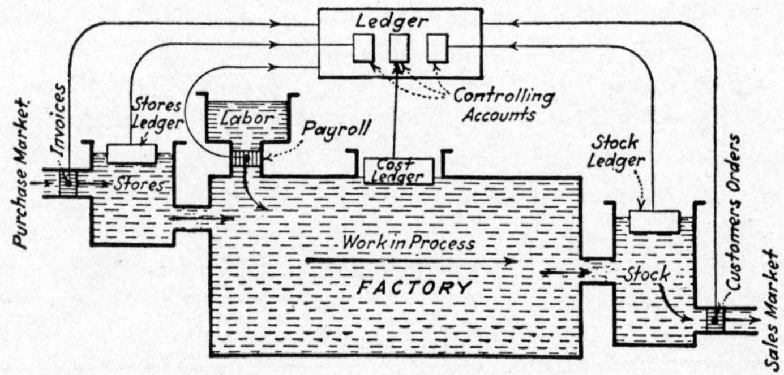

Fig. 46.—Relation of costs to accounting.

payroll. The value of *all* shipments is measured by the sales orders. With these and other values that can be measured with exactness the main ledger accounts can be made to balance *exactly* so far as *total* values are concerned. In other words, the general books can always be made to show exactly how the concern stands *in relation to the outside world and whether the enterprise is making or losing money.*

The general books, however, cannot show whether money has been made or lost in connection with any individual job unless a separate account has been opened in the main ledger for this job and all debits and credits incurred in connection with it posted therein. If the number of shop orders is small and the number of debit and credit items also small such a procedure could be carried out and one general ledger would suffice. In ordinary manufacturing a ledger of this kind would be too bulky and recourse is had to a subsidiary ledger called a **cost ledger.** The cost ledger is usually a card system or a loose-leaf ledger. When a job is placed in production an account is opened in the cost ledger by placing in it a card or loose leaf bearing the job number on which can be recorded all labor, material, and other items of cost properly chargeable thereto. The summary of such an account would give the shop cost of the article under consideration without reference to the main ledger. It is better, however, to carry the totals of the cost ledger to **controlling accounts** in the main ledger, for reasons that are more fully explained in Art. 223. Cost finding in its best form is a subsidiary function of the accounting system of the enterprise. Similar remarks apply to the stores ledger, stock ledger, plant ledger, and finished-parts ledger if there is one.

191. Recorded and Predetermined Costs.—The most common form of cost finding and the first form historically is that wherein the costs of production are determined by recording all labor, material, and other items of cost *after* the operations have been performed. Such costs are known as **recorded costs.** It was shown in Chap. XIII, however, that it is possible to predetermine the labor and material *actually* used in any products if careful planning of all productive processes is in use. Such costs are known as **predetermined** and **standard** costs since they are based upon standardized performances. The advantage of being able to predetermine costs is obvious, particularly when work must be contracted for at a predetermined price, as is often the case. Recorded costs will be discussed first since the limitations of predetermined costs will thus be better understood.

192. The Elements of Cost.—In producing manufactured goods of any kind, by any process, the manufacturer buys supplies which, for convenience, he classifies as raw material. He transforms this raw material into finished product in his factory, adding to its purchase price the cost of the labor expended in the transformation and such other factory expenses as are chargeable indirectly to the operation, in order to find the total cost. The most natural and convenient primary classification of the elements of cost is, therefore, **material, labor,** and **expense.** It should be noted, however, that all values with which the manufacturer is concerned are in the last analysis labor values. Material becomes valuable, in general, only as labor is performed upon it, and its *potential* value, as a natural product, is usually a small part of its value in a fabricated state. All efforts to reduce cost are, therefore, efforts directly or indirectly to eliminate labor values; or in other words to increase the output per labor hour.

The labor element of cost is usually divided into two classes. All work done directly upon the product and recognizable as pertaining only to the operations upon it is called **direct** or **productive labor.** But all labor around a factory cannot be connected directly with some piece of production. Thus the fireman, the engineer, the oiler, crane men, errand boys, office help, etc., are employed in activities that are *general* and not *specific,* or the time that they are employed on any one job is so short as to make intelligent distribution of their labor uncertain. Such labor is called **indirect**[1] or **nonproductive labor.**

In a similar way there are two classes of materials. All material entering directly[2] into the product is usually classed as **direct material.** But, again, there are many other materials used in a factory that do not enter directly into the product. Thus coal, oil, materials for repairs, etc., are all elements of cost chargeable against product, but not going directly into it, or connected with any one particular piece of work. Such material is called **indirect** or **expense material.**

Again, there are items of **expense** that are neither labor nor material, as, for instance, rent, taxes, insurance, depreciation, etc. These all form part of the cost of production but cannot be connected directly with some particular piece of product.

In computing the cost of production of a given part it is clear that it is possible to allocate the direct labor and direct materials chargeable against it; but the indirect labor and material and the expenses, such as rents, etc., are not so readily allocated. These indirect charges are usually gathered together under the general title of **burden, overhead expense,** or simply **expense.** The total cost of production, therefore, is made up, as before noted, of labor, material, and expense.

The cost of general administration accounting, etc., and also the cost of selling the product, are also of the indirect kind and hence are included in the expense. But these functions are independent of production; they are administered by officers who are not directly responsible for manufacturing costs and who should be held strictly accountable for their own expenditures. The manufacturing superintendent should be held accountable only for the costs of actual production and the cost ledger should show the relative proportions of expense chargeable to each of these divisions of the organization. Expense, therefore, divides itself naturally into manufacturing or **factory expense, administrative** or **general expense,** and **selling expense.** In many instances the administrative and selling expense are grouped together under the name of **general expense.** It will be assumed sometimes in this discussion that this grouping is sufficiently accurate, but the general principle should be kept in mind. It is often highly important that the cost of the sales should be carefully separated from the administrative expense in order to allocate such expenditures accurately and to fix the responsibility where it belongs.

[1] The terms *direct* and *indirect* are preferable to *productive* and *nonproductive.* All labor should be, in a strict sense, productive, though perhaps not applied directly to any article of product.

[2] There are often material items that enter directly into product that cannot very well be accurately charged against specific pieces of work. Thus nails, screws, glue, etc., enter directly into product but often in such small quantities as to make accurate accounting of them impossible.

Where the selling expense is large compared with other expenses this separation should always be made.

The several subdivisions of cost and the several steps in their summation may be shown graphically as in Fig. 47. The sum of the direct labor and direct material is known as the **prime** or **flat cost.** The **shop cost,** called also **manufacturing** or **factory cost,** is found by adding the factory expense to the prime cost. This is the summarized cost that the factory superintendent is held responsible for, and includes all items properly chargeable against production *up to and including the delivery of the finished product to the stock room or shipping floor* as the case may be. Here the financial responsibility of the factory superintendent stops.

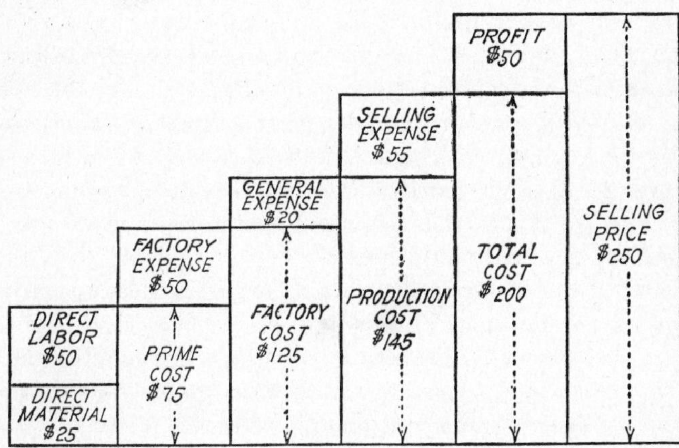

Fig. 47.

The **production cost** is the factory cost plus all other expenses such as salaries of officials, clerical services, etc., that are properly chargeable to the *administration* of the factory. The **total cost** is the productive cost plus the cost of advertising, shipping, transportation, etc., incident to marketing the product, and usually designated as **commercial** or **selling expense.** To make a profit the product must be sold for more than the total cost and the **selling price** is, therefore, the total cost plus the profit. The relative proportions of these items will, of course, vary considerably with the character of the work and the organization of the factory. The figures given in Fig. 47 are hypothetical, but not improbable for general manufacturing.

It is to be noted that all the items included in the total cost are fixed by the nature of the product and the efficiency of the organization. The profit is, in a way, arbitrarily fixed. It is clear that for a given capitalization and a required percentage of profit thereon, the percentage that must be added to the total cost to make the selling price will depend on the *volume*[1] of the output. If this volume is large compared to the capitalization, the percentage added for profit may be comparatively small; if the volume is small as compared to the capitalization the percentage added must be larger. And if this percentage is so large as to make the selling price too high, competition will prevent sales. In such a case the output must be increased in volume or the cost of production must be decreased to obtain the desired profit.

It should be carefully noted, also, that a given percentage on the total sales is not obtained by adding that percentage of the total cost to the total cost. Thus, if the total cost is \$75 and it is desired to make 25 per cent on the total sales to give the required profit on the investment, the sales price would not be obtained by adding 25 per cent of \$75 to the total cost of \$75, since that would give a sales price of \$75 + \$75/4 = \$93.75, and the difference between the sales price and the cost, or (\$93.75 − \$75) is not 25 per cent of \$93.75. If, however, 33⅓ per cent is added to the total cost the sales price is \$100 and 25 per cent taken from this leaves the total cost or \$75, hence the profit would be 25 per cent of the sales price and would bear the correct relation to the profit desired on the investment. Care should be exercised that operations involving percentage are based on correct theory, otherwise undetected financial loss is liable to occur. Errors of this kind are more frequent than might be supposed.

193. Classification of Expense.—The items that usually enter into the factory expense are those that are incurred in actual production and that cannot be charged directly to some particular piece of work. The items that enter into the general expense are of two classes, namely, **administrative** and **selling expenses.** In many cases, as has been noted, it is advisable to record the selling expense separately in order that the efficiency of the selling department may be determined, even though both classes are treated as one in determining selling price. The dividing line between factory and general expense cannot always, however, be sharply drawn because industrial conditions vary so widely. Thus the duties of the president, treasurer, and similar officers may include supervision of both manufacturing and sales, and their salaries should be distributed accordingly. In some cases the selling and administrative cost may be so small that they can be, without great error, included in the factory expense. In many cases it is desirable to distribute such items as interest, taxes, and insurance in the factory expense, while in others it is sufficiently accurate to throw them all into the general expense. The following, however, are representative items of factory expense:[2]

[1] The use of statistical data such as the *ratio of output to inventory* is well instanced here (see also Art. 107). Note also that the capitalized value may, and often does, exceed the actual or inventory value.

[2] For a very detailed list of factory expense see Alford, L. P. (Ed.), "Cost and Production Handbook," p. 1008.

Superintendence.
Light.
Heat.
Power.
Salaries of watchmen, etc.
Factory office salaries.
Indirect labor.
Interest.
Rent.
Insurance.
Taxes.
Repairs and betterments.
Depreciation.
Defective material and spoiled work.
Experimental (for factory).

As before stated, the items that enter into general expense include administrative expenses and those incurred in marketing the product and will, therefore, include such items as:

Salaries of general officers.
Advertising.
Legal expenses.
Correspondence.
Expense of sales.
Collecting.
Accounting.
General office expenses.

In Fig. 48 there is shown a classified analysis of the cost of production, including selling costs, as it occurs in an average manufacturing plant. Only typical items are shown since the detail in which it is necessary or desirable to take account of expense depends upon the industry and the size of the plant.

This classification is in general accord with the average practice of skilled accountants. The nature of most of the above-named expenses and the reason for so classifying them are self-evident, but there are a few that will require further discussion. These are interest, rent, taxes, insurance, repairs and betterments, depreciation, defective material and spoiled work, and expenditures on experimental work.

194. Interest and Rent.—Accountants and economists are not unanimous in their opinions as to the conditions under which interest should be charged against product. Clearly if the manufacturer rents land or buildings or machinery the rent that he must pay the owner represents a manufacturing expense and is a just and proper charge against product. If, now, he is manufacturing a varied product with an equipment of varied value, housed in buildings of different character and cost, it certainly is obvious that he should distribute the burden of this rent with reference to the value of his equipment if he wishes to obtain the correct cost of the several lines of product; and the same remarks hold true if his plant is built and equipped with borrowed capital on which he must pay interest.

If, however, the manufacturer *owns* his land and equipment he is under no such obligation and, apparently, need not include a charge for interest on his investment in computing his cost. There are good reasons, nevertheless, why this should be done. Clearly the money that he has invested in his plant would yield him the prevailing market interest if he simply loaned it and made no effort himself to employ it. Or, if invested in land and buildings, it should yield him interest in the form of rent, with no appreciable effort on his part. Unless, then, he takes this interest factor into account he cannot tell whether or not he is obtaining remuneration for his own exertions or in return for the added risk that he assumes in working his own capital.

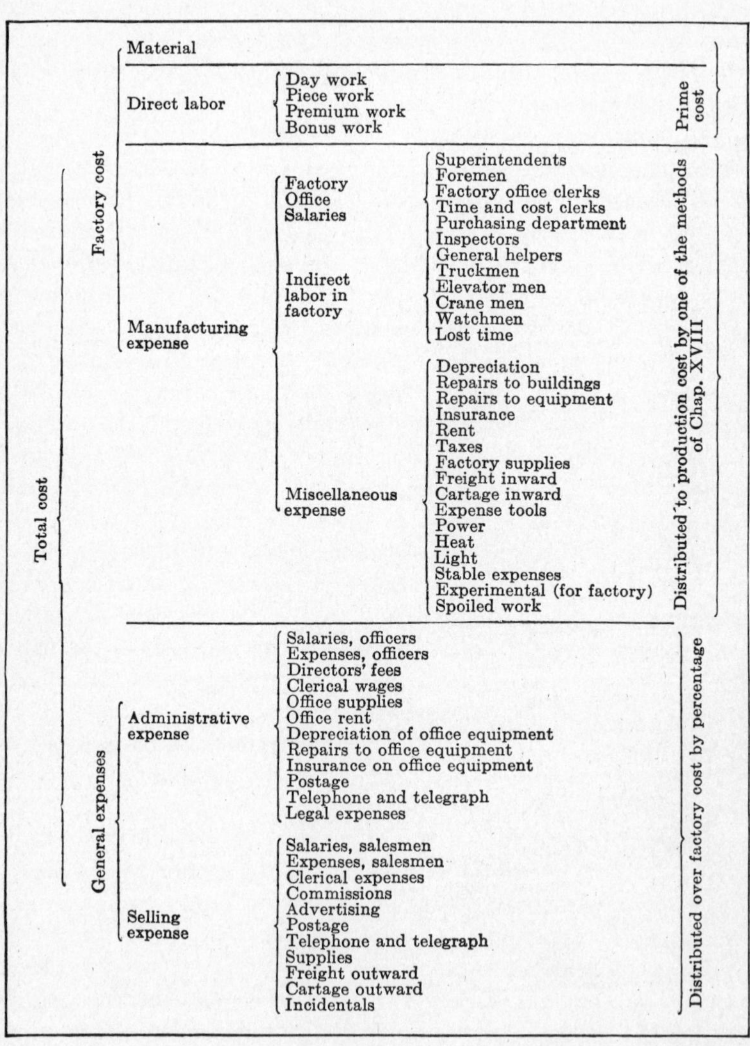

FIG. 48.—Distribution of production and selling costs.

Unless, moreover, he distributes this interest charge in proportion to the value of his equipment he cannot obtain a correct idea as to what part of his product is paying him the best returns, if his manufacturing problem be at all complex. The counter crediting of such interest charge so that the profit and loss account will show the total profit is a matter of bookeeping only. The manufacturer that owns his plant has, of course, an inherent advantage over the man that rents his plant or capital. The latter *must* make a minimum profit in order to pay his interest, the former not having this limitation.

195. Insurance and Taxes.—It is held by some accountants that these items, like interest, are attributes of capital and do not belong to manufacturing expense. Economically this may be true, but the object of cost keeping is not to decide points in economics but to *determine costs*, and if the plant is complex and the product varied these items should be distributed in the factory costs.

196. Repairs and Betterments.—Care should be exercised in charging off the cost of repairs. Obviously, all ordinary repairs and replacements made necessary by wear and tear are chargeable against production. In the case of rebuilding a machine or making extensive improvements upon it, however, it may be allowable to consider the work a betterment that will add to the productive capacity of the machine, and hence creditable to capital or plant investment, the inventory value of the machine being raised accordingly. Care should be used that such betterments really do add to the income-producing capacity.

197. Depreciation.—Depreciation and repairs are intimately connected and the former is so important that it is considered justifiable to make it the basis of a subsequent chapter (see Chap. XIX).

198. Defective Material and Spoiled Work.—If a certain class of work is unusually difficult, so that bad castings or spoiled work are likely to occur to a much greater extent than in the ordinary run of work, the extra expense incurred thereby should be charged against the particular class of work concerned, and should be considered as an allocable productive expense. The occasional bad casting or piece of spoiled work should not, in general, however, be charged against the particular job in which it occurs; but the cost of all such items should be distributed in the factory expense, thereby distributing the loss over the entire output in the same way as insurance. If this is not done the cost of the penalized job may be excessively and unjustly high. If the spoiled piece is one of a large lot it may be proper to charge off the cost of the spoiled part against the cost of the lot. Lost time, *i.e.*, time paid for but yielding no returns, as in the case of a delay through breakdowns, is of the same general character. Such charges, however, should be entered in the costs as a separate item so as not to cause confusion in making estimates on work where such losses may not apply, thereby raising the estimated cost unnecessarily. It is of as much importance not to have estimates too high as it is to avoid having them too low. One causes loss of business through failure to secure contracts, while the other causes financial loss on the contracts taken.

199. Experimental Work.—Experimental work that has for its object the development of better manufacturing facilities is obviously a factory expense. Experimental work that is conducted for the purpose of securing engineering data is somewhat different in character. Thus in developing a new line of goods it may be necessary to do a considerable amount of preliminary designing and experimenting. The cost of this may often be carried to a special **development account,** and if the preliminary work is consummated by placing the proposed line of goods in production, this development account may be charged off against the product over a predetermined amount of production. If this is not advisable, or feasible, the preliminary work must be charged off in the general expense.

200. Other Characteristics of Expense.—From the foregoing it will be evident that no serious difficulty is involved in finding the cost of the direct labor and material entering into the production of a given part. It is also evident that it is possible, without great complication, to classify the many items included in factory expense and to find the total amount of each item for any given period of time. It is not difficult, as will be seen, to charge off the *total* expense charges against production so that *total* costs are fairly accurate, but it is exceedingly difficult, except in simple cases, to apportion to each shop order the correct amount of each expense account so that it will bear its own share, and only its own share, of the burden. The reasons for this may be made a little clearer by considering more fully some of the characteristics of expense items. Direct material and direct labor are specific, tangible things that, as has been shown, can be accurately evaluated for any piece of work. But expense is variable in character and effect and does not attach itself in a tangible form to the work as it passes through the shop. The real problem of cost keeping is to apportion the expense items so that each job shall bear its own just share of burden. Unless this can be done with some degree of accuracy there is no way of computing the true selling price of the several lines of work, even though the *total* costs may be sufficiently accurate to fix profitable prices.

The total expense of production is, in general, divisible into two classes, namely, *constant* and *variable.* Constant expense includes all items necessary, so to speak, to the mere *existence* of the business, while variable expense includes all items connected with the *activities* of the business. Thus rents, insurance, taxes, and depreciation of buildings remain practically uniform no matter what the volume of business in the shop may be; or if they change at all, they do so occasionally and perhaps by large increments and then they remain stationary again for a long time. Many of them, moreover, can never become zero no matter what the state of the business may be. Salaries of general officers and those that are not affected by a change in volume of business are also fairly fixed in character.

Expenses, on the other hand, such as clerical help, unskilled labor, power, oil, and similar operating supplies are affected quite sensitively by a change in the volume of business and go up and down with it *though not usually in direct proportion.* Thus it takes a certain minimum amount of power to turn the engine and shafting when no productive work is being accomplished. Any additional power required will evidently be some function of the volume of the work moving through the shop, the exact relation depending on the character of the work. In general then, the relation of power to volume may be expressed by the equation:

$$P = C + f(V),$$

where P = power required, C = a constant, and $f(V)$ = some function of the volume of work. Many other expense items are of this general character, the relations usually being far from simple. Evidently the amount of either constant or variable expense that a job must bear is dependent on the *volume* of work passing through the shop, this amount increasing as the volume decreases.

It follows, also, from the above that profits do not vary directly in proportion to the volume of business transacted. As the volume of business decreases the amount of expense that must be added to the flat cost of every article manufactured constantly increases, because of the irreducible minimum expense. If the fixed expense is comparatively high the decrease in business need not be great before the increased expense on each article swallows up all profit, and any further decrease in business will result in a deficit (see Art. 222).

A very disturbing element in allocating expenses is the manner in which some of them vary with *time.* Thus rents, insurance, and taxes are direct functions of time and can be reasonably predicted. The repairs on a cupola, on the other hand, involving the use of both expense material and labor, are necessary because of the wear and tear incident to the work of the previous week or month. Expense supplies may be purchased today because of favorable market conditions and their use may be extended over several weeks or months. Evidently it would not be accurate to charge off accumulated expenses of this kind against current production. Such expenses must be spread out and averaged over a reasonable period of time, even though this period be somewhat arbitrarily fixed because of the difficulty of determining it accurately. In practical cost keeping averages of this kind must be employed for another reason. In most cases once a month is as often as it is convenient or possible to close the books and determine summarized costs. If, now, every job could be started on the first of the month and finished on the last day of the month, it would be possible to assign to each job, as accurately as the method employed would allow, its own share of the indirect expense incurred during the month it was in production. But jobs are finished regardless of the day of the month and, in most instances, it is desirable to bill them when shipped, so as to collect the payment. Indirect expense must, in such cases, be charged off on the basis of the summarized costs of the previous month or other periods of time, the proportions for the current month usually not being available.

The proportion of certain expenses that various jobs should bear is dependent on the size or weight of the product. Thus, theoretically,[1] small parts should not be called upon to bear the cost of operation and maintenance of large cranes, large machine tools, and large equipment generally. Clearly a large casting should bear more of the expense incurred in repairing the cupola than should a small one. The same difficulty arises with articles of different character. An article of one kind may give rise to indirect expenditures that are unnecessary in articles of another kind.

A similar complexity appears in considering the clerical work of the office and similar expenses. It may require more of such work to put a small complex machine through the shop than it would to put through a very large and more costly machine. And it can be seen that, in general, the cost of clerical work incident to a large and varied line of manufacturing is so complex as to render absolutely accurate allocation unprofitable even if it were possible. As in the former case it must be turned into the expense and distributed as intelligently as possible.

201. The Classified Expense Order-number List.—From the foregoing it will be seen that the relation between factory expense and general expense will vary greatly with the character of the business, its size, and complexity. A careful analysis of these relations must be made, therefore, and a classified list of expenses prepared, covering in detail the cost accounts that are deemed necessary.[2] In a large works these accounts may be numerous, one large manufacturing company in this country dividing its expense items into over 130 accounts. All work or material not chargeable directly to product must be charged to the proper expense account, and in order to do this each account must be identified by a number or letter. In small works, where great detail is not needed, the mnemonic (see Chap. XI) system of labeling accounts has been found satisfactory. Thus the account for *repairs to buildings* may be marked *R. B.*; expenses for *power, heat, and light, P. H. L.*, and so on. The use of such symbols is, however, limited, and in large works cannot, in general, be extended beyond general classifications of machinery

[1] It will be shown later that although, theoretically, small parts should not be taxed with expense incident to large tools, in practice this procedure is often necessary to prevent the cost of certain classes of work from being so excessively high as to make it unmarketable. Such a condition, however, is indicative of a weakness against competition in some line of product.

[2] See "Cost and Production Handbook," p. 1008 for an extended list of expense accounts.

or accounts. In some works the accounts are designated by numbers, whole numbers being used for the expense accounts, which usually are comparatively limited in number as compared with manufacturing accounts, for which some decimal notation based on the Dewey decimal system is used.

202. The Sources of Cost Data.—It is fundamental that if accurate costs are to be compiled no productive work should be performed without an order bearing the proper order number, and every man working on direct production must account for all of his time on some form of time card. No material may be drawn without an order bearing an order number to which the material is to be charged. All men working at indirect labor must also account for all their time on time cards bearing the correct expense order number to which such labor is to be charged. Other sources of expense such as gas bills, telephone service, messenger service, etc., will appear as bills or pay vouchers. In fact no work may be done, no material used, and no money expended for other services unless there is some identifying document that is returnable to the cost department.

All direct labor and direct material will be charged up on the proper cost-ledger sheets since they can be identified directly by their respective job-order numbers. All expense items will be distributed to the classified expense-order list to be discharged into the costs afterward, by methods to be described. It will appear that there is no difficulty in securing fairly accurate allocation of direct labor and direct material to the several accounts to which they belong. *The real problem of cost finding is to distribute the summarized expense accounts fairly and equitably against the production or direct job numbers.*

METHODS OF DISTRIBUTING FACTORY EXPENSE

203. General.—From the foregoing it is obvious that absolutely accurate distribution of expense is a very difficult, if not impossible, problem except in the very simplest cases, the complexity of the problem increasing with the complexity of the industry. In fact, different lines of work in the same factory may demand different methods of cost accounting, which is another reason for careful departmentalization aside from those arising from productive processes. These features, no doubt, account to a considerable extent for the failure, often, of large expansions in a factory, or the consolidation of factories, to produce expected results. In the process of enlargement some vital characteristic of the accounting may be lost sight of. The effect of this lost item may not have been serious in the smaller groups, but may prove very disastrous to the enlarged organization. The necessity of an accurate system of cost accounting needs no defense. It is as much a high-grade tool as a high-grade lathe or planing machine; but, compared to the installing of a first-class machine tool, the problem of instituting even a fairly accurate cost-keeping system is, in a large works, almost infinitely more complex.

Now the manufacturer, as a rule, is much opposed (and often with good reason) to complex systems. What he wants, usually, is something simple and direct; and between the need of accuracy, on the one hand, and the dread of complexity and added clerical help, on the other, the system adopted is often a compromise. As a consequence there have grown up a number of approximate methods of solving this problem and the characteristics and limitations of the most important of these will be very briefly discussed. The fundamental idea on which these systems are based is to use some tangible feature of the job as a basis of comparison, and by it to measure off the proper expense that the job should carry. It has already been noted that direct material and direct labor attach themselves to all jobs in a definite, tangible, and measurable manner. The *time* element of direct labor is, therefore, also a tangible quantity; and if a machine is employed in the work the time of such machine service can be accurately determined. The following methods of distribution based upon the above factors are those in most common use, namely, by material; by percentage on wages; by percentage on prime cost (labor and material); by man hours; and by machine rates. Another and more accurate method by so-called production factors has been advocated of late and will also be discussed briefly.

204. Distribution on Material as a Basis.—In simple continuous processes where the output consists of one uniform product as in a rail mill, a salt works, or a cement plant, it is obvious that if the expense incurred during a given period be evenly divided over the output for the same period the distribution will be correct. If the running conditions do not change materially, little error will be introduced if the expense incurred during the next preceding period of time be used as a basis. This is so, not because of the inherent accuracy of the method, but because *distribution* in a strict sense is not needed in such cases but only simple *division* of the indirect expense. In fact, in such simple cases the direct labor or the flat cost would be just as accurate as a basis. But if the product varies from time to time,[1] or if there is more than one line of product, these simple relations no longer exist and the introduction of material values into the computation of expense distribution is very likely to distort the results.

205. Distribution on Direct Labor as a Basis.—The use of the direct labor as a basis of distribution is based on the supposition that the indirect expense chargeable to a job is proportional to the direct labor expended upon it. It is, perhaps, as generally used as any other method, probably because of its simplicity. If the total direct labor for, say, a

[1] Thus a saw mill will turn out more *board feet* of product when cutting large-sized product than when cutting smaller pieces, the indirect expense remaining practically the same. It is not customary, however, to take cognizance of this fact in distributing the expense.

month should be $5,000, and the indirect expense for the same time $2,500, then the indirect expense is 50 per cent of the direct labor and by this method the indirect expense would be distributed by adding 50 cents to every dollar expended for direct labor. If, for instance, a machine has been built during the period considered, the material for which amounted to $200 and the direct labor to $400 the factory cost would be:

$$\$200 + \$400 + (\$400 \times 0.50) = \$800.$$

In practical operation the percentage used is, for reasons already explained (see Art. 200), not that of the current week or month but of the next preceding period or the average of several preceding periods.

If the work is of practically the same size and character, and if the wage rate does not differ greatly, the above method may, in many instances, be sufficiently accurate. But the method becomes more and more erroneous as the difference in size and character of parts become greater. Thus a job involving $5 worth of labor by a man using a hammer and file is burdened by this method with as much expense as one involving a similar direct-labor charge if done on a $20,000 boring mill and requiring the service of a high-priced overhead crane. Yet the interest and depreciation on investment necessary to perform the latter operation are very much greater than for the former both as to cost of tools, floor space, etc., to say nothing of the greater expense for heating, lighting, and insuring that part of the shop that houses the boring mill. Again, as the volume of work fluctuates all lines of work seldom vary equally, the difference being more marked when the difference in size is great, and in such cases one line may have to bear interest and similar fixed expenses belonging to other lines to an undue amount.

One of the greatest defects of this method is its failure to take proper cognizance of the effect of elapsed time upon the costs. A job that takes a rapid man, earning 50 cents an hour, 3 hours to perform, is taxed the same amount as another job done under the same conditions by a cheaper man getting 30 cents an hour and consuming 5 hours for the work; and the shop cost of the article does not differentiate between the two. Now in manufacturing, especially, "time is money." Profits depend not on cost alone but on quantity of product (see Art. 200); and the work of the slow man involving a longer use of tools, floor space, light, etc., is obviously more costly than that of his more rapid neighbor.

It is evident that if all pieces of the same size were machined in the same shop, as is often the case in a very large works that has been departmentalized along these lines, a varying and more equitable percentage could be applied to each class; and this is sometimes done in such cases. This principle has also been applied to shops doing mixed work by classifying the work and applying different percentages to the different classes, the larger parts carrying the heavier burden. Undoubtedly, if this can be done and if a graded percentage can be intelligently fixed, it will give better results than the flat percentage method, in all cases where there is variation in size and weight. The difficulties of doing this are, however, usually considerable.

206. Distribution on Prime Cost as Basis.—There would seem to be little justification for this method of distribution and, as far as the writer is aware, it is little used. If the value of the material used in the product is very small compared to the labor put upon it the method approaches the use of direct labor as a basis; while, on the other hand, if the material values are very high compared to the direct labor, the method approaches the use of direct material as a basis, and in either case is subject to the limitations and errors of these methods already discussed. In mixed manufacturing, where one piece may have a high material value and low labor value and the next piece may have the relative values of these items reversed, it is self-evident that the distribution of expense by this method will be neither logical nor accurate.

207. Distribution on Man Hours as a Basis.—In distributing the expense on this basis it is assumed that the expense chargeable to a piece of work is proportional to the *number of man hours* expended on it. It might seem that this system would give the same results as the percentage-on-wages method already discussed, and this would be so *if all men received the same rate of pay,* since then the labor cost would be proportional to the time consumed. Thus suppose that, as in the case cited in discussing the percentage-on-wages system, the total direct labor for the month is \$5,000 and that it is made up of 10,000 man hours at 50 cents per hour. Assume as before that the total indirect expense for the month is \$2,500. Let the material cost of the job considered be \$200 as before, and let the direct-labor charge upon it be made up of 800 man hours at the given rate of 50 cents or a total, as before, of \$400. Then the expense per man hour chargeable against any job is $\frac{\$2,500}{10,000} = 25$ cents per man hour and the expense chargeable against the job under consideration is $0.25 \times 800 = \$200$, the same as in the percentage-on-wages plan, and the factory cost is $\$200 + \$400 + \$200 = \$800$ as before.

But suppose that the wage rate is variable, as it usually is, and that the labor cost of the above job consists of 1,000 man hours at 40 cents an hour or \$400 as before. Now the expense chargeable against it is $1,000 \times \$0.25 = \$250$, and the total shop cost is $\$200 + \$400 + \$250 = \$850$. Again if the direct-labor cost consists of 400 hours at \$1 an hour the total shop cost will be $\$200 + \$400 + \$100 = \$700$; so that even though the labor cost may be the same the factory cost will be different if the time consumed varies.

This method has, therefore, the advantage over the percentage-on-labor plan of accenting the value of the time element in costs, the factory cost in general increasing and decreasing with corresponding changes in the time consumed. Like the other system, however, it fails to take account of the difference in size and value of the equipment used, all jobs consuming the same amount of time being burdened equally, though in one case the workman may be using a hammer and chisel and in another a very costly machine tool. Like the percentage-on-wages system it will give satisfactory results only when the class of work and the machines employed are fairly uniform in size. Or, as Mr. Church[1] has expressed it, "where we have a simple set of facts to represent, their representation is an equally simple matter."

208. Distribution by Machine Rate.—The machine rate is a very old conception and no doubt has its origin in an instinctive effort to equalize in some degree the varying cost of production caused by the use of tools and processes of varying size and value. It was in use long before the days of refined accounting methods, so common today, and in its original form made no attempt to insure an accurate distribution of the total factory expense. It attempted, rather, simply to equalize such factors of expense as naturally attach themselves to machines and processes as, for instance, power, interest on investment, depreciation, and repairs. The entire equipment was divided into classes by size or value, and a graded charge per hour was fixed for each class, a machine in this sense being any tool or process from a vise to the largest boring mill. Thus the charge per hour for a vise hand might be 50 cents, while the hourly rate for a large boring mill might be $5.

The theory on which the machine rate rests is, without doubt, much more accurate than that which underlies any of the methods previously discussed. Most of the items of expense do not connect themselves naturally with *wages* but do most naturally gather around *machines* and *processes*. Nor do they collect as a uniform layer over wages or time but gather in varying quantity around machines and processes. The rate of pay and the time consumed being equal, it costs a great deal more to do a piece of work on a large mill than on a vise, since the larger tool costs more originally, and such items as repairs, power, insurance, heat, light, housing, etc., are all greater in like proportion. It was most natural, therefore, that this method should be extended to the problem of distributing the *total* shop expense, for it is to be especially noted that this method of distribution applies the burden at the time and place that the work is performed; and if the machine rate is correct for the existing conditions of production the result must be much more accurate than that of any of the averaging methods discussed, for all cases where the machines and processes vary in size and value.

In the ordinary method of determining machine rates for the purpose of distributing the total expense, all items of expense are apportioned so that each machine or process bears its own just share of the expense as

[1] CHURCH, A. H., "Expense Burden," p. 34.

nearly as possible. The total of such allocated expenses assigned to any machine[1] is then divided by the *estimated* number of hours the machine may be expected to be in operation during the period considered, this estimate being checked, if possible, by records of past performances. This gives the hourly rate of the machine and every job that passes through it is charged accordingly. Obviously, if this allocation be correct, and if each job be properly assessed as it passes through the several processes, and also *if all machines are in operation the exact time estimated,* all the indirect expense will be distributed in proportion to the use that has been made of the various machines and processes.

The theory of the method, as before stated, seems very accurate; but the difficulty begins when any departure is made from the estimated time that machines are in operation. If a machine fails to run up to this normal time an undercharge is made; if it is in operation more than the normal time an overcharge is made. This last may not be so serious, but when the volume of the work is even slightly decreased and a few machines[2] become idle, a large undercharge is incurred. This undistributed expense due to machines being idle does not appear in the cost of production and is lost sight of until it appears in the totals of the profit and loss account. Any approach to accuracy depends, therefore, on every machine and process being in operation the exact amount of time used in estimating the machine rate. Such conditions seldom prevail in any shop.

There is one objection that is sometimes raised against the machine rate, and that is the large amount of expense that, under this method, is charged against a job that is done in a machine larger than is actually required for the process, because of smaller machines being oversupplied with work. This makes the cost of this so-called "penalized" job appear excessive; and if taken as a guide for future work is misleading. On the other hand, the fact that it is high is an instant indication that the most economical process is not being employed and points at once to a weakness in the manufacturing equipment. It is better to know that the cost is high, and to be able to find the reason, and make such allowance as may be necessary, than it is to have an undiscovered weakness in the manufacturing processes.

209. Distribution by Production Centers.—The inherent advantages of the machine rate have led A. Hamilton Church[3] to propose a more

[1] A machine in this sense would be any actual machine, or a vise, or in fact any *place* where a workman is employed, if full distribution of expense is to be attempted in this manner.

[2] The error from this source is magnified by the fact that in dull times the large machines whose rates are highest, and hence discharge more expense per hour, are usually the first to be out of work, and the last to come into operation as times improve.

[3] See "Distribution of Expense Burden," p. 46; also "Production Factors," by the same author.

refined application of its underlying theory. Suppose the factory under consideration to consist of a large number of small units separated physically from each other but supplied from central sources with such general requirements as heat, light, and power in such a way that all such requirements can be accurately charged up against each unit. Suppose, further, that these units are of different sizes and contain processes and machines of varying character and size. Let it be further supposed that the owner of the factory operated some of these units personally and rented others to employees. Obviously, he could not, and would not, charge off his general shop expenses by any system of *averaging*, but would be compelled to consider each unit separately, keeping a separate record of each and every "service" or "production factor" and of the exact amount supplied to every production unit or "production center" as these units may be called. Thus it would be possible to apportion to each unit the expense incurred because of the land and building it occupied, the insurance and depreciation of the building, and the cost of heating, lighting, and supplying power. Other items of general service such as transportation, stores, telephone service, supervision, etc., might be more difficult to apportion accurately; but a fair approximation could be made, in fact, would have to be made, the owner keeping a *separate account* of each and every service rendered.

Obviously, also, if a tenant renting one of these units wished to compare his costs of production with a neighbor, whose unit was larger or smaller, he could reduce his several expenses to such a form as would make comparison easy. Thus, his rent could be expressed as so many dollars per square foot of ground occupied, and his light and heat in similar terms; and if he had more than one machine in his unit these rates could be used in determining the relative cost of production between machines. Knowing, moreover, just what these several expenses were for a given period of time he could add thereto those expenses that were directly connected with his tool or process, such as interest, depreciation, oil, etc. Then by estimating or otherwise determining the number of hours that his machine or process would be in operation during that time, he could calculate a machine rate, as explained in the foregoing paragraph, that would discharge all this expense as the work passed through his machine or process. His floating expenses that could not be so reduced *would be discharged as a supplementary rate,* which would also care for discrepancies in his estimates of his machine hours.

Now Mr. Church contends, and with good reason, that these conditions do not change simply because the walls are taken away from the small units and a large building, housing them all, is erected instead. His argument is that the manufacturer should still keep these several expenses as separate accounts,[1] and still considering each machine[2] or process as a "production center," assess it for each service according to an accurately determined or "scientific" rate. The production factors that can be so treated and the methods of reducing them to chargeable terms he lists as follows:

Land-building factor, measured by..........	floor area.
Power factor, measured by.................	horse power used.
Lighting factor, measured by...............	floor area.
Heating factor, measured by................	floor area.
Organization factor, measured by...........	simple division.
Supervision factor, measured by............	special determinations.
Stores-transportation factor, measured by.....	special determinations.

In addition each machine or production center would be charged with the expenses arising out of the character of the machine itself as, for instance, interest on first cost, insurance on the tool itself, repairs, supplies, and wear and tear on cutting tools and special fixtures. All of these, as before noted, can be reduced to a machine-hour rate and can be charged off as the work moves through the machines or processes.

The philosophy of this method is sound, and where it can be realized it will no doubt give very accurate results. There are, however, several serious difficulties in operating it. The preliminary study and preparation necessary to install such a system might be great even in factories of moderate size, and in very large works would be exceedingly difficult if not impossible. Some of the production factors, such as heat, light, and insurance on buildings can, perhaps, be allocated in almost any factory with an approach to accuracy. In the case of power, especially where large amounts are used in a variable way for testing, and where complex systems of shafting and belting, air and hydraulic distribution serve many and varied machines, accurate allocation is impossible; or at least would require such an elaborate system as to make the net gain realized doubtful. In many cases, however, approximations can be made that are sufficiently accurate for the conditions and much more accurate than any of the other methods of expense distribution that have been described.

210. Machine Rates by Production-center Method.—Figure 49 illustrates the computation of a modern machine rate based upon the methods of Mr. Church. It is reproduced in an abbreviated form from the thesis of Professor R. M. Barnes, a former student in the College of Engineering, Cornell University. In this study it is assumed that the

[1] Mr. Church's system of control accounts by which he proposes to keep track of the several production factors is most interesting. See A. H. Church, "Production Factors," p. 138.

[2] Machine and process here, as before, meaning any piece of apparatus or, in the case of handworkers, a stationary place to work.

1	2	3	4	5	6	7	8	9	10	11	12	13	14	15	16	17	18	19
MACHINE NO.	NAME. AND MAKER	RATED HP.	PRESENT VALUE (NEW)	WORKING AREA FOR ONE MACHINE	NUMBER OF MACHINES	HOURS IN USE PER MONTH PER GROUP	AREA COVERED BY GROUP	FLOOR AREA CHARGEABLE TO GROUP	HP. HOURS PER MONTH PER GROUP	PRESENT VALUE (NEW) PER GROUP	DEPRECIATION PER MONTH PER GROUP	POWER COST PER MONTH PER GROUP	MISCELL-ANEOUS CHARGES PER MONTH PER GROUP	SPACE CHARGE PER MONTH PER GROUP INCLUDING INTEREST	MACHINE VALUE CHARGE PER MONTH PER GROUP INCLUDING INTEREST	TOTAL CHARGE PER MONTH	HOURLY RATE	ROUNDED MACHINE RATE
1	2 SPINDLE J. & L. FLAT TUR. LATHE	7.5	3800	144	7	1037	1008	1801	3880	26600	199.00	46.25	77.30	277.50	502.50	1102.55	1.060	1.06
2	14" SURFACE GRINDER P. & W.	15.0	2400	256	3	450	768	1370	3380	7200	54.00	40.30	33.50	213.00	136.00	476.80	1.060	1.06
3	3B LAPOINTE BROACH	8.0	800	250	4	519	1000	1790	2076	3200	54.50	25.00	38.70	275.70	60.50	454.40	.880	.88
4	J. & L. FLAT TURRET LATHE	5.0	3000	153	11	1829	1680	3010	4570	33000	247.00	54.00	136.00	463.00	626.00	1524.50	.834	.84
5	14" FAY AUTOMATIC LATHE	7.5	2500	50	15	2496	750	1340	9350	37400	405.00	111.50	186.00	206.00	706.00	1614.50	.646	.65
6	6-A SEMI-AUTOMATIC LATHE	7.5	2800	66	7	1093	462	824	4100	19600	104.00	49.00	81.50	126.00	370.00	731.50	.668	.67
7	14" NATCO MULTIPLE DRILL	10.5	4300	120	1	150	120	215	750	4300	32.20	8.95	11.20	33.10	81.30	166.75	1.110	1.11
8	NO. 53 ACME AUTOMATIC LATHE	5.0	2900	155	4	506	620	1110	1265	11600	125.50	15.10	37.80	171.00	219.50	568.90	1.120	1.13
9	14" SENSITIVE DRILL SPINDLE	1.0	325	45	2	90	222	398	45	650	4.85	.35	6.70	61.20	12.30	85.60	.952	.96
10	13-B MILLING MACHINE B. & S.	7.5	2125	130	6	918	780	1400	3440	12750	138.00	41.00	68.40	215.50	241.00	703.90	.766	.77
11	CADILLAC CENTRE MACHINE	1.0	150	80	1	148	80	143	74	150	1.60	8.80	10.90	22.00	2.85	46.15	.312	.32
12	NO. 14 PLAIN GRINDING MACHINE	15.0	2725	227	6	942	1362	2480	7060	16350	122.50	84.20	71.00	381.50	309.00	968.20	1.026	1.03
13	NO. 2 AUTOMATIC SCREW MACHINE	5.0	3350	144	2	179	288	515	44	6700	72.50	5.35	13.35	79.30	126.70	297.20	1.658	1.66
14	NO. 55 ACME AUTOMATIC LATHE	3.0	2025	80	1	85	80	143	127	2025	21.95	1.50	6.34	22.00	38.20	89.99	1.058	1.06
15	PEW AUTOMATIC LATHE	3.0	2200	225	2	183	450	805	275	4400	47.60	3.30	13.60	124.00	83.20	271.70	1.480	1.48
16	GRIDLEY AUTOMATIC LATHE	5.0	2475	108	1	109	108	193	272	2475	26.80	3.20	8.10	29.70	46.70	114.50	1.050	1.05
57	HIGLEY CIRCULAR COLD SAW	2.0	250	112	2	230	224	400	230	500	5.40	2.75	17.15	61.50	9.45	96.25	.414	.42
58	BATH NO. 1 UNIVERSAL GRINDER	2.0	1800	192	5	752	960	1720	960	9000	67.50	11.40	56.00	263.00	170.00	567.90	.755	.76
59	CINCINNATI POLISHING JACK	3.0	200	62	5	728	310	555	465	1000	10.80	5.55	54.20	85.40	18.90	174.85	.240	.24
60	15-TON LUCAS POWER PRESS	2.0	300	50	1	28	50	90	50	300	3.25	.60	2.05	13.85	5.70	25.45	.910	.91
61	THOMPSON BUTT WELDER	10.0	400	80	2	189	160	286	800	800	13.65	9.55	14.10	44.00	15.15	96.45	.510	.51
62	NORTON EMERY WHEEL	3.0	150	55	2	277	110	187	165	300	3.25	1.95	20.60	30.30	5.70	61.80	.223	.23
63	BENCH GRINDING WHEEL	2.0	75	20	2	184	40	72	60	150	1.15	.71	14.50	11.10	2.85	30.31	.156	.16
BENCH	BENCH		40	150	50	8400	7500	11430		2000	41.65		625.00	2066.00	37.80	2770.45	.330	.33
	TOTALS					50339	38582			570300		1425.13		10657.45	10777.82	31478.53		

FIG. 49.—Machine rates.

plant is a new one and that the machine tools are arranged in groups of like kind. Referring to Fig. 49, columns 1 to 6 are self-explanatory. Column 7 shows the estimated machine hours per month for each group. This is the most difficult item for which to fix a value. If the volume of the output is known this value can be calculated, otherwise it must be assigned from experience or from records of performance covering a considerable period of time if such records are to be had. Column 8 is obtained by multiplying the values in column 5 by those in column 6.

Column 9 gives the total floor areas chargeable to each group. The areas shown in column 8 are only those actually occupied by each group and do not include the aisles, shop offices, and other areas which provide service for the groups. This is computed by distributing the total floor area to the several groups in proportion to the areas in column 8. In making this calculation the areas of the cafeteria, general offices, and unused space, if any, are deducted from the total area before allocation is made. Thus:

	Square Feet
Total floor area	78,400
Cafeteria area = 2,800 square feet	
General offices = 6,600	
9,400	9,400
Total shop floor space	69,000

Now the total area occupied by the machine groups is the total of column 8, or 38,582 square feet. Hence the factor of allocation is $\frac{69{,}000}{38{,}582} = \mathbf{1.79}$. As an illustration, therefore, the floor space chargeable against the first group of machines is $1{,}008 \times 1.79 = 1{,}801$ square feet.

Column 10 gives the horse power hours per month per group. The estimated horse power for each machine is listed in column 3. It will be in accordance with good practice to consider that the actual consumption of power will be one-half of the estimated normal amount. Therefore,

$$\frac{\text{Column 3} \times \text{column 7}}{2} = \text{column 10 or for group number 1}$$

or

$$\frac{7.5 \times 1{,}037}{2} = 3{,}880 \text{ horse power hours.}$$

Column 11 is the product of columns 4 and 6. From these values and with assumed scrap values and length of life the depreciation for the groups has been computed and listed in column 12. The methods of computing depreciation are fully discussed in Chap. XIX and will not, therefore, be repeated here.

The cost of power has been assumed at 1.6 cents per kilowatt-hour or 1.192 cents per horse power hour, since 1 horse power = 0.746 kilowatt.

The power cost per group, therefore, column 13, is found by multiplying column 10 by 1.192; or for the first group the power cost is

$$3880 \times 1192 = \$46.25.$$

There are always miscellaneous expenses properly chargeable to production but which are difficult to allocate to the production centers. Some of these expenses are for services rendered directly to the production centers and some are for general services that affect the centers indirectly. Thus oil, waste, etc., are chargeable directly to the production centers, while superintendence, sweeping and cleaning, tool room, attendance, etc., affect the production centers indirectly. In order to allocate all expenses as accurately as possible it would seem fair to charge one-half of these miscellaneous expenses directly to the centers and the other half to the general space factor. Hence,

Miscellaneous supplies, oil, waste, etc.	$1,500
Indirect labor, cleaning, superintendence, tool room, etc.	4,500
All other minor expenses not otherwise allocated	1,500
Total	$7,500

One-half of this amount is to be distributed on the basis of machine hours, hence column 14 = column $7 \times \frac{3,750}{50,339}$ = column 7×0.0745. For the first group, therefore, $1,037 \times 0.0745 = \$77.30$. Column 15 lists the **space charge**. This charge includes the **land-building factor, the heating factor**, and the **lighting factor** of Mr. Church, and such other items as may be charged off on the basis of floor area without great error. The computations in this case are as follows:

Two acres of land at $3,000	$ 6,000.00	
Cost of buildings	353,000.00	
	$359,000.00	$359,000.00
Transmission equipment	$ 25,000.00	
Furniture and fixtures	31,250.00	
Miscellaneous equipment	50,000.00	
	$106,250.00	106,250.00
Total cost of plant less machinery		$465,250.00
1. Interest on $465,250 at 6 per cent, per month		$ 2,326.25
2. Taxes on $465,250, per month		777.00
3. Insurance on plant, building, etc., per month		1,862.00
4. Water, heat, and light, per month		1,000.00
5. Depreciation on buildings, per month		1,325.00
6. Depreciation on equipment, per month		966.00
7. Half of miscellaneous charges, per month		3,750.00
		$12,006.25

Then the space charge per square foot per month is

$$\frac{12{,}006.25}{78{,}400 \text{ (total floor area)}} = 0.154 \text{ per square foot,}$$

and column 15 = column 9 × 0.154, or for the first group

$$1{,}801 \times 0.154 = \$277.50.$$

Column 16 lists the charges for interest, taxes, insurance, repairs to machinery, and general maintenance charges that may be charged off on the basis of value to the several production centers. These charges are based upon the total of column 11 and are as follows:

Taxes upon $570,000 per month	$ 951
Insurance upon $570,000 per month	2,140
Interest at 6 per cent upon $570,000 per month	2,852
Machine repairs at 0.0015 per cent upon $570,000 per month	856
General repairs at 0.007 per cent upon $570,000 per month	3,990
Total machine-value charge	$10,789

$$\text{Then column 16} = \frac{\text{column } 11 \times 10{,}789}{570{,}300 \text{ (total of column 11)}} = \text{column } 11 \times 0.0189$$

and, therefore, for the first group 26,600 × 0.0189 = 502.50.

Column 17 lists the total monthly charges and is the sum of columns 12 to 16. Thus for the first group:

12. Depreciation charge, per month per group	$ 199.00
13. Power charge, per month per group	46.25
14. Miscellaneous charge, per month per group	77.30
15. Space charge, per month per group	277.50
16. Machine-value charge, per month per group	502.50
Total monthly charge	$1,102.55

The hourly rate is found by dividing this total monthly charge by the total estimated hours of service of the group. Thus for the first group this charge is $\frac{1{,}102.55}{1{,}037} = \$1.06$. As these hourly rates are based upon certain approximations, it is a reasonable procedure to round off the computed hourly rate to the second decimal place. Column 19, therefore, lists the rounded hourly rates that may be used to allocate the expense to the several groups of machines. If, then, each group actually operates the estimated time listed in column 7 the total expense will be allocated in a fairly reasonable manner. If, however, the machines operate longer than this estimate an excess amount of expense will be distributed, while if the operating time is less than the estimate part of the expense will remain undistributed.

211. The Machine Rate and Supplementary Rate.—An effort[1] has been made to compensate for the error introduced into the machine rate

[1] Church, A. H., "The Distribution of Expense Burden," p. 46.

when machines do not run up to their estimated normal time by the introduction of a so-called **supplementary rate.** The operation of this auxiliary rate is as follows. Such expenses as can be apportioned to machines and processes are so allocated and charged off, as before, by a machine rate. A record is kept of all expense actually charged off in this manner and at the end of the month the total of such distributed expenses is subtracted from the total expense that should have been distributed. The difference is the undistributed or unabsorbed expense, and Mr. Church suggests that this may be distributed as an hourly charge over the several jobs or by proportioning it over the jobs as a percentage on the expense[1] already allocated to them. While this procedure will no doubt allocate all of the expense, there are certain well-grounded objections to these methods, which are discussed in the succeeding section.

212. Distribution of Unabsorbed Expense.—When a factory is running at normal capacity and care has been exercised to allocate the expense of each article in proportion to the use that has been made of the facilities of the shop in producing it, the comparative costs of all articles should be fair and logical. If the output is *increased,* and all costs of production thereby decreased, no line of production can suffer. But should the volume *decrease* the case is different. Suppose, for instance, that the volume decreases so that all the large tools are idle and the lines of product on which they are normally used are no longer produced. Under all of the methods of expense distribution that have been discussed, the expense incident to these large tools when idle is distributed against lines of product that make no use of these machines. This is true even of the production-center and supplementary-rate method, the supplementary rate being introduced for the very purpose of collecting expenses due to idleness and distributing them over the product in process.

The degree of error in the costs due to fluctuation in volume of work under the averaging methods of expense distribution will depend upon circumstances. If the machines and equipment do not vary greatly in value small variations in the volume of business will not introduce serious errors into the costs because of idle machines. In departments where there is considerable difference in the size and cost of equipment, however, the error thus introduced may be very great. This is especially true in such cases for the reason that when the volume of work diminishes the larger and more expensive equipment is the first to be left without work—and it is also the last to resume operations as business improves. Since the fixed expense belonging to the larger equipment is, in general, much larger in proportion than that belonging to the smaller machines, the latter may have an expense burden laid upon them which is prohibitive to sales. And even when the equipment does not vary greatly in size

[1] For an illustration of the application of the supplementary rate, see Sterling H. Bunnell, "Cost Keeping for Manufacturing Plants," p. 152.

and value, and there is a marked decrease in the volume of business, considerable illogical distribution results with all of the methods that have been described.

It was noted in Art. 192 that one of the fundamental functions of a cost system is to show clearly the expense items for which each departmental head is responsible and, following this procedure, it is customary to hold the manufacturing superintendent responsible for manufacturing expense. It does not seem fair, however, to hold him responsible for expenses due to idle equipment when he is in no way to blame for such idleness; nor does it seem fair to include the expense of idleness in current costs, since obviously it confuses and distorts such costs with changing volume of business. It has been advocated, therefore, with good reason, that the expense distributed against any one product should be strictly proportional to the use it has made of the manufacturing facilities; and that any other expense should be disposed of in some other manner.

H. L. Gantt, discussing this problem in an interesting paper,[1] argued that "the indirect expense chargeable to the output of a factory bears the same ratio to the indirect expense necessary to run the factory at normal capacity as the output in question bears to the normal output of the factory." That is, if the production falls to, say, half the normal volume, this production should be burdened with only one-half the normal expense, so that, everything else remaining the same, the manufacturing costs would not change with change in volume of product. The undistributed expense would be charged to the Profit and Loss account, thus placing the responsibility for rising costs with the management, where it rightly belongs.

It was noted in Art. 200 that expense is of two kinds—constant or fixed expense and variable expense. Fixed expense is that due to the existence of the plant and includes interest, rent, taxes, etc. Variable expenses such as clerical help, unskilled labor, power, oil, etc., change with the volume of business. The value of fixed expense can never become zero, and there is an irreducible minimum value below which it cannot fall. Variable expense, on the other hand, may vary from zero through a wide range depending upon the volume of business transacted. An investigation of a number of plants by N. T. Ficker indicated that fixed expense averaged 40 per cent of the total expense during normal operation. The effect of constant expense in distorting the costs increases, therefore, as the volume of work diminishes. It should be noted that the expense that is distributed by the supplementary rate is composed principally of fixed expense and, therefore, if there is much error in estimating the probable time of operation of the several machines and

[1] See *Jour. Am. Soc. Mech. Eng.*, August, 1915.

processes, the supplementary rate may greatly distort the costs in dull periods.[1]

With these characteristics of expense in mind Mr. Ficker has proposed that "the expense chargeable against the shop should be that portion of the constant expense which the current activity is of the normal activity, plus the actual current variable expense." That is, if the activity of the enterprise for a given time is found to be 70 per cent of the normal activity, the expense which should be charged against the manufacturing or producing department should be 70 per cent of the constant expense in normal times, plus the actual variable expense that is justly chargeable against the productive operations for the period. Mr. Ficker would carry all undistributed expense to a separate account and dispose of it either by discharging it through costs during periods when business was good or by charging it to profit and loss.

In judging of the merits of these plans it should be remembered that under any of the simpler averaging methods of expense distribution the entire expense, fixed and variable, is charged against current production. But the supplementary rate burdens current production only with that fixed expense that is not distributed because of error in estimating the machine rate. If the estimated time of operation of each machine and process agrees closely with the actual periods of operation, the machine rate will absorb the fixed expenses belonging to each machine and a large part of the estimated variable expense; and the error introduced into the costs because of decrease of business may not be great under this method. The great difficulty in operating the supplementary rate is in estimating accurately the periods of operation, keeping in mind times of great depression. There probably will be periods in every business when there will be a considerable amount of undistributed expense that does not belong, logically, to current production, but which must be accounted for in some manner, whether in the costs or elsewhere.

In comparing the accuracy of distribution by the machine-rate system with the averaging methods formerly discussed, it must be kept in mind that some of the production factors themselves are based on averages. Buildings are not heated or lighted at the same rate all the year round, repairs to buildings and machinery are not proportional to elapsed time, and expense material may be bought today that may not be used for several weeks or even months. As already noted, moreover, it is not always possible, or at least desirable, to wait until the end of the month to bill goods that are shipped early in the month. If bills are to be sent out promptly with the shipment, the production factors and supplementary rate must be based on records of previous performances; in fact, in a large works, where many small shipments are made daily, this supplementary rate would have to be determined by previous per-

[1] Ficker, N. T., "Shop Expense Analysis and Control," p. 129.

formance, for the work of going back over the month's shipments and making a redistribution would involve a very great periodic increase in clerical labor. Any claims to refined accuracy in this, or in fact in any other method of distributing expense, must, therefore, be taken with caution. Nevertheless, the machine rate offers a more logical method of solving this problem than any other.

It should be fully noted, also, that the ratio of burden to direct labor, or burden to prime cost, or the ratio of indirect labor to direct labor is not necessarily an index of the efficiency of the factory. It is true, of course, that all indirect expenses should be carefully guarded, for they tend naturally to increase unnecessarily unless carefully watched. As the quantity to be produced increases, however, it becomes increasingly easy to separate mental and manual processes and to apply transfer of skill; and the application of these principles usually increases the ratio of the indirect-labor charge to the direct-labor charge. To illustrate, suppose there was just enough of some product to keep five men busy on standard lathes, but not enough to warrant the purchase of an automatic lathe for the work. Then the direct-labor charge would be the wages of the men employed, and if the work was of small size involving no high-priced designer the indirect-labor charge would be small. If, now, the quantity is increased so as to warrant the purchase of a full automatic machine for the work, and the work is, consequently, transferred from a general-machine floor to an automatic-machine floor, the labor on the parts will probably be of the indirect class entirely, as the duties of the men in the automatic room are so varied as to make accurate allocation impossible. It is clear, however, that in this case the total cost of the parts concerned will be greatly reduced, though the indirect charges will be greatly increased, and the direct-labor charges reduced to zero. As a matter of fact it may be that a high direct-labor charge and a low indirect-labor charge may be an index of bad management rather than an index of cheap production.

213. Summarizing Costs.—Where the number of cost items is comparatively small a single card in the cost ledger will suffice to summarize labor, material, and expense for each production order. If, however, the job be a large one and consists of several component parts whose costs are desired it may be necessary to have a **master cost card** and several subsidiary cards for the components. Again, if the labor and material items for a given job are very numerous a **labor-cost sheet** and a **material-cost sheet** may be of service in collecting labor and material charges as they accrue, only the totals of these cards being carried to the master cost sheet. Practice in this respect must vary considerably with circumstances and the form and rulings of the cost cards will vary accordingly. When the job is completed and all labor and material items have been posted upon the master card the expense is added, the total forwarded to the accounting department, and the job-order number is closed against further charges.

In large enterprises the number of time cards, material issues, move cards, etc., becomes very great and the problem of handling these documents expeditiously assumes importance. A number of mechanical devices have been designed to facilitate these operations. Thus the recording time stamp for stamping the time of issue and receipt of documents is in common use. In sorting and tabulating returns such as time cards, again, such machines as the Hollerith tabulating machine should be especially noted. In this system the data are recorded on small cards by means of a perforating machine which operates somewhat like a typewriter. These cards are then sent through a sorting machine which automatically sorts them into the required classification.

214. Distribution of General Expense.—The general expense[1] consists, strictly speaking, of two parts, the **administrative expense** of operating the factory and the **selling expense.** This expense cannot, usually, be charged against specific production orders, the connection between selling and manufacturing being usually vague. It is often possible, however, to apportion this general expense between the several *lines* of product with some degree of fairness, especially when the works are so large that the administrative and sales department are, of necessity, departmentalized. These expenses are usually distributed over the factory cost as a percentage. Thus, suppose that the total output of the factory for a given month is $200,000 and that the general expense for the same period is $50,000. Then the percentage by which the factory cost of each article must be increased in order to absorb the general expense is $\frac{50,000}{200,000} = 0.25$ or 25 per cent. Similar reasoning applies if the general expenses are apportioned to departments.

It may be desirable in some works to keep the sales expenses entirely separate from the general administrative expenses, in which case the selling expense is sometimes distributed as a percentage over the gross cost, *i.e.*, the factory cost plus administrative expense.

PREDETERMINED COSTS

215. General.—It will be obvious that the method of finding costs by recording the transactions after the work is performed is applicable to a wide range of industry. It is particularly applicable to enterprises doing a variety of work with products of considerable magnitude and requiring some time for their completion, as in shipbuilding or the construction of a line of large engines. Such costs will necessarily reflect variations in

[1] The duties of some officials may be divided between these two divisions of the work and their salaries would then be so distributed.

the market prices of material and labor and will change considerably with changing conditions. It will be equally obvious that some means of recording total costs for each item of product is necessary if for no other reason than to insure that a profit is being made.

Such recorded costs, however, are open to the criticism that they record the result of operations *after* they have occurred. Recorded costs of this character, while showing what the costs really *are*, do not show what they *should have been*, and it is something of a task to analyze such costs and to determine from them whether they are higher than they should be, though much can often be done to this end. Moreover, there has been a growing desire among manufacturers to be able to predict costs more accurately than heretofore, and the methods based upon time and motion study have done much to forward this idea. Predetermined or predicted costs usually arise from an effort to control costs in advance in much the same way that a budget controls expenditures of any kind. It will be clear, however, that no manufacturer can place implicit faith in predicted costs of any kind and all such costs must be checked in some manner by actual costs of some sort. The degree of refinement to which prediction can be carried intelligently and the degree of completeness to which predicted costs must be checked will depend upon the circumstances and may vary considerably.

216. Estimated Costs.—It is often necessary to estimate the cost of work prior to production for the purpose of securing contracts. Thus a manufacturer may estimate the cost of a power house or a shipbuilder may estimate the cost of a ship for the purpose of bidding upon the work. In such cases detailed prediction is not possible and recourse must be had to recorded costs of product similar to that which is being considered. The accuracy of the estimate will depend upon the accuracy of the recorded data. And in the absence of recorded costs of product closely similar to that upon which the estimate is made, personal judgment usually becomes a factor in the problem. Estimated costs of this character are usually checked by the cost-finding methods described in the foregoing, the job orders being issued so that comparison of the estimated and actual costs is facilitated. The new recorded costs with the estimated costs may form the basis of future estimates.

217. Standard Costs.—It will be obvious, however, from the discussion in Chap. XII that in many instances it is possible to determine costs in advance of production with a considerable degree of accuracy, and if the processes and conditions of production have been standardized it is possible to realize these predictions quite closely. In some instances the operations to be performed have been repeated so frequently that very accurate recorded costs are available, and in others it is possible to make time and motion studies of the work, thus providing an accurate foundation for cost prediction with little or no recourse to personal judgment. Such costs have become known as *standard costs* and have come into considerable use.

In general, the method is applicable only to plants that manufacture the same lines of goods over a considerable period of time, so that the computing of the standard costs takes cognizance of the variations in expense discussed in the preceding chapter. In establishing such costs a forecast must be made of the proposed volume of production for the period considered, and then detailed computations made for the labor, material and expense involved in carrying out the program.

The applicability of the method depends largely upon the degree of complexity involved in checking up the standard costs and determining the cause of any variation from these standards. Thus in general it will be very costly to set standard costs and then check them by detailed job-order recorded costs. Standard costs are, therefore, most applicable where they can be checked by comparatively simple means, as in industries which use repetitive processes. A simple case is provided by the shoemaking industry. Suppose a shoe manufacturer has produced during the past two years 100,000 pairs of shoes at $2.25 a pair. The labor costs per shoe are standardized by piece rates and are therefore very accurately known, and the amount of material per shoe is also accurately known. Expense accounts have been kept for a number of years, so that the amount of expense that must be allocated to each shoe is also known, for any given volume of product. Market conditions indicate lower prices of material so that the standard cost per pair is fixed at $2.10. Production could be started and advance sales safely made upon this basis if the total actual costs of labor, material, and expense are recorded and checked up against the standard costs of these items, and this procedure is often found to be adequate.

Several interpretations and procedures have been advocated under the name of standard costs, but space limits this discussion to what is in most common use. The most general practice is to predetermine as closely as possible the labor, material, and expense for the work in hand. As has been noted, this can be done with considerable accuracy under modern methods, and where standardized conditions exist in the factory these predicted quantities can be realized quite closely. Recorded costs are made only in such detail as will furnish a check on the predicted costs and permit analysis of variation from them.

A practical example may make the idea clearer. Figure 50 shows an analysis of standard costs presented by Mr. Charter Harrison, but modified slightly for the purposes of this discussion. In the upper part of the table there are tabulated the standard unit prices of the several types of apparatus and the estimated sales by units and volume for the month. At the right hand are shown the actual number sold, the sales at standard prices, and the actual sales as billed to customers. This last amount, the actual receipts, is $68,100.

Model	Standard sales price	Budget sales		Actual sales		
		No.	Amount	No.	At standard sales prices	Billed
18B	$200.00	35	$ 7,000.00	30	$ 6,000.00	$ 6,300.00
24A	280.00	70	19,600.00	75	21,000.00	21,000.00
30A	310.00	40	12,400.00	38	11,780.00	11,780.00
36F	420.00	10	4,200.00	6	2,520.00	2,520.00
42R	450.00	42	18,900.00	40	18,000.00	18,000.00
45B	520.00	5	2,600.00	8	4,160.00	4,000.00
Repair parts.......	....	...	4,000.00	...	4,500.00	4,500.00
		202	$68,700.00	197	$67,960.00	$68,100.00

Factory cost		
Material..........	$23,827.06	
Labor..........	12,370.56	
Expense..........	3,632.10	$49,829.72
Gross profit..........		$18,270.28
Administrative and selling expense..........		15,900.00
Net profit for month..........		$ 2,370.28
Budgeted net profit..........		3,471.41
Decrease in profit as budgeted..........		$ 1,101.13

Analysis of profit variation	
Decrease in sales..............	$ 216.28
Increase in factory cost.........	865.07
Increase in general expense.....	159.78
	$1,241.13
Increase in sales price..........	140.00
Net loss on budget............	$1,101.13
Variation in inventory brought forward this month..........	$3,759.42
Total..................	$3,759.42
Issued direct to sales..........	865.25
Increase for month............	$2,894.17

Analysis of cost variation	
Material variation	
Price......................	$400.00
Waste....................	58.00
Spoilage....................	117.00
Total....................	$575.00
Productive labor	
Piece-work variations..........	$ 250.00
Set-up allowances............	50.00
Extra day work..............	100.00
Total....................	$ 400.00
Expense variation due to decreased volume of work......	$3,181.47
Decreased expense............	397.05
Total....................	$2,784.42
Net increase..................	$3,759.42

FIG. 50.—Analysis of standard costs.

In the next lower division of the analysis the actual shop cost as recorded in the controlling ledger accounts is shown to amount to $49,829.72, leaving a gross profit of $18,270.28. Subtracting the administrative expense from this leaves $2,370.28 as the net profit for the month. But the predicted or expected profit was $3,471.41, hence there is a deficit from the expected profit of $1,101.13.

In the next lower division of the analysis on the left-hand side this deficit is analyzed, as are also the variations in inventory. On the right-hand side the variations in material costs advanced $575, labor increased $400, and expense increased $2,784.42, making a total net increase in costs of $3,759.42.

With this analysis in hand, the manager may readjust his prices or he may by investigation reduce the variations until his standard costs are attained. The ease with which he may do the latter will depend upon the detail with which he has predicted his costs and the corresponding detail with which he has recorded the actual costs. In the example given monthly totals only are compared, but the plan can be extended to any desired degree of detail. An important feature claimed for standard costs is that only the exceptional cases of variation need be attacked, which in many cases reduces the time and labor required for cost reduction.

It will be noted that in Fig. 50 the direct labor, the direct material, and the expense are compared severally with predetermined totals. Now it will appear from the preceding discussion that while it is possible to predetermine direct labor and direct material with some degree of accuracy, it is not possible to do so for expense. It is not possible under any known system to predict with accuracy each item of expense material and labor that will be needed for a given piece of work since, as has been explained, many of these items are not directly connected with the work; in fact, the connection may be very remote. The total of expense items can, however, be closely controlled by budgeting them as suggested in Fig. 50. Budgeting is the assignment of a fixed amount of expenditure for a given purpose for a definite period of time. A cost system and a budget system are not necessarily coexistent in any plant, but a budget system can be of great use to a cost system and in some instances, such as in standard costs, some budgeting is essential for predicting and checking costs. A fuller discussion of budgeting is given in Chap. XXII, to which reference should be made in connection with this article.

PROCESS COSTS

218. General.—In continuous processes, or, in other words, where, owing to the conditions of manufacture, the lots of material follow each other in such a manner that the workmen cannot distinguish one lot from another, the production-order method does not apply, and the system of arriving at cost must be different from that outlined in preceding chapters, though the fundamental principles are the same. A consideration of a simple case, such as that of a cement mill, may make the general method clear. Here the material flows in a continuous stream through the several processes, and the output is more dependent on the machines than on the workmen. The material, moreover, passes through all of the machines, so that the mill, so far as finding total costs is concerned, may be treated as a single machine. The problem is still further simplified in this case by the fact that the material in process at any one time is not of great value as compared with the monthly output, and therefore can be neglected in computing costs. Furthermore, the material passes through the mill rapidly, and at no time is there a large amount of labor tied up in work in process.

It is evident that all that is necessary, so far as total costs are concerned, is to find the total labor and expense incurred during a given period, and divide this total by the output for the same period; this output may be expressed in terms of weight or bulk; that is, in terms of pounds or barrels. The dividend so obtained will be the amount which must be added to the material cost of each unit of output to cover the labor and expense of production. Obviously, these computations can be made more frequently than in the case of the more complex production-order methods.

219. Detail-process Costs.—If it be desired to know the cost of each process, or department, of a continuous-process industry, labor and expense costs must be kept by processes or departments, but they may be distributed, as before, by simple divisions on a material basis, and this will indicate the general method to be pursued in more complex cases. It is usual in such cases to issue a standing-order number to each process, and to charge to this number all labor and expense, if the latter can be segregated. The total amount of these items for any period, divided by the total weight or volume of all of the manufactured product passed through the process for the same period, will give the unit cost which must be charged against each unit of material that has passed through the process. If the expense cannot be allocated to each process, the unit labor cost can be ascertained as indicated in the foregoing treatment, and this cost can be used as a basis for distributing the burden of expense to each unit of product.

Thus, in a factory consisting of several simple continuous processes, each process involving a separate and distinct series of machines, it would be difficult, in general, to segregate accurately all of the expense; hence compromise methods, like those described in this chapter may have to be employed in such cases for allocating the expense.

220. More Refined Process Costs.—The foregoing discussion assumes that the material passes rapidly through the process, or series of processes, and that, therefore, the labor and expense collected at the end of the week or month, as the case may be, belong, approximately at least, to the material that has passed through during that period. If, now, the time required to pass the material through the process, or series of processes, is considerable, this assumption does not hold true, but part of the labor and expense collected at the end of the accounting period will belong to the material that has passed through, and the remainder will be chargeable to material in process. The longer the period of fabrication, as compared to the accounting period, the more marked will this condition be. If it is necessary to take this relation into account, as it may be, the cost accounting will involve keeping a record of material that has been issued to the process in question, and of the amount that has issued from it during the accounting period, in order that at the end of the period the quantity remaining in process may be determined. The theory of this method is simple, though the arithmetic may be somewhat confusing in complex cases.

It should be noted, however, that this refinement is necessary only in extreme cases. In process production, as under the production-order method, goods should, in general, be shipped as soon as possible after completion. It is not possible to hold all the goods manufactured during an accounting period until the end of that period, so as to be able to compute accurately the cost of production; therefore, this cost must generally be computed upon the basis of experience in manufacturing similar goods. It will be noted, also, that many expense items can be allocated only approximately; and, where more than one line of goods is in process, accurate allocation is as difficult under the process-production system as under the production-order method. No definite rules can be laid down for these more complex process methods; each problem must be studied independently, individual judgment entering largely into the solution of the problem involved in each set of conditions.

221. Other Difficulties of Process Accounting.—The discussion assumes that the processes considered are continuous, and that all the material of each kind passes through the same series of machines. If the combination of machines and processes varies from day to day, all the difficulties discussed under the production-order method appear at once. If this takes place, even though there may be some semblance to continuous production, it is better to pass the material through in lots, assigning a production order to each lot. Even then, there will be forms of process production that will be troublesome to the cost-finder.

In intermittent industries, for instance, there are processes which are continuous in character, and which use considerable expense material, the cost of which is difficult to allocate. Processes where material is dipped in insulating fluid—japanning and baking processes, etc.—are instances of this kind. In processes like cement making it is possible to weigh the material, and to use the weight as a measure of labor and expense. But in processes like those others just mentioned, such a measure of labor and of expense material is difficult to obtain. Thus, in plating or dipping, the superficial area of the material treated is the proper criterion for measuring expense material, and this area is difficult to obtain. The expense material itself may be measured, but here again more than one kind of product may be treated at the same time, a condition which makes the allocation difficult, if not impossible. Similar remarks apply to baking processes, where several kinds of products may be baked simultaneously, and where the accurate allocation of direct labor and indirect expense may be impossible. No rules can be laid down for complex cases like these, but a knowledge of correct principles, combined with good judgment, will always indicate compromise methods that will give accurate enough results without too much complication.

222. Costs in Management.[1]—It was noted in Art. 100 that cost returns may be of great service in the management of the plant when consolidated into administrative reports and especially when put into graphic form. When properly interpreted, they may illuminate other phases of industrial management. In Fig. 51 let AB represent the *fixed costs* of a certain concern and AC the *variable costs* for varying volumes of production measured from AB. The ordinates under AC measure the *total costs.* Let OD represent the *total income* from sales. Then the ordinates between OD and AC measure the profit or loss for any volume of production. Thus for full capacity the profit measured by CD is $833,000. The point P is the **break-even point,** where costs just equal the income, and below that point, which is about 42 per cent of full capacity, the plant will run at a loss. If the fixed costs are higher as at $A'B'$ and the variable cost line still passes through the point C the profits at full capacity will be the same as before but the volume can drop only to P' or about 60 per cent before the break-even point is reached.

The assumption that variable costs are proportional to volume of product and that AC is therefore a straight line is true for simple cases only, where each unit of product absorbs the same amount of labor and material and where sales costs are proportional to volume. In more complex plants where the product varies in size and variety and where sales costs may have no definite relation to volume of product, the line AC will, in general, be an irregular one which must be plotted from cost data (see Art. 199). The general principle of Fig. 51 is instructive, however, and the diagram is very useful in studying the effect of changes in fixed and variable costs.

223. Diagrammatic Representation of Accounting Relations.—It was noted in Art. 190 that in best practice cost accounting is an integral part of the general accounts and the general relations are indicated in Fig. 46. A discussion of the complete routine of general accounting is

[1] See also Art. 104.

beyond the limits of this book, but an outline of this procedure is presented in Fig. 52 through the courtesy of Professor John Bangs. The upper part of the diagram shows the principal accounts in the general books with which costs are concerned, while the lower part indicates the factory accounts similarly involved. In the lower part of the diagram, labor and material are indicated as flowing from left to right, as in Fig. 46. The movements of the vouchers, or other controlling documents, are

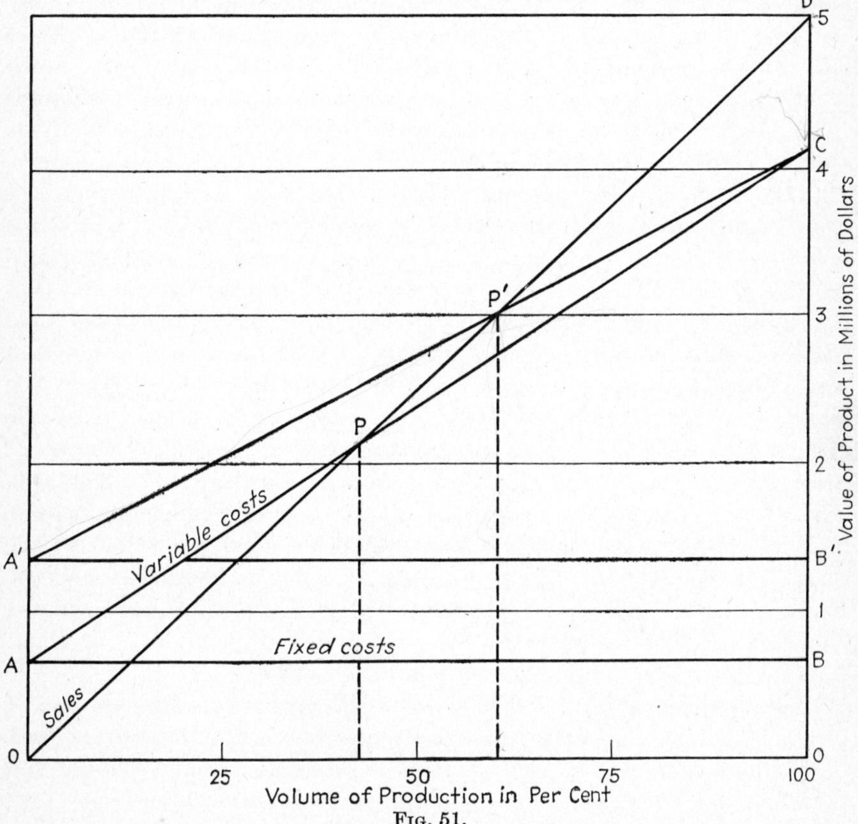

FIG. 51.

indicated by the heavy numbered lines, which the student may follow much as he would an automobile road map.

Beginning, then, at the top, vouchers payable flow to the market for material and labor as indicated by path 1. No material or labor of any kind should be purchased except through some form of voucher or order, which is posted on the credit side of vouchers payable. Through these vouchers (path 1) direct material, direct labor, and expense flow into the factory. All material is charged into the raw-materials account, all direct labor is charged into the direct-labor account, and all expense is similarly charged into the expense account. When direct material is drawn by the production department (path 2), it is charged out of the raw-material account and charged into the work-in-process account. When direct labor is used in production, it is charged out of the direct-

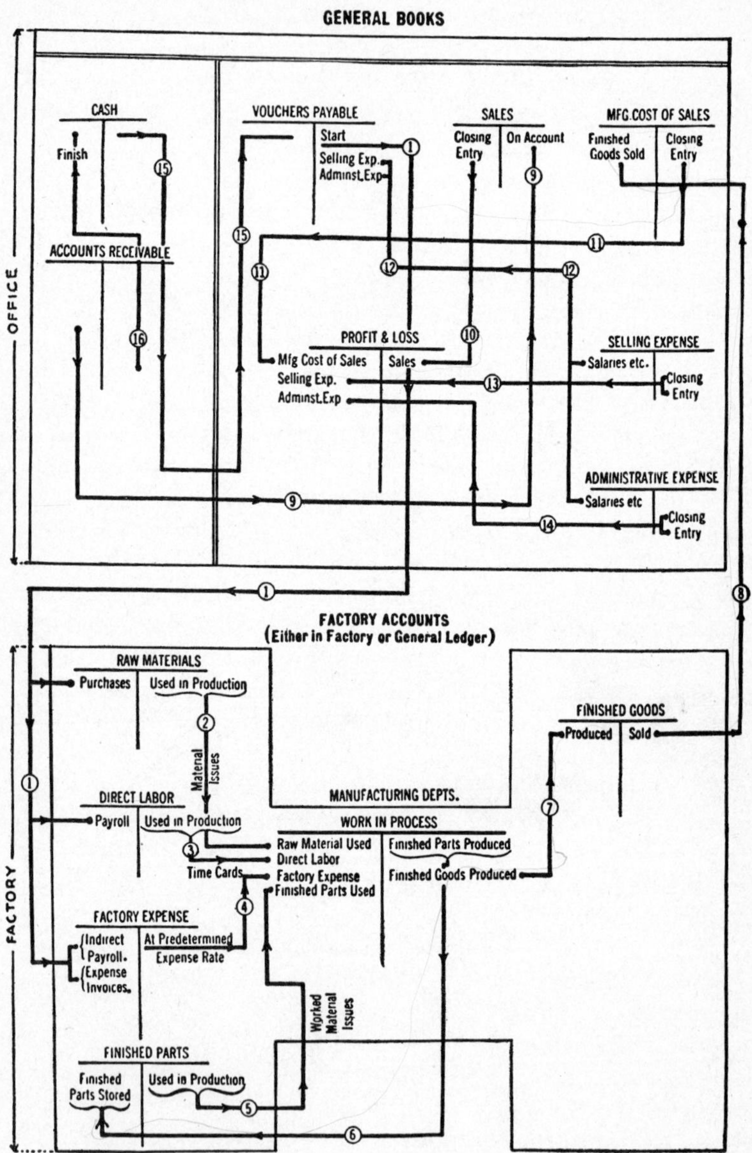

Fig. 52.—Diagrammatic relation between costs and general accounts.

labor account (path 3), and charged into work in process. In a similar manner, expense labor is charged out of the factory expense and charged into work in process (path 4).

If finished parts are used in assemblying the product, they are charged out of the finished-parts account and charged into work in process (path 5). On the other hand, if finished parts are produced in the factory, for either assembly or repair parts, they are charged out of work in process and charged into the finished-parts account (path 6). Care must be used in such transactions that the factory expense due to production is charged against the finished parts only once, and not duplicated in the transfer.

As work progresses in the factory, the several order numbers are charged in the cost ledger, with all labor, material, and expense expended upon them. The sum of all such charges constitutes the total amounts charged into the work-in-process account. As product is completed, it is charged out of work in process according to the value shown in the cost records, and charged into finished goods (path 7). When goods are sold, their value is charged out of the finished-goods account and charged into manufacturing-cost-of-sales account (path 8). It now remains to determine whether a profit or loss is made in the transactions, and this is determined by the profit and loss account, into which the several accounts bearing upon this matter are closed, as follows.

The manufacturing cost of sales is debited with the value of goods sold, and this is carried as a debit to the profit and loss account (path 11). To this account, in a similar manner, are carried the closing entry of the selling-expense account (path 13) and the closing entry of the administrative expense (path 14). The sales are carried to the profit and loss account as a credit (path 10), and the difference between the two sides will show whether a profit or loss has been incurred, due to the production and sale of goods.

The sales account is balanced by debits to the accounts receivable, whether these be in cash or notes covering the sale (path 9). From these accounts receivable also come the cash (path 10) that flows again by path 15 to enable vouchers payable to start more material and labor through the factory.

A clear distinction should be drawn between the profit and loss statement and the balance sheet. The first shows the result of trading operations to date. But the balance sheet shows the entire status of the enterprise. To make up the balance sheet, all accounts and subsidiary ledgers must be balanced and closed into it. Thus the stores ledger, the cost ledger, and the stock ledger in general will record material, raw, in process, and finished, that have not been sold but whose values are needed to balance expenditures made for productive purposes.

224. Summary.—From the foregoing brief outline of the methods of distributing expense, it will be seen that the problem is usually a difficult one and not, in general, capable of exact solution. There are, however, certain fundamental principles that should not be lost sight of, no matter what the system adopted may be. The method adopted should be as simple as the problem will admit. Thus, it should be folly to install an elaborate machine-rate method in a continuous-process plant manufacturing a single commodity, where a percentage-on-material method is amply accurate. Again, in cases where a few lines of goods are made on small machines of low value the percentage-on-wages or the hourly-burden method may be fully adequate. Where the lines of production vary widely in size and character these simple systems are not sufficiently accurate, and the careful manager will go as far as he can in the direction of the machine rate. Almost any shop can be departmentalized and the indirect expense distributed with a fair degree of accuracy between departments. How far beyond this the manager can go economically will depend on conditions. In any case he should see to it that *all* costs are distributed. On the other hand, if he employs a professional organizer to assist him he will do well to have a clear understanding in the beginning of just what costs he desires to obtain and not install a lot of useless detail, the expense of which more than offsets the gain. There is a great difference between *principles* and the *detail* to which they may be carried. The expert organizer should be a master of the principles involved and be able to install a satisfactory system; the manager, on the other hand, should be able to guide him in the matter of detail. The two working together should be able to install a system that will obtain the desired results at minimum expense.

References

ALFORD, L. P. (Ed.): "Cost and Production Handbook," p. 941.
———: "Management's Handbook," p. 1313.
BANGS, JOHN R., JR.: "Industrial Accounting for Executives."
CAMMAN, E. A.: "Basic Standard Costs."
CHURCH, A. HAMILTON: "Expense Burden."
———: "Manufacturing Costs and Accounts."
———: "Production Factors."
FICKER, N. T.: "Shop Expense Analysis and Control."
FRANKLIN, B.: "Cost Reports for Executives."
GILMAN, STEPHEN: "Analyzing Financial Statements."
LEE, M. A.: "A Practical Drawing-room Course," *Mech. Eng.*, August, 1923.
SCOVELL, CLINTON H.: "Cost Accounting and Burden Application."

CHAPTER XIX

THE DEPRECIATION OF WASTING ASSETS

225. Nature of Depreciation.—The assets of any industrial undertaking are usually divisible into two classes, namely **fixed assets** and **floating assets.** Under fixed assets are included land, buildings, and machinery necessary for the work; while under floating assets are included the purchased materials operated on, with such supplies, cash, bills receivable, etc., as are a necessary part of the business. The total amount of the assets may be fairly constant, but the distribution of this total among the several classes of assets may vary constantly with variations in the business. Now, manifestly, some of these forms of assets are stable and do not necessarily change in value, or if they change it is by slow degrees. Thus the land may appreciate slowly, or the purchasing power of the cash may slowly increase or decrease depending on many circumstances.

Other forms of invested capital, however, constantly tend to decrease in value whether the business is operated or not. Thus, the buildings waste away because of the action of the elements and also by reason of wear and tear incident to the industry. Machinery and furniture of all kinds tend to wear out and must be renewed. Purchased material, that has been fabricated into salable product, may depreciate greatly if held in store too long, either from the action of the elements or from being superseded by other types of product. Even unworked material may depreciate to scrap value by reason of changes in design or manufacturing processes, especially if it is of special character and not a standard market commodity. These two last forms of depreciation are particularly likely to occur in new industries where the development is rapid.

Invested capital may be lost in one of two ways; and for convenience these may be distinguished as **losses on capital account** and **losses on revenue account.** If an uninsured ship is lost at sea or an uninsured building is burned, the loss is clearly a loss of capital that has nothing to do with depreciation. To replace such losses the owner must furnish new capital whether he takes it from his surplus savings or borrows it elsewhere; but clearly no allowance for wasting depreciation that he makes on his remaining property can properly be said to replace the loss.

Losses on revenue account are those incurred as the result of trading. Thus, if a company begins business with a total capital of $200,000 and at the end of the year has its original equipment (having suffered no loss on capital account) but finds that after proper allowance is made for wasting losses it possesses only $150,000, it has suffered a loss of $50,000 on revenue account. Depreciation is one of the elements that enter into and intimately affect loss or gain on revenue account and the above distinction is important.

Investments that unavoidably deteriorate through the action of the elements or through wear and tear incident to the industry are termed **wasting assets.** Evidently they will vary in character with the character of the business, and a careful investigation should be made of every undertaking to determine just what wasting assets it includes in order that proper allowance can be made for them by setting aside money from revenue sufficient to keep the capital account intact. Depreciation has become of increasing importance with the extension of income tax laws.[1]

A careful distinction must sometimes be made between the several ways in which assets may lessen in value. In the case of the appraisal of a public-utility enterprise as, for instance, a street-car system or a telephone system, where toll rates are to be fixed upon the basis of the valuation, the following forms[2] of lessening value may be, and often are, recognized:

1. **Wear and tear or maintenance.**
2. **Physical decay or decrepitude.**
3. **Deferred maintenance or neglect.**
4. **Inadequacy.**
5. **Obsolescence.**

226. Wear and Tear or Maintenance.—From the moment a building is erected or a machine is put into service, deterioration begins because of the action of the elements or the use of the building or machine. Thus, the bearings of all machines wear more or less, the paint on the building begins at once to wear off, the commutator of a dynamo must be replaced, or a new tire must be put upon a wagon wheel. Deterioration of this kind, that can be compensated for by proper repairs and renewals, is usually known as **wear and tear.** Depreciation of this sort varies greatly in its effect with different classes of apparatus. In some cases the effect is very great in the beginning of the life of the asset, slowing up as time goes on; while in other cases the reverse may take place, the deterioration, because of wear and tear, becoming greater in effect as the end of the working life of the asset approaches. In interchangeable manufacturing, where extreme accuracy is required, wear and tear that under ordinary conditions would be allowable may render a machine useless for its purpose to the degree that it may be cheaper to replace it than to repair the wear. In this class of depreciation may also be included the results of accidents or sudden damage from unforeseen causes, and when these are abnormally great they should be charged off over a considerable length of time so as not to augment the current operating expenses

[1] See *The National Accountant*, August, 1937, p. 6.

[2] For a more detailed list see Ewing, Matheson, "The Depreciation of Factories."

excessively (see Art. 207). It is customary, in most plants, to charge the expense of compensating for wear and tear, which is the most apparent form of depreciation, to operating expense, thus making it a direct charge against production.

227. Physical Decay or Decrepitude.—Even when a machine is kept in first-class repair, or when a building is kept properly painted and repaired, there is a general deterioration that goes on continually that cannot be thus compensated for, and in time the structure or machine will reach such a state that nothing short of complete renewal will suffice. In many cases this gradual lessening of value by age will be at least as rapid when the asset is not in use. Buildings, boilers, insulated wire, and similar assets will waste away by the action of the elements as rapidly when standing idle as when in operation, and it is common experience that such properties, in time, reach a state of decay where repairs are no longer economical. Such deterioration is called **physical decay** or **decrepitude.** A horse is a most excellent example of this form of depreciation. His shoes can be kept repaired but the gradual breaking down of his physical powers cannot be stayed by any manner of repairs or renewals. He must be *replaced.*

228. Deferred Maintenance.—It is clear that even though repairs and maintenance are properly provided all physical assets will, in course of time, depreciate below their original value, even though their productive powers are as high as in the beginning. In fact, after a few years it is probable that, even with the best of maintenance, a plant of any kind cannot be put in a condition that will exceed 85 per cent of its original value. If, however, the proper repairs and maintenance are not provided, the value of the asset will fall below the value it should have if properly maintained, and the amount it may fall is known as **deferred maintenance** or **neglect.** Deferred maintenance is a measure of the amount that must be expended to restore the asset to normal working condition and is, therefore, a measure of the efficiency of the management or its financial ability. Such depreciation is important in appraisal work where interests other than of the management are concerned.

229. Inadequacy.—Even though the asset may be kept in full repair it may become uneconomical or even useless because of increased demands of the service, though it may still be fully adequate to do the work for which it was installed. Thus an engine may become too small for the work required, or locomotives may become too small to be economical for the increased service demanded. If heavier locomotives are installed they may make heavier rails necessary, though the old rails may not be worn. An overhead crane may be in good repair and of modern type, but may be found inadequate to meet the requirements due to growth. This kind of decreased value is called **inadequacy,** or **supersession.** It clearly has no connection with age or time of service or the physical condition of the asset so far as wear and tear are concerned.

230. Obsolescence.—Assets may become of lessened value because of the introduction of new types of apparatus or new inventions or processes. This is particularly true in any industry or business that is developing rapidly. Thus, in the development of the textile industries of New England, a heavy burden was imposed upon manufacturers because of the rapid development of new machines, that gave a great advantage to other men seeking an opening in the field and compelled the older owners to scrap their machinery long before wear and tear had become noticeable. The same effects were very common in the electrical field during the early periods of development and still prevail, in fact, in many lines of that industry. The history of street-car traction is a remarkable instance of the effect of obsolescence. The change from horse cars to cable cars, from cable cars to electrical propulsion, and the very rapid growth of this last system was marked by the abandonment of much apparatus long before wear or decrepitude would have compelled such a step. It would now appear that this form of transportation has been rendered obsolete by the gasoline-driven bus. Such depreciation is called **obsolescence.** It is very similar to inadequacy in its effect but proceeds from different causes. Machinery or other assets thrown out of use by reason of inadequacy may still have a high market value; but machinery abandoned because of obsolescence is, in most cases, valueless except for scrap since here the economic use of the asset is destroyed regardless of its size. Inadequate machinery may be of good service in some other place or under other conditions.

As before noted, any or all of these forms of lessening value may be important in appraising properties where conflicting interests are concerned, as in the valuation of railways or other quasi-public enterprises, or in differences of opinion between stockholders and bondholders. In the case of simple depreciation of factories, where the owner is desirous only of knowing the total of such losses, these several classes of wasting losses may be, and usually are, grouped under two heads, namely, **depreciation,** which includes the effects of wear and tear, decrepitude, and deferred maintenance, and **obsolescence,** which includes inadequacy also. The effect of the first group included in depreciation can, obviously, be estimated by observation, or, if data are available, some systematic method of compensating for these effects can be adopted. Obsolescence, however, cannot always be adjudged visually, but it is possible often to make estimates on the probable life of the asset at the end of which it will be obsolete. A discussion of the methods of providing for these losses will be given in a succeeding article.

231. Relation of Depreciation to Capital-Depletion.—Many undertakings must face what may be termed **obligations.** Thus, money may have been borrowed, payable at a definite future time. Machinery may be installed in a rented factory under the agreement that it becomes the property of the landlord after a given fixed time; or valuable patents may have been acquired whose value is comparatively short-lived. To meet these obligations an annual sum may be set aside from revenue, thus forming a **sinking fund** that, under compound interest, will accrue to the desired amount at the expiration of the allotted time.

The importance that should be attached to distinguishing between sums of money set aside out of revenue for specific purposes will, clearly, depend on the nature of the business and the manner in which it is owned and operated. Sometimes neither a reserve nor a sinking fund is necessary, but allowance must nearly always be made for depreciation and obsolescence and care should be taken, if only one fund is set aside, that it shall be sufficient to cover not only the specific purpose for which it may be intended but depreciation and obsolescence as well, if these are not cared for in some other manner. In general, the larger the undertaking the more important it is that these accounts be segregated, while in small plants provision for wear and tear, obsolescence, and other contingencies is often made under the one head of allowance for depreciation, thus greatly broadening the significance of the term. In large undertakings, on the other hand, the conflicting interests of stockholders and bondholders may make it undesirable to establish large reserves for unforeseen contingencies, as it is difficult, often, to convince stockholders of the necessity for such funds, which they would prefer to see distributed in dividends. For this reason reserves are often hidden under the general name of depreciation, though the practice can scarcely be commended. The federal income tax laws regulate closely the rates of depreciation for industries engaged in interstate commerce. Accountants for such industries should therefore acquaint themselves with these regulations before setting up depreciation reserves.

The capital investment of practically all industrial enterprises includes some wasting assets; and it is evident that they should be carefully considered. These wasting losses are in reality a charge against production, and the fact that they do not make themselves known through the payroll, the material requisitions, or bills payable renders them all the more elusive and dangerous. Suppose, for instance, that an enterprise is started with $100,000 total assets, divided into $60,000 fixed assets, $25,000 worth of material in process, and $15,000 cash. Suppose that at the end of 10 years the owner has disbursed $20,000 in profits, but on taking a careful inventory he finds his fixed assets to be worth only $30,000, his material in process to be worth $20,000, and his cash to be $10,000, or a total of $60,000. Clearly, his apparent profit of $20,000 has been made at the cost of a loss of $40,000 from his capital;[1] in fact, his *apparent* profits were taken *out of capital*. The following basic rule may, therefore, be stated: **no profits should be declared until all losses to capital through the revenue account have been replaced from revenue.**

This principle is even more clear in considering undertakings that are

[1] It is assumed that he has no liabilities in either case.

limited in extent or time, and where the operation of the property necessitates the **depletion** of some of its capital assets. Thus, in the case of a man who acquires a piece of coal land and sinks a shaft for the purpose of taking out the coal, his investment is represented by the purchase price of the land and the cost of his shaft and equipment, with such cash, etc., as may be necessary for operation. When the coal has been removed the land and machinery may be valueless, or nearly so, depreciating yearly as the coal is removed. Clearly, he must sell the coal at a price that will return him his original investment plus the cost of operating, plus such a profit as he may expect to make on his investment. Goodwill, patent rights, and similar investments, that depreciate with time, are of the same character and must, in general, be returned to capital out of revenue before they expire; and profits cannot be said to have been made till all such wastes have been returned to capital.

The relation that depreciation bears to assets and profits is not always easy to see. Floating assets such as cash, bills receivable, and materials in process can be readily evaluated and usually the books of any concern give minute details of these accounts. But the actual changes that have taken place in the value of buildings and equipment are seldom accurately known, first because it is (as will be seen) difficult to evaluate these changes, and second, because, as noted, these changes in value do not *force* themselves upon the attention of the accountant as do other items of manufacturing expense. This fundamental relation is nevertheless clear, that it is not safe to declare profits[1] of any kind until assured that all wastes of the assets have been replaced. It may be noted here that the care that will be exercised in enforcing this important principle often depends on the character of the parties owning the industry. To the individual owner, or to simple partners, the above reasoning will appear sound and will usually be followed as far as possible or desirable. When, however, the business is owned by a stockholders' corporation and has issued bonds that are held by so-called bondholders, there is a diversity of interest that may affect the rate of depreciation greatly. The bondholder does not run the business and has no vote in its management, but simply loans money to the corporation, taking a bond as security and receiving interest on his loan, usually at a fixed rate. Evidently his bond is secured only so long as the assets that it represents remain unimpaired, and hence he will most naturally want to see depreciation of all wasting assets fully restored, even though no dividends are paid beyond the interest on the bonds, which have first call on any payments. The stockholders or apparent owners of the industry, however, are interested more in the *profits* of the business. They may be, and often are, a con-

[1] The term profit is here used in a general sense, meaning any surplus in the trading account after wasting capital losses have been replaced. Strictly speaking, however, profit is any surplus left after *interest* on capital investment has been allowed (see Art. 194).

tinually changing body and would not, in general, be concerned if profits were paid out of capital, because of inadequate allowance for depreciation. Unless, therefore, the officers of such a corporation do make proper allowance for depreciation before declaring profits they are not dealing fairly with the bondholders who are their creditors. It is to be noted that excess allowance for depreciation usually does no injury to either bondholders or stockholders, since it serves only to make the bondholders' security more secure and leaves a surplus in the hands of the stockholders for administration. As will be seen later, however, there are limitations also to this procedure.

This divergency of interest often occurs where a building or factory is rented by the manufacturer. The owner is interested in obtaining his fixed rental, and also in seeing that the plant is kept in thorough repair. The tenant is interested in upkeep only so far as it affects his profits. A written agreement is essential in such cases, as this divergent point of view is often the cause of legal action.

232. Relation between Depreciation, Repairs and Renewals.— Expenditures made for repairs and maintenance tend, naturally, to offset depreciation due to wear and tear, but it is only in certain cases that they may be considered as completely balancing depreciation losses. Where the plant consists of a large number of units that wear out so quickly as to need frequent renewals, the very fact that it is in full working order is sufficient proof that depreciation is fairly compensated for. Again, in very large and permanent undertakings, such as railroads, where a large amount of repairs, renewals, and additions is constantly under way, it is often assumed that depreciation is thus fully compensated for. Evidently there should be an obvious increase in the plant yearly to insure that such is the case; otherwise there is danger that a gradual lessening of value may really be taking place. For, in general, it cannot be assumed that the ordinary running repairs and renewals compensate for depreciation. A machine or building may be kept in prime repair and worn parts may be replaced from time to time; but in spite of the best of care, there is, and must be, a general wearing out of the asset till nothing short of complete renewal can be considered.

It is, of course, true that extensive repairs may, in some cases, be considered as offsetting a certain amount of depreciation, but such allowances should be made with care. In a similar manner some renewals may be considered as additions to capital. Thus, suppose a boring mill that was originally worth $10,000 is sold to a second-hand dealer for $2,000 and a new mill bought for $20,000, being paid for by the $2,000 from the sale of the old mill and $18,000 taken from earnings. Clearly, it would be fair to make an addition to the capital account of $10,000, provided, of course, that the earning power of the new mill was greater than the old one in proportion to the difference in price. By similar reasoning it can be seen that renewals may just balance depreciation;

but care should be taken that such renewals are not considered as additions to capital unless they really increase the earning capacity of the plant. In fact, new additions to the plant should not be considered as additions to capital unless it is clear that they increase the earning power, and also that the investment in the additions is not compensated for by the deterioration of the older part of the plant, for which no provision has been made in the form of a reserve fund.

233. Methods of Depreciation.—From the foregoing it will be clear that the object of computing depreciation is to make sure that all deterioration of the wasting assets is fully restored before any profits are declared. The values of the continuous and unavoidable wastes in the plant are taken from revenue and transferred to the floating assets in the form of cash or some other floating asset, and if the computation for depreciation is correctly made the total assets will remain constant in value.[1] The funds so set aside from revenue may be employed in the business in other ways, or they may be placed at interest, if not needed in the business, thus forming a reserve fund that may be drawn upon for renewals or repairs of such a character as may be justifiable.

While the necessity of making allowance for depreciation is generally admitted, there is little unanimity of opinion as to the methods to be pursued in making such an allowance. This is naturally so since industrial enterprises differ widely, and besides, what may be *desirable* may not always be *expedient*. There is often, however, too great a lack of knowledge of the fundamental principles involved, and systematic methods of providing for depreciation are the exception and not the rule. Some managers are content to consider the amount spent from revenue for additions, repairs, and renewals as sufficient to compensate for depreciation. The limitations of this procedure have already been discussed. Others are content to take the difference between an estimated percentage of depreciation and the cost of repairs and renewals as a measure of the depreciation; but such rules are of a necessity rough approximations. Probably the most common way of ascertaining depreciation is to take an inventory of all assets, visual examination being made of each and every tool and appliance, and the apparent value noted. The sum of the values thus found is the apparent valuation of the plant, and by comparison with former records the depreciation may be determined. This would seem to be the most practical and satisfactory method, particularly where the books of the concern are closed at stated periods, say annually, and a balance made of all accounts. There are some disadvantages, however, in this method, because of the large amount of time, trouble, and expense involved, especially if the plant is a large one; and in very busy seasons it may be very undesirable to take such an inventory, particularly if it

[1] Of course additions may be made to capital from some outside source or by adding to it from the profits, but this does not affect the above principle so far as the original capital is concerned.

involves a suspension of work. A visual examination of a machine, moreover, may or may not give a correct estimate of its real value. A machine several years old may appear to be in first-class order, nevertheless its working life shortens yearly and due provision should be made against the time when it must be replaced or is rendered obsolete. It requires rare judgment and great experience accurately to estimate plant values visually. A periodical survey of the whole plant is, however, a very valuable and necessary proceeding, as it may serve as a check upon any systematic method of computing depreciation.

Some care must be exercised in placing a valuation on any industrial property, since the purpose of such a valuation is to show what it is worth as an asset. Equipment may have several values, depending on how it is viewed. There is a great difference in the value of a plant as a going concern to its owners, and the value of the same plant to a purchaser if it is disposed of at forced sale to satisfy obligations. Every tool depreciates considerably in market value the very first time it is used, though its intrinsic worth may not change. It would not seem fair, however, to evaluate such property at the lowest price, namely, forced-sale value, so long as the concern is a going one, unless the business is exceedingly profitable and the owners can afford to carry the value of the plant at a sum that is on the extreme side of safety.

In appraising[1] public utilities several kinds of value may be, and often are, recognized. Thus the **service value,** or the value of the asset as measured by its present effectiveness for the purpose for which it was installed, may be important in such cases. This may be high, though the property may be considerably depreciated, theoretically. Another basis for valuation of utilities and one that has been approved by the courts of some states is the **cost of reproduction** of the asset considered, by new apparatus of the same kind and efficiency, at the current market prices.

If from the original cost, if it be known, or from the estimated cost of reproduction new, there be taken the total depreciation, the so-called **present value** is obtained. This is the value that is most used in evaluating factory assets for inventory purposes and will be discussed more fully later.

In making an evaluation of any asset, care should be used to separate recoverable values from those that are irrecoverable. The *total* cost of a machine is its purchase price plus freight, cartage, and cost of installation, including the foundation. A machine does not change in value if moved from one position in the shop to another, but the outlay incident to erecting it in the original location vanishes the moment it is moved, and cannot be regarded as recoverable in any sense. In fact, it may be an expensive matter to remove or remodel the old foundation to make the site available for other operations. Such items of expenditure, therefore, should not be included in the inventory value of the machine, but

[1] Floy, Henry, "Valuation of Public-utility Properties," p. 12.

should be charged to a preliminary expense account and written off independently and as quickly as possible by depreciation methods.

In addition to the physical assets that are **tangible,** that is, assets that are visible, there are usually other items that are **intangible** and invisible, that are, nevertheless, assets in a true sense. In this class would be listed all development expense such as engineers' surveys, legal expenses of organization, cost of franchises or permits, salaries, and all other expenses incident to, and chargeable against, construction, and similar expenditures that are a part of the cost of the plant but do not show as visible or tangible property in the inventory. Such expenses are a true part of the cost of the plant but are not easy to recover if the plant is sold. Best practice carries all such expenses in a separate **development account** and makes provision to depreciate it out of existence by means of sinking-fund methods to be described later. Intangible assets, such as cost of franchises, patents, and short-lived assets, in general, that are not a part of construction expense should also be carefully segregated and provision made for writing them off as quickly as possible.

From the foregoing it will be clear that there is a difference in the valuation that should be placed upon an asset depending on the purpose for which the valuation is made. Setting aside the modifying influences that arise in making such valuations of property for the purpose of fixing rates for public service and similar cases, it is clear that for the usual purposes of inventory this value will lie between the original or cost value and the ultimate or scrap value of the machine. The rate at which the value of the asset will fall from the original value to scrap value will depend on several factors and may vary with changing circumstances. It is customary in most well-operated plants to establish *average* rates of depreciation, these rates varying with the character of the plant, so that each asset or class of assets can be depreciated yearly without much trouble, and to check the results by partial or complete visual examination at longer periods. These depreciation rates may be adjusted from time to time as variations in the business or extensive repairs and renewals make it necessary or desirable. The three principal factors involved in establishing such rates are:

1. The first cost of the asset, whether building or machine.
2. The estimated productive life of the asset.
3. The residual or scrap value of the building or machine.

The two factors that tend most to modify any systematic scheme of depreciation are:

1. Extensive repairs or renewals.
2. Obsolescence[1] of the asset due to change in productive methods or the introduction of new machines or processes.

[1] There may be cases where changes in processes may cause machines to *appreciate* in value, but such cases are rare. Land often appreciates in value.

These relations may be made clearer by the **plant ledger sheet** (Fig. 53), on which is recorded the financial history of a milling machine which was purchased, new, for $2,975, and for which the freight charge was $25, thus making its inventoried value $3,000. The residual or scrap value was placed at $600. The **wearing value** or amount that is to be depreciated is, therefore, $3,000 − $600 = $2,400, and it will be assumed that this depreciation is to be distributed over 10 years of producing life in equal amounts of $240 per year.

MACHINE NO. 3A MILLING MACHINE	LOCATION FLOOR 2 ROW 8 NUMBER 46
MAKER KEMPSMITH MACH. CO.	COST - 2975 FREIGHT - 25
PURCHASED FEB. 5 1916	ESTIMATED LIFE. 10 YEARS
NEW OR SECOND HAND NEW	PROBABLE SELLING VALUE 600
WEIGHT 3050 LBS.	RATE OF DEPRECIATION STRAIGHT LINE

DATE			REMARKS	TOTAL COST	SCRAP VALUE	WEARING VALUE	ANNUAL DEPREC.	DEPREC. RESERVE	PRESENT VALUE
Feb	5	16	Installed	3000 00	600 00	2400 00	240 00		
Jan	1	17					240 00	240 00	2760 00
Jan	1	18					240 00	480 00	2520 00
Jan	1	19					240 00	720 00	2280 00
Jan	1	'20					240 00	960 00	2040 00
Jan	1	21					240 00	1200 00	1800 00
Feb	5	21	Motor Drive Installed	500 00	700 00				2300 00
Jan	1	22					320 00	1520 00	1980 00
Mar	6	22	Thoroly Repaired, New Spindle	200 00				1320 00	2180 00
Jan	1	23					370 00	1690 00	1810 00
May	6	24	Machine Sold for $1800						
			Loss = $10						
			FOR ATTACHMENTS SEE REVERSE SIDE						

Fig. 53.—Plant ledger.

The plant ledger shows that for the first 5 years this procedure was carried out, $240 being carried annually to the depreciation-reserve account and the inventory value decreased by that amount until at the end of the fifth year this value had fallen to $1,800.

Early in the fifth year (1921), however, a motor drive was attached to this machine, the cost of which was $500, and the inventory value was increased to $2,300, while the residual value was increased to $700. The new wearing value was, therefore, $2,300 − $700 = $1,600, and a new annual depreciation rate of $320 was set for the 5 remaining years of estimated producing life. In January, 1922, the machine was depreciated on this basis. In March, 1922, the machine was thoroughly repaired and a new spindle and spindle bearings installed. It was considered that these renewals would offset depreciation to the extent of $200 and, therefore, this amount was deducted from depreciation reserve and added to the inventory value, but it was not considered wise to change the residual value of $700. A new depreciation increment of $370 was set, therefore, and in 1923 the machine was depreciated upon this basis. In May, 1924, the machine was sold for $1,800 and a loss of $10, therefore, was incurred, since the residual value plus the wearing value at that time was $700 + $1,110 = $1,810. This loss would be carried to the profit and loss account.

The machine might, of course, have been retained beyond the 10 years of estimated producing life and it might be found to be useful for many more years. On the other hand it might have been in first-class condition any time during the course of the estimated life, but be almost valueless because of changes in manufacturing processes or because of new inventions. Special tools are much more likely to be thus affected than are those of standard design and type.

The probable life of any machine or building varies with the industry and the class and character of the equipment. Care and character of service, and the hours of actual use also contribute to this variation. For this reason, while it is necessary to assume a working life in arranging a system of depreciation, the inventory values as given by any system should be checked occasionally by actual examination, particularly where obsolescence is possible.

The ultimate selling value of any machine will, obviously, depend on many factors, and must, in general, be estimated. In the extreme case, the ultimate value will be the value of the machine as scrap and this, again, would depend on the materials of which it is made and the difficulty of reworking them. Thus small, complicated apparatus, composed of various materials as steel, cast iron, and brass, are often costly to dismember; while very large and thick castings are expensive to break up.

The rate at which the asset shall be depreciated from the original cost to scrap value over the assumed life requires special consideration. The assumed rate will lie, in general, between two extremes. If the asset has been kept in first-class repair and has not suffered from obsolescence, its value for the purpose for which it was installed may decrease very slowly for a long time, actual depreciation becoming very rapid only near the end of its productive life. To carry any wasting asset at a high valuation for a long period of time is, however, courting disaster, if there is any danger whatever of any readjustment of the business that would involve an appraisal of the property, particularly if such readjustment resulted in a forced sale; and most prudent managers carry the value of their plant on their books at a constantly decreasing value to guard against such a contingency.

The market or commercial value of a machine, on the other hand, falls very rapidly during the first part of its life, though its producing power and value as a going asset may not decrease. As before noted, it would be obviously unfair to depreciate suddenly all new assets during the first years of their life, and in the case of new enterprises such a procedure would often render profits and progress impossible. Thus, a special machine might be a very valuable and profitable investment to a going concern, but would be worth scrap value only, at a forced sale, the day after it was built. For these reasons the rates of depreciation usually adopted lie between these two extremes, thus compromising the advantages and defects of both, the rates being selected so as to lean toward either extreme, as desired, depending on the character of the asset under consideration.

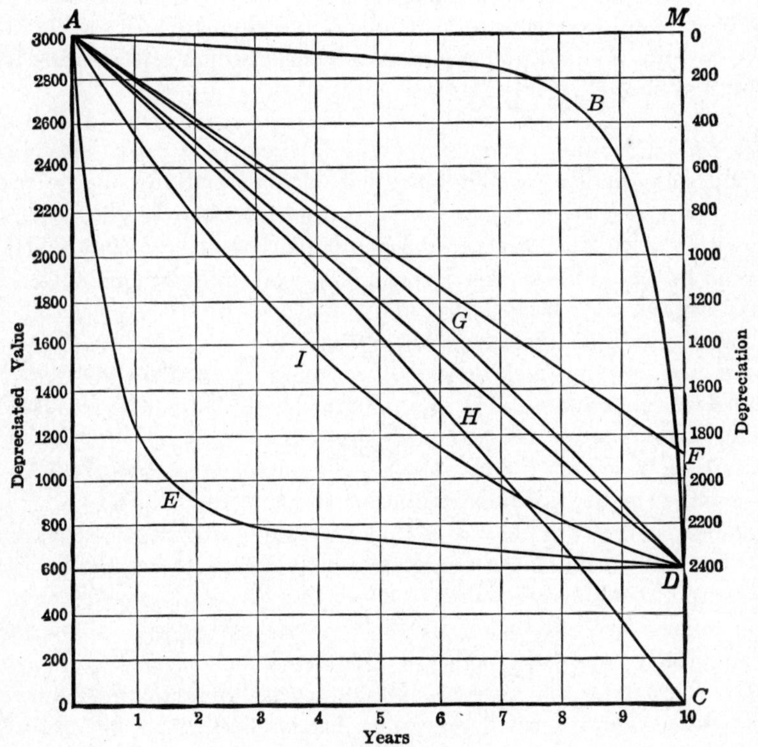

Fig. 54.—Depreciation curves.

Thus, referring to Fig. 54, suppose a milling machine that cost $3,000 is to be depreciated to a sales value of $600 in 10 years. If it be desired to depreciate the asset very rapidly so as to reduce it quickly to forced-sale value the depreciated value would lie along some such curve as *AED*, dropping rapidly in the early years and more slowly in the later years. If, however, the inventory was to be based upon the service value and the asset was kept in good repair, the depreciated values would lie along some such curve as *ABD*, falling very slowly at first, but dropping very rapidly as the machine neared the end of its productive life. Obviously, an infinite number of curves could be drawn between these extremes, depending on the circumstances and the judgment of the appraiser. In practice, however, it is customary, for convenience, to adopt some systematic mathematical method for progressively lowering the value of the asset, the most important of these methods being the **percentage-on-original-cost plan,** the **percentage-on-diminishing-value plan,** and the **sinking-fund plan.**

Under the percentage-on-original-cost method the total depreciation, that is, the difference between the cost and the scrap values, is divided by the estimated producing life, and an amount equal to the dividend is deducted from the value of the asset annually. Thus, in the above example, the annual depreciation of the milling machine would be $\frac{\$3,000 - \$600}{10} = \$240$, and the depreciated values of the machine would lie along the straight line *AD* (Fig. 54); hence the name **straight-line method** sometimes applied to this plan of depreciation. Because of its simplicity and because it gives a fair compromise between the conflicting difficulties discussed, this method of depreciation is used more, perhaps, than any other.

An argument in favor of the above method is that in a new business, with scanty income during the early years, it does not make such a heavy demand on income as other methods to be described. An argument against the above method is that depreciation *really* is much greater in the early years of an asset than in the later periods. Undoubtedly, the diminution in value of a machine tool is much greater during the first or second year of its life than during the tenth or fifteenth. Another argument against the method is that it is often more desirable to depreciate heavily during the early years when repairs and renewals are not costly, and to deduct less during the later years when repairs and renewals begin to be more burdensome, thus keeping the annual deduction from revenue fairly constant.

For these and other reasons some managers prefer the percentage-on-diminishing-value method. Under this method a fixed percentage is taken from the value as depreciated the preceding year, and not from the original value. Thus, if the percentage of depreciation be taken at 15, the value of the tool at the end of succeeding years will be as shown by the curve *AID* (Fig. 54). The method of depreciation by percentage on diminishing values evidently enforces a heavier reduction in value in the early life of the asset and in the case of an entirely new enterprise this method may make profits impossible unless a very long producing life is assumed. It is applicable particularly where it is desired to make a rapid reduction in the value of an asset of perishable or short-lived character.

Table 7 gives the comparative values and the amounts of depreciation by these methods for the case noted above. It will be noted that the annual amounts set aside are much greater in the percentage-on-diminishing-value method during the earlier years and less in the later years. Table 7 gives the depreciated value of unity for different rates and terms of years by the percentage-on-diminishing-value method, and may be found useful in assigning a rate of depreciation for an assumed working life.

TABLE 7.—COMPARISON OF METHODS OF DEPRECIATION

Time	By percentage on original value or straight-line method		By percentage on diminishing value	
	Value at time noted	Amount of depreciation	Value at time noted	Amount of depreciation
Beginning	$3,000	......	$3,000	
End of first year	2,760	$ 240	2,550	$ 450
End of second year	2,520	240	2,168	382
End of third year	2,280	240	1,843	325
End of fourth year	2,040	240	1,567	276
End of fifth year	1,800	240	1,332	235
End of sixth year	1,560	240	1,132	200
End of seventh year	1,320	240	962	170
End of eighth year	1,080	240	818	144
End of ninth year	840	240	695	123
End of tenth year	600	240	591	104
Total amount written off	......	$2,400	......	$2,409

The percentage on diminishing value is computed as follows:

If V = the original value,

V' = the residual or scrap value,

n = the number of years,

x = the percentage of depreciation,

Thus $x = 1 - \sqrt[n]{\frac{V'}{V}}$

or for the example in Table 6,

$$x = 1 - \sqrt[10]{\frac{600}{3{,}000}} = 1 - \sqrt[10]{0.2} = 1 - 0.85 = 0.15.$$

It should be noted that when the scrap value is small as compared to the original value, the rate of depreciation is very high for a normal working life, and approaches 100 per cent as a limit as the scrap value approaches zero. This method is not adapted, therefore, to such cases. Recourse should then be had to the percentage-on-original-cost plan or a curve assumed that will fit the necessities of the case.

TABLE 8.—DEPRECIATED VALUE OF UNITY AT DIFFERENT RATES FOR TERMS OF YEARS

Years	1 per cent	1¼ per cent	1½ per cent	2 per cent	2½ per cent	3 per cent	4 per cent	Years
0	1.000,000	1.000,000	1.000,000	1.000,000	1.000,000	1.000,000	1.000,000	0
1	0.990,000	0.987,500	0.985,000	0.980,000	0.975,000	0.970,000	0.960,000	1
2	0.980,000	0.975,156	0.970,225	0.960,400	0.950,625	0.940,000	0.921,600	2
3	0.970,299	0.962,967	0.955,671	0.941,192	0.926,859	0.912,673	0.884,736	3
4	0.960,596	0.950,930	0.941,336	0.922,368	0.903,688	0.885,292	0.849,346	4
5	0.950,990	0.939,043	0.927,216	0.903,921	0.881,099	0.858,734	0.815,372	5
6	0.941,480	0.927,305	0.913,308	0.885,843	0.859,068	0.832,972	0.782,757	6
7	0.932,066	0.915,714	0.899,608	0.868,126	0.837,591	0.807,982	0.751,477	7
8	0.922,745	0.904,267	0.886,114	0.850,763	0.816,652	0.783,743	0.721,389	8
9	0.913,517	0.892,964	0.872,822	0.833,748	0.796,235	0.760,231	0.692,534	9
10	0.904,382	0.881,802	0.859,730	0.817,073	0.776,329	0.737,424	0.664,832	10
11	0.895,338	0.870,779	0.846,834	0.800,732	0.756,921	0.715,301	0.638,239	11
12	0.886,385	0.859,895	0.834,131	0.784,717	0.737,998	0.693,842	0.612,709	12
13	0.877,522	0.849,146	0.821,619	0.769,023	0.719,548	0.673,026	0.588,201	13
14	0.868,746	0.838,532	0.809,295	0.753,643	0.701,559	0.652,836	0.564,673	14
15	0.860,059	0.828,050	0.797,155	0.738,570	0.684,020	0.633,250	0.542,086	15
16	0.851,485	0.817,699	0.785,198	0.723,798	0.666,920	0.614,253	0.520,402	16
17	0.842,943	0.807,478	0.773,420	0.709,323	0.650,247	0.595,825	0.499,586	17
18	0.834,514	0.797,385	0.761,819	0.695,136	0.633,991	0.577,950	0.479,603	18
19	0.826,169	0.787,417	0.750,391	0.681,233	0.618,141	0.560,612	0.460,419	19
20	0.817,907	0.777,574	0.739,135	0.667,609	0.602,572	0.543,794	0.442,002	20
21	0.809,728	0.767,855	0.728,048	0.654,245	0.587,620	0.527,300	0.424,332	21
22	0.801,631	0.758,257	0.717,128	0.641,171	0.572,930	0.511,655	0.407,349	22
23	0.793,615	0.748,778	0.706,371	0.628,348	0.558,606	0.496,306	0.391,055	23
24	0.785,678	0.739,419	0.695,775	0.615,781	0.544,641	0.481,416	0.375,413	24
25	0.777,822	0.730,176	0.685,338	0.603,466	0.531,025	0.466,974	0.360,396	25
26	0.770,043	0.721,049	0.675,058	0.591,396	0.517,749	0.452,965	0.345,980	26
27	0.762,343	0.712,036	0.664,932	0.579,568	0.504,806	0.439,376	0.332,141	27
28	0.754,720	0.703,135	0.654,958	0.567,977	0.492,185	0.426,194	0.318,855	28
29	0.747,172	0.694,346	0.645,134	0.556,618	0.479,881	0.413,408	0.306,101	29
30	0.739,701	0.685,667	0.635,457	0.545,485	0.467,884	0.401,006	0.293,857	30
40	0.688,972	0.604,622	0.546,321	0.445,701	0.363,232	0.295,711	0.195,366	40
50	0.605,006	0.533,157	0.469,689	0.364,171	0.281,988	0.218,065	0.129,885	50

TABLE 8.—DEPRECIATED VALUE OF UNITY AT DIFFERENT RATES FOR TERMS OF YEARS.—(*Continued*)

Years	5 per cent	6 per cent	7½ per cent	10 per cent	12½ per cent	15 per cent	20 per cent	Years
0	1.000,000	1.000,000	1.000,000	1.000,000	1.000,000	1.000,000	1.000,000	0
1	0.950,000	0.940,000	0.925,000	0.900,000	0.875,000	0.850,000	0.800,000	1
2	0.902,500	0.883,600	0.855,625	0.810,000	0.765,625	0.722,500	0.640,000	2
3	0.857,375	0.830,584	0.791,453	0.729,000	0.669,922	0.614,125	0.512,000	3
4	0.814,506	0.780,749	0.732,094	0.656,100	0.586,182	0.522,006	0.409,600	4
5	0.773,781	0.733,904	0.677,187	0.590,490	0.512,909	0.443,705	0.327,680	5
6	0.735,092	0.689,870	0.626,398	0.531,441	0.448,796	0.377,149	0.262,144	6
7	0.698,337	0.648,478	0.579,418	0.478,297	0.392,696	0.320,577	0.209,715	7
8	0.663,420	0.609,569	0.535,962	0.430,467	0.343,609	0.272,490	0.167,772	8
9	0.630,249	0.572,995	0.495,764	0.387,420	0.300,658	0.231,617	0.134,218	9
10	0.598,737	0.538,616	0.458,582	0.348,678	0.263,076	0.196,874	0.107,372	10
11	0.568,800	0.506,299	0.424,188	0.313,811	0.230,191	0.167,343	0.085,899	11
12	0.540,360	0.475,921	0.392,374	0.282,429	0.201,418	0.142,232	0.068,720	12
13	0.513,342	0.447,366	0.362,946	0.254,186	0.176,240	0.120,905	0.054,976	13
14	0.487,675	0.420,524	0.335,725	0.228,768	0.154,210	0.102,770	0.043,981	14
15	0.463,291	0.395,292	0.310,546	0.205,891	0.134,934	0.087,354	0.035,184	15
16	0.440,127	0.371,575	0.287,255	0.185,302	0.118,067	0.074,251	0.028,148	16
17	0.418,200	0.349,281	0.265,711	0.166,772	0.103,309	0.063,113	0.022,518	17
18	0.397,214	0.328,324	0.245,782	0.150,095	0.090,395	0.053,646	0.018,014	18
19	0.377,354	0.308,624	0.227,349	0.135,085	0.079,096	0.045,599	0.014,412	19
20	0.358,486	0.290,107	0.210,297	0.121,577	0.069,209	0.038,760	0.011,529	20
21	0.340,562	0.272,701	0.194,525	0.109,419	0.060,558	0.032,946	0.009,223	21
22	0.323,533	0.256,358	0.179,936	0.098,477	0.052,988	0.028,004	0.007,379	22
23	0.307,357	0.240,958	0.166,441	0.088,629	0.046,365	0.023,803	0.005,903	23
24	0.291,989	0.226,501	0.153,957	0.079,766	0.040,569	0.020,233	0.004,722	24
25	0.277,390	0.212,911	0.142,411	0.071,790	0.035,498	0.017,198	0.003,778	25
26	0.263,520	0.200,136	0.131,730	0.064,611	0.031,061	0.014,618	0.003,022	26
27	0.250,344	0.188,128	0.121,850	0.058,150	0.027,178	0.012,420	0.002,418	27
28	0.237,827	0.176,840	0.112,711	0.052,335	0.023,781	0.010,562	0.001,934	28
29	0.225,935	0.166,230	0.104,258	0.047,101	0.020,808	0.008,977	0.001,547	29
30	0.214,639	0.156,256	0.096,439	0.042,391	0.018,207	0.007,631	0.001,238	30
40	0.128,512	0.084,162	0.044,225	0.014,781	0.004,790	0.001,502	0.001,133	40
50	0.076,945	0.045,331	0.020,281	0.005,154	0.001,260	0.000,296	0.001,014	50

In the sinking-fund method of providing for depreciation, a sum of money is set aside annually such that at compound interest it will accumulate,[1] by the end of the producing life of the asset, an amount equal to the original cost of the asset less its scrap or sales value. If V be the value to be accumulated at the end of n years, r be the rate of interest plus 1 and I the amount to be invested annually, then,

$$I = \frac{V(r - 1)}{r^n - 1}.$$

Thus, in the foregoing example, if $190.80 is set aside annually at 5 per cent interest, it will accumulate at the end of the 10 years to a total of $2,400. This method is shown graphically in Fig. 54, where the curve *AGD* represents the depreciated value of the same machine by this method, the vertical ordinates between the line *AM* and the curve *AGD* being the total of the sums set aside annually plus the accumulated interest. It is apparent that this method depreciates the asset less in the early years than either of the other methods.

While apparently this method differs from the straight-line method, it is in reality identical in principle. In both cases a fixed amount is set aside annually, but in one case it is retained in the business as part of the working capital, while in the other it is set aside in a bank or in some interest-producing investment. In Fig. 54, the line *AF* indicates the progressive sum of the amounts set aside annually for a sinking fund for the above case, while the vertical distances between *AF* and *AGD* measure the accumulated interest. In a similar way, if the sums of money retained annually from profits in the straight-line method be considered as earning only as much as that set aside in the sinking-fund method, the accumulated interest will be shown by the line *AHC* and it will be noted that the required depreciation of $2,400 would be accumulated between the eighth and ninth years. In many instances it may be desirable and necessary actually to set aside a sinking fund as a guarantee against contingencies or obligations, especially where diverse interests are concerned in the distribution of the profits. On the other hand, it does not seem to be a good financial policy for a private concern to set aside earnings to draw interest at bank rates when, by retaining them in the business, a greater interest can, presumably, be earned. For if the business cannot earn more than bank interest, it might as well be out of existence so far as profit producing is concerned.

The accounting of the sinking-fund method, furthermore, as usually applied to depreciation, may be faulty. The problem of depreciation is to set aside from revenue an amount equal to the diminution in value that *has already occurred.* As has been noted, the exact rate at which

[1] For annuity tables giving accrued values of annual payments at various rates of interest, see Kent, William, "Engineer's Pocket Book," and handbooks generally.

depreciation occurs is difficult to fix; but it is clear that if the depreciation is really \$240 annually instead of \$190.80, the former amount should be set aside and the asset depreciated accordingly. The final total depreciation will, of course, be the same in the above case for all the methods discussed, but if the asset considered is one that wastes rapidly, its real value at any other time than the end of the working life will be more accurately expressed, perhaps, by a curve such as *AID* than by *AGD*. Sinking-fund methods are, therefore, more universally applicable to the problem of writing off intangible assets such as patents, franchises, development expenses, etc., and for meeting definite obligations at a definite future time and where the intervening values are not so important.

As before noted, there are other methods of depreciation in use, some of which are simple and may be very satisfactory for certain circumstances, though their basic principles may be arbitrarily chosen. The following method given by W. M. Cole[1] may be taken as an illustration. In this method the depreciation is calculated by multiplying the **wearing value** (original cost minus scrap value) by a fraction, the numerator of which is the remaining number of years of life the machine is estimated to possess, and the denominator the sum of the year numbers of the total estimated producing life. Thus, in the example quoted above, the estimated total life is 10 years and the denominator is, therefore,

$$10 + 9 + 8 + 7 + 6 + 5 + 4 + 3 + 2 + 1 = 55,$$

and the numerator for the first year is 10, for the second 9, for the third 8, and so on. The depreciation at the end of the first year would be $(3{,}000 - 600) \times 10/55 = \$436$; at the end of the second year it would be $(3{,}000 - 600) \times 9/55 = \$393$, and so on. The depreciation applied by this method is at least as heavy during the earlier years as that computed by percentage on reduced value, and the method should, therefore, be used with caution unless it is desired to obtain a heavy depreciation during the early years of the asset.

234. Classification and Rates of Depreciation.—In practically all enterprises the character of the several assets and their rate of depreciation vary greatly, and due account must be taken thereof. A flat rate of depreciation over the entire plant may, of course, be safe so far as allowing for *total* depreciation is concerned, but seldom gives any indication of the manner in which it should be distributed. A careful classification should, therefore, be made of all capital accounts and these again subdivided in such detail as will allow of intelligent depreciation rates. The following is a typical classification of factory equipment: **Preliminary expenses, goodwill, land, buildings, power-house machinery** (engines, boilers, etc.), **fixed plant and machinery, small loose plant, horses,** and **terminable assets,** such as mineral deposits or leases.

[1] Cole, W. M., "Accounting and Auditing," p. 273.

The treatment of these several classes will depend very greatly on circumstances, and nothing more than general suggestions can be offered. To be on the safe side, however, the manager must shape his course by trying to reduce the book value of his plant to what it would actually bring in the market, this value being usually much less than the cost price or even than the actual value of the plant as a "going concern." With this in mind all irrecoverable expenses such as preliminary legal expenses, surveys, etc., and all unsalable assets, such as foundations, will be written off as rapidly as possible. The same remarks apply, usually, to such short-lived assets as patents and goodwill. It is comparatively unusual, today, to find that the land occupied by a factory needs to be depreciated. Land values are, in most localities, on the increase, but an appreciation of value of the land occupied by a factory should be discounted if the remodeling of the site for other purposes involves the removing of massive foundations, chimneys, etc.

The rate of depreciation for buildings will, of course, vary considerably with the character of construction and the work that they house. Thus, heavy stone and brick buildings used for storehouses will far outlast cheap wooden or even steel-frame buildings used for such severe service as forge shops, or industries requiring the use of heavy cranes that severely rack the framework. Again, the life of machinery will depend on the excellence of its original construction and the service to which it is devoted. A portable hoisting engine would not be expected to last as long as a Corliss engine in a well-kept engine room; and a large boring mill, if used infrequently, will outlast many renewals of small tools.

The following list (Table 9)[1] may be taken, therefore, as giving average values only, for buildings and machinery kept in a fair state of repair, and *including obsolescence*. Column 4 gives the rate that must be applied by the percentage-on-original-cost method to reduce this original cost to the residual value noted in column 2 during the estimated life of the asset. Column 5 gives corresponding rates for the method of percentage on diminishing values. It will be noted that these last rates are, as a whole, much higher than the former. While it may be *desirable*, as before noted, to depreciate very heavily in the early years of the life of the asset it is often not so *expedient*, and actual depreciation rates, even if based on the principle of diminishing values are usually lower than those given in column 5, the difference often being compensated for by renewals and extensive repairs, thus practically extending the life of the asset.

Engineering expenses for production, drawings, and patterns should, when possible, be charged to specific production orders. Where this is

[1] For a detailed list of depreciation factors and estimated length of life of various properties, see Horatio Foster, "Engineering Valuation of Public Utilities and Factories," p. 194, or Henry Floy, "Valuation of Public-utility Properties," p. 188. See also Alford L. P. (Ed.), "Cost and Production Handbook," p. 1243.

TABLE 9.—ESTIMATED LIFE AND FACTORS OF DEPRECIATION

Character of asset	Probable life of asset in years	Ratio of scrap value to original value	Percentage on original cost	Percentage on diminishing value
Reinforced concrete buildings	50	0.10	1.8	4.5
Brick or steel-frame buildings, easy service	40	0.10	2.25	5.5
Brick or steel-frame buildings, severe service	20	0.10	4.5	11
Good, wooden buildings, easy service	30	0.10	3	7.5
Good, wooden buildings, severe service	15	0.10	6	14
Steam engines	15 to 30	0.10	6 to 3	14 to 7.5
Steam boilers	15 to 30	0.10	6 to 3	14 to 7.5
Boiler-room feed pumps	20	0.05	4.75	14
Engine-room instruments and gages	10	0.05	9.5	26
Steam piping, valves, and fittings	10 to 15	0.05	9.5 to 6.3	26 to 18
Portable engines and boilers	10	0.05	9.5	26
Gas engines	10 to 15	0.05	9.5 to 6.3	26 to 18
Turbogenerators	20 to 30	0.10	4.5 to 3	11 to 7.5
Electric generators	20 to 30	0.10	4.5 to 3	11 to 7.5
Electric motors	20	0.10	4.5	11
Storage batteries	10	0.05	9.5	26
Switchboard and instruments	15	0.05	6.3	18
Heavy machine tools	25	0.10	3.6	9
Light machine tools	15 to 20	0.10	6 to 4.5	14 to 11
Shafting, hangers, and pulleys	20 to 30	0.05	4.75 to 3	14 to 9
Belting	10 to 25	0	10 to 4.0	

impossible, as in the case of the development of a *line* of machines, such expenses should be carried to a **development account** and charged off over a definite number of machines. Particular care should be used in crediting patterns as an asset. If used frequently, they soon wear out, and if not used, they are not only of little value but often occupy valuable storage space that could be used for other purposes. Metal patterns, of course, have an intrinsic residual value.

Small loose plant such as hand tools, chains, ropes, foundry flasks, etc., wear out so rapidly that they should be carried at a very low value. The better way to consider much of the small loose plant is to renew it entirely out of revenue and charge it off as expense. Horses should also be carried at a nominal value because of their perishable character. Terminable assets, such as mineral deposits, leases, loans, etc., are best cared for by means of a sinking fund, as explained in Art. 233.

A complete inventory should be maintained listing all buildings, machinery, and tools. This inventory is most conveniently formed on the card-index or loose-leaf principle, a card or leaf being provided for each item. Figure 53 illustrates such a card, and it will be noted that it gives a life history of the machine, including original cost, weight, location, residual value, rate of depreciation, repairs, and additions, and also the history of any special attachments that may have been used with it. Records of this kind constitute a **plant ledger.** A ledger may be maintained for standard plant and one for special fixtures if desired. The plant ledgers with the cost accounts, the stores, and stock ledgers, constitute an inventory of the material assets of the plant.

235. Investment and Distribution of Depreciation.—It is clear that the setting aside of funds out of revenue to compensate for depreciation is equivalent to transferring a part of the fixed assets to the floating assets, the total value of the assets remaining unchanged if the computations are correctly made. The primary object of this reserve is to provide for repairs and replacements, and if not needed for this purpose it may be employed elsewhere in the business; or, if not needed thus, it should, of course, be invested so that it will be earning interest. The relation between depreciation, repairs, and capital account has been discussed already in Art. 232, and the principles therein noted should be carefully observed in making "betterments" which may be either repairs, additions to capital, or a combination of both. Generally speaking, all prosperous enterprises tend to grow in size, and if earnings set aside for depreciation are used to extend the plant, care should be taken that such additions are not credited to the capital account if their value is offset elsewhere by uncared-for deterioration.

Depreciation, as has been noted, is a just charge against production and should, properly, be included in the manufacturing expenses and distributed with them. The somewhat common practice of fixing costs without including depreciation, trusting to profits being large enough to declare a dividend after deducting depreciation, cannot be considered a safe policy, especially where the books are closed but once a year. The argument may be used that to include depreciation in factory costs might raise the total cost above the market price, and that it is better to wait till the end of the year to see what allowance can be made for depreciation. This argument is, of course, fallacious. *Cost* is *cost*, and the manufacturer that has included all items of cost in his manufacturing expenses can see much more clearly where he must *reduce manufacturing costs* to meet competition, and the manufacturer that can meet competition is the one that will eventually survive. The practice of including depreciation in the general expense as a percentage of the total wasting assets is, of course, safe so far as *total* costs are concerned, but all the arguments in Art. 177 regarding the distribution of expense in a scientific manner apply also to depreciation; and with advances in cost-keeping methods, this item of expense will be distributed more as a machine rate and less as a uniform percentage on labor or time elements of cost. In continuous industries it is easy, of course, to charge off depreciation. Thus in cement mills it is common practice to add a certain amount per barrel or sack to care for this item, but, as noted in Art. 220, when manufacturing processes become more complex, the problem is more difficult and requires careful consideration. Each department should, if possible, bear its own share of depreciation and one line of goods should not be burdened with the wear and tear or obsolescence charges belonging to another.

236. Conclusion.—In concluding this brief outline of the principles of depreciation it may be well to repeat that it is seldom possible to lay down exact rules for any kind of plant. Conditions change from year to year; the machine or process that is valuable today is obsolete tomorrow, and the state of trade may and usually does modify greatly what may be a very desirable course of procedure. In dull times it may not be possible to depreciate as fully as desired, and in good times it may be desirable to make a greater allowance than might be really necessary under normal conditions. The fact remains, however, that depreciation is an important expense that cannot be neglected, and a well-defined system, even though it cannot be rigidly adhered to, will assist materially to a clearer understanding of the problem. The slower the deterioration the more important it is that depreciation be executed *systematically*, since, where the life is short, renewals from revenue are more frequent and force themselves upon the attention of the manager. Long-lived assets, therefore, need more careful consideration in order that the accumulated, uncared-for deterioration of years may not be the means, as it often is, of wrecking the enterprise.

References

ALFORD, L. P. (Ed.): "Cost and Production Handbook," p. 1215.
———: "Management's Handbook," p. 1350.
FLOY, HENRY: "Valuation of Public-utility Properties."
FOSTER, HORATIO A.: "Engineering Valuation of Public Utilities and Factories."
LEAKE, P. D.: "Depreciation and Wasting Assets."
MATHESON, EWING: "The Depreciation of Factories."
National Machine Tool Builders Association, "Manual of Cost Procedures."
Reports of the Commissioner of Internal Revenue.
SALIERS, E. A.: "Principles of Depreciation."

CHAPTER XX

EQUIPMENT POLICIES

237. General.—While considerable attention has been given to the general problem of plant location, construction, and equipment as illustrated in Chap. VIII, not so much thought has been bestowed upon the economic or financial features of this problem. It is still common practice to buy costly equipment upon the advice of foremen or superintendents without careful examination of the possible gains or losses that may be incurred by the transaction, and deplorable mistakes of this kind are not uncommon when they could be obviated by simple mathematical calculations. It will appear from the discussion in the preceding chapter that no investment in equipment can be considered successful unless during its producing life it will pay a fair return upon the capital expenditure after all expenses incident to its operation have been refunded, including any loss in capital value from depreciation or depletion of any kind. The element of time necessarily enters into all such considerations, since expense includes interest, rent, and other items involving time. The quantity of product to be produced is also a factor since there is an intimate relation between the volume of product and profit. It is not sufficient that goods be produced at a cost lower than the market price, but the volume of goods made and sold must be such that the margin between cost and market price will return a fair profit upon the investment. These basic considerations must enter into any discussion of the economics of equipment, though as will be seen these considerations may be somewhat complicated mathematically.

A survey made by L. P. Alford (see *Manufacturing Industries*, October, 1927, p. 277) would indicate that a large number of manufacturing plants operate without a definite equipment policy, though there would appear to be the same reasons for logical and careful expenditures for equipment as for labor and material. In well-managed plants the purchase and replacement of all tools are a well-defined function. This function is recognized in Fig. 16, where the production-equipment engineer is responsible directly to the works manager. The general problem of equipment may be divided for convenience into two parts, namely the problem of equipping a new plant for a definite purpose, and the problem of making changes in or additions to the equipment of an existing plant.

238. New Equipment.—The problems of equipping a new plant lie between the extremes of intermittent production and those of continuous manufacturing. Thus, consider the equipping of a shipyard. The tools are practically all of standard design for general service and their size is dictated by the maximum size of ship that is to be built. A large amount of experience and judgment must enter into the selection of each piece of equipment, and even the volume of work is a matter of conjecture and estimate. The productive life of the large equipment is long, and simple depreciation methods are about all that is necessary as a policy.

At the other extreme consider a high-speed continuous plant for producing typewriters or automobiles. Here managerial policies decide exactly what shall be manufactured and also the rate of production. The equipment selected is closely adapted to the work and may be very special in character. The capacity of all major tools is quite accurately known and the selection and arrangement of the equipment offer little difficulty. But the working life of the equipment may be short either because of the severe work to which it is subjected, or because its accuracy is soon destroyed. Furthermore, a change in the design of the product may make all special tools obsolete long before they are worn out. This is particularly true of jigs and fixtures, which in many industries involve a large expenditure and are useless except for the specific purposes for which they were built. In such cases the equipment policy cannot be safely left to chance, but becomes a major financial consideration, since here the factory costs may be seriously affected by rapid changes in plant equipment. Such a policy should envisage not only skillful purchasing of all equipment, but also the financial relations affecting cost of product as reflected from changes in plant of any kind.

In this connection it may be noted that in continuous production the design of the product affects the character of the equipment much more than in general or intermittent production, and such design should always be conducted particularly with the productive process in mind, if high efficiency is to be attained. This relation has been more fully recognized of late, as indicated by the appearance of the term **product engineering** in technical literature.

239. Replacement of Equipment.—The manufacturing equipment of a plant may be classified as *permanent* and *transient*. Permanent tools are those that have a fair expectancy of working life, such as lathes, planers, etc. Transient tools include taps, dies, jigs, fixtures, etc., whose working life is short at best, and often limited to the production of the particular job for which they have been built. Permanent equipment is listed among the assets of the company as capital investment. Transient tools, while often representing a large investment, are charged off, in best practice, to the cost of production and their value recovered directly from sales. If a permanent tool is properly depreciated to the end of its producing life and then sold for the scrap value as recorded in the plant inventory (see Fig. 53), no loss on capital account will be incurred. But if for any reason it becomes necessary or desirable to replace such a tool before the end of the estimated working life, care must be taken to avoid such a loss. There are three ways in which this problem may be handled.

1. The unamortized, or present value, of the old tool less the scrap or resale value may be carried directly to the profit and loss account as a loss on capital account, the new tool being listed in its place in the inventory.

2. The unamortized value of the old tool less the scrap or resale value may be deducted from the savings incident to using the new tool over a predetermined number of years, and carried to the depreciation account, thus restoring the full capital value of the old tool. This method can be logically applied where the tool in question has a fairly long working life.

3. If both the new and the old tool are obviously short-lived, as is often the case with comparatively small metal-cutting equipment, many manufacturers consider that replacement is not advisable unless the savings due to the use of the new equipment will pay not only for the new tool, but also for any unamortized value of the old, or replaced tool, within a given number of years. This time limit will, of course, depend upon the conditions and character of the tools. For this case, the following formula by Professor R. M. Barnes may be useful:

Let X = the number of years in which equipment will pay for itself.
A = the cost of the new equipment installed in the plant.
B = the depreciated value of tool less scrap or resale value.
C = the interest charge on new equipment.
D = the number of pieces produced per day by new equipment.
E = the labor cost per piece with old equipment.
F = the estimated labor cost per piece with new equipment.
G = estimated number of working days per year for new equipment.
H = savings (or losses, plus or minus) in fixed charges per year other than interest.

Then
$$X = \frac{A + B}{(E - F)DG + H - C}$$

A more extended solution of the problem of replacement will be found in a paper presented before the American Society of Mechanical Engineers by J. A. Shepard and C. E. Hageman, May, 1925. While developed primarily as a discussion of the economics of material-handling machinery, it is applicable to a wider range of problems. The following factors are involved:

Debit Factors:

A = percentage allowance on investment.
B = percentage allowance to provide for insurance, taxes, etc.
C = percentage allowance to provide for upkeep.

D = percentage allowance to provide for depreciation and obsolescence.
E = yearly cost of power, supplies, and other items which are consumed, total in dollars.

Credit Factors:

S = yearly savings in direct cost of labor in dollars.
T_a = yearly savings in labor burden in dollars.
T_b = yearly fixed charges in dollars on mechanical equipment employed as a standard of comparison or which will be displaced.
U = yearly saving or earning through increased production in dollars.
X = percentage of year during which equipment will be operated.

Other Factors:

I = initial cost of mechanical equipment.
K = unamortized value of equipment displaced less its resale or scrap value.

Results:

Z = maximum investment in dollars which will earn simple interest.
Y = yearly cost to maintain mechanical equipment ready for operation (fixed charges).
V = yearly profit in excess of simple interest from operation of mechanical equipment.
P = yearly profit from operation in percentage on investment.
H = years required for complete amortization of investment out of earnings.

Then,

$$Z = \left[\frac{(S + T_a + U - E)X + T_b}{A + B + C + D}\right] - K \tag{1}$$

$$Y = I(A + B + C + D) \tag{2}$$

$$V = (S + T_a + U - E)X + T_b - [Y + (KA)] \tag{3}$$

$$P = \frac{V}{I} + A \tag{4}$$

$$H = \frac{100 \text{ per cent}}{P + D} \tag{5}$$

It will be obvious that this general method of computing probable gains or losses due to the installation of new machinery and apparatus is capable of wide application. An illustrative example will be found in the article from which this reference is taken. Also a similar application and illustration of the use of such methods in connection with the use of jigs and fixtures will be found in a paper presented by Professor J. W. Roe before the American Society of Mechanical Engineers, December, 1928.[1]

[1] See also an article on use of electric industrial trucks in *Trans. Am. Soc. Mech. Eng. Materials-handling Bull.*, January–April, 1928.

It will be noted also that these mathematical deductions are essentially applications of the law of diminishing returns. Thus equation (1) limits the expenditure that can be made and yet earn the desired interest. The history of manufacturing is filled with illustrations of installations made solely with the idea in mind of securing production, but at an expenditure entirely beyond the point where interest on the investment was possible.

It should be noted also that all of these methods of computation rest upon certain assumptions or estimates. Thus the number of working days during which the apparatus is to be employed is necessarily an estimate, as are other factors in these equations. These equations therefore should be used with discretion. But they do indicate approximate results that are far superior to the older methods, which often were little more than guesses.

CHAPTER XXI

THE COMPENSATION OF LABOR

240. Basic Features.—It is almost axiomatic that the industrial problems dealing with materials, machinery, and the physical side of industry are relatively important only as they bear on the greater problems of human existence, and for this reason the problem of rewarding men for services rendered is by far the most important and at the same time the most difficult of all industrial problems. This is necessarily so because it bears so directly on the great problem of distribution of wealth, and because it touches so closely upon human nature with all its ambitions, hopes, and fears. The problem has been with man from the beginning, changing in aspect as he has changed his methods and ideals, and will probably continue to be with him to the end.

It was inevitable that the changed industrial methods discussed in the foregoing chapters, with the changed personal relations resulting therefrom, should bring with them new methods of compensating labor. Under the older and simpler methods the relations between master and man were personal and often very close. The apprentice, and sometimes the mature workman, were often treated like members of the employer's family, a relation that now survives only in a few callings, such as agricultural service. Nor was this relation wholly lost even after the introduction of modern tools began to specialize men, so long as the number employed by any one man was comparatively small. Furthermore, under the simpler methods, where the tools of industry were within comparatively easy reach of all, and especially in this country where congested populations had not yet appeared, where land was still plentiful and the avenues to all industry still easily accessible, the law of supply and demand was much more effective in regulating the compensation of labor than at present.

As the new industrial methods advanced and aggregation and specialization became more effective, these simple relations were obliterated. These influences constantly tend to separate men into classes, and as numbers increase, the workman is separated farther and farther from the employer, till today, in all large industries, labor has lost all personal attributes and appears to the employer as a commodity to be purchased at the lowest market price. True, the employer is interested, and perhaps more so than ever, in securing efficient help, but the securing of this help is delegated to others and the working agreement is based on strict business principles with little or no personality entering into the bargain. As competition became keener the employer found that he must either improve his methods or cut his wage rates. The first became increasingly difficult and was often impossible, while the latter always appeared to be a natural and defendable procedure under the old day-rate system of compensation. The idea of obtaining increased output by increased pay came as a later development of the study of labor compensation.

The workman, on the other hand, cut off from the ownership of his tools and finding himself increasingly dependent on the employer for his daily bread, brought face to face daily with new labor-saving machinery, and observing the degradation of labor that nearly always followed its introduction, most naturally set up what defences he could against these tendencies that carried him toward an ever-decreasing compensation. As the individuality of the worker was lost in that of the class, organization against common danger was easy and natural. Labor unions are a most natural result of our changed industrial methods. They cannot be legislated out of existence but will, like their prototypes, the old guilds, persist until the causes of their growth are removed by changes in our industrial organization.

As a net result of these changes, labor compensation is no longer a simple matter based on the law of supply and demand, but is more likely to be based on a sharp bargain driven between two opposing parties with many complex and confusing conditions that tend to modify this law or render it at least very sluggish in its action. It is this very complexity of influences that makes the labor problem so difficult of solution because it renders exact information difficult to obtain. A continued struggle between organized labor demanding all that it can get, and organized capital banded together to oppose stubbornly the demands of labor, cannot be expected to result in a solution of the problem.[1] If there is hope of a peaceful solution it must lie in a systematic and scientific investigation of the *facts* of each case; and if contending parties cannot settle their differences amicably on such a basis, communal control of some kind will undoubtedly enforce a settlement or suggest a remedy. It should be particularly noted, however, that legislative action, boards of arbitration, or any other communal instrument cannot be expected to render satisfactory decisions that will be permanent until much more is known of the exact facts concerning labor than is usually available at present. The discussion of the wage systems that follows may make the above points clearer.

To the manufacturer, whose capital investment in machines is large, the question of wages has much greater importance than their numerical

[1] This is not intended to convey the idea that no progress can be made through collective bargaining (see Art. 279).

value would indicate. The wages of a machine operator may not be great, but the output of the machine he controls may be very great, and any failure or slackness on his part may be reflected manyfold in the decreased production on his machine. It does not pay, therefore, to have inefficient men operating expensive machines, where effectiveness or deficiency on the part of the workman is multiplied manyfold in the product. And, furthermore, as a perfectly general principle, the more efficient the workman the greater will be the output for a fixed capital investment and fixed conditions of production. And this output will be obtained at lower unit cost, since it will be obtained without appreciable additional manufacturing expense, for such expense in general does not vary in proportion to output but tends to remain constant through a considerable range of variation of output. It is clear that low-paid workmen may not always be the cheapest; in fact, a low rate of pay is likely to indicate a low rate of output. This idea forms one of the basic features of modern pay systems that recognize the importance of obtaining the best results out of every man, even though increased compensation is necessary to secure this result.

241. The Basic Wage.—A clear distinction should be made between the *mechanisms of wages* or *wage systems* that are described in succeeding sections of this chapter, and *basic wages*. In any community at any given time there is a general wage level that usually does not vary materially in the several enterprises for the same service. These basic wages will vary widely between various callings depending upon the character of the calling, the training and skill required, etc., and it will vary somewhat within each given calling depending upon the skill and productivity of the worker. The economic laws that fix these basic wage levels are complex, and economists are far from agreeing upon the several theories that have been advanced to explain wage levels. Any discussion of these theories[1] is beyond the limits of this book. It will be obvious, however, that the wage level cannot permanently exceed the point which will permit of a fair return upon capital investment, nor can it be permanently below the minimum requirements of the standard of living of the particular group involved. Between these levels, however, the wages of any group will vary depending upon a number of conflicting factors. A few of the most important of these will be briefly discussed.

Perhaps the most potent influence affecting the basic wage is the supply of, and demand for, labor. Obviously if labor is very plentiful men will work for what they can get and when labor is scarce they will demand all they can obtain. This tendency is modified or accented by the relative strength of labor organizations and protective combinations of employers. For this reason, also, employers are, as a rule, in favor of

[1] For a summary of these theories see ALFORD, L. P., (Ed.), "Management's Handbook," p. 911. See also ELY, RICHARD T., "Outline of Economics," Chap. XXI.

immigration, while labor organizations are strongly opposed to the same. Legislation affecting immigration will therefore, in general, affect wages.

There has been a growing tendency among progressive managers to try to set the basic wage on a more liberal basis than that dictated by the purely competitive conditions just described. Not a few companies, whose profits will permit of such a procedure, have established basic wage rates considerably above those fixed by strictly competitive considerations. This procedure may not always spring from utopian ideals and may be only a method of drawing the best workmen in the community to the plant. But, aside from this, there is a growing belief that the workman is entitled to a living wage and that the cost of living should be taken into account in setting the base rates. There may be a great difference between the amount of money that a man is able to earn and the amount that he should have to enable him to maintain himself and his family as they should be maintained for the best interests of society. This fact has long been recognized, but Henry Ford was one of the first to make a practical experiment along these lines by paying considerably more than the prevailing wage, provided certain conditions of living were observed by the recipients of these higher rates. It is an open question, of course, how far an employer should undertake to dictate the personal affairs of an employee or to impose paternal regulations upon him, even though these regulations are accompanied by higher rates of pay. It should be remembered also that few manufacturers are in a position, financially, to justify any such system of labor reward as has been established by Mr. Ford.

There is much food for thought, however, in this experiment and it is pertinent to inquire whether there is not a more humane and more progressive basis of labor reward than the prevailing wage that is fixed by a competitive system. Major George D. Babcock[1] has made a very interesting attempt to find a basis of labor reward which would take into account the logical factors upon which such labor reward should depend. The discussion of this effort is beyond the limits of this book, but it will repay reading, and it is interesting to note that Major Babcock states: "No attempt has been made as yet to determine the correct wage rate for the workers or in any way to establish fundamental values for their efforts." Major Babcock took the prevailing wage rates for the year 1905 as base rates, giving good reasons for so doing. The rates that he established, therefore, while *relatively* fair and just, rested, as he frankly states, upon an assumed base rate. It may be that it is not possible to establish any logical basic wage rate and that some other basis of labor reward must be resorted to if industry is to serve all humanity in a fitting manner and if there is to be industrial peace.

[1] Babcock, Major George D., "Taylor System in Franklin Management."

But in any case the economic theory of wages held during the first quarter of the nineteenth century which stated that: "the natural price of labor is that price which is necessary to enable the laborers, one with another, to subsist and to perpetuate their race without either increase or diminution" has long since been discarded. Not only has this "iron law of wages" been proved to be untrue by the present condition of a working population immensely greater than at that time, but there is a growing feeling that industry was made for men and not men for industry, and that industry can and should provide the workers with decent conditions of life. One of the most interesting manifestations of this belief is modern legislation in behalf of a "living wage."

242. Legislation and the Basic Wage.—Efforts to regulate wages and working hours have been tried since ancient times. The Code of Hammurabi,[1] promulgated about 2250 B.C., fixed the wages of all artisans, physicians, and veterinarians. It would be interesting to know how successful he was in his attempt to change economic law by legislative enactment. English[2] industrial legislation runs back to early days and should be read for an understanding of modern legislation. These early English laws were often not in favor of the worker but quite the reverse. Thus one of these early acts required "all artificers and laborers hired by time to be and continue at their work at or before five o'clock in the morning and continue at work and not depart until between seven and eight of the clock at night—two and a half hours in the course of the day being allowed for meals and drinking." The first modern English factory act that favored the worker was passed in 1802 and was introduced into Parliament by a master manufacturer, Sir Robert Peel.

In this country many states have enacted legislation regulating the hours of labor, especially of women and minors, and a few have passed minimum wage laws. The first important federal legislation was the National Industrial Recovery Act of 1933. This act provided for the establishment of "codes of fair practice" in the several industries and callings, regardless of state boundaries, fixed minimum wages and maximum working hours, prohibited unfair practices such as selling below cost of production, and provided for collective bargaining between employer and employee. This act clearly legalized some practices that were forbidden by existing anti-monopolistic legislation. It was declared unconstitutional by the U. S. Supreme Court on the ground that it attempted to regulate industry *within* the several states. But before that event the unworkability of such a complicated, costly, and cumbersome system was quite obvious.

[1] The original code, carved in cuneiform characters upon a block of black diorite about 8 feet high, is in the Louvre museum in Paris. The English translation is by Robert F. Harper.

[2] See TAYLOR, R. W. COOKE, "Modern Factory System."

The most recent effort of this kind in this country is the Federal Fair Labor Standards Act of 1938. This act provides that all organizations engaged in *interstate* commerce shall pay a minimum wage of 25 cents per hour for the first effective year of the act, a minimum of 30 cents per hour for the second year, and a minimum of 40 cents per hour during the six next succeeding years. The maximum working hours are to be 44 for the first year, 42 for the second year, and 40 thereafter for six years. Child labor is prohibited. The constitutionality of this act has not as yet been tested but undoubtedly will be in the near future.

Without in any way questioning the desirability of the purposes of this act certain questions naturally arise. First, it should be remembered that law cannot *create* wealth. It may *encourage* or *discourage* the processes whereby it is created and it may modify the *distribution* of wealth. It remains to be seen whether the low wage areas in which the act is expected to lift the wage level can create the necessary wealth for such a program. Again, the hours of labor in industrial plants have fallen from about 66 per week to about 40 per week in about 70 years without the aid of federal legislation, and it is questionable how far such laws can hasten what is essentially an economic process involving the volume of production (Art. 1). The French government was recently compelled to revoke a similar enactment because it was found that the necessary production could not be attained in that country with a 40-hour week. Lastly, the policing of such a comprehensive program, the difficulty of deciding what is interstate and what is intrastate, the litigation that is sure to follow will be a very heavy burden that must be borne eventually by industry, already very heavily burdened by taxation. Time and experience only will prove the wisdom or uselessness of such legislation.

At present there is much discussion on the feasibility of paying workers an *annual wage*. From the standpoint of the worker this idea may appeal more as a measure of security than as an incentive to increased production. The idea is based on the belief that the standard of living depends upon the wage income and that the annual industrial pay roll can be augmented to provide all workers with an assured minimum annual income variously estimated by its advocates to be anywhere between \$1,100 and \$2,500. It is difficult to understand wherein a minimum annual wage differs, in principle, from a minimum hourly or day wage except in the added security it suggests which might justify it. But as a means of fixing a basic wage it meets with the following difficulties. In 1937 there were roughly 10 million available workers in the manufacturing industries. An annual wage of \$1,200 would require an annual pay roll of 12 billions of dollars, which is 2½ billions more than the total manufacturing pay roll for that year. The actual number of workers in the manufacturing industries was about 8.5 millions and the average annual wage was about \$1,111. Since the beginning of the century the proportion of national income that has gone into wages has risen from 54 per cent to 66 per cent for all callings and the percentage for the manufacturing industries is now about 80[1] per cent, with a tendency for these percentages to increase. That is, industry has always paid wages *in proportion to productivity.* It is possible that these percentages may be raised somewhat for those now actually employed, especially if this is accompanied by increased production. But in addition industry must be *expanded* in order to absorb the entire group of eligible workers. The mere setting of a fixed wage of any kind, whether in an individual factory or in the industry as a whole, does not expand the pay roll, as all experience shows, unless the increase is within the economic range of the business. If it is beyond the economic limit of the enterprise or industry such fiat wages usually result in increased unemployment, as has been fully demonstrated in coal mining and some other industries. The real problem of the basic wage is to expand industry and increase the use of its products. Any legislation that restricts this process simply adds to unemployment.

It is important therefore to remember that the several *incentive* wage systems that are discussed in the following sections are *wage mechanisms* only and that they are of less importance than the base rate, which is the most important problem before industry today.

243. The Primary Pay Systems.—There are only two fundamental methods of rewarding labor: one is by paying the man for the amount of *time* that he spends on the work, and the other by paying him for the *amount of work* that he performs. The first method is usually characterized as **day work** because the rate of pay is most usually by the day, or *per diem.* The second is usually called **piece work** since compensation is by the piece or job. All other wage systems are combinations of these two principles in varying proportions. Some of these combinations are occasionally termed **profit-sharing systems** because of certain *gain-sharing* features that are incorporated in them. This is erroneous in two particulars. No money paid out directly as a reward of labor can by any stretch of imagination be classed as profit, which is always an undistributed balance after all costs of production are paid in full. Nor can any money distributed as profit be considered as a wage payment, for the same reason. Profit-sharing schemes are in the nature of an extra reward, not only for skill and industry, but for faithfulness of service over some considerable period of time, usually a year. **Gain-sharing** is a correct name for the new pay systems to be described, such as premium and bonus systems, for the element of gain-sharing is embodied in them; but they are, nevertheless, combinations of the two primary methods named above.

[1] See "National Income and Its Elements," by National Industrial Conference Board; also *Metal Trades Digest*, October, 1938, p. 2.

244. Incentive-wage Systems.—It is well known that workmen when left to their own initiative do not, in general, produce anywhere near their capacity. Formerly this was attributed wholly to indolence or unwillingness, both of which are contributing factors, and the usual method of overcoming this difficulty was to "drive" the workers through domineering foremen. The investigations of Taylor and his successors have shown, however, that the average worker is not only inefficient because of faulty inherited methods, but he is also uninformed concerning the maximum capacity of machine tools and processes. But Taylor found, as others had found before him, that, while workmen can be instructed and methods improved, the worker's interest in increased production can, in general, be stimulated only by an appeal to his own interests. He found that to get the maximum output from average machine-shop workers it was necessary to pay 30 per cent more than the average base rate. To obtain the maximum from laborers on work calling for severe bodily exertion it was necessary to pay from 50 to 60 per cent more than the base rate. To obtain the maximum from machinists on the more delicate and difficult work it was necessary to pay from 70 to 80 per cent above the base rate, and for work requiring skill, brains, strength, and close application, as in the operation of a large steam hammer, it was necessary to pay as high as 100 per cent above the average rates. In his first experiments in advanced management he, therefore, recognized this principle in his differential price rate, giving an impetus to certain ideas already recognized and put into operation by F. A. Halsey, whose work will be discussed in a later section.

An incentive-wage system should, first of all, be of benefit to both employer and employee; that is it should decrease costs and at the same time permit the ambitious worker to raise his earnings above the prevailing base rate; no element of philanthropy or paternalism should enter into it. It should guarantee a basic wage comparable with prevailing wages in the district. The system should be easy to apply and easily understood by the worker so that he can calculate, accurately, his increased earnings. Complicated systems which the worker cannot readily understand are of doubtful value. As a corollary the incentive reward should be directly connected with the worker's efforts and not be distant and dependent upon general conditions or the work of his fellows. And, lastly, the basis of the system must be set, if possible, so as to be permanent. Nothing so quickly leads workmen to distrust such systems as changes in basic rates and principles. This means that before such a system is introduced careful time study, motion study, and standardization as described in the preceding chapters should be resorted to before incentive rates are set, if permanency is desired. Rates set upon guesses or estimates are not likely to be long successful.

There have been many experiments with incentive-wage systems, but only those that are best known and which illustrate basic principles will be discussed. In the following classification of the best known of pay systems, each group is classified under the name of the original system in that group, or that system which best illustrates the principle on which the several plans are based.

Group	Plans
Day work	Straight day work Multiple time plan Measured day work
Piece work	Straight piece work or 100 per cent premium plan Taylor differentiated piece-work plan Merrick multiple-piece plan
Halsey and similar gain-sharing plans	Halsey premium plan Manchester or standard-hour plan Haynes or "Manit" plan Bedeaux "point" plan
Emerson and similar gain-sharing plans	Emerson efficiency plan Wennerlund efficiency plan Knoeppel efficiency plan Rowan plan
Gantt task and bonus plan	Gantt task and bonus plan

DAY WORK

245. General Features.—Under the day-work system of wages the employer buys the *time* of the worker. The unit of time bought may vary from one hour to one year, so that the term "day work" is, in a way, a misnomer, handed down to us from the time when the day was a more common unit for wage payment. The higher the grade of the employee the longer, as a rule, is the time unit. Thus managers, treasurers, and higher officials are usually engaged by the year, though most usually paid by monthly installments. Foremen and engineers may be hired by the month, other classes by the day or hour. As the unit of time bargained for becomes greater, less supervision, presumably, is needed to obtain value received, since the men on monthly or yearly salaries are usually not numerous, comparatively, and are selected with a view to being enough interested in their work, or what is more likely, loaded with enough responsibility, to insure good service.

The method of day work is, without doubt, the oldest method of rewarding labor, and the reason for its inception is not difficult to see. In the beginning of any civilization industry is simple and *general.* The farm hand was required to do many and diverse duties, each one occupying, perhaps, a short portion of his daily service, which was not limited to definite hours but set in accordance with the necessities of the case. Domestic service of today is an excellent example of this form of employment, of which only a few types have survived. Much of the early manufacturing industry was of this same general character. A machinist of 50 years ago was expected to do all manner of work on a large range of machines working, perhaps, on many jobs in the same day. Taking into account the more or less paternal attitude of the old employer toward his workman, the day-work method was a very natural system and not without its advantages. Where the number of men employed was small and personal relations close, the employer was able to reward diligence and skill in something like a just proportion; and he depended on personal observation, either on his own part, or through the use of not more than one intermediary, to insure a fair return from each man for the wages paid. The personal element was a large factor, and there was always the hope for the abler men that through industry they might rise either to a higher paid position, or get into business for themselves.

246. Defects of the Day-work Method.—As the influences of aggregation and specialization began to make themselves felt, and the personal relations vanished, the day-work method became less and less applicable. As the personality of the workman was merged by these influences into that of a class, it became more and more difficult for the individual to make his superior qualities known and more and more difficult for the employer to reward industry and skill in adequate proportion. The employer ceased to *hire men*, as men, and began to *buy labor* like any other commodity. The inevitable result was that the better men, unable to obtain higher pay than their more inefficient fellows, organized their class and endeavored to raise the wage level of the entire class as the only means of obtaining the desired compensation.

On the other hand, workmen on day pay had great opportunity of restricting output, even in spite of rapid advances in machinery, since little was known as to the possibilities of production with the new tools. The workmen, instinctively feeling that he could influence the law of supply and demand in his favor by limiting the output,[1] did not work up to his capacity, and under these circumstances production tended to mediocrity or even to the standard of the poorer workman. Any efforts to *drive* men to higher output are almost invariably met by stubborn organized class resistance, while the employer who pays only the rate earned by the poorest man may get only the output he pays for, even from his very best men.

Day work, therefore, has often proved inadequate and unfair to both employer and employee in modern mass production involving large numbers of men and specialized labor. It is a system that is adapted naturally to *general work* and even here in its simplest form is fully

[1] The workman should not be censured for this tendency. Self-preservation is the first law of nature. With the most apparent effects of the new system staring him in the face and his economic independence taken from him, it is not to be expected that he would be willing to suffer any current loss because, economically, future generations would be benefited. It must be remembered that the economic benefits resulting from new methods do not always accrue to those directly interested in the industry affected.

adequate for small numbers only. It will remain in use, however, in many places where it is, and where it is not, suitable, simply from its inertia.

If T = time worked in hours, R = rate per hour, then the worker's earnings, $E = TR$.

247. Measured Day Work.—H. L. Gantt[1] very ably pointed out how the usefullness and effectiveness of day work might be extended by separating each man's work from his neighbor's and by keeping a careful record of individual performance, thus restoring, in a measure, the possibility of individual superiority and reward, and obtaining a clear and more accurate idea of the time actually required to do a given piece of work. This, he thought, might make possible a more intelligent incentive reward in the way of higher wages. Incentive rewards for day workers in the form of group bonuses is discussed elsewhere. The idea was not followed up immediately, but later on appeared as the **multiple time plan.**[2] Under this plan the worker is paid a day rate up to a standard production and a higher day rate if this standard is exceeded. There may be one or more standards and corresponding increases in day rate. More recently the idea, in a more developed form, has appeared under the name of **measured day work.** In this more modern system a careful study is made of each and every operation to determine a fair base rate by evaluating its characteristics and requirements and rating these in terms of percentage. Thus characteristics that might be considered[3] are:

1. Skill required.
2. Responsibility involved.
3. Mental application required.
4. Physical application required.
5. Working conditions.

To such criteria as these some employers add a number of "basic points" to take account of local conditions and possibly to insure a fair minimum wage.

This process, it will be noted, is merely an evaluation of the worth of the several operations *in relation to each other.* The final basic day rates are then set in accordance with prevailing wage rates, labor conditions, and company policies.

To these basic day rates an extra compensation is given, based upon percentage applied to the characteristics of the worker, for instance, quantity of production, quality of production, versatility, dependability, etc. If the worker does not qualify sufficiently high he earns only the base rate. It is stated that where the plan is in successful operation the

[1] "Work, Wages, and Profits," p. 59.

[2] See Alford, L. P., (Ed.), "Cost and Production Handbook," p. 622.

[3] See Rositke, R. H., "Measured Day Work," *Factory Management and Maintenance*, February, 1937.

base rate constitutes from 75 to 85 per cent of the total measured day rate.[1]

PIECE WORK

248. General Features.—In piece-work pay systems the man is paid for the *amount of work performed* and not for the time expended. Thus, suppose a man earning $3 per day was making bolts for his employer. His pay would not change under the day-pay system whether he made 10 or 15 bolts daily. But suppose he were paid *by the bolt* at the rate of 15 cents[2] each. Then he must make 20 bolts to earn $3. Any falling off in his production would mean lowered daily earnings, while any increase in his production would mean an increase in pay. If the rate per piece is fair to both employer and employee this would seem to be an ideal system in many ways, as it apparently restores to the ambitious workman the opportunity to secure the increased compensation due him on account of his greater skill or diligence. If it successfully stimulates production it lowers the cost of the product, since the increased production is obtained with practically no increase in overhead costs. Thus, suppose in the above example that the material cost per bolt is 10 cents, and the machine rate[3] (see Art. 208) for the equipment he is using is $2 per day, then the cost per bolt to the employer for various rates of production would be as shown in Table 10.

TABLE 10.—EARNINGS AND COSTS UNDER PIECE WORK

Number of bolts per day	Material cost	Workman's earnings	Machine rate	Total shop cost	Cost per bolt
10	$1.00	$1.50	$2.00	$4.50	$0.45
15	1.50	2.25	2.00	5.75	0.38⅓
20	2.00	3.00	2.00	7.00	0.35
30	3.00	4.50	2.00	9.50	0.31⅔
40	4.00	6.00	2.00	12.00	0.30
50	5.00	7.50	2.00	14.50	0.29

The workman, therefore, make a higher wage, the cost of the product is lessened, and the output per dollar of investment is increased, so that both employer and employee are benefited.

Piece work is evidently not adapted to cases where many pieces of different character are handled daily. It lends itself naturally to repeti-

[1] For a summary of job evaluation see *Bulletin of National Association of Cost Accountants*, Dec. 1, 1938.

[2] Piece rates are usually set somewhat lower than the corresponding day rate.

[3] The effect of including material cost and machine rates in total costs should be carefully noted. The first does not affect the *difference* in total costs but does affect their *ratio*. The second affects their difference as well. Costs that do not include labor, material, and burden are misleading for purposes of comparison, especially if compared with other costs where these items enter in different proportions.

tive work, that is, where many pieces of one kind are to be made. It can be applied to advantage, however, to small numbers of parts where the work to be done on each is of sufficient magnitude to make intelligent estimates of time allowances possible.

If N = number of pieces produced, r = rate per piece, then the worker's earnings, $E = Nr$.

249. Difficulties and Objections.—Piece work is, of course, not new, and has probably existed in some form or other from early antiquity. For reasons already discussed it did not, however, obtain a strong foothold in our industrial organization in the beginning. When the limitations of the day-wage method discussed in Art. 246 began to make competition more difficult, and as the volume of production increased, employers naturally turned to the piece-rate system as a means of increasing production and reducing cost. These very limitations of the day wage, however, have been, in a large measure, the reason for one of the greatest difficulties in introducing piece rates. Under modern conditions the discouraging effects of day work had tended, as already noted, to reduce greatly the output, so that with the advance in modern tools and methods little was really known regarding the possibilities of production or what really constituted a fair day's work. The records of work already accomplished were, therefore, unreliable as a guide in setting piece rates, and the estimates of a busy foreman were likely to be little better than guesses.

When, therefore, piece rates were introduced, based on these unreliable sources, it was found that the workman under this stimulus could produce much more than it was supposed he could. An examination of the foregoing table (the data of which are taken arbitrarily but are fairly representative) shows that under these conditions the increase in wages is very much greater in proportion than the decrease in cost. The result was that the employer either from cupidity, or because he really believed the worker was obtaining more than a fair share of the returns, "cut" the piece rate to a lower figure.

If the new piece rate allowed of it, and if the ambition of the worker was not killed by the first cut, and he again succeeded in raising his wage to a high figure, the rate was again cut; and this cycle was repeated till the discouraged worker refused to exert himself further and perhaps found himself working much harder than formerly with little or no advance in his wage.

The general effect of this penalizing process upon the good workman is to teach him to limit his production to that of the poorer man, and to awaken class consciousness. He quickly sees that an advance in wages cannot come through his own extra exertions and he naturally turns to organization as a means of securing by might what he feels should be his by right; and he is willing that poorer men shall be overpaid in order that he may receive something near what he feels is his just due. The logic is perfectly clear and he cannot be blamed for the result.

Piece work has also been opposed upon other grounds. The average workman much prefers day pay because it involves no risk as to the amount he is to receive. In some respects there is a good reason for this objection. If the workman on day pay encounters extra hard castings, or if his production is interfered with by reason of a breakdown or other unforeseen contingency over which he has no control, the entire loss occasioned thereby falls, not on him, but on his employer; while on piece work he would be a loser to the extent of his probable earnings. It has been opposed by labor unions on ethical grounds,[1] because it is asserted that the system awakens greed in the workers and stimulates unrestricted competition between them, with the result that discord, suspicion, and the destruction of brotherly feeling soon take the place of harmony and goodwill. While the truth of this assertion is denied by some, the writer knows by personal experience that there is a considerable amount of truth in the statement. Competition between workmen has the same effect as competition between employers or corporations, and this principle must often be taken into account in introducing new wage systems.

And, finally, the workman is prone to object to any method that tends to increase production, simply because it does tend to do so. He may not be able to explain just why, but as before noted, he instinctively feels that by restricting production he can affect the law of supply and demand in his favor. He is interested in his own welfare, and not that of the men of the future; hence economic arguments based on the ultimate gain accruing from increased production do not impress him. This attitude, shortsighted as it may be, is reflected in union regulations that, while allowing the use of piece work, often fix a maximum number of pieces that any man may turn out in a day.

It will be noted that the defects and objections to piece work may be those due to bad management (including lack of accurate knowledge) or to inherent defects in the method itself. Piece work has been operated very successfully where the rates have been accurately set and have been maintained, and where a correct understanding existed between employer and employee. There are many cases where it can be used to advantage, but its success will depend on a careful observance of the advantages and disadvantages noted above.

250. One Hundred Per Cent Time-premium Plan.—An interesting variation of piece work known by this title[2] has the following features:

[1] O'Connell, James, President International Association of Machinists, "Piece Work Not Necessary for Best Work in the Machine Shop," *Eng. Mag.*, Vol. 19, p. 373, 1900.

[2] Estes, L. V., "Comparison of Wage Incentives," *Industrial Management*, September, 1920.

1. A task *time* is set for each operation.
2. A specified *rate per hour* is set for each class of work.
3. The worker receives 1 hour's pay at his established rate for each task-hour's work that he performs.

Thus suppose that, as before, the worker is making bolts and that the task time is 1 hour for every 2 bolts and that the hourly rate is \$0.30. Then the amount earned for making, say, 20 bolts, would be $^{20}\!/_{2} \times \$0.30 = \$3$ without reference to the actual time acquired to do the work.

The advantage claimed for this method is that the premium is on *time* instead of money. Mr. Gantt in his task and bonus system, described in Art. 262, also makes the bonus a function of the time saved. The basis of reward for increased effort in this plan is permanent for given conditions and does not need to be changed when changes take place in the basic wage. In the case of straight piece work it is sometimes necessary to change the rate per piece when there are marked changes in the base rate, which is not desirable from the viewpoint of either the relations with the worker or methods of accounting. This plan also makes it possible to reward workers for faithful service through higher hourly rates without changing the basis of the incentive to increased production.

251. Taylor Differential Piece Rate.—While this plan is little used at present, it is discussed because of the principle on which it is based, namely the offering of a low piece rate for low production and a higher piece rate for higher production. In the original use of day-rate and piece-rate plans, no effort was made to determine just what a fair day's work should be. The difficulties that ensued have been discussed in Art. 246. Taylor proceeded on the assumption that through time study it is possible to fix quite accurately a standard of performance and that by standardizing all conditions of production and by careful instruction, workers could reach this assigned standard (see Chap. XII).

To encourage the workman to reach the standard of performance Mr. Taylor established two piece rates, a high piece rate when the standard is attained, and a low piece rate when the standard is not attained. Thus, if, as before, the standard production is 30 bolts per day, the piece rate for that output, and beyond it, might be 15 cents per bolt; but for any production below 30 the rate might be 10 cents per bolt. There is every incentive, therefore, toward maximum production, for the workman receives not only a high piece rate if he reaches and exceeds the standard, but receives the full piece rate, per piece, as high production rises, after he has attained the standard performance and not simply a portion of it, as under the Halsey and other plans. Taylor's plan[1] differs from any that preceded it in that it seeks to determine definitely just what the output of a good man should be and to set the standard performance so that only good men can attain the higher price level, but to reward

[1] TAYLOR, F. W., "A Piece-rate System," *Trans. Am. Soc. Mech. Eng.*, June, 1895.

liberally those that can. It also penalizes the poorer worker in greater degree than is done in straight piece work, since the lower piece rate is purposely set very low to spur the man to try to attain the higher rate. The day wage is not assured to the worker under this plan.

To make an approximate comparison with other methods, suppose that analysis shows that with improved facilities 30 bolts per day may be taken as a fair day's work. Suppose also that an upper rate of 15 cents per bolt is sufficient incentive to the workman to meet this standard, and let 10 cents be taken as the lower rate. It will be fair to assume that the machine rate will be increased to say $2.50 because of the more expensive planning department necessary. Then the costs and earnings under this system will be as shown in Table 11 following:

TABLE 11.—EARNINGS AND COSTS UNDER TAYLOR DIFFERENTIAL PIECE RATE

Number of bolts	Material cost	Day wage	Piece rate	Workman's daily earnings	Machine rate	Total shop cost	Cost per bolt
10	$1.00	Not assured	10	$1.00	$2.50	$ 4.50	$0.45
15	1.50	Not assured	10	1.50	2.50	5.50	0.36⅔
20	2.00	Not assured	10	2.00	2.50	6.50	0.32½
30	3.00	Not assured	15	4.50	2.50	10.00	0.33⅓
40	4.00	Not assured	15	6.00	2.50	12.50	0.31¼
50	5.00	Not assured	15	7.50	2.50	15.00	0.30

252. Advantages and Criticisms.—The Taylor[1] differential piece rate recognizes very fully that low wages do not mean cheap product. Thus, in the above example, the cost of 20 bolts per day is as great as at 40 bolts per day. It is evident, however, that in order to reduce the price and at the same time pay a high piece rate a large quantity must be produced. Under Taylor's method of expert analysis, prediction, and preparation, however, the good workman has more chance of reaching this high output than under other plans that depend on the initiative of the workman alone. The Taylor plan aims to determine just what the maximum product should be under best conditions, leaving nothing to the worker's initiative, but paying him a good rate to insure his cooperation. The criticism usually made of the Taylor system is that it takes away the workman's initiative and tends to make an automaton of him. While this may seem to be the immediate effect upon skilled workmen, the ultimate effect of this method would be no different from that of the introduction of any labor-saving device or any division of mental labor

[1] The data selected for the several tables are what might well be expected in practice. Accurate comparison of the systems cannot, however, be drawn from these data, as the basic rates may be varied so widely.

from manual labor. All such influences tend to subdivide and reclassify labor, putting the planning into the hands of the more able, and the actual execution into the hands of the less able. The Taylor system, of which this plan of payment is a part, is a very able analysis of the theory of division of labor, both mental and manual. To what extent it may come into use will depend on grounds other than those already considered.

It is objected also that the method, by measuring accurately a man's capacity for work, puts into the hands of the employer an enormous power that he hitherto has not possessed. This also is true, but is no argument against accurate measurement. There is no reason why an employer should not know just what value he is purchasing in labor, as he does in buying material. He must not, however, be allowed to use this power unjustly. Clearly, rates could be set by this method that would exclude all but the very best men from participating in industry, and because of the increased product the market demand could be filled. It is questionable, to say the least, whether it is better to have production concentrated in the hands of a few or to have every man producing as efficiently as he can and being paid accordingly.

253. Merrick Multiple Piece Rate.—The only difference between this plan and Taylor's is that it offers three graded piece rates instead of two. The first step is set at 83 per cent of standard on task production and the second at the task point. This gives three piece rates: one for beginners, one for average workers, and one for first-class men, thus modifying the severity of Taylor's lower piece rate. It will be clear that the principle is capable of further extension and possibly with advantage in some cases.

HALSEY AND SIMILAR GAIN-SHARING PLANS

254. The Halsey Premium Plan.—The Halsey Premium Plan[1] was the first of the modern gain-sharing plans and is a well thought out effort to meet some of the difficulties of day work and piece work already noted. It is especially important as it was the pioneer[2] in a new method of rewarding labor. Under this plan it is optional with the workman whether he elects to work on the premium plan or not, and his day's pay is assured to him whether he earns a premium or not, provided, of course, that he is not so incompetent as to be undesirable. Under this plan a standard time, *based on previous experience*, is allowed for the work in question. For every hour that the workman can shorten this time he is paid a

[1] HALSEY, F. A., "The Premium Plan of Paying for Labor," *Trans. Am. Soc. Mech. Eng.*, Vol. 12, p. 755.

[2] This is true, at least, so far as modern times and the machine industries are concerned. The idea seems to have been employed, however, in earlier days in other industries, but such use as was made of it had made little impression on wage systems in general. See also CHURCH, A. H., "Rational Management," *Eng. Mag.*, April, 1913, p. 29.

fraction of his hourly wage as a premium. In Mr. Halsey's original illustration the fraction selected is one-third; but, as he noted, this is a question that must be settled by good judgment. In practice it varies from one-quarter to one-half of the hourly wage. Thus, suppose a job normally requires 10 hours to complete, and the workman's pay is $3 for the 10 hours. If he can reduce the time of the work to 8 hours his premium will be $\frac{2 \times 30}{3} = 20$ cents and his earnings for the 8 hours will be

$$(8 \times 0.30) + 0.20 = \$2.60$$

or at the rate of $3.25 per day of 10 hours. The labor cost to the employer is, therefore, 40 cents less than on day work. Or suppose, again, that as in Art. 248 the workman is paid $3 per day and is producing normally 20 bolts daily. If, under the stimulus of the premium plan, he produces 30 bolts daily he would save one-half of a day in time and his bonus would be ($\frac{1}{3}\ \frac{300}{2}$) = 50 cents, thus making his daily wage $3.50. The labor cost per bolt would also fall from 15 cents each to 11⅔ cents. If, on the other hand, he should fail to make 15 bolts he would still receive his full normal day's pay of $3. The wages and costs for various numbers of bolts under this plan and with these data are shown in Table 12.

Table 12.—Earnings and Costs under Halsey Premium Plan

Number of bolts	Material cost	Day wage	Premium	Workman's earnings	Machine rate	Total shop cost	Cost per bolt
10	$1.00	$3.00	0	$3.00	$2.00	$ 6.00	$0.60
15	1.50	3.00	0	3.00	2.00	6.50	0.43⅓
20	2.00	3.00	0	3.00	2.00	7.00	0.35
30	3.00	3.00	0.50	3.50	2.00	8.50	0.28⅓
40	4.00	3.00	1.00	4.00	2.00	10.50	0.26¼
50	5.00	3.00	1.50	4.50	2.00	12.00	0.24

If S = standard time, T = actual time taken, and p = premium percentage, then the workman's earnings, $E = RT + p(S - T)R$.

255. Advantages and Disadvantages.—Since this system insures the workman his full day's pay it is easy to introduce. No changes are needed in the regular shop methods, or at least no conspicuous changes, and the workman is not compelled to work for a premium unless he so desires. Because of this conciliatory characteristic of the plan it has been much used. It is simple in its operation and every man can compute just what his premium will be. The standard times are posted in the shop and each man by keeping account of his own performances can readily compute his own premium. These standard times, as before noted, are based on previous records, with such shortening of these records as may seem desirable or necessary. No radical shortening of the records, however, is made unless new methods or appliances are put in operation.

Under this plan the workman does not obtain the entire benefit of the gain in product that he produces, as he does in straight piece work. This, however, is true of all incentive plans except piece work, and this defect, if such it may be termed, is offset by the assurance of a daily wage. Perhaps an advantage of the plan is that the employer, since he is obtaining part of the gain, is less likely to reduce the premium rate or lower the basic wage.

An argument often advanced against the plan is that the rates are set by judgment or are based on records that do not represent the workman's full capacity and that, as a consequence, the workman easily makes large premiums, thus tempting the employer to reduce the standard time. The same argument holds against piece work as ordinarily practiced. In the light of more modern advances in time study there is some truth in this criticism, but there is no reason why basic rates for this system cannot be based on so-called scientific time studies. On the other hand, the lowering of the standard time much below previous records makes the introduction of any bonus or premium plan more difficult. The success of the Halsey plan is due largely to its simplicity, ease of introduction, and fairness.

256. Manchester Plan.—Under this plan a minimum daily wage is assured up to some selected percentage of the task, and from this point on the incentive reward is by piece work. It will be evident that such a plan lacks the incentive force of straight piece work, but it embodies the conciliatory principle of the Halsey plan and is, therefore, useful in certain cases. If the incentive is expressed in hours instead of pieces this plan is known as the **Standard-Hour Plan.**

257. Haynes Plan.—In the Haynes plan,[1] the standard of performance is set by time study and is expressed in **manits,** a manit being a standard *man-minute* of work. The day's wage is assured where the work is not well standardized and the standard of performance low, the value of the time saved is divided between the worker, the supervising force, and the company, five-tenths going to the operator, one-tenth to supervision, and four-tenths to the company. It differs in this respect from the Halsey plan, in that supervision is recognized in the division of the savings. Where the work is standardized on the basis of time study and the required performance is consequently high, the savings are divided between the worker and the supervising force, five-sixths of it going to the operator and one-sixth to supervision. The company receives its share of the gain in the decreased time over day work. The standards are set so that the ordinary good workman can make as high as a 30 per cent bonus above his hourly wage. The bonus paid to the supervising staff is credited to a bonus fund, and the cost of time lost by the workers

[1] See *Trans. Am. Soc. Mech. Eng.*, December, 1924.

by delays and waiting because of faulty supervision is charged against this fund, the difference, if any, going to the supervisors. No manits are credited to the worker for product that does not pass inspection. This plan differs from the Halsey plan only in having a minute as a basis of measurement instead of an hour, and in its recognition of supervision in the division of the premium.

258. The Bedeaux Plan.—In the Bedeaux system the standard of performance is also the amount of work assigned to be done in one minute and is designated as a **point** or "B." The rate of pay is also reduced to the minute basis and the task is defined as 60 × B × hours. The day's wage is assured and the standard task is set on the basis of careful time study. The savings are divided between the worker and management in the ratio of 3:1. The number of "points" produced by every worker and the amount of the premium he has earned are posted daily so that every worker can see what his earnings were for the previous day.

An advantage claimed for this system is that it enables comparisons to be made between departments by comparing the **total point hours** produced by each. The total point hour for a department is determined by dividing the total number of points produced per day by the total number of hours worked. Thus if the total number of points produced by all workers of a department for the day was 5,600, and the total number of hours worked was 80, then the point hour for the department would be $\frac{5,600}{80} = 70$, which could be used as an index of efficiency against other departments.

If, as before, R = rate, T = time taken, and S = standard time, then the worker's earnings are

$$E = TR + .75(S - T)R.$$

Since a B = $\frac{1}{60}$ of an hour

$$S = \frac{\text{standard B's}}{60}$$

and

$$T = \frac{\text{earned B's}}{60}$$

EMERSON AND SIMILAR GAIN-SHARING PLANS

259. Emerson Efficiency Plan.—In the Halsey and similar plans the premium or bonus that is assigned to the worker is a fixed proportion of the gain that he makes over the task point, so that these gains follow straight lines (see Fig. 55). For this reason, these plans are sometimes called **constant gain-sharing plans,** though in the opinion of the writer the name is not well chosen. It will be evident, however, that almost any curve may be drawn from the task point (Fig. 55) that is satisfactory to both employer and employee. The Emerson[1] efficiency plan, so called, while aiming to attain results similar to those attained by the Halsey and like plans already discussed, proceeds on a principle somewhat different from any of them, though some features of the plan are similar to some features of these other methods. Like the Halsey and Gantt systems, Emerson assured the workman his day wage. Like Taylor and Gantt, he made a careful study of the details of production and established a standard performance that represents a full and fair task for the worker. For the attainment of this standard a large bonus is offered, as in the Gantt method, but smaller bonuses may be earned before reaching this standard, thus agreeing in a way with the Halsey plan.

To make this method clear, suppose that a job is standardized at 120 hours. If the workman performs the task in 120 hours his efficiency is said to be 100 per cent. If he takes 240 hours his efficiency is 50 per cent. If he takes only 100 hours his efficiency is 120 per cent, and so on. No bonus is paid the worker unless his efficiency reaches 66⅔ per cent; he receives only his day pay. At this point he receives a very small bonus, but the bonus increases as his performance rises, till at 100 per cent efficiency he receives 20 per cent of his day wage as a bonus. For greater performance greater bonuses are paid until at 140 per cent efficiency the worker receives 60 per cent of his wages as a bonus. The bonus rates for the several efficiencies are given in Table 13, from which it will be seen that the bonus for the lower efficiencies is very small but increases rapidly as the efficiency rises.

In the practical operations of this method of Mr. Emerson's, the bonus is calculated monthly and not for individual jobs. Thus, if a man's wages are \$0.30 per hour, and if during a given month he has worked 240 hours, doing in that time jobs whose total standard times have been set as 210 hours, his efficiency is $^{210}/_{240} = 87.5$. His wages are \$72, his bonus (see Table 13) is 7.94 per cent of his wages, or \$5.72, and his earnings \$77.72. The advantage of this monthly award is that it tends to make the worker desirous of making a bonus on *every* job since the averaging in of a number of poor performances with a few good ones would, in all probability, mean the loss of any bonus that he may have earned on these good performances.

Above 100 per cent efficiency this plan gives the worker all the time he saves plus 20 per cent of his actual time wages. From 66⅔ per cent of standard up to standard, therefore, the worker's earnings are $E = RT + K(RT)$, where K is taken from Table 13. Above standard $E = RT + (S - T)R + .20RT$.

To make an approximate comparison with the other systems, let the standard performances as before be 30 bolts and the day wage \$3; then the earnings and costs under the Emerson plan are as given in Table 14.

[1] EMERSON, HARRINGTON, "Efficiency."

As in all bonus systems where the workman receives a large part of the apparent gain, the output must be large in order to reduce the cost, and as a consequence, the standard performance must be set so high that only the best men can attain it. The system is, therefore, selective in its operation, though not so markedly so as the Gantt and Taylor systems, since there is some provision made for all men that can attain an efficiency of 66⅔ per cent.

TABLE 13.—EMERSON BONUS RATES

Efficiency, per cent	Bonus per $1 wages	Efficiency, per cent	Bonus per $1 wages	Efficiency, per cent	Bonus per $1 wages	Efficiency, per cent	Bonus per $1 wages
67	0.0001	78	0.0238	88	0.0832	99	0.1881
68	0.0004	79	0.0280	89	0.0911	100	0.20
69	0.0011	80	0.0327	90	0.0991	101	0.21
70	0.0022	81	0.0378	91	0.1074	102	0.22
71	0.0037	82	0.0433	92	0.1162	103	0.23
72	0.0055	83	0.0492	93	0.1256	105	0.25
73	0.0076	84	0.0553	94	0.1352	110	0.30
74	0.0102	85	0.0617	95	0.1453	120	0.40
75	0.0131	86	0.0684	96	0.1557	130	0.50
76	0.0164	87	0.0756	97	0.1662	135	0.55
77	0.0199	87.5	0.0794	98	0.1770	140	0.60

TABLE 14.—EARNINGS AND COSTS UNDER EMERSON PLAN

Number of bolts	Material cost	Day wage	Efficiency, per cent	Bonus	Workman's daily earnings	Machine rate	Total shop cost	Cost per bolt
10	$1.00	$3.00	0.33⅓	0	$3.00	$2.50	$ 6.50	$0.65
15	1.50	3.00	0.50	0	3.00	2.50	7.00	0.46⅔
20	2.00	3.00	0.66⅔	$0.03	3.03	2.50	7.53	0.37⅗
30	3.00	3.00	100	0.60	3.60	2.50	9.10	0.30⅓
40	4.00	3.00	133⅓	1.59	4.59	2.50	11.09	0.27¾
50	5.00	3.00	166⅔	2.60	5.60	2.50	13.10	0.26⅕

260. Wennerlund and Knoeppel Plans.—These plans are both modifications of the Emerson efficiency plan. In the Wennerlund plan, bonus payments begin at 75 per cent of task and follow an empirical curve much like Emerson's up to task or 100 per cent. From there on the increment of bonus increases by 1.2 per cent for every 1 per cent gain in efficiency, which gives a straight line as in piece work. The day wage is guaranteed up to 75 per cent of task.

The Knoeppel plan guarantees day wage up to 67 per cent of task and from there on to task the bonus payments follow an empirical curve as in the Emerson plan. At this point there is a step up of 5 per cent and thereafter the increments follow a straight line. These modifications of the Emerson plan are given especially to note that the variations that can be made with any of these plans are endless.

261. The Rowan Plan.—In this plan[1] a percentage is added to the day rate, this percentage being computed by the fraction $\frac{\text{time saved}}{\text{standard time}}$, or expressed as an equation

$$\text{Premium} = \text{day rate for time consumed} \times \frac{\text{time saved}}{\text{standard time}}.$$

Thus, if the standard time were 10 hours and the day rate \$3 and the workman completed the job in 8 hours, his premium would be \$2.40 × $\frac{2}{10}$ = 0.48 and his pay for the *piece* would be \$2.40 + 0.48 = \$2.88 or at the rate of \$3.60 per day. Using the same data as in the other systems the several items for various rates of production would be as shown in Table 15. Twenty bolts per day are taken as a basic day-rate production.

TABLE 15.—EARNINGS AND COSTS UNDER ROWAN PREMIUM PLAN

Number of bolts	Material cost	Day wage	Premium	Workman's daily earnings	Machine rate	Total shop cost	Cost per bolt
10	\$1.00	\$3.00	0	\$3.00	\$2.00	\$ 6.00	\$0.60
15	1.50	3.00	0	3.00	2.00	6.50	0.43⅓
20	2.00	3.00	0	3.00	2.00	7.00	0.35
30	3.00	3.00	\$1.00	4.00	2.00	9.00	0.30
40	4.00	3.00	1.50	4.50	2.00	10.50	0.26¼
50	5.00	3.00	1.80	4.80	2.00	11.80	0.23⅗

The worker's earnings under this plan are $E = RT + \left(\frac{S - T}{S}\right)RT$.

It will be noted that under this plan the earnings of the workman can never exceed twice his day rate. The value of the controlling fractions, $\frac{\text{time set} - \text{time consumed}}{\text{time set}}$ constantly approaches unity, as the time consumed approaches zero, hence the premium can never exceed the day rate multiplied by unity and, therefore, the earnings can never be more than twice the day rate. It also pays the worker more liberally for the earlier, and hence easier gains, but makes it increasingly difficult to make higher gains, thus practically discouraging very high production. This plan of computing the premium differs from the original Halsey method in this particular, as the latter places no limit to the continual

[1] ROWAN, JAMES, "A Premium System of Remunerating Labor," *Proc. Mech. Eng.* (British), 1901, p. 865.

increase of earnings. There seems to be no more reason for limiting earnings than for limiting production, but the plan has the advantage, if it may be so called, of lessening the employers' desire to cut the basic rates as production and earnings increase. This plan has not been much used in this country, though at one time it was in extended use in England.

THE GANTT TASK AND BONUS PLAN

262. General Features.—It is evident that the differential piece rate is a difficult one, in general, to introduce, because of the fear on the part of the workmen that he cannot attain the higher rate and is, therefore, condemned to a lower wage and ultimate dismissal. The late H. L. Gantt,[1] a former associate of Mr. Taylor, devised a plan that obviates this difficulty and yet holds out the reward for good performance. In the Gantt plan a very careful study is made of the work and conditions exactly as advocated by Taylor, and from this study determination is made of just what a good standard performance should be under the best conditions that can be established. On the basis of these observations a definite **task** for a given time is set, and if the worker can accomplish this task he receives a **bonus** in the form of an extra time allowance, usually from 25 to 50 per cent of the time allowed for the task; hence the name **task and bonus** which is associated with this plan.

If the workman fails to accomplish the task he receives only his day rate, which is guaranteed to him. The plan, therefore, has the good features of the Halsey plan in insuring the day rate, and hence makes it easy of introduction, and embodies, also, the good features of the Taylor plan in that it makes a high rate of production possible and offers a great inducement for high performance.

The worker's earnings up to task are $E = TR$ and above task point, $E = SR + \frac{1}{3}SR = 1\frac{1}{3}SR$.

To illustrate, suppose that as in the previous example of the Taylor method, the standard performance is 30 bolts daily, and that the day rate is \$3 as before. Suppose, also, that the bonus is $33\frac{1}{3}$ per cent of the time allowed. The time allowed for 1 bolt is, therefore, 0.333 hour. If the workman makes just 30 bolts per day he earns a bonus and is given credit for $(10 + \frac{10}{3}) = 13.33$ hours, which at 30 cents per hour is \$4 per day. If he does not make the 30 bolts he does not earn a bonus and his pay is at the day rate of \$3. If, on the other hand, he should exceed the task and make 40 bolts he would be given the time allowed for 40 bolts plus a premium of one-third that time. Thus, the time allowed for forty bolts is $0.333 \times 40 = 13.33$ hours, the premium would be $\frac{13.33}{3} = 4.44$ hours, and the worker's daily earnings would be $(13.33 + 4.44) \times 0.30 = \$5.33$.

[1] See *Trans. Am. Soc. Mech. Eng.*, Vol. 23, 1902, p. 341; also GANTT, H. L., "Work, Wages, and Profits."

Table 16 shows the earnings and costs under the Gantt bonus system for the same data as have been assumed for the previous examples.

A study of the first and fifth columns will show that this system gives day pay when the bonus is not earned and piece-work pay when the bonus is earned. In the example given, for instance, the day pay is $3 and the piece rate is 13.3 cents.

TABLE 16.—EARNINGS AND COSTS UNDER THE GANTT BONUS PLAN

Number of bolts	Material cost	Day wage	Bonus	Workman's daily earnings	Machine rate	Total shop cost	Cost per bolt
10	$1.00	$3.00	0	$3.00	$2.50	$ 6.50	$0.65
15	1.50	3.00	0	3.00	2.50	7.00	0.46⅔
20	2.00	3.00	0	3.00	2.50	7.50	0.37½
30	3.00	3.00	$1.00	4.00	2.50	9.50	0.31⅔
40	4.00	3.00	1.33	5.33	2.50	11.83	0.29½
50	5.00	3.00	1.66	6.66	2.50	14.16	0.28⅓

263. Advantages and Disadvantages.—As before noted this plan is easy to introduce and it is humane in its operation. Under the methods advocated by Gantt, special attention is given to the training of the workmen, both in the skill necessary to earn the bonus and also in habits of industry.[1] A careful study is made of all the conditions, all obstacles are removed, and every assistance is given to the worker that may help him to earn the bonus. The task must necessarily be set high since the output must be large to reduce the unit cost greatly, and since the bonus is large and the workman gets all the apparent gain. A further incentive to production is provided by giving a bonus to the foreman[2] when a given proportion of men under him earn their bonus. This encourages the foreman, not only to teach the men all he can, but to keep all obstacles from before them. The system has undoubted merit, and under Mr. Gantt's personal direction it was very successful in many plants. It does, however, like the Taylor plan, divide the workers into two classes, those that can earn a bonus and those that cannot, and this feature has been criticized. It is questionable, however, if this effect is any greater than the necessary difference in wages that must always exist where men are paid on merit.

264. Other Incentive-wage Systems.—It will be obvious that an infinite number of variations of the incentive methods illustrated in the preceding articles can be made, and a number of such variations have been devised and put into practice. Roe and Lyttle in "Management's

[1] See "Work, Wages, and Profits," p. 115.

[2] See Art. 132.

Handbook" list six other "systems" so called, namely, Parkhurst, Bigelow, Barth, Diemer, Ficker Piece Rate, and Ficker Time Rate. All of these are modifications or combinations of the principles that have been discussed and derive their names from the men who have conceived these modifications. They do not advance any new principles and will not, therefore, be discussed in detail. No doubt any and all of them are applicable under certain circumstances, though some of them do not comply with the requirement laid down in Art. 244, that a successful incentive system must be simple and such that the worker can easily compute his added reward.

RÉSUMÉ

265.—It is difficult, if not impossible, to draw accurate comparisons between the several methods of payment discussed in the preceding articles because of the different foundations on which they rest and the widely differing practice they lead to; and the tabulated figures given for each method must, therefore, be taken as suggestive rather than conclusive. They do, however, make it possible to compare these systems so as to show clearly the relative importance they may possess in the eyes of the employer and the employee. In making this comparison it must be remembered that the interests of these two classes of men are not always the same. The employer naturally employs labor as cheaply as he can, the worker naturally offers his labor at as high a price as he can command. The employer wishes large output; the worker is in general not interested in increasing his output *unless his compensation increases accordingly.* The fact that increased output eventually benefits not only the employer but also the employee has little or no influence on the worker. He is not willing, and justly, to forego present profits for the sake of prospective gains that are, after all, somewhat problematic and uncertain. Hence he wishes as high a wage as he can obtain regardless of output; in fact, he is inclined to look upon increased output with distrust as leading to a full market with a resulting drop in labor values.

The employer also desires low unit costs. If he can obtain this and also obtain great output his position is very favorable. There is a great advantage, however, in large output even if the shop costs do not materially change; since the greater his output per dollar of investment the greater is his percentage of profit for a given gain per piece sold. Clearly, it is more profitable to sell 1,000 pieces per month than to sell only 1, the gain per piece being the same in both cases. A wage system, therefore, that will stimulate output even though it does not materially reduce the unit cost, is a desirable matter.

In comparing these new wage systems with day work it would seem fair to consider day work at its best, and not to compare them to day work where the worker is producing a small fraction of what he is capable of.

Such conditions, are, perhaps, too common, but they are due to defects in management rather than in the principle of day work. It would not seem to be unfair to estimate that the worker on day pay is producing two-thirds of what he is capable of under the existing conditions. Hence, in the illustrations cited, where 30 bolts is considered a good day's work under best conditions, 20 bolts may be taken as a good performance under the ordinary conditions and surroundings.

In Fig. 55 the line *ACK* represents the worker's pay for any hourly output whatsoever at 30 cents per hour; 20 bolts daily being considered a fair day's work. If, now, the worker is put on piece work at a rate equivalent to his day-work performance, or 15 cents per bolt, his earnings will be represented by the line *OB*, and when he reaches the performance of 20 bolts per day or 2 per hour his hourly rate rises to 30 cents. Should he fail to produce 15 bolts, his decreased earnings would be represented by *OC*.

Since the Halsey system and all its modifications, as illustrated by the Rowan plan, are not based on changes in surrounding conditions or facilities, it would not be expected that they could stimulate the output beyond that attainable by piece work. The advantage of this system is that it insures the workman his day rate and under these methods his curves of earnings are *ACG* and *ACPH*, respectively, and both of these curves lie below the piece-work curve, hence the remuneration per piece is less by these methods than by the piece-work plan. They are, however, much more likely to secure the maximum product of 20 pieces since they insure the day rate and workmen may look upon them with less distrust.

The Taylor, Gantt, and Emerson methods proceed on the general principle that not only does increased compensation stimulate the output but that still greater gains can be made by making the conditions surrounding the workman the very best and by instructing him in the very best method of procedure. It has been assumed in this case that these methods will increase the output 50 per cent or to 30 bolts daily. Then the pay of the worker under these several methods is fairly well represented by the lines *ONDB*, *ACNPM* and *ACF*, respectively. It is assumed that the piece rate under the Gantt system may be somewhat lower than under the Taylor system in order to produce the same incentive, since the Taylor plan does not insure day's pay. The lines *OC* and *ON* measure rates of pay below the standard wage of 30 cents, but the Halsey, Rowan, Gantt, and Emerson curves and that part of the Taylor curve that measures earnings above 30 cents per hour lie between the straight piece-work curve *CB* and the day-rate curve *CK*. That is, the reward of the worker is, in general, greater on piece work and less on day work than by any of the other pay systems for all outputs above the standard rate of 15 pieces per day. This is necessarily so in the Halsey and Rowan plans from their very nature. It is true of the other plans because the great increase in output under these new methods is due only in part to increased remuneration (the effect of which has already been shown to have limitations), and in greater part to the extended division of labor under these methods and the assistance given the worker. The latter is, therefore, not entitled to a proportionate reward as in straight piece work, and if he were it could not be paid without increasing the unit costs above piece-work costs, since the planning of the work and the

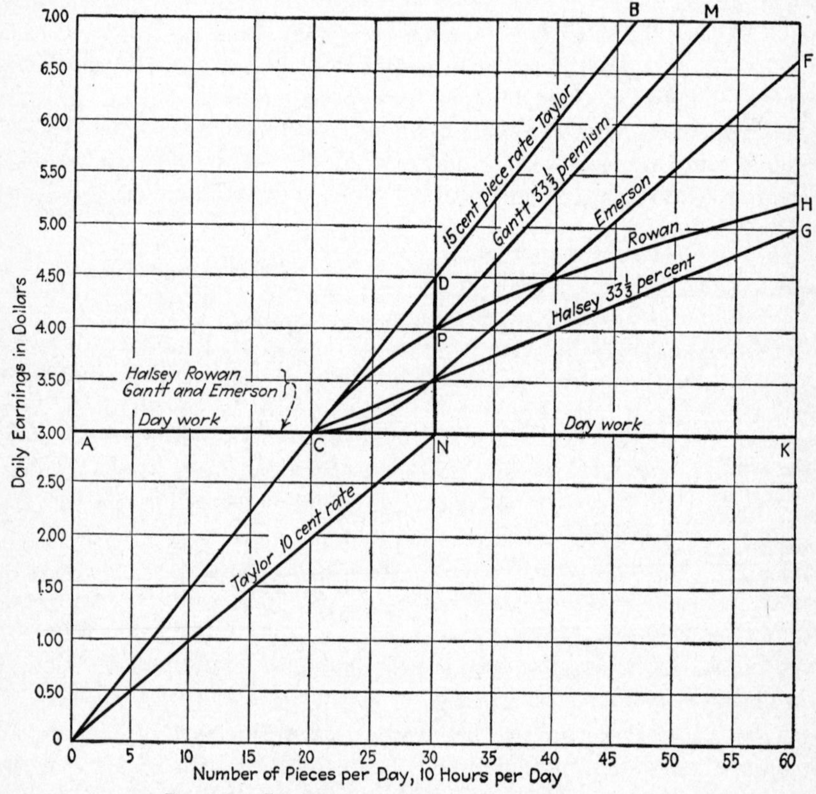

FIG. 55.—Graphic comparison of wage systems.

training of the workmen under the new systems are items of expense that must be included in the costs. It is clear, however, that these more advanced methods of rewarding labor are effective in raising the output while paying higher wages than could be paid under ordinary day or piece work, at the same time keeping the costs as low as, if not lower than, when the increased output is obtained by financial stimulation alone.

It is obvious that the cost per bolt for a large output will be less under day work than under any of these methods that pay higher rates for higher output, and it is also clear that the unit cost will be less under the Halsey plan and its modifications than under piece rates, since the worker receives a portion only of the gain accruing from his increased activity. The effect of the Taylor, Gantt, and Emerson systems on unit cost is not so clear, and the assumption so often made, that increased output necessarily means decreased unit cost, is not warranted except when other factors remain constant. The increased output under these methods is due, as before stated, to the incentive of high wages and to a detailed planning of the work accompanied by expert advice to the worker. The cost of his last feature may make a large addition to the shop burden and, therefore, the unit wage cost is not a correct measure of the total unit cost. In the examples cited it was assumed that an increase of 50 per cent in output could be obtained by these advanced methods with an increase in the machine rate of 25 per cent, which would seem to be conservative. To make comparison easier the unit cost under each method (*i.e.*, the last column in each of the foregoing tables of cost and earnings) are tabulated in Table 17.

Table 17.—Comparison of Costs under Various Systems

Number per day	Cost per bolt in cents					
	10	15	20	30	40	50
Day work	60	**43⅓**	35	26⅔	22½	20
Piece work	45	38⅓	**35**	31⅔	30	29
Taylor piece	45	36⅔	32½	**33⅓**	31¼	30
Halsey premium	60	43⅓	**35**	28⅓	26¼	24
Emerson	65	46⅔	37⅗	**30⅓**	27¾	26⅕
Rowan	60	43⅓	**35**	30	26¼	23⅗
Gantt	65	46⅔	37½	**31⅔**	29½	28⅓

The black-faced figures in the table denote the costs for the highest probable output under each system. It will be noted that generally in each case the cost for day work is lower, and for piece work higher than for any other system except in the smaller outputs, where some of the advanced systems naturally give higher costs because of increased shop burden. But it is evident that if the remuneration or the added shop burden in the Gantt, Taylor, or Emerson system should be much more than what has been allowed, the reduction in cost over simpler systems would be problematical. It should again be noted, however, that even when there is no reduction in cost the gain in output is highly important and desirable.

An instructive comparison of several wage plans has been worked out by Professor M. A. Lee and is illustrated in Fig. 56. It is assumed that the working day is 8 hours and that it is desirable to fix the minimum hourly wage at 45 cents or $3.60 per day. It is known that 120 pieces per day is a good performance and that for this an hourly rate of 67½ cents per hour or $5.40 per day would be good wages in the locality. The point J represents this good performance and the several pay systems are drawn through this point, thus giving the bonus or premium for each number of pieces and the corresponding daily wage or piece rate as the case may be. This analysis is very helpful in selecting a wage plan for specific requirements.

As previously stated, these mathematical statements must be taken as approximate and as indicating general principles only. They are such,

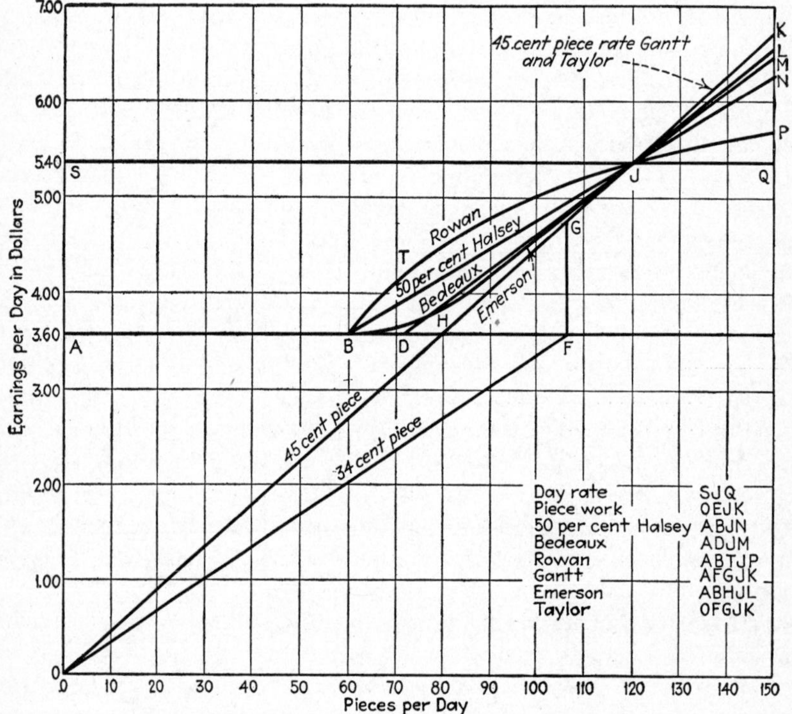

FIG. 56.—Graphic comparison of wage systems.

however, as might occur and may, therefore, assist in visualizing the relations that exist between these much discussed methods. Each shop is, of course, a problem by itself, and a method that may be satisfactory in one may not work at all in another. It is also obvious, as has been stated, that an infinite number of pay systems can be devised along the lines of the advanced methods discussed. The importance of these new methods does not lie so much in the fact that they assist in securing greater output at lower cost and higher wages, as in the *tendencies* that they portend. It really does not matter very much what pay system is used so long as it is just to employer and employee, insuring to the one full value for his money, and rewarding the other fully for his effort.

There are, however, two very important features involved in these new methods that deserve more than passing thought. Under the older system of day work it is necessary in most cases to *drive* the worker in order to obtain his best efforts. Under piece work this is not necessary, but the worker has to take chances against losses sometimes beyond his control, and this he is not inclined to do and often cannot afford. The newer methods frankly recognize that men must be paid for extra exertion, and this is a step in the right direction away from slave-driving methods.

The other feature is even more important. Under day work, piece work, and to a large extent under the Halsey plan, the conditions of production are not changed where added incentive is given to production. Under the Taylor, Gantt, and Emerson methods radical changes are involved, affecting not only the equipment but the workman himself. The introduction of the planning department, functional foremanship, and other features of advanced management so closely connected with these modern pay systems portend a much further application of division of labor than heretofore contemplated. The effect of these changes on the workman will be marked, as these influences tend to disintegrate still further the trades and to reclassify workers into new groups. Mr. Taylor[1] expressed this idea very clearly when he said: "The full possibilities of functional foremanship, however, will not have been fully realized until almost all of the machines in the shop are run by men who are of smaller caliber and attainments and who are, therefore, cheaper than those required under the old system." The new wage systems are, therefore, closely tied up with radical changes in management and are, in a way, not comparable with old methods in their ultimate effect on the workman.

Furthermore, the new methods approach the problem of remuneration from a new viewpoint. Labor is measured exactly, all obstacles are removed as far as possible, and the worker is expected to reach a predetermined performance in exactly the same way in which a scientific farmer determines the efficiency of a cow or the output of a hen. This, in itself, is not of importance; *but if these methods are to be used as a means of eliminating all that fall below a given standard* it opens up a grave and perplexing problem. In the case of the farmer it is an easy problem; in the case of men and women it is not so easy.

It will be seen, then, that modern wage systems are closely interlocked with systems of *management*,[2] and back of this again, often forgotten, but never absent, awaits the greater problem of humanity and human exist-

[1] *Trans. Am. Soc. Mech. Eng.*, Vol. 24, p. 1295.

[2] The results of statistical surveys of the extent to which incentive wage systems have come into use in this country will be found in *Factory Management and Maintenance*, October, 1937.

ence. The time was when wages were settled without much regard to this greater problem, but unless all signs are misleading it will soon be the great factor in both industrial management and reward.

266. Group Bonuses.—In some kinds of work the result depends upon the coordinated efforts of several people. In such cases a **group bonus** for increased production has been found to be effective. Such bonus methods are easier to install than the individual methods that have been discussed, but they are applicable only to certain conditions. If applied to a group of operators whose work is unrelated the good men are likely to suffer through the laxity of the poorer ones, and vice versa. In this respect group bonuses are not unlike the profit-sharing plans that are discussed in Art. 267. If, furthermore, the work is not closely related and of such a character that the workers cannot cooperate harmoniously, ill feeling is likely to arise among them.

267. Profit-sharing Methods.—The student of industrial problems turns naturally to a consideration of cooperative methods as a means of restoring, in a measure, what the workman has lost by separation from the tools of production; and many comprehensive attempts have been made to realize some of the benefits of cooperation in actual practice. A few have met with some measure of success, where the conditions were favorable, but the great majority have been failures.

One of the most common forms of this idea is the profit-sharing scheme whereby a certain percentage of the profits is distributed at fixed intervals, usually annually or semiannually, in some definite ratio to all employees that have been in the employ of the firm for a stated term. The difference between this plan and the wage systems discussed should be clearly noted. Under all of these wage systems the extra reward is *individual*, is based on diligence and skill, and is paid at once. Under profit sharing the bonus comes at long intervals and as a result of many conditions that are obscure and conflicting to the worker. The conditions, furthermore, that fix the possibility of such reward are, to a large extent, not under the control of the worker, and any extra effort he may make may be more than offset by foolish mistakes in management or unfortunate trade conditions. The reward is too remote to interest him to the same extent as the pay systems discussed. This method of bonus award also makes no distinction between the diligent and lazy, which is manifestly unfair, and incidentally this is one of the basic troubles that lie at the root of all cooperative schemes. It would appear that such unjust discrimination must tend to kill personal incentive and ambition and to reduce all efforts to mediocrity. Any system that eliminates personal ambition and individual incentive is foreordained to failure.

The same remarks apply, in a general way, to schemes which permit employees to invest in shares of the company's stock on advantageous terms. As a means of bettering the financial status of the employee and of obtaining his interest, they no doubt are valuable; but they should not in any case be looked on as rewards for increased diligence. As Mr. Going has well said: "There is no necessary automatic and manifestly just relation between an employee's efficiency or faithfulness and his ability to save money and invest in stocks. The most deserving man in the company's service may have a large family, or a sick wife, or dependent parents, and he may have to turn aside from the opportunity to become an investor and see it go to someone whom he knows (as perhaps only one workman can know another) is less worthy." What he needs and desires is immediate and proportionate reward for his labor.

There are other difficulties in the path of profit-sharing schemes. Workmen are always willing to share the profits but are neither willing, nor as a rule able, to share the losses. Nor is there any just reason why they should participate in the losses since these are matters, in a way, beyond their control. Any arbitrary division of profits will, in general, be looked upon as a gratuity and not as a reward for extra effort or diligence.

QUALITY AND OTHER INCENTIVES

268. Quality Bonus.—All of the incentive methods of remuneration discussed in the foregoing accent increase in the *quantity* produced. But *quality* is often more important than quantity and it is a foremost consideration in most products. In general, dependence is placed upon inspection methods (see Chap. XVII) to insure quality, and it is general practice to pay the worker only for the product that passes inspection and is up to the prescribed standards. It is common experience that the work of inspection must be performed with increasing vigilance as the efforts to increase production are accelerated, and for this reason incentives to quantity production must be used with care where quality is the foremost consideration.

A rigidly enforced inspection system naturally penalizes the worker for poor product and some good results have been obtained by offering a **bonus** or **financial reward** for a high percentage of quality production. Such bonuses can be used in connection with any wage system. They have been used with success in mixing colors[1] where quality is highly important. It is fundamental, of course, that standards for quality bonus awards must be set with at least the same care as with quantity bonus.

269. Bonus for Waste Elimination.—In industries where product is to be cut from stock material such as hides, boards, or cloth, a quantity incentive is likely to lead to excessive wastes through careless and hasty cutting. In such cases bonuses based upon the percentage of waste,

[1] Lichtner, W. O., "Time Study and Job Analysis," p. 336; also Landsburg, R. H., "Industrial Management," p. 303.

which is, of course, a measure of the material saved, have been found to be effective. Carl Bigelow gives a full account of the application of such a system to the cutting of product from boards in *Mechanical Engineering* for January, 1923. The application of such bonus methods to leather cutting and cloth industries is obvious.

270. Other Forms of Bonus.—It will be obvious that the principle of bonus reward for increased effort is capable of very wide[1] application. Bonuses have been devised for **length of service,** for **prompt attendance** at work, and for **accident reduction.** Bonuses have also been arranged to stimulate **continuity of operation.** Where there is a large number of similar machines in operation, as in textile industries, such bonuses can easily be based upon the percentage of the total time they are in operation, since each machine is producing when in operation. An interesting clock known as the Malcolm Efficiency Clock has been devised for automatically indicating the efficiency with which machines are kept in operation. This clock is geared to the machine whose operation is to be measured so that if the machine is kept in continuous operation the Malcolm clock will register in advance of the regular time clock. Thus, if at 5 P.M. the Malcolm clock registered 5.45, the time bonus earned would be 45 minutes. Change gears permit of variation in the premium time that can be earned. In case of a breakdown the workers are paid day pay.

References

ALFORD, L. P. (Ed.): "Management's Handbook," p. 911.
BABCOCK, MAJOR G. D.: "Taylor System in Franklin Management."
EVERSON, HARRINGTON: "Efficiency."
GANTT, H. L.: "Work, Wages, and Profits."
LYTLE, C. W.: "Wage-incentive Methods."
Bulletin of National Association of Cost Accountants, Dec., 1938.
TAYLOR, F. W.: "Shop Management," *Trans. Am. Soc. Mech. Eng.*, Vol. 24.

[1] A bonus system has been in operation in the Departments of Drawing and Machine Design in Cornell University for many years. The work is divided into blocks and a time is set for the completion of each block. If the student can complete the work in less than the assigned time and if the work is of the required quality he may use the time thus saved as he chooses.

CHAPTER XXII

MEASURES OF MANAGEMENT

271. General.—One of the most marked tendencies of modern management is an effort to measure more accurately all industrial results and all forms of effort. The advent of modern cost accounting and the continuous inventory made possible more frequent summaries of the state of the business and there is a constant search for still more advanced methods that will give the manager instantaneous knowledge of what is transpiring and better control over the processes of production. Without doubt, this tendency has been due, in some measure, to the advent of the engineer into managerial work. Measurement of engineering factors is inherent in his profession and the measurement of performance as illustrated in all phases of public service, taxicab service, etc., has long been one of his problems. Almost automatically, therefore, he tries to measure all forms of activity. It was this impelling motive that started Taylor upon his classical experiments, and the most refined efforts to measure human productivity are simple extensions of his original ideas.

The difficulties of the problem are manifest. Management is, and must remain, partly personal in character, and as Professor Roe[1] truly states:

> Those elements which constitute an art, and are based on personal skill, leadership, and imagination as well as the vital element of integrity, can and should be left to judgment as heretofore.

But nevertheless measurement should be substituted for judgment wherever that can be done. Until very recently *all* managerial results were *judged*. Today not a few of these results are being *measured*.

Again quoting Professor Roe:

> There is a great difference between judgment and measurement. To judge is to arrive at a conclusion or decision by weighing or comparing. To measure is to ascertain quality, dimensions, or quantity by comparison with a *standard*. In judging things they are compared one with another. In measuring them all are compared with the same thing, namely, the standard. Comparison is common to both, but the use of an agreed-upon standard as the basis of comparison distinguishes measurement from judgment. Paintings are judged, pistons are measured. Judgment is the more widely applicable process. Measurement is possible only where a standard can be used. Measurement where applicable is the more definite and satisfactory because all agree to compare with the same thing, the standard.

[1] Roe, Professor Joseph N., "Measures of Management," *Mech. Eng.*, November, 1923.

It will appear also that, while it may be easy to measure the mechanical features of industry, it becomes increasingly difficult to measure industrial effort as it tends to become mental in character. As has been shown, there is little difficulty in measuring the work of a mechanic, whether operating a machine or doing a handicraft operation. But it is impossible to measure the work of a highly developed designer or that of a manager whose vision, personality, and energy are the moving forces in the enterprise. And, in general, it may be stated that it is much easier to measure *line* operations than *staff* services. Thus, Professor Roe, in trying to set up measures for the several departments of a manufacturing plant, states that he has been unable to discover a standard or means of measuring performance in cost accounting which would be satisfactory or generally applicable. These limitations may be clearer, perhaps, after a discussion of some features of management that can be measured.

272. Data and Measurement.—A clear distinction should be drawn between collected data and *measurement*. Industrial data, for the most part, record *accumulated* results over a given period of time. They are simple statements of facts. Thus, a balance sheet shows the accumulated assets and liabilities by classes and items for the period since the last sheet was compiled. This may have been a month or a year, depending upon the practice. A sales report gives a record of actual sales and sales expenses over some given period, a weekly labor report records the expenditures for various classes of labor by the week or month, and many similar reports will occur to the reader.

Simple summarized statements or averages of this sort may be useful for certain purposes, but all statistical material can, in general, be made much more effective by combining or contrasting, and it is often necessary to consider data from more than one report to obtain best results. The most common method of comparison is by forming a *ratio*, as explained in Art. 103, which should be reread here.

Measurement, then, it should be noted, involves a *standard* to which reference is made. In some cases, it is desirable to measure simple accumulated data against standards but, in general, ratios such as have been discussed in the preceding form the best basis for measuring management. In the case of the power plant referred to in Art. 103, the conditions are predominatingly mechanical and it is possible to set up a standard to which comparison can be made and management measured with considerable accuracy. The possibility of such accurate measurement decreases as the conditions depend more and more upon the personal equation, and the element of judgment becomes increasingly important in measuring results.

The problem and possibility of measuring management are well illustrated by the balance sheet. A balance sheet is a statement of the accumulated values of assets and liabilities. The *difference* between the assets and liabilities is a measure of the prosperity of the concern. But the balance sheet also provides comparative data that can be used to measure[1] other characteristics of the enterprise. Thus the ratio $\frac{\text{current assets}}{\text{current liabilities}}$ is commonly accepted as a measure of the borrowing capacity or credit of the enterprise. If this ratio is equal to 2, the condition for extending loans is considered satisfactory by credit men, hence, in this case, the standard is 2 and the advisability of loaning money to the concern is increased or lessened as the ratio is greater or less than 2.

It may be, however, that the current assets may consist partly of merchandise inventory that might be difficult to sell in an emergency. Some credit men prefer the ratio $\frac{\text{quick assets}}{\text{current liabilities}}$ therefore, as a criterion of borrowing capacity, where quick assets contain only those items such as cash and ready receivables. If this ratio is equal to or greater than 1 the condition is considered satisfactory or, in other words, the standard for this criterion is 1.

From balance-sheet data and other accounting data it is obvious that many similar ratios may be evolved that will be helpful as measures of management if they can be applied intelligently. J. H. Bliss, who has written[2] very understandingly on this topic, has suggested the following ratios:

Factor Measured	Ratio
1. Earning power	$\frac{\text{surplus net profits}}{\text{net worth}}$
2. Profit on turnover	$\frac{\text{surplus net profits}}{\text{volume of business}}$
3. Operating efficiency	$\frac{\text{operating profits}}{\text{total capital}}$
4. Profit earned on turnover	$\frac{\text{operating profits}}{\text{volume of business}}$
5. Capital turnover	$\frac{\text{volume of business}}{\text{total capital}}$
6. Results of merchandising	$\frac{\text{gross earnings}}{\text{volume of business}}$
7. Trend of operating results	$\frac{\text{costs and expenses}}{\text{volume of business}}$
8. Effect of general policies	$\frac{\text{property expenses}}{\text{investment and sales}}$
9. Cost of borrowed capital	$\frac{\text{total cost of borrowed funds}}{\text{average amount of capital borrowed}}$
10. Cost of total capital	$\frac{\text{cost of borrowed money} + \text{fair return on net worth}}{\text{average amount of total capital}}$

[1] For a more extended and very clear discussion of balance-sheet ratios see GILMAN, STEPHEN, "Analyzing Financial Statements."

[2] BLISS, J. H., "Management Through Accounts"; "Management's Handbook," p. 1260, edited by L. P. Alford.

Factor Measured	Ratio
11. Inventories turnover	$\frac{\text{average annual inventory}}{\text{cost of sales for year}}$
12. Use of capital in receivables	$\frac{\text{volume of business}}{\text{amount of accounts receivable}}$
13. Turnover on fixed property investment	$\frac{\text{volume of business}}{\text{capital invested in plant and equipment}}$
14. Credit condition	$\frac{\text{current assets}}{\text{current liabilities}}$

Other writers[1] give other ratios, depending upon the angle from which the problem is viewed. The view of the banker who is asked for a loan may be somewhat different from that of the manager who is simply seeking information as to the prosperity of his plant. Space will not permit even listing of such other ratios nor will it permit discussion of the reasoning upon which any such ratios are based. For these the reader is referred to the books to which reference has been made. The logic upon which some of them is based is almost obvious; while in the case of others, the reasoning is more involved. Reference is made to these ratios here largely as a preface to other matters that follow.

273. Standard Ratios.—While there is little difficulty in setting up a ratio that will indicate almost any characteristic of the business, it is not so easy to set up a *standard* ratio by which to measure the result. In the case of the power plant discussed in the preceding, there is no difficulty in finding a standard by which to measure the ratio of kilowatt-hours to coal consumed, since here the operation is almost entirely mechanical and a standard ratio for best performance is not difficult to determine. In the case of the ratio $\frac{\text{current assets}}{\text{current liabilities}}$ judgment and experience appear to show that a value of 2 indicates a sound condition. Again for the ratio $\frac{\text{quick assets}}{\text{current liabilities}}$ a value of 1 is logical, since that value insures the ability to meet all liabilities at any time and through any emergency. No doubt other standards can be assigned by experience and judgment, to others of these ratios, that will hold true for any and all enterprises. However, all writers upon the topic have had difficulty in determining such standards for other ratios with any such degree of logic as pertains even to these three ratios just referred to.

A common method of securing standards of reference is to compile corresponding data from a large number of similar enterprises and from these to deduce *average* values that may be so used. The *U. S. Census Reports* and other such official compilations contain many data of this kind and both Alexander Wall[2] and J. H. Bliss[3] collected data of

[1] See also ALFORD, L. P. (Ed.), "Cost and Production Handbook," p. 169.

[2] WALL, A. H., "Balance-sheet Analysis," *Management and Administration*, November, 1924.

[3] BLISS, J. H., "Management Through Accounts."

this kind from an examination of many balance sheets. This method has been quite widely used for other purposes. Such data are by their very nature *averages* and, while such averages may have important uses, their use as a guide in any particular instance is attended with danger. This lies in the very fact that they are *averages* and may be made up of items that are very far apart. As Stephen Gilman, in discussing this matter, very aptly points out, the average of 11 and 13 is 12, and in this case 12 is somewhat representative of the data considered. But the average of 2 and 22 is also 12 and in this case the average is very remote from either of the quantities averaged and not at all representative.

The fallacy of thus averaging industrial data may be made clearer by considering the case of the power plant already alluded to. Power plants are of varying size and of widely varying efficiency measured by the ratio of pounds of coal per kilowatt-hour. In the largest and most efficient plants, as found in large cities, the coal burned per kilowatt-hour approaches one pound. But in districts where coal is cheap and where, consequently, it will not pay to install very efficient machinery this ratio may be as high as four. Similar conditions are found in many small and poorly maintained plants. An average of all the power plants of the country would, therefore, give a ratio much higher than the minimum obtained in high-grade plants. A knowledge of such an average, while interesting from some angles, would be entirely useless to the chief engineer of a large, efficient plant who was looking for comparative data to assist him in making his plant more profitable. What he really needs is information from plants *of the same size and character as his own.*

Again, the data that might be obtained from a small plant manufacturing a very high-class automobile in small numbers and of a necessity, therefore, asking a large profit per car would be utterly useless as a guide to a manufacturer producing a cheap car in large quantities against strenuous competition. And to average such data as a guide for automobile construction companies, in general, would be manifestly illogical.

Now, any given field of manufacturing is much more varied in character than either of those quoted above. Thus, to attempt to deduce average ratios from such fields as agricultural machinery, leather manufacturing, electrical machinery, etc., with their great spread both as to size and as to character, is obviously illogical.

Furthermore, averages of this sort must necessarily include many companies whose financial condition is unstable if not on the verge of disaster. The large proportion of industrial concerns that pay no dividends on common stock has already been noted, and there are always many companies that are about to go to the wall, sometimes ignorant of the reasons therefor. And again, there is often a reasonable doubt as to whether the balance sheet represents accurately the true state of the business. The true value of all "receivables" and of the merchandise inventory may or may not appear upon the balance sheet, depending upon the viewpoint of the management in compiling it.

Gilman, therefore, is quite right when he states that standard ratios of this kind are not feasible except where:

1. A large number of balance sheets taken at the same time are available.
2. The corporations furnishing the balance sheets are financially sound.
3. The corporations operate under similar geographic conditions.
4. The balance sheets are of recent date.
5. The deviations of the individual ratios from the average are not too great.
6. Accounting methods throughout the industry are substantially uniform.
7. The business policies which influence ratios are substantially uniform.
8. The products manufactured and sold are substantially similar.

That is to say, average ratios are meaningless unless the conditions under which they are formed are closely similar, a combination which as Mr. Gilman states is so rare as to be negligible. This is not to say that average ratios are not without their uses. Obviously, information of this kind from similar successful industrial plants should be of great use to the industrial manager even though they are suggestive only. But it is also clear that the wise manager will try to establish ratios based upon an analysis of his own business showing what he *must* do to make a profit and not be misled by blind reference to what someone else is doing that may or may not be applicable to his particular case.

An interesting and important example of the blind use of industrial ratios was the practice of gaging the efficiency of the shop management by the ratio $\frac{\text{indirect labor}}{\text{direct labor}}$. For many years this ratio was almost a sacred number which, if it exceeded some arbitrary chosen value, was an index of bad management. This idea had its origin naturally in the old idea that only those who actually produced constituted *productive labor* and all others no matter how helpful they might be were *nonproductive*. Happily, these terms have largely disappeared. When industry was a matter of handicraft or of use of simple machines it was true that the extravagant use of "helpers," clerks, etc., had to be carefully watched; in fact, this still holds true in all industry today. But it will be remembered that any extension of division of labor or of transfer of skill is necessarily accompanied by coordinative influences in the form of clerical help or skilled supervision which by nature is indirect labor. Functional foremanship as visualized by Taylor involved a great increase in indirect labor with a greater proportional increase in production. And so long as the law of diminishing returns is not transgressed this extension of indirect labor is justified. It has always been difficult for managers of the old school to appreciate the significance of these relations.

Consider, for instance, the case where, say, 20 men are producing a certain article on standard lathes. Their wages are all of the direct-labor class. If, now, this work is transferred to the automatic-lathe department and the old lathes sold, all direct labor on this work disappears and is replaced by the indirect labor of the supervising experts in the automatic department. For, in general, the services of such experts cannot be assigned to particular machines, but is charged off as indirect labor. Here, then, the abolition of all direct labor and an increase in the indirect labor are accompanied by a lowering of productive costs. Any and all ratios that are used as criteria of efficiency should be carefully examined to make sure they apply to the case in hand.

Several efforts have been made to develop ratios that would give intelligent comparisons between industrial data. Brief reference only can be given to the most important of them. Joseph W. Roe presented one of the first of these studies for measuring the efficiency of plant operation. It will be found in the Transactions of the American Society of Mechanical Engineers, Vol. 45, p. 825. Roe's ratios are based upon the standard accounting data available in any well-managed plant.

This was followed in 1929 by a paper presented before the same society by Messrs. L. P. Alford and J. E. Hannum (Vols. 51, 52) in which it is proposed to measure industrial effectiveness in terms of *man hours.* The unit proposed is 1,000 man hours or a **kilo-man hour** (abbreviated to **kmh** for convenience). The authors of this notable study point out that the *kmh* is useful not only in measuring efficiency in a given plant, but is equally reliable for measuring the relative efficiency of similar or dissimilar industries. While no doubt the plan has limitations, it presents a new idea in industrial measurement. Labor turnover, discussed in Chap. XXIV, is a measure of the stability of the working force.

274. Forecasting and Budgeting.—One of the most important and promising developments in the field of management is the growth of efforts to *measure in advance* the expenditures and costs of industrial operations through **forecasting, budgetary control, standard costs,** and similar devices. Many of the factors involved in budgetary control, standard costs, etc., such as the quantity to be manufactured, the probable cost of raw material, and other items, depend upon conditions in the field of general business that are usually not very well known. It was quite natural, therefore, that efforts should be made to apply logical methods of analysis to the conditions of the business world with the hope of forecasting these factors upon which the successful administration of productive processes depends.

There are two general methods by which it may be attempted to forecast future business possibilities, namely,

1. By referring to a curve or curves that forecast the business cycle on the theory that the patterns of such curves repeat themselves.

2. By gathering sales statistics for a single enterprise or group of enterprises of similar character and charting a manufacturing budget upon such information.

A number of organized agencies have been formed for forecasting business conditions and several are now in existence. One of the most scientific of these attempts was that made by the Harvard Committee on Economic Research, which published for some years in its *Weekly Letter* (now discontinued) three **index curves,**[1] namely Curve **A—speculation;** Curve **B—Business;** and Curve **C—Money.** Curve A is based upon New York bank debits and industrial stock prices; Curve B, upon bank debits outside of New York City and upon commodity prices; and Curve C upon the value of commercial notes. Economic studies such as these appear to indicate that business conditions run in "cycles" that are periodic in character. While this is a somewhat controversial assump-

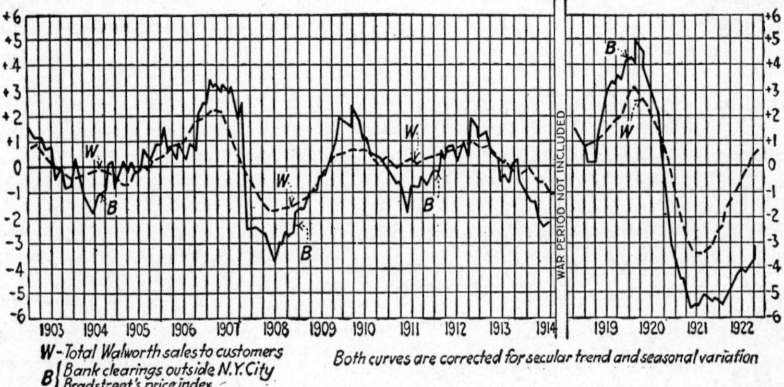

Fig. 57.—(*Reproducd by courtesy of Harvard University Committee on Economic Research.*)

tion, there appears to be considerable truth in it. If it is basically sound it would appear as though each industry could discover similar index curves that would synchronize, more or less, with the Harvard or other similar curves of general tendencies, and thus serve as a means of predicting future manufacturing policies. Corroborative evidence that these assumptions are true is difficult to obtain; the best evidence of the character known to the writer being that presented by Howard Coonley[2] of the Walworth Manufacturing Company. Mr. Coonley, in investigating this matter for his company, found that the curve of sales of the company corresponded quite closely to Curve B of the Harvard Committee. Figure 57 shows[3] these curves and their marked coincidence. With this as a basis Mr. Coonley's company was able to forecast production and to make an operating budget to correspond with considerable accuracy. Thus he states that:

> Our actual sales came within 0.5 per cent of our estimate. Cumulatively the first 6 months were 8 per cent in excess of the estimate; the first 9 months were

[1] For a full discussion see *Weekly Letter*, May 19, 1923.

[2] See "Scientific Management Since Taylor," p. 141; and also a series of articles by Mr. Barber in *Management and Administration*, October, 1923.

[3] Reproduced by permission from "Scientific Management Since Taylor."

4.3 per cent, but the full year's figures were so close to the estimate as to be a coincidence. We do not expect again to equal this particular record.

It is not to be expected that such accurate results can be obtained by industry in general even with careful compilation of statistics. Henry Dennison,[1] reporting a survey of forecasts made in 1921 to 1927, states:

> In 500 forecasts of general prices just over one-half were found correct, just one-quarter were incorrect, and about one-fifth negative, that is to say neither harmful nor helpful in their results. The ratio of helpful to injurious predictions was 18 to 10. In 433 forecasts concerning the volume of general business nearly two-thirds were correct, one-sixth incorrect, and one-sixth negative. The ratio here of the helpful to the injurious was 37 to 10. Five hundred forecasts on individual prices were tested. As with the predictions of general prices these ranged a little better than one-half correct, a little better than one-quarter incorrect, and one-fifth negative.

This is not a highly encouraging record but, as Mr. Dennison states,

> Exactness in prediction can hardly be expected as yet, though careful forecasting should have chances in its favor over random guessing, just as weather forecasting has.

If a forecast such as that described in the foregoing can be made, it is obvious that the expenditures of the plant can be budgeted with some assurance. Budgeting has long been in use and in enterprises whose principal function it is to *disburse* money, such as educational, governmental, and eleemosynary institutions, a budget is a prime essential to successful management. Budgeting of the expenditures of profit-making establishments is a more recent development. Budgetary control in its essence consists of the formulation of a policy for the future and then by analysis of the past to lay out a financial program that will bring this policy to a successful conclusion. Obviously, the *degree* to which it is possible to budget future operations will vary widely but there are few enterprises that cannot use the principle to some degree with great advantage.

Four principal steps are necessary in establishing and operating a budget, namely:

1. The establishment of a master policy for a fixed period of future time.

2. A statement of this policy to department heads with a request for estimates of expenditures for the time assigned. This request should be accompanied by all information, past and present, that will aid the department head in making an intelligent estimate.

3. The coordination of these departmental estimates into a master budget by the adjustment of deviations from normal and the addition of

[1] Recent Economic Changes, Vol. II, p. 505.

such margins and allowances as managerial judgment and experience may dictate.

4. Insuring that the budget is carried out by systematic periodic checking and the issuance of periodic reports to departmental heads. This later necessarily calls for a good accounting system and cost-finding methods.

The degree to which the policy of the future can be determined governs the degree to which budgeting control can be made effective more completely perhaps than does any other factor. In the case of governmental and institutional management, these policies can be determined with some accuracy. Thus, the state or city can decide in advance just how much shall be spent for administration, roads, buildings, etc.; the hospital can decide just how many patients it can house; the university can dictate just how many students it will admit. In such cases, budgets can be laid out with some accuracy and administered successfully. Many such budgets have long been in use.

The case of the manufacturing plant is somewhat different and varies all the way from mass-production plants with a fairly well-defined market to those that do a contract business that may vary widely in volume and character. In many well-established businesses, however, sales estimates can be made that will serve as a basis for budgeting. It may be noted in passing that the necessity or desirability of establishing some sales policy for the future has given rise to some interesting efforts to forecast future business conditions by using the trend of certain market indexes as a guide. Industrial statistics of this character appear to be gaining in importance, and the manager who is interested in budgeting must necessarily inform himself concerning these efforts. If any future policy as to the volume and character of product can be established, it is possible for the manager to budget some part, at least, of his expenditures.

It will be obvious that the particular activities that are to be subjected to budgetary control will depend upon the business and the judgment of the executive as to the relative influence the several activities may have upon the success of the business. The control may range from simple allocation of departmental expense to control of all important factors. In any case, the experience of the past should logically be considered in estimating the future, and here again arises the problem of ratios and trends.

Harold V. Coes,[1] who has written very clearly upon this topic, states:

> There is no set of standard ratios expressing the various fundamental relationships between expenses and sales, manufacturing expense and cost of sales, etc. These must be determined for each individual business from a study of

[1] See *Trans. Am. Soc. Mech. Eng.*, Management Division, p. 29, January–April, 1928.

past records, and then checked against such ratios for the industry, or important units in the industry, as can be obtained. The application of these previously determined ratios, then, to the various items of expense in the various divisions of the business will constitute the budgeted expense items.

It will be noted that this statement harmonizes with the conclusions drawn in Art. 273 concerning general financial ratios. Coes also lists

TABLE 18.—FUNDAMENTAL OPERATING RATIOS

Ratios	Years					Maximum or minimum per cent
	1922	1923	1924	1925	1926	
$\frac{\text{Cost of sales}}{\text{Net sales}}$	79.9	79.2	78.1	77.8	80.1	75
$\frac{\text{Manufacturing expense (burden)}}{\text{Net production}}$	29.4	24.0	26.8	26.1	23.5	22
$\frac{\text{Manufacturing expense}}{\text{Net sales}}$	24.5	22.0	24.3	24.7	20.2	20
$\frac{\text{Raw material inventory}}{\text{Net production}}$	40.1	42.0	41.9	39.8	38.9	35
$\frac{\text{Process inventory}}{\text{Net production}}$	30.1	32.0	31.0	29.9	29.2	26
$\frac{\text{Direct material}}{\text{Net sales}}$	37.5	35.2	37.2	38.5	39.1	35
$\frac{\text{Direct labor}}{\text{Net sales}}$	23.4	22.8	20.9	21.7	22.0	20
$\frac{\text{Indirect labor}}{\text{Direct labor}}$	47.0	46.5	46.1	45.8	45.2	40
$\frac{\text{Finished-goods inventory}}{\text{Net sales}}$	10.8	10.4	10.1	10.5	10.0	10
$\frac{\text{Total inventory}}{\text{Net sales}}$	24.3	24.0	23.8	24.2	23.0	20
$\frac{\text{Fixed expense}}{\text{Total manufacturing expense}}$	28.1	28.3	27.9	27.2	27.5	25
$\frac{\text{Working capital}}{\text{Net sales}}$	35.1	34.8	35.5	34.2	33.1	30
$\frac{\text{Gross profit}}{\text{Net sales}}$	21.1	20.9	21.9	22.2	19.9	25
$\frac{\text{Selling expense}}{\text{Net sales}}$	10.9	11.0	11.4	12.2	12.5	11
$\frac{\text{Net profit}}{\text{Net sales}}$	4.3	4.7	5.1	5.5	3.9	5

the controlling ratios shown in Table 18 with an illustration of the trend of ratios over five years and a deduced maximum or minimum ratio as may be judged best for budgeting purposes. If such statistical data are not available, estimates must be made by departmental heads based upon such experience as may be available. All of the items shown in Table 18 are usually available where a good cost-accounting system is in operation. Any detailed discussion of the methods of making departmental estimates for budgeting purposes is beyond the limits of this discussion.

A budget, like all coordinative mechanisms, is not automatic in its operation, nor can it in any way take the place of intelligent superintendence. It will be effective largely as the entire group of administrative heads become interested in it and are enthusiastic in making it operative. Care should be taken that periodic statements are issued to each officer interested, showing expenditures to date and balance available. Much of the excess and variation in expense is due to lack of watchfulness, and it is surprising how quickly and effectively a budget system will remedy some of these wastes.

A budget, is, of course, an *estimated* course of procedure. It may, and often does, occur that changes in operating conditions may make it necessary to revise the budget. In doing so, care should be exercised that this is not done in such a drastic manner that the work of production will suffer through unnecessary penuriousness.

A **flexible budget,** that is, one that can be readily modified to meet changes in the market, can always be operated where arrangements have been made to obtain frequent and prompt information on such changes. The General Motors Corporation[1] is reported to operate under such a plan. Obviously small enterprises should have no trouble in keeping the budget flexible.

References

Alford, L. P. (Ed.): "Cost and Production Handbook."
Dennison, Henry S.: "Recent Economic Changes," Vol. II, p. 503.
Gilman, Stephen: "Analyzing Financial Statements."
Kinsey, J. O.: "Budgetary Control."
Williams, John H.: "The Flexible Budget."

[1] Gilman, Stephen, "Analyzing Financial Statements," p. 421.

CHAPTER XXIII

THE MECHANIZATION OF INDUSTRY

275. Changes in the Industrial Picture.—It would appear to be unnecessary to call attention to the fact that industry has changed tremendously during the last half century. Yet it is safe to say that few have given serious thought to the exact character of these changes, though most people have been impressed with some of the manifestations of modern methods and all have been affected to some degree economically by them. Some of these changes are familiar to all.

First, there is the growth in the *size* of industrial plants that has been referred to in Chap. IV, which should be reviewed at this time. Not only have industrial plants grown from small beginnings to immense proportions, but it is no longer unusual to see very large industrial plants built and fully equipped before any production is started. In many cases, the organization of the personnel and the procedure and system for the conduct of the business are all planned in advance of productive operations.

Again, the *character* of industry has changed very materially. A few industries, such as carriage making, harness making, blacksmithing, etc., have either disappeared or have shrunk to small proportions as compared to former days. Many of the industries that survive under their old names have been greatly changed internally. Thus, consider the men's clothing industry. The U. S. Census of 1900 lists 28,014 establishments making men's clothes, employing 191,043 persons, with an output valued at over $415,000,000. The Census of 1925 lists only 4,000 such establishments employing only 175,332 persons, but with an output valued at $1,087,238,000, which, making due allowance for the difference in the value of the dollar, represents a very large gain in value of output per worker. In 1935 there were 1,797 establishments listed, employing 183,000 persons, and the output had fallen to $503,819,000, owing no doubt to the depression. Again, in 1900 there were 23,560 *custom* shoemaking establishments, employing 9,689 persons, as compared to 1,900 *factories*, so called, employing 143,000 persons. In 1925 there were only 1,460 shoemaking establishments, but they employed 206,922 persons and their output was valued at $925,383,422. In 1935 there were 1,024 establishments, employing 202,113 persons, with an output valued at $643,872,000. In other words, these industries have been completely changed from handicraft to machine production, with corresponding changes in the workers involved. Practically all of the industries that have survived under old names have been affected more or less in this manner. The Census of 1900 was the last to recognize handicraft factories, as such. It is true, of course, that many small custom tailor shops, shoemaking shops, blacksmith shops, etc., still survive, but they do so by serving small special needs. The volume of their output is negligible compared with that of factories in the same line.

Considering industry as a whole, the results are equally significant. In 1900 the value of the output per worker for industry as a whole was about $1,600. In 1919 this ratio had risen to about $7,500 but in 1935 it had fallen to $6,200. Again making allowance for the difference in the value of the dollar, this is a great gain which can be attributed only to improved methods.

Another significant change has been the marked increase in capital investment per worker. The Biennial Census for 1925 gives the investment per worker in 1849 as about $560. By 1919, this ratio had risen steadily to nearly $5,000, the yearly increase in capital being always greater in proportion than that of the workers employed. These data are not available for 1935. That is, the industrial worker is being separated farther and farther from the possibilities of personal ownership of the tools of industry, and is becoming increasingly dependent upon capital and management for the opportunity to earn a livelihood. It is still possible, of course, for a handicraftsman to establish himself in a small way in such personal services as shoe repairing, clothes cleaning and repairing, etc., and if he can obtain possession of some new product that is marketable, and particularly if it is patentable, he may still begin in a small way. But competition in established lines of product is, in general, beyond his financial means. For that matter, large industry, in general, is beyond the financial means of the individual, mass financing through stocks and bonds being necessary for all large enterprises. It has already been noted that over 15,000,000 people in the United States own stock or bonds in commercial or industrial enterprises.

In addition to this influence due to the rising cost of equipment, a similar tendency is appearing in the increased use of power. From 1914 to 1925, the horse power per industrial worker increased from 3.3 to 4.3, and it is common knowledge that this ratio is increasing. The growth in *total* horse power in the United States is also worthy of note. Data are lacking in the Census of 1900 as to the total horse power in use at that time, but the Census of 1914 shows the total horse power in use in *manufacturing* as 22,264,343, and this was increased by 1925 to 35,772,628. The *total* prime-mover capacity in use in the United States is in the neighborhood of 1,250,000,000 horse power.[1] It is estimated that this is about four times as great as that of Great Britain or Germany and ten times as great as that of France. More significant still is the fact that the per capita wealth of the United States bears the same ratio to the per capita wealth of Great Britain that the per capita horse power here does to the per capita horse power there—a relation that might naturally be expected.

[1] Potter, A. A., "Technological Trends and Their Social Implications."

It should be a natural result of the extended use of *time-saving* and *labor-saving* machinery.

The growth in the size of central-station machinery should also be noted. The great Corliss engine built for the Centennial Exposition in Philadelphia in 1876, which was considered to be an epoch-making machine, was of 1,400 horse power. The first large turbogenerator built by the General Electric Company, about 1900, was of 5,000-kilowatt capacity. Today, single units of 50,000-kilowatt capacity are common, combined units of 100,000 not unusual, and one of 208,000-kilowatt capacity has been constructed. A survey of our public utilities in the *Blakemore Analytical Reports*, dated December 20, 1922, gives the total horse power of prime movers in this industry in this country as 3,000,000 in 1902; 12,000,000 in 1912; 24,000,000 in 1922 and a prospective 30,000,000 in 1930. In 1935 it was estimated to be 32,670,000. No better index of the increased use of power both in home and factory could be had, and these figures are most impressive.

Two other developments should be mentioned that have profoundly affected modern industry, namely, transportation and communication. In both of these fields of development the progress has been rapid both as to size and extent of equipment and as to rapidity of performance. Both land and marine transportation have greatly accelerated exchange of goods nationally and internationally and are tending more and more in this country to equalize the economic advantages formerly enjoyed by one section of the country as compared to others, with a consequent tendency for industry to migrate to new centers and for new competing centers to develop in new territory. Modern methods of communication have at the same time eliminated time and space so far as this field is concerned. The net result of the development of these fields has been to *accelerate* greatly the entire field of commerce and manufacturing. The United States is much smaller economically than it was 50 years ago and continues to shrink so far as these particulars are concerned.

Lastly, the phenomenon of new industries and the new callings connected therewith are worthy of more than passing notice, for in the character of the productive methods by which these industries have been built is found the answer to some of the most difficult modern industrial problems. Some of these new callings, like the automobile and airplane plants are built upon and are extensions of old trades and callings. Others, like the electrical industries, while resting primarily upon old trades and callings, have developed many ramifications and adaptations of these old trades into what are practically new callings. Still others, while having their genesis in chemical processes, must necessarily be constructed through the use of the old mechanic arts. All of them have been affected by the modern productive methods that have been discussed. The magnitude of some of these new industries is most impressive. A few data concerning them will be found in Art. 27, which should be read at this point.

It should be particularly noted that a new industry producing a new product that tends to supplant an old product does not necessarily eliminate the old industry. The new product may find an enlarged field, leaving the old product to do the same and perhaps hold part of the old field. The telephone, for instance, did not entirely supplant the telegraph, nor will the radio entirely supplant either of them. The electric light did not eliminate gas producers, nor has oil displaced coal. The motor truck and autobus, in a similar way, will find their place in transportation, but they are not likely to eliminate railroads. By similar reasoning, synthetic products, such as rayon, probably will not displace cotton and linen, but will make a place for themselves in our industrial economy. We shall, no doubt, witness the development of many new synthetic products to supply the lack of natural animal and vegetable products as the supply of these products diminishes, and we may expect to see many new products brought forth either to satisfy new needs or to cater to our comfort or amusement.

Brief reflection will show, therefore, that there is a great tendency toward what has been aptly called the **mechanization of industry.** By this is meant the doing of the world's work by power-driven machinery, particularly by automatic and semiautomatic machinery, instead of by the use of handicraft methods aided by man power and animal power. While the mechanization of industry has no doubt greatly increased man's productive powers, it has at the same time affected the human element in industry in such a manner as to give rise to some apprehensions as to the resultant good of thus changing industrial methods.

These changed manufacturing methods are to a large degree applications of transfer of skill and, as explained fully in Chap. III, all such applications are accompanied to some degree by one or all of four results, namely:

1. Further separation of the worker from the ownership of the tools of industry.
2. Degradation of labor.
3. Extension of the field of labor.
4. Elevation of labor.

The first of these will be even more evident from the discussion of the preceding paragraphs and the discussion in Chap. III should be reread in connection with what follows. The progress of modern manufacturing has been accompanied by continual changes of this character. New processes and improved machinery have been and are now constantly reducing the amount of skill required in old occupations, even to the extent of eliminating some callings. In some cases the displaced workers have found occupation elsewhere, while in other cases much real suffering has resulted. In a few industries, complete readjustment has been

PLATE IX.—Main assembly floor of A. O. Smith Corporation's automatic plant for manufacturing automobile frames. In parallel lines the left-hand and right-hand side bars of the frames and the several cross bars come forward from the far end of the floor where they are formed automatically from sheet steel. On the way they receive various machining operations automatically at the near end. These parts are assembled and riveted together by the automatic riveting machine in the foreground.

accomplished, as in callings such as shoemaking, textiles, clothing and others, which, barring revolutionary inventions, is not likely to be disturbed. But in other lines of work, invention and manufacturing progress are still active and demotion of the worker is still in progress.

As an offset to this demotion of the skilled worker, there appears the extension of the field of industry to persons of lesser skill. The new industrial methods have enabled many thousands of comparatively unskilled persons to take important parts in many industrial fields formerly closed to them. Today, in nearly every large manufacturing industry, the unskilled or semiskilled labor greatly outnumbers the skilled workers, and products of great accuracy are produced by such organizations. The principle of the extension of the field of labor is a very broad one. As more and more skill has been transferred to hand and machine tools, it has become increasingly easy for unskilled men and women to take part in what were formerly highly skilled industries. The *actual* production of automobiles, watches, typewriters, shoes, etc., is conducted very largely by semiskilled labor. The tremendous absorbing power of American industry rests largely upon the principle of the extension of labor through the use of semiautomatic machinery, and is one of the greatest forces that underlie Americanization of the foreign worker. Brief consideration of the many new industries that owe their existence to science and invention should convince the most skeptical of the truth of these statements.

As an illustration of a highly developed case of mechanization of industry, consider the plant of the A. O. Smith Corporation of Milwaukee, shown in Plate IX, for manufacturing automobile frames. It is the largest and most highly developed example of a power-driven automatic manufacturing plant yet constructed and is, in effect, a large automatic machine. This plant literally takes steel plates and turns them into automobile frames automatically. Space permits of mention of only a few details. Plate IX shows the main machine floor looking toward the end where the plates are received. At that end the plates are cut and pressed automatically into the several component parts of an automobile frame. They are carried through several operations, finally arriving at the end of the shop nearest the observer. Here a machine picks up the side-bar subassemblies and crossbars, clamps them together, and drives the rivets into place automatically. This automatic riveting device can be plainly seen at the end of the picture nearest the observer. The frames can be seen in the several "stations" that they occupy successively, and to which they are moved periodically and automatically. Each of these stations is fitted with riveting heads which can be identified by their circular form. Rivets are fed by compressed air to these heads. When the frame is in place in any given station, the rivets are shot into place by compressed air, the riveting heads swing into operating position, "drive" the rivet, and swing back into "idle" position—all automatically.

It is difficult to give anything but a vague description of this great automatic plant; it must be seen to be appreciated. But some of the data concerning it may help to visualize its operating efficiency. The plant uses 1,000,000 pounds of steel every 24 hours of operation, which it turns into 7,000 automobile frames. The plant performs 4,000,000 automatic operations daily, all of which must be accurately done. It takes 40 minutes to manufacture a frame and the plant can be changed from one style of frame to another in from 6 to 8 hours. The entire plant is electrically operated, requiring 2,000 horse power.

Now, while this plant is highly interesting as a piece of manufacturing machinery, it is doubly so when the human element is considered. To make the same number of frames with standard machinery and ordinary methods would require over 1,000 men. The automatic plant employs only 200 men and, naturally, they do not need to be as skillful as the worker in the simpler plant so far as actually attending the machinery is concerned. Of course, such a plant requires the services of a number of skilled engineers, tool makers, and repair men. But the economic gain, so far as men is concerned, is obvious. While the A. O. Smith plant is a somewhat extreme case of automatic production it is, nevertheless, typical of the tendency of modern industrial methods where quantity production is practiced, and it illustrates clearly the displacement of labor by transfer of skill. Whether this great automatic machine transgresses the law of diminishing returns remains to be seen.

Consider, on the other hand, the automobile industry itself. Here is a gigantic business built up in a few years, employing many thousands of workers directly and many more thousands indirectly, supplying materials and accessories to the factories proper. The workers in these great factories can for the most part engage in this form of production only because of the mechanization of industry.

Or consider again the plant of the American Telephone and Telegraph Company, at Kearney, New Jersey. This plant, designed especially for the purpose, recruited in a brief time 12,000 workers and proceeded to make telephone apparatus. Now, in all probability a very small portion of these workers had ever seen the inside of a telephone or worked at that sort of work. Yet because of these new methods, they can engage in the work with little or no trouble. It should also be especially noted that this plant and the A. O. Smith plant did not grow from small beginnings, but were designed and built as entirely new enterprises, all methods and processes being designed and built before production started.

Modern industry then develops in two principal ways: (1) by the growth and expansion of old industries, and (2) by the development of entirely new industries producing new products. The old industries tend constantly to change in character through the use of improved and new methods and an extension of division of labor. They tend to partake less of handicraft and to employ more transfer of skill. As a consequence, the output per man constantly increases and this, combined with the changes due to the introduction of time-saving apparatus, tends to **technological unemployment** without reference to extremes of good or bad times. Some of the workers thus displaced find employment in other old industries and many are absorbed by the growth of new industries. The extent of this unemployment so far as skilled workers are concerned is hard to gage and data are lacking. Periodically the fear is expressed that the tendency for unemployment from these causes is increasing. Quite recently many articles to this effect have appeared in the press. As a matter of fact, this fear is as old as the present industrial system and from the foregoing (see also Chap. III), industrial progress under modern methods is not possible without degradation of labor and extension of the field of labor.

The Census of 1900 comments upon these tendencies as follows.

> A factor that has had a real tendency to lower the actual earnings of the wage-earner in many industries is the displacement of the skilled operator by machinery which permits the substitution of a comparatively unskilled machine hand. This tendency is noticeable in many lines of industry. Its effect are twofold: to reduce the number of employees producing the same or an increased quantity of product and, hence, to lower the total wages of the group; and to reduce the average rate of wages because of the lower degree of skill required. The effect of the introduction and improvement of machinery upon the condition of the skilled artisan is an economic question of the greatest importance. . . . In the boot and shoe industry an increase of 18.3 per cent in value of products resulted from an increase of 22.2 per cent in value of machinery and tools used with only 6.9 per cent increase in number of wage-earners and an apparent decrease of 2.5 per cent in wages paid.

While this is a true picture of the *primary* effects of the application of modern methods, it gives only a part of the picture. It ignores the great reduction of cost of the product and also ignores the expansion of the shoemaking industry by extension of the field. Subsequent Census Reports do not corroborate the doubts expressed in the Census of 1900. That Census lists the number of workers in the shoe industry, both handicraft and factory, as 153,620, and gives their annual earnings as $63,304,-244, or about $415 per annum per person. In the Census of 1925, the number of workers in this industry is listed as 206,922, with annual earnings of $225,788,000, or about $1,090 per person. In 1935 this industry employed 202,113 persons, with total annual earnings of $172,-349,000, or $852 per person. The purchasing power of the dollar in 1925 was about 66 per cent of that of 1914 and 53 per cent of that of 1900, but even making allowance for this shrinkage in purchasing power, there has been a considerable gain in real wages since that time.

Similar data are found for the printing industry. The Census of 1900 lists the number of workers in this industry as 162,992, with earnings of $84,249,963, or about $517 per person per annum. The Census of 1925 gives 251,276 persons thus employed with earnings of $438,832,974, or $1,746 per person per annum. In 1935 this industry employed 245,376 persons, with total annual earnings of $428,778,000, or $1,790 per person. Again making due allowance for the depreciation of the dollar, the gain in real wages is considerable. Furthermore, comparisons such as those quoted from the Census of 1900 do not take into account the increased employment due to the building of machinery for these industries. In 1925 the value of the printing machinery produced in the United States was estimated at $69,216,683, and the value of the shoemaking machinery was appraised at $11,769,137. It should be remembered also that each of these industries, like the automotive industry, has many ramifications that would be difficult to follow but all giving employment to workers. The Census reports furthermore indicate that the percentage of the total population "gainfully employed" in manufacturing industries has not been materially altered, which must have been the case if the fears expressed by the Census Report[1] just quoted had been realized.

It will be clear, however, that as industry is mechanized and the output of the worker progressively increased, old industries must be expanded and new ones developed, or else the working hours must be reduced, if unemployment due to these modern methods is to be avoided. In passing, it should be noted that the hope for new industries lies in industrial research—a point that was fully stressed by President Hoover during his presidency and has been emphasized by other farseeing industrial leaders. Particularly, we shall need more industries that produce goods of economic value rather than those that cater solely to our amusement. There will be no lack of the latter in any case. The automobile and the radio to a certain degree fulfill both functions, and it should be remembered that most of the new industries tend to "pay their way." They may, like the automobile and radio, start out almost solely as amusements, but in a short time commercial uses are found for them and they become real factors in our economic life. If it were not for this feature of many new industries, the increase in manufactured products would soon slow up and unemployment become a greater problem than it ever has been. It is very difficult at any time to draw a distinction between necessities and luxuries. What is a luxury to one is a necessity to another. The automobile is a luxury to many but a necessity to the doctor and many others. No doubt there is a large number of products that have little or no economic or esthetic values that are forced upon the public by so-called "high-pressure" salesmen's methods. The

[1] See ALLEN, R. I., "Science Versus Unemployment," *Science*, May 23, 1939.

extension of installment purchasing also has had a great influence upon the sales of both luxuries and necessities.

Lastly, one is led naturally to speculate as to the economic level we may attain with our present prospects of industrial growth and disregarding any possibility of a radical advance in manufacturing principles, such as came in through the Industrial Revolution. It is axiomatic that to *have* the good things of life we must *produce* them and, theoretically, at least, there can be no over-production so long as people are in want and economic desires remain unsatisfied. The two great problems therefore are *production* of economic goods and intelligent *distribution* of the same. On the side of production, great gains can still be made in three particulars. First, there can be a wider application of modern methods of production. There is a wide difference between highly developed enterprises such as the best examples of automobile production, the highest type of steel plants, etc., and the poorest and least efficient manufacturing plants of the country, so far as equipment and production processes are concerned. An equally wide variation exists between the best type of management and the poorest type. A study from this angle of the manufacturing plants that go into bankruptcy would be most enlightening. Great gain can also be made by reducing industrial waste. We are, as a people, most wasteful, both individually and as a nation. The *Report*[1] of the Committee on Waste of the American Engineering Council estimates that American management is responsible for 50 per cent of our industrial waste, and this estimate is probably not far wrong. Anyone well acquainted with industry will testify to the possibility of great economic gains through the use of better equipment and better management.

And if marked gains are made they will most likely come because of wider recognition of these shortcomings. It has already been noted that in many highly developed instances of modern production, the old law of diminishing returns has already become effective to some degree and that there are definite limitations to the use of transfer of skill and division of labor. It may be expected, therefore, that as industry, as a whole, is made more efficient the rate of gain measured either in terms of output per worker or output per dollar of invested capital will decrease, unless some new and radical methods of production come into being, which at present appears to be unlikely. In this regard, it is interesting to notice that the output per dollar of investment has been decreasing as far as Census reports give such information. This ratio since 1850 has been as follows: 1850, 2; 1860, 1.87; 1870, 2; 1880, 1.85; 1890, 1.44; 1900, 1.43; 1919, 1.39; and in 1929 the ratio of the value of products of all *corporations* to their combined assets was .92 (see also Art. 37). It should be remembered, of course, that the primary values on which these ratios are

[1] See "Waste in Industry," p. 9.

based are to a large extent estimates. But it is significant, at least, that in the face of such a great gain in production, not only quantitatively as a whole but also a great gain per worker, this ratio should show a steady decrease. It may be noted in passing that industrial and commercial failures may not necessarily be unmitigated calamities. It may be that this is the only way in which the incompetent manager can be eliminated. It is to be regretted that there is not some way of preventing the obviously incompetent from obtaining the credit which results in financial troubles for others, not only when he fails, but while he is in business and possibly selling at prices that are ruinous to himself and his competitors.

Productive gains, then, appear to be possible through more modern equipment, better management, and the elimination of industrial waste, and progress is undoubtedly being made along these lines in many progressive plants and even in some industries as a whole. Great possibilities still exist in the field of production, and it would appear that the *science* of production is well advanced. But production cannot exist without distribution, and our knowledge of this side of our industrial economy appears to lag far behind. This is not to be wondered at, for distribution is much more complex than production, involving both national and international relations. Disregarding all international aspects of the matter, there is much to be learned concerning the financing of our industrial enterprises and the financial relations that should exist between the employer, the employee, and the purchasing public. Thus, it has been impressed upon us most fully of late that those who produce are also purchasers and, obviously, the more they have to purchase with, the more they will produce. We need more information, therefore, as to the flow of money from the employer to the employee through wages and back to the employer through purchases. Again, as stated, it is estimated that 15,000,000 or more workers in the United States own industrial securities of some kind, and if this tendency continues at the present rate the ownership of industry may assume a different aspect. Most interesting still is the phenomenon of deferred-payment purchasing on the part of the populace to the extent of $5,000,000,000 or more. Of course, installment purchasing of land, homes, and even diamonds and other goods of somewhat *permanent* value has long been in vogue. But the wholesale purchasing of automobiles, radios, refrigerators, and a large number of other *short-lived* products is comparatively new and raises a number of new economic questions that have a direct bearing upon the extension of mass production. Another equally important group of problems in distribution is found in the field of agriculture. Here again, production apparently is greater than consumption, and yet food is not cheap nor the farmer prosperous. It would appear that any great advance in production and any consequently marked rise in the economic status of the people as a whole must wait upon a more intelligent solution of the problem of distribution. Much study is being given to this problem by the ablest economists of this country, but at this writing there is no tangible evidence of any great advance in the science of distribution. It is by far the most important of all industrial problems and constitutes a study of first magnitude for the economist, the engineer, and the statesman.

276. Responsibility.—Unemployment, of course, is due to causes other than mechanization of industry. Dull times, business failures, overproduction, changes in style, supersedure of old products by new ones, and many other minor influences are all factors in this problem. It has been only of recent years that any serious study has been made of these causes with a view of ameliorating the seriousness of the problem. It should be noted, however, that many suggestions advocate national, state, or municipal aid by regulating the time and manner of expending funds upon public improvements. Thus, it is urged that public buildings, roads, harbors, etc., should be constructed as far as possible in dull times so as to straighten out the unemployment curve. The gigantic experiment along these lines now being conducted by the federal government should throw much light on the efficacy of such methods.

The merits of these many and wise suggestions are not here under discussion, but it is desirable to note that there is a rising consciousness that unemployment is a matter of public concern. This of itself is a recognition that we are living in a new industrial era. Under the handicraft system of a century and a half ago, the worker could be something of a self-sustaining economic unit with the tools of industry accessible to him. As has been noted in the preceding pages, this is no longer true. The worker, and for that matter the employer also, is closely "geared," so to speak, into the great modern industrial machine. If he is thrown out of gear it may be, and often is, difficult for him to get into contact again. The public, in general, has been greatly benefited by these new methods and processes and logically, therefore, it should be responsible for the cost of these gains.

This does not in any way absolve the individual employer from doing all he can within his own sphere of influence to ameliorate these difficulties, if for no other reason than for humanity's sake. But it is fairly clear that individual efforts on the part of the employer, be he ever so kindly and fair minded, are not sufficient to solve this problem. It is a problem for economists and statesmen as well, since it affects the entire community as a whole, and for that reason most of the efforts along this line have socializing tendencies. The time has probably arrived when the economic *gains* resulting from new inventions must be more carefully weighed against the probable resulting economic *distress*. The rapid introduction of a mechanical cotton picker or of a synthetic fiber that would displace cotton would work drastic hardships upon a colored population already on a low subsistence level. Possibly we should regulate the *rapidity* with which major inventions are permitted to disturb the economic balance until some of the complexities of the industrial system are better understood. State employment bureaus, old-age pension systems, workmens' compensation insurance against injury, national safety campaigns, and other similar efforts on the part of the community, the state, and the nation, all indicate the growing dependence of the worker upon organized industry and the decline of economic independence based upon the ownership of tools and equipment. Undoubtedly, our social system is being modified by the new industrial methods and it is to be hoped that wise industrial and political leadership will keep us from the rocks of paternalism, on the one hand, and the whirlpool of communism, on the other.

CHAPTER XXIV

INDUSTRIAL RELATIONS

CORRECTIVE INFLUENCES

277. Introductory.—It will be clear that the introduction of such refined and far-reaching industrial changes as are discussed in the foregoing chapters would necessarily be accompanied by changes in the worker's industrial status and consequently in his social environment. These changes, as has been noted, are not always to his advantage, and where such a danger threatens it is only natural that corrective influences should make themselves felt. Some of these corrective measures are revivals of old movements that had disappeared because of lack of economic necessity. Others are the direct result of modern conditions. These influences fall naturally into two distinct classes, namely those that arise from the efforts of society to protect itself against certain features of these modern methods, and those that arise from the desire on the part of those who are directing industry to improve conditions within the several callings. The first group may be considered as regulatory methods applied from the outside of the industrial field, while the second group represents movements within industry itself. Of the first group, those movements that touch industrial problems most closely, and which tend constantly to modify industrial methods and conditions, the following are perhaps the most important:

1. Industrial legislation.
2. Labor unionism.
3. Industrial education.
4. The arts and crafts movement.

The second group of movements constitutes what has become known as personnel administration or industrial relations and will be discussed in succeeding sections. Only the briefest mention of the salient features of the first group[1] can be given here. Reference is made to them solely to call the attention of the student to the fact that they are integral factors in our industrial system. They are very closely related to factory management, and their causes and probable effects should be carefully studied. Like all other phenomena, there are definite causes for their existence, and they will grow or abate as these causes persist or are removed.

[1] For an extended discussion of these topics see KIMBALL, DEXTER S., "Industrial Organization," 3d ed. p. 359.

278. Industrial Legislation.—Industrial legislation, contrary to popular opinion, is far from being a new issue. History[1] in all ages abounds with instances of the legal regulation of industry and in many countries the same effect has been obtained by custom or caste. Nor has industrial legislation always favored the worker. To the contrary, it has sometimes been aimed against him where economic conditions gave him the upper hand (Art. 242), as instanced by the Statute[2] of Laborers of 1351. It is in fact a comparatively recent conception that the community should have little or no jurisdiction over the methods of conducting industry. It so happened that at the time of the Industrial Revolution the workman was totally unprotected, legally, and the mutual protection of the old guilds had vanished. As has been noted, the attitude of the ruling classes was one of **laissez-faire** and tended to exalt unduly the rights of the individual and to minimize his responsibility. The first efforts of reformers who sought legal help in rectifying the evils of the new factory towns met, therefore, with little attention and less sympathy; and it was not until diseases[3] incident to the conditions in these factory towns broke out that these reformers obtained a hearing.

The fight for legal regulation of factories was led by such men as Robert Owen, Richard Oastter,[4] and Sir Robert Peel and the first modern factory act in England was passed in 1802. Its effects and those of the four succeeding acts were almost nil, although they were based upon the findings of commission after commission appointed to investigate the evils of the factory system. A brief statement, even, of the slow and discouraging growth of this movement would be out of place here, although it will repay reading. It was not until 1891, or 100 *years after the great inventions*, that a factory law was enacted in England that in any adequate way regulated some of the evils that they had unloosed.

While conditions were never quite so bad in America, industrial legislation has grown steadily as the various states have become more and more thickly populated and the problems of existence have become more and more complex. Thus the industrial legislation of the older states, such as Massachusetts or Connecticut, is voluminous and governs details of industry to a degree quite startling to one who has not inquired into it. This form of legislation is growing very rapidly, in keeping with the growing public sentiment that the state has police powers over all industry and that the community has a right to regulate the manner in which industry may be conducted in its midst, and that there is just as much need of regulating productive industry as of regulating and licensing the professional callings, such as medicine and law.

[1] See The Code of Hammurabi, Art. 242 of this book.

[2] Taylor, R. W. Cooke, "The Factory System and the Factory Acts," p. 51.

[3] *Ibid.*, p. 53.

[4] Taylor, R. W. Cooke, "Modern Factory System," pp. 209–211.

It would be useless to attempt, here, even a synopsis of the industrial laws of the various states, as they vary in character with the character of the industries of the state and the degree to which these industries have been developed. In their most highly developed form, as in Massachusetts, they exercise control over factory construction in so far as ventilation, sanitation, fire protection, etc. are concerned. They regulate the installation of machinery, such as elevators, and prescribe that care must be exercised to make all machinery safe for the workman. They also carefully regulate the hours of labor, child labor, employment of women, regularity of payment, etc., in great detail. The aim, in general, is to protect the public from the dangers of the business as a whole, and to protect the workman against the dangers of his calling. In the past they have, usually, been negative and prohibitory and were seldom *constructive* in character. This follows from the nature of their inception which is almost always the prohibiting of abuses. Of late, however, constructional legislation has appeared in considerable volume.

Evoked originally to correct certain abuses in places where *congregated* labor was a factor, they have spread with great rapidity to include nearly all forms[1] of industry. How far they will extend is difficult to predict, but recent legislation, such as the federal Fair Labor Standards Act of 1938 (Art. 241) and other acts to be discussed, and the creation of commissions to regulate industry are very significant, and no factory owner, manager, or employee can afford not to study carefully this factor in production when the new methods of intensified production and so-called scientific management are under such close scrutiny.

More significant, perhaps, is the growing tendency of the federal government to *regulate* industry where national problems are concerned. The work of the Interstate Commerce Commission and of the Federal Trade Commission and other federal enactments of this character are noteworthy examples of this tendency. How far this movement may progress only the future will show.

One of the most important federal enactments is the so called Social Security Act of 1935. Under this act the federal government, beginning with the year 1942, will grant pensions to workers[2] in certain industries who are 65 years of age. It may also make grants to aid the several states that have pension systems of their own and it may also make grants to the several states to assist unemployment insurance, the relief of dependent children, etc. The necessary funds are to be raised by a tax

[1] A few callings such as *domestic service* seem to be still without legislative regulation.

[2] This act, officially called the Federal Old-Age Benefits Act, makes these provisions concerning the beneficiary

(1) "He is at least 65 years of age and,

(2) The total amount of wages paid to him with respect to employment after Dec. 1936 and before he attained the age of 65 was not less than $2000."

on both employer and employee. The plan is therefore of the nature of enforced savings. While the national government has pensioned army and navy veterans and has hospitalized its employees and wards this is the first time in our history that it has embarked upon so wide a program with the prospect that it may be broadened to include all workers. The arguments pro and con that are advanced concerning this program are many and somewhat conflicting. It should be noted, however, that this act implies that large numbers of people may no longer hope to save a competence and that the care of the aged and needy is no longer a problem for the individual, city, or state. It has assumed national importance. It should be added that several European countries have had some such legislation for some years past.

279. Labor Unionism.—It was noted in Art. 19 that labor unionism began in 1827. Labor unions naturally grew up as **craft unions,** that is, by skilled trades such as carpenters, painters, etc. In time these many unions were amalgamated into the American Federation of Labor. At no time during the first 30 years of this century had the percentage of all persons gainfully employed, who were members of labor unions, exceeded 7 per cent except in 1920, when it rose to 10 per cent, declining again to 7 per cent in 1930. However, because of their strategic position labor unions have often exercised great influence as illustrated by the railroad and building trade unions.

In the meantime the great industrial changes described in Chap. V and VI were bringing together large bodies of semiskilled workers who were not eligible for membership in the craft unions. Hence arose a demand for unionization based upon the *industry* rather than on *trades.* The answer to this demand was the Committee for Industrial Organization, at first ostensibly a committee of the American Federation of Labor, and organized in 1935. But the differences between the two groups have steadily widened and in 1938 the new group changed its name to the Congress of Industrial Organizations. At present these organizations are very antagonistic, one bidding for membership on the basis of craft unionism and the other on the basis of industrial unionism. A recent investigation (1937) records[1] the membership of the American Federation as 2,995,500 and that of the Congress of Industrial Organizations as 3,623,500, with about 605,704 union men not affiliated with either group. The combined membership of the two great groups was therefore about 22 per cent of those gainfully employed as listed in the census of that year. Obviously the acrimonious differences between these two great bodies greatly weakens their position before the public. The position of the Congress of Industrial Organizations has been greatly strengthened by the National Labor Relations Act, commonly known as the Wagner Act, enacted by the federal government in 1935. This act

[1] Brooks, R. R. R., "When Labor Organizes," p. 342.

affects all enterprises (railroads excepted) that are engaged in or whose operations affect the flow of interstate traffic. It provides that employees have a right to organize for the purpose of collective bargaining and employers are strictly prohibited from influencing in any way this right to organize and to select representatives for the purpose of *conducting collective bargaining.* The general tenor of the act is that the employer has an undue advantage in such matters which can be offset to a certain extent by collective bargaining. Several state legislatures have passed laws patterned on this act to cover *intrastate* industries. The Wagner Act has been approved by the United States Supreme Court with reference to interstate commerce.

If the influence of the act becomes widespread, it will open a new era in our industrial life. The natural antipathy of employer to labor unions may not be ended but some methods of opposing them will be prohibited. This will mean the end of company unions, so called. Labor union membership will no doubt be increased with normal industrial conditions. Whether the new bargaining power of the unions will result in a higher wage scale is a debatable question. The change will in time no doubt affect, if it does not abolish, all such employer activities as group insurance, sick benefits, pensions, and other paternalistic efforts of the employer which are discussed in succeeding sections of this chapter.

Granting also that collective bargaining is here to stay it should be remembered that successful fruition of any such far-reaching plan will require much time and patience if the experience of England and other countries may be taken as a criterion. And there is no assurance that labor unions will be able to agree among themselves as to the most desirable form of organization. New Zealand, which has gone farther perhaps than any other country with industrial legislation of this sort, is at this writing badly disturbed over the very same difference that separates the two great labor groups in this country. Sweden,[1] however, appears to have had considerable success with collective bargaining.

280. Industrial Education.—Prior to the modern industrial era, education of any kind was limited to the needs of the clergy and the ruling classes. The rapid growth of pure and applied science created a demand for men trained in these fields, hence arose the modern colleges of engineering, medicine, agriculture, etc. The disappearance of the old apprenticeship system necessitated the establishment of vocational schools to supply young men and women for the trades and callings. The state has recognized the fact that good citizenship depends largely upon ability to make a living, hence arose a widespread system of vocational schools. But there are many other educational activities of this kind, such as private enterprises, part-time schools, continuation schools, etc. As yet

[1] For an illuminating discussion of Swedish cooperatives see *Harvard Business Review*, Summer Number, 1938.

no very clear state[1] or national plan of vocational schooling has been devised, though some such measure is needed to clarify the situation. Brief reference is made to this topic, in so far as it is a part of factory management, in later sections.

281. The Arts and Crafts Movement.—The arts and crafts movement typifies the resentment of the artist and art lover against the machine-made product. It owes its origin to William Morris and his writings,[2] and has for its general purpose the preservation of the artistic side of production. While quite important for some years, it is comparatively less important now, since machine-made products can often be quite artistic, as illustrated by the product of the Jacquard loom and the modern shoemaking machinery. Yet the arguments of Morris and his followers, which were approved by men such as Ruskin, Emerson, and Elbert Hubbard, are well worth reading. The latest manifestation of Morris' idea is found in the so-called "styling" of automobiles, which in some instances appears to be overdone.

INDUSTRIAL RELATIONS—PERSONNEL ADMINISTRATION

282. Introductory.—The Industrial Revolution, by separating the industrial worker from the ownership of the tools of industry, made him almost entirely dependent upon the employing class for his means of subsistence. Unfortunately for him, the employing class of a century and a half ago held ideals vastly different from those held by the progressive employer of today, and, as a consequence, the workers in the industries immediately affected quickly found themselves in a deplorable condition. As the employer of the Industrial Revolution, with his narrow money-grubbing view, has given way to the intelligent educated employer of the present, two distinct principles or points of view have developed in our social and political creed. The first is the idea that the public has a right to regulate the manner in which industry is conducted in its midst, in so far as industry affects matters of common interest. This tenet is the basis of **industrial legislation** which is now being experimented with, and the limitations of which cannot be seen at the present time. The second idea is that every employer owes a duty to his employee over and above that required by law and as expressed in the wage agreement, that he is in a large sense his brother's keeper, and that his responsibility is a true stewardship. From this last idea has grown the field of effort now variously known as **industrial relations, personnel administration, employee's service, etc.,** which includes all endeavor on the part of employers to better the personal relations that exist in industry. It is now widely recognized that the personal relations in industry are matters of major importance, and in large enterprises the **personnel**

[1] See "Education for Life," by the Regents of the State of New York.

[2] See MORRIS, WILLIAM, "Hopes and Fears for Art."

manager holds a position of trust (see Fig. 13). Like all the functionalized activities that have been discussed, the personnel department will vary in size and scope with the size and character of the plant.

The first man in modern times to recognize these ideas and to put them into practical operation was Robert Owen, who in 1800, at the age of twenty-eight, became managing owner of the New Lanark Mills, about 20 miles from Glasgow. The village contained about 1,300 people in families and between 400 and 500 pauper children between five and ten years of age. These children were "parish apprentices," that is, children from the poorhouses placed in the mill village under agreement with the pauper overseers. Practically the only law governing these people was the will of the manager.

Owen himself has recorded the conditions that he found at New Lanark. He says:[1] "The people lived almost without control in habits of vice, poverty, idleness, debt, and destitution." The state of the pauper children, many of them mere babies, was particularly distressing. When it is considered that this was conceded to be the best-managed mill village in the kingdom one wonders what the others were like, and, indeed, it is difficult to believe the many well-authenticated accounts of the dire straits into which the manufacturing population had fallen by reason of the unrestricted application of the new methods.

Owen[2] had long pondered a plan for improving such conditions and now had an opportunity for putting his theories in effect. Against great difficulty, including opposition from the employees themselves, he gradually built up a model village the equal of which did not exist and has seldom, if ever, been seen elsewhere. His reforms included improved sanitation in homes and factory, recreative facilities, library and schools, methods of purchasing supplies for the workmen at low rates in such a way that they would not be cheated, elimination of drunkenness, and the reduction of the working day to 10 hours; 13 and 14 or even 16 hours being the length of the working day elsewhere. In fact, he anticipated practically every item of welfare work that has been attempted since.

Owen carried on this work through good and bad times, at one time paying full wages for four months during which the mills were idle, at a cost of $35,000. It was only in recent years that this idea was revived in the form of **unemployment insurance,** which some forward-looking companies are now operating. But in spite of what, to his partners and many others, seemed an extravagant and useless outlay of money the business prospered and paid handsomely, the village becoming a model of its kind.

[1] Sargent, W. L., "Robert Owen and His Social Philosophy," p. 27.

[2] The story of this model village and the point of view of this great reformer will repay reading. See Lloyd Jones, "Life of Robert Owen," and also W. L. Sargent, "Robert Owen and His Philosophy."

Differences with his partners compelled his retirement from the partnership and the village relapsed into its old state. Owen took up other activities looking toward legal protection of factory employees and to promulgating his theories of industrial organization. These theories, frankly socialistic, have not and probably will not be realized but nevertheless the world is deeply indebted to this fearless reformer, philosopher, philanthropist, and manufacturer.

The ideas that he introduced at New Lanark were not followed to any extent until a few years ago, when they were revived, particularly in America. The work has, in general, been conducted closely along the lines of Owen's experiment, and in some instances great sums of money have been expended by single individuals or companies interested in this work. The following classification, modified and abbreviated somewhat from one developed by J. E. Walters,[1] may be helpful in visualizing the field.

1. Employment.
   a. Labor turnover.
   b. The personnel supply.
   c. Job analysis.
   d. Job specifications.
   e. Selection and placement.
   f. Discharges.
   g. Rehiring, etc.
2. Personnel Maintenance.
   a. Promotions.
   b. Transfers.
   c. Wages and rewards.
   d. Ratings.
   e. Shop rules.
   f. Employees' organizations, etc.
3. Training and Education.
   a. Training executives.
   b. Training foremen.
   c. Training workers for foremanship.
   d. Job instruction.
   e. Training apprentices.
   f. Adapting college graduates.
   g. General industrial education, etc.
4. Accident Prevention and Safety Instruction.
   a. Mechanical safeguards.
   b. Safety education.
   c. Safety inspections, etc.
5. Health Conservation and Factory Hygiene.
   a. Physical examinations at and subsequent to hiring.
   b. First aid and medical treatment.
   c. Hospital and nursing services.
   d. Shop sanitation, ventilation, etc.

[1] See Walters, J. E., "Applied Personnel Administration," p. 53.

6. Employees' Service.
   a. Financial betterment and training in thrift.
   b. Recreational and social activities.
   c. Industrial housing, gardens, parks, etc.
   d. Restaurants, stores, etc.

Because of a more enlightened view on the part of industrial management and partly because of modern industrial legislation, the first five of this group of activities are well recognized today as legitimate and justifiable features of management. The sixth group, which embodies items formerly known as **welfare work,** is not so firmly established.

283. Labor Turnover.—Not many years ago there could be found in the older manufacturing states many small factory towns where the same families of employers and employees had carried on industries for several succeeding generations. Every individual of the community was well known and his abilities and shortcomings were public knowledge. Industry, furthermore, was broad and general, and each worker in the skilled trades, at least, was expected to perform many functions in a satisfactory manner. The problem of employment was not a difficult one, since practically all the workers were well known and where strangers were to be employed the judgment of the foreman was all that was necessary. Modern methods have changed these relations and factory towns such as these just described have now become the exception. The increased size of factories, the increased facilities for migration, the influx of alien labor, and other causes have made a wide gap between employer and employee, while the requirements of modern industry, so far as the worker is concerned, have become increasingly narrow and specialized. At the same time, many new lines of industry have come into existence. The problems of inducting men and women into industrial positions *where they will fit,* and of securing permanency in the working force, are no longer simple problems; in fact they present one of the most important, and at the same time most difficult, phases of modern industry.

One of the most marked results of these changed conditions is the shifting character of the personnel in many factories. This difficulty has long been known to factory managers, but the study of its economic aspect is comparatively new. The late Magnus Alexander made a most interesting and important investigation of this matter. His report covers the experience of 12 factories which gave employment to 37,274 employees at the beginning of the year, 1912, and 43,871 at the end of that year. The net increase for the year was, therefore, 6,697, but during that period 42,571 people were hired and, as a consequence, 35,874 must have been dropped from the employment rolls during that same period. The factories examined were fairly representative in character and size, the range of work covering large steam engines, electrical apparatus, automobiles, and fine tools and instruments. The smallest factory employed 300 people and the largest had more than 10,000 employees on its payroll. In these 12 factories it was found that about 73 per cent of the employees engaged during the year had not worked in these factories before, while about 27 per cent had worked in them at some previous time.

As a corroboration to this statement it was found by other investigators that in a certain large carpet factory near Philadelphia 75 per cent of the employees had been in the employ less than 1 year, 9 per cent from 1 to 2 years, 5 per cent from 2 to 3 years, 4 per cent from 4 to 5 years, and only 1 per cent of the employees had been in the employ more than 5 years. While this last example may not represent average conditions it is true that this state of affairs and that reported by Mr. Alexander are undoubtedly too common, and this constant shifting of workers is a source of great industrial loss. The term "labor turnover" has been given to this change in the personnel of the factory force, and it is measured as a percentage. The National Employment Managers' Conference in 1918, agreed upon the following definition[1] and method of computing labor turnover.

Labor Turnover for any period consists of the number of separations from service during that period. Separations include all quits, discharges, or lay-offs for any reason whatever.

Percentage Labor Turnover for any period is the ratio of the total number of separations during the period to the average number of employees on the force report during that period. The force report gives the number of men actually working each day as shown by attendance records.

To illustrate, assume that the number of separations in a given week is 360 and that the average *daily* attendance for the week is 1,200. Then the percentage of labor turnover on a yearly basis is

$$\frac{360}{1{,}200} \times 52 = 0.30 \times 52 = \textit{ratio} \text{ of } 15.60 \text{ or } 1{,}560 \textit{ per cent} \text{ of } 1200.$$

It should be noted that this ratio by itself may not always convey a correct impression of the change that has taken place and it is always desirable to know the *stability* of the factory force. Thus a turnover of 100 per cent may be caused by the entire force changing during the year, or it may be caused by one-tenth of the force changing ten times during the year. As Mr. Slichter states: "The turnover statement in addition to the total number of changes should show also the number of the men on the payroll at the beginning of the year who remained continuously in the employ of the company throughout the year." A factory might easily have a labor turnover of 100 per cent and still find that 80 per cent of its employees had remained constantly on the payroll.

[1] Frankel L. K., and A. Fleisher, "The Human Factor in Industry," p. 68.

There is no unanimity, however, as to the exact method of computing labor turnover, and there has been much discussion of this topic. J. E. Walters[1] lists five others besides the one discussed in the foregoing, and states that 75 per cent of the companies he investigated use the formula $T = \frac{100S}{M}$ where T = labor turnover for 100 employees, S = total separations including quits, discharges, and layoffs, and M = the average number on the payroll for the period considered. Thus if a factory has an average of 1,000 persons on its payroll and has 100 separations per month, the turnover for that month would be

$$T = \frac{100 \text{ (separations)} \times 100}{1{,}000} = 10 \text{ per cent for the month.}$$

The idea is capable of wide expansion and variation, and it would not appear to be of great importance what formula is used provided it is properly interpreted and gives the management some measure of the exodus of men from the plant. Labor turnover, it will be noted, is a measure of the stability of the working force (see Chap. XXII).

284. The Causes of Labor Turnover.—The many reasons why men are discharged or quit their jobs divide naturally into two classes, (1) those that are due to some lack or misfortune on the part of the employee, and (2) those that are due to some remissness on the part of the employer. On the part of the employee will be found incompetence, insubordination, drunkenness, laziness, a general roving spirit which makes it difficult for him to stay long in one place, and, lastly, those misfortunes over which the worker has little or no control, such as accidents, sickness, or death. On the part of the employer may be found such causes as low wages, bad working conditions, failure to protect the worker against accident, a bad attitude on the part of superintendents and foremen toward the employees, thus preventing the growth of interest and friendly feeling; unfairness in making promotions, and inefficient management in general. To these should be added such factors as the fluctuating character of some industries and the seasonal demand for certain products, for which neither employer nor employee is to blame. Such investigations as have been made go to show that a large percentage of the trouble is due to incompetence on the part of the workers, and this in turn is due partly to faulty methods of selecting employees and to lack of proper facilities and methods for training them for the work in hand, when it is special in character and different from that in other factories or other lines of work. It should be remembered that industry of all kinds has become very complex and highly specialized, so that a worker well trained in one line may find himself entirely out of place in an industry that apparently differs but little from those with which he is familiar. The great

[1] See "Applied Personnel Administration," p. 212.

outstanding fact should be kept in mind that in many industries it is customary to "hire and fire" many more men in any given time than are regularly employed.

285. Cost of Labor Turnover.—While the facts discussed in the preceding paragraph have been generally known for some time, it is not commonly appreciated how great an expense may be involved in hiring and training workmen, nor are the detailed costs which make up this total expense generally understood. These detail expenses may be summarized as follows: interviewing new men; medical examination, if one is required; investigating the records of applicants and studying the sources of labor supply; instructing new men regarding their specific duties and regarding factory rules and regulations; wear and breakage of machines and tools by inefficient or unskilled men; reduction in production due to unfamiliarity of new men with machines and surroundings; cost of work spoiled by new and perhaps inexperienced men; and similar causes.

It will be obvious that the total cost will vary with the class of work and the character of the employees, and it is not easy to obtain mathematical data that are reliable or conclusive, but such data as have been obtained are somewhat startling. Mr. Alexander stated that he learned, by inquiry from a number of managers, that the average estimate for discharging a man and replacing him was between $50 and $100. In his investigation he classified the employees considered into five classes as follows: (1) highly skilled mechanics, (2) mechanics of lesser skill who can be trained in two or three years, (3) operators and piece workers who require only a few months to train, (4) unskilled laborers and helpers, (5) clerical helpers in shops and offices. Mr. Alexander gave the estimates, shown in the following table, of the costs of replacing these several classes of workers with new men and of rehiring old employees. The investigations of other men corroborate generally the costs given by Mr. Alexander, some giving even higher figures. The important question concerning these investigations and results is not their relative accuracy so much as the startling size of these totals as given by all who have investigated this problem. It is believed that managers, as a rule, are not well informed on this source of loss.

Group	Hiring	Instruction	Wear and breakage	Reduced production	Spoiled work	Total cost	Cost of rehiring
1	$0.50	$ 7.50	$10.00	$20.00	$10.00	$48.00	$10.00
2	0.50	15.00	10.00	18.00	15.00	58.00	20.00
3	0.50	20.00	10.00	33.00	10.00	73.50	35.00
4	0.50	2.00	1.00	5.00	......	8.50	5.00
5	0.50	7.50	1.00	20.00	......	29.00	10.00

286. Methods of Reducing Labor Turnover.—The foregoing discussion naturally suggests ways and means of reducing labor turnover. Among the most important remedies are:

1. Improved methods of hiring and discharging men.
2. Facilities for training new men for their duties.
3. Reducing fluctuations in the volume of work.
4. Offering better financial inducements to remain in service.
5. Medical supervision and care to safeguard the employee against sickness and accident.
6. A human interest in the employee with a view to securing his interest and making him contented.

It has already been demonstrated that remedies such as these are helpful in reducing the labor turnover, and obviously these remedial efforts involve modern employment and labor-maintenance methods as listed in Art. 284.

MODERN EMPLOYMENT METHODS

287. The Employment Department.—It has been noted (see Chap. V) that it is good administrative policy to have each person perform as few functions as possible. The separation of functions and the development of specialists for each duty are in strict accord with the theory of division of labor, and employment problems are no exception to this rule. In small shops where the employees are few, employment work must be performed, for obvious reasons, by the superintendent or foreman; but in plants employing 500 or more employees this work should be in the hands of one man who should devote all of his time to employment problems. Many modern plants are now doing this and the centralized employment office under a special employment manager is rapidly becoming the rule rather than the exception in large institutions. If the plant is large enough to justify a complete plan of personnel administration the employment department will naturally be included in the larger organization.

The primary duties of an employment manager are to find and develop the sources of labor supply; to examine applicants for positions, and to select new employees whose qualifications will fit the needs of the factory; to study and to classify these needs and reduce them to written statements so that applicants can be fully informed, in advance, of what will be expected of them in the factory.

288. Sources of Labor Supply.—Many employers have no clear idea of their labor supply, the great majority depending upon personal applications, selecting those who may appear competent. While such methods may suffice for small shops, a large works should have definite and well-known sources of labor supply. This can always be supplemented by careful inquiry among reliable employees. It often occurs that workmen know of friends or others who would make desirable employees. Obviously such inquiries should be made only of those employees who are trustworthy and satisfactory from the standpoint of labor questions in general. Another source of labor supply is found in employment agencies. Agencies engaged in supplying highly trained men such as engineers and teachers are usually useful and reliable. Those supplying cheaper labor are not so reliable, though they are often useful in furnishing large numbers of workers at short notice, as is sometimes needed in railroad work. State and municipal labor bureaus have not been very successful as a rule.

Advertising is simply a means of increasing the number of personal applications. It is much used, and with good success, for obtaining men for the higher positions where the applicant is expected to furnish unquestionable records and credentials. It may also be used effectively where an immediate increase in labor is essential and where quality cannot be too closely considered. It is not a good method for securing a permanent supply of well-trained, reliable men.

One of the best methods of securing good workers, if the plant is large enough to afford such a plan, is through an apprenticeship system in connection with educational methods. Industrial education of some kind or degree is rapidly becoming an essential requirement for factory workers. In many places satisfactory cooperative arrangements can be made with local public schools so that a constant stream of well-trained boys and girls pass into the industries. Many large plants have auxiliary school shops organized for this special purpose, and cooperative school and shop methods are becoming more common daily. No large plant can afford to neglect this method, for in all probability it is the ultimate solution of the problem and the only solid foundation upon which an industrial community can be sustained. A more general consideration of industrial education is given in a succeeding section.

289. Empirical Methods of Selecting Employees.—Whatever means are employed to get in touch with sources of labor supply, some method must be adopted for selecting those that are to be hired. For the most part these methods of selection are still empirical, reliance being placed upon the personal judgment of the superintendent, foreman, or employment manager supplemented by recommendations of some kind. The value of the latter is problematical, except as concerns personal character, unless the work for which the worker is engaged is very much like that to which he has been accustomed. There is no doubt that personal judgment based upon long experience is not to be dismissed lightly, and the writer has seen some magnificent organizations of men built up solely upon the keen judgment and insight into human nature possessed by a single superintendent. This was easier to do, however, when work was more general in character and when the workmen employed were of the all-round type now rapidly disappearing. In hiring such men the specifications of the work to be done were covered by the experience and skill of good workmen of the class required, and selection became largely a matter of judging personal characteristics, in which work some men are naturally gifted, and hence become highly efficient in selecting reliable workers.

While the need of judgment and insight into human nature still remains the most important feature of employment work, the conditions of industry have changed. Any employment manager who is to hire men for any large industry must recognize the fact that to do so successfully he must have accurate specifications of the work to be performed and that he must match these specifications with the experience of the worker or provide some method of preliminary training before the worker will fit into the vacancy which is being filled. For these reasons some advanced managers have adopted methods not unlike those in use in colleges and governmental activities to eliminate, so far as possible, the employment of workers who are sure to be misfits. It may be of value to review briefly some of these advanced, yet logical, methods.

290. Specifications of Work to Be Performed.—There still remains much work that is simple to describe and of which the general characteristics are easy to understand. It often occurs, however, that those who hire men know very little about the exact requirements of factory work, and until comparatively recent years little or no work had been done in classifying operations with reference to the personal attributes of the worker who is to perform the task. The work of Taylor, Gantt, Gilbreth, and others referred to in Chap. X gives ample proof of this statement. It was comparatively easy to match the all-round ability of the old mechanic against the general character of industry of a few decades ago. But extreme division of labor, by reducing industrial operations to a few functions, has instituted a need for workers of a few characteristics. Thus one job may require dexterity, another quickness of vision, another concentration, or any combination of these personal attributes. Clearly it is not an economic policy to employ men for duties for which their personal characteristics and training do not fit them, but this cannot be avoided unless the requirements of the position to be filled are clearly definable. It is helpful to both for the employment manager and for the foreman to endeavor to specify in writing just what the requirements of every position are before hiring a man to fill the place. An analysis of the character of an industrial operation has come to be known as a **job analysis,** and the written description of the work based upon such an analysis, which may be used by the employment manager in selecting workers, is known as a **job specification.** The degree of refinement to which such methods may be used will depend naturally upon the size and character of the plant. Much attention has been given to this problem in recent years and the reader is referred to "Applied Personnel Administration," Chap. X, by J. E. Walters, and to "Cost and Production Handbook," by L. P. Alford (Ed.), p. 1349, for fuller information.

291. Psychological Tests.—The work of the experimental psychologist is slowly developing a more scientic basis for classifying men than has hitherto been possessed. Laboratory methods are now developed that will measure all manner of human attributes, including such very refined functions as mental processes themselves. The best-known worker in this field was the late Professor Hugo Münsterberg, whose writings on this subject have been noteworthy. An extended effort is now being made to apply psychological methods to vocational guidance and selection. There is also a well-defined effort to connect physical appearances with mental attributes. Thus, Dr. Katherine Blackford has advanced the idea that physical appearances can be used as a basis of classification for industrial fitness. She has undertaken to show that a man is not short or tall, blonde or brunette by accident, and that the shape of his nose and the outline of his face have all evolved through definite experiences of his ancestors. She has also applied these theories to the selection of men for the industries in a practical manner. The work of Holmes W. Merton[1] in this field has met with considerable favor among industrial employment managers.

While the background of these philosophies may be sound, it is questionable whether they have as yet been advanced to the stage where they can be applied intelligently to the problems of industrial selection. It should be remembered that this is a most difficult and elusive problem, and it will probably be some time before it will be possible to lay aside personal judgment and measure men and women as inert material is now measured. This phase of industrial progress, nevertheless, should be carefully studied by the progressive manager.

292. Mechanical Tests.—It is a well-established fact that a man's natural bodily characteristics fit him better for one kind of physical activity than for others. Thus oarsmen, sprinters, baseball players, and other athletes have clearly distinguishing bodily characteristics which experienced trainers look for in selecting men. In a more detailed manner, each worker's arms and fingers fit him naturally for certain kinds of work in preference to others. The experimental psychologist long ago developed methods for testing the human machine and measuring its possibilities but, as yet, these methods have not come into common use in selecting men. These psychological and physiological tests include the measurement of speed and dexterity of both hands, range of eyesight, ability to comprehend verbal instructions, power of imitation, power of concentration, mathematical speed, quickness of thought, etc. The

[1] See publications of the Merton Institute.

interested reader will find in the *Industrial Management Magazine* for 1916 and 1917 three very instructive articles by William F. Kemble, which discuss some simple mechanical methods for testing the common manual and mental requisites, and which will amply repay reading. The "wiggly block" devised by Johnson O'Connor is an excellent example of the use of mechanical equipment in placement work. Not a few large corporations are now applying such mechanical and mental tests to applicants for positions. The telephone companies, for instance, have carefully drawn specifications defining the work of telephone operators, and have specified not only the type of girl best fitted for this work, but have also developed laboratory methods for testing applicants.

293. Fitting the Worker to the Job.—No matter how small the part which the worker is to perform, care should be taken to see that he thoroughly understands his work. This is particularly true in starting a new employee at work. All difficulties should be removed from his path as far as possible and every precaution taken to make him feel at home, and to familiarize him with his new surroundings. In work of special character, this preliminary instruction may be truly educational and many companies have found it a good investment to establish schools of one kind or another to promote the progress of their employees in the work of the factory. Aside from these general educational efforts, however, it will be found that it pays to instruct the worker in the particular work in which he is engaged. H. L. Gantt has made a real contribution to this subject in his writings on task and bonus work. He found that great increases could be made in the output of workers who were, in the beginning, only mediocre performers, by careful and systematic instruction in the details of the operations to be performed. If such instruction leads to higher output and consequent higher pay, one of the first causes of labor turnover is removed. Obviously, this is a better method of securing a permanent force of men than by the old method of "hiring and firing," retaining only those who happen to qualify.

294. Other Employment Functions.—In large plants where the personnel division is well developed, medical examination is required of all applicants for work. Since medical supervision is also an important part of personnel maintenance, reference to this phase of employment will be deferred to that discussion. Where personnel work is well developed, the personnel director not only selects the workers but he is usually consulted concerning promotions, transfers, discharges, and rehiring. Thus if a worker does not fit into one place, the placement officer may transfer him elsewhere instead of discharging him. This officer will also inquire into the reasons why any man leaves the employ, and he will in general through his personnel records act as a source of information concerning all such matters.

PERSONNEL MAINTENANCE

295. General.—The second duty of the personnel director in a well-managed shop is to make a study of plant conditions as they affect the employees. Such a study will include consideration of the methods by which men are introduced to their work. This item may be of broad significance and may include preliminary preparation of an educational character. If an apprenticeship system is in operation, or if extension-school methods are in use, the personnel director should be in close touch with, if not in actual control of, these functions. He should also study carefully the conditions under which the men work with a view to discovering any conditions that work adversely to a spirit of cooperation between the men and the management. This study should include the manner in which men are treated by the foremen, the hearing of complaints and grievances, methods of promotion, transfers from one department to another, adjustment of wages, and, most particularly, the employment manager should examine every case of discharge or other cause for an employee leaving the service. He should also study the cause and effects of absences.

It may be objected that many of these duties are now, and should remain, in the hands of the foreman, and many foremen will object to having these functions taken from them. Most of the functionalized positions in modern management have had to make their place against these very same arguments. The trained designer, the tool maker, the storekeeper, the cost finder and others that are now considered essential to good organization were called into being by the same demands for more refined methods that are now indicating that low labor turnover and more economical production can be secured by a more intelligent study of the problems of employment. Many employers have already recognized that this problem is a far-reaching one and have given the personnel director wide powers.

296. Conditions of Employment.—Careful selection of employees and thorough instruction as to their duties are not enough in themselves, however, to insure permanence in the working force. The conditions under which men work must be satisfactory. Every worker desires good pay, short hours, steady employment, and work that will not prove too much of a physical, mental, or nervous strain upon him. These conditions are somewhat fundamental and the degree to which they are realized has much to do with the worker's contentment. It should be remembered that attractions of a minor sort will not retain the interest of workmen unless these more important conditions are fulfilled.

A good personnel department will, therefore, look carefully into the hours of labor and the rates of pay as compared with other plants and industries. Careful investigations should be made of all disagreeable features involved in the work, and every effort should be made to minimize or remove these disagreeable features. The agreeableness and disagreeableness of a job should be taken into account in setting the wage rates, and systematic efforts should be made to remove all distracting and uncongenial surroundings. Men always produce more and are better contented when their surroundings are agreeable.

In factories involving a variety of work, and consisting of many departments, it may occur that a worker may not be satisfactory in one department, but may do very well when transferred to another. In progressive shops, therefore, where a personnel manager is installed, the individual foreman can discharge a man only from his own department and the personnel manager has the privilege of placing him elsewhere if he so desires. In this connection it should be noted that there is much to be desired in many foremen. No one man should be picked with such care as the foreman, for he alone represents the management to the workman. To get work out of men and yet retain their friendship and their loyalty to the organization is a fine art and every manager will do well to see that his foremen maintain the right attitude toward the workmen. Arrogant, blustering ways, unfair methods, and, above all, unjust discharge[1] do not pay dividends and they belong, furthermore, to an age that is rapidly passing away. If no personnel manager is employed, the superintendent should know the full reasons for every discharge. It should be difficult for a good worker to get employment in a good plant and, once in, it should be as difficult for a rival concern to induce him to leave, and to this end he should be protected against unjust and discourteous treatment.

297. Reducing Fluctuations in Output.—Many large factories make what are known as seasonal goods. Thus the market for arc lamps is active in the fall, and hence the busy manufacturing season is during the summer. Straw hats must be made during the winter to meet a sudden and large demand in the spring. Unless such fluctuations in product are counterbalanced by other goods, the labor force must fluctuate with the volume of the work. Some of the trades, as bricklaying, fluctuate not only because of the season but because of the unavoidable irregularity in building operations.

In many industries this is a difficult problem to combat, yet it is one of the most serious causes of labor turnover in many shops. Unemployment is one of the most dreaded of all ills to which the worker is exposed. He naturally, therefore, prefers a shop where employment is steady, and no doubt many industries would be better off financially if production

[1] The recent rulings of the National Labor Relations Board are markedly against unfair discharge and in not a few instances the men so discharged have been reinstated with back pay.

were equalized over the year, even though this would involve a lower interest on investment. It would be more than offset by the reduced cost of labor.

TRAINING AND EDUCATION

298. Training Foremen.—As has been stated, no men in the entire organization of an industrial plant should be selected with such care as the foremen. On the foremen depend, to a very large degree, the spirit and morale of the plant. To the workman the foreman represents the management, and he interprets the attitude of the foreman as that of his superior officers. Many modern enterprises, therefore, are training their foremen and subforemen in the principles of sound administration. Such training usually includes instruction in the principles of organization, economies of production, cost finding, etc. But it also includes discussions of personnel problems and the relation of the human element to successful administration. The aim of such a course should be to make the foreman a broader and better executive and to enable him to understand more clearly the value of the human elements involved. Two general methods are in use for this work. In the first all executives of the plant meet regularly to listen to talks on the several topics given by men carefully selected for the purpose. In the second method the men from several plants are collected into groups that have common problems for discussions of these problems. Sometimes outside reading is advised in connection with the discussions. Such reading is to be highly recommended. In fact, if a foreman can be induced to acquire the habit of reading in connection with his work, other educational work is scarcely necessary. Educational work similar to that just described is also carried on by some enterprises for the benefit of its salesmen.

299. Educating the Worker.—Industrial education, as an effort on the part of the public to supply certain deficiencies in the modern industrial system, has been mentioned in Art. 277. It is now quite generally conceded that the public schools should train all boys and girls in such general branches of knowledge as are required for good citizenship and should also, as far as is possible, give each child a mental background or elementary training in industrial methods before he or she is permitted actually to engage in a distinct vocation. The growing tendency of the several states[1] to pass laws prohibiting boys and girls from entering industry until at least sixteen years of age makes the necessity for such preliminary vocational training increasingly necessary. It is obvious, on the other hand, that no matter how extensive the work of the public and private schools may be in this regard, there will always be a certain part of the worker's training that can be given only within industry itself. The school can supply general background, basic technical knowledge,

[1] See also the Federal Fair Labor Standards Act, Art. 242.

and a limited amount of technical skill. But a complete mastery of technique and a full knowledge of industrial methods and of *industrial conditions* can be obtained only in the atmosphere of industry itself. This is true of all grades of education from the grammar grades to the college. No general solution of the problem of adapting workers to modern industrial processes has been developed as yet, but the most important of those now in operation will be briefly discussed.

300. Apprenticeship Schools.—When it was fully realized that modern industrial conditions had made the old apprenticeship system obsolete, the first reaction of manufacturers was to fall back upon the public-school system and demand that it give trade training. The limitations of this system that have been discussed were quickly discovered and not a few industrial enterprises set up **apprenticeship schools** wherein the advantages of school methods could be realized in close connection with real shop conditions. For the most part such schools are found only in large enterprises that can afford to operate them, and in such industries as still retain a considerable demand for a wide range of skill or technique. Thus the Westinghouse Electric and Manufacturing Company, the General Electric Company, and a number of the larger railroads have successful schools of this kind. The apprenticeship school operated by the Atchison, Topeka and Santa Fe Railway appears to have been very successful, and no doubt there are many plants in other lines of industry where such schools can be operated to advantage.

301. Specific Job Instruction.—In many industries, particularly those that produce in large quantities, there is a very large number of operations that require only a limited amount of skill or knowledge, and general trade skill and knowledge, such as it is aimed to impart by apprenticeship methods, are not required. In many such industries it has become quite common practice to train workers for specific jobs before employing them at actual production. This form of training can be accomplished in two ways. The first is an adaptation of the old apprenticeship methods. The new employees are placed under the supervision of special instructors and are given intensive training for a short period on the factory floor and on regular machines under actual working conditions. Obviously this method is very flexible and can be adapted to small plants.

The second method is through the use of special schools that may be in a separate room or may be placed on some portion of a production floor and hence in the atmosphere of the industry. During the late war, when it was necessary to train large numbers of workers in special jobs, many of these schools came into existence under the name of **vestibule schools.** Usually the work is conducted on regular machines and with regular products. The cost of such schools is high because of the expensive equipment required, and, therefore, it is not likely to be much used except in large enterprises.

302. Adaptation of College Men.—The limitations of public schools in preparing men for industry hold also for colleges and universities. Many industries, however, have found the product of these higher institutions most desirable, if not essential, particularly the graduates of technical colleges. Large enterprises such as the Westinghouse Electric and Manufacturing Company, the General Electric Company, the Western Electric Company, and others long ago established special methods for adapting technical graduates to their needs. Other enterprises in other lines have followed their example. These courses are sometimes called **special apprenticeship courses** but they are really **courses of adaptation.** In such courses the recruit is passed as rapidly as possible through a number of departments so that he can become acquainted quickly with the *art* of the business of which he presumably has a knowledge of the *science*. Even where no formal course has been organized this general method of introducing the college man into industry through a preliminary period of adaptation is rapidly gaining ground. The General Motors Corporation established in 1926 an Institute of Technology. This is a cooperative school designed to train employees for greater responsibilities in the corporation. The Chrysler Institute of Technology, with a similar purpose in view, is licensed by the state of Michigan to confer engineering degrees. The usefulness of this function remains to be seen.

303. Cooperative Education.—Practically all of the educational methods described in the foregoing have been, or are being, operated in cooperation with public-school systems, Y.M.C.A. evening courses, or university courses. Two distinct methods of cooperative training should be noted. In the first, or truly cooperative method, the worker spends part of his time in actual study in the school and part in actual work in the plant with which the school is cooperating. Usually there are two sets of students, one working in the plant while the other attends classes in the school, and vice versa. A regular course of study and work is planned in advance.

In **continuation-school** work the worker is employed regularly in the plant and is relieved during a part of the day to attend classes; or the classes are conducted in the evening so as not to interfere with the shop work. In every large city there are many opportunities for workers to attend **extension courses,** so called, that are offered by educational institutions, usually through evening classes.

ACCIDENT PREVENTION AND RELIEF

304. Accident Prevention and Relief.—In no phase of industrial philosophy has there been such a quickening of our conscience as in the matter of industrial accidents. This has been due partly to a fuller realization through statistical studies of the enormous losses thus entailed.

The U. S. Department of Labor estimates[1] the total annual number of industrial accidents for a recent year in the United States as 2,453,418, of which 21,232 are fatal. The monetary loss due to this dreadful toll is estimated at $1,022,264,866. The older philosophy of management assumed that the worker was sufficiently skilled or careful to look out for himself, and if he was injured because of negligence on his part or on the part of a fellow worker the employer was not to blame and could not be called upon for financial compensation. Today it is commonly believed that it is the employer's duty to see that every precaution is taken to prevent accidents of every kind, and that if an accident does occur the owner must assume the financial responsibility. This, in effect, compels each industry to pay for its own losses due to accidents instead of turning the incapacitated workers adrift to be a charge upon the general public.

As a result of this changed point of view there is an unprecedented interest in accident prevention in this country in which large corporations, such as the U. S. Steel Corporation have led the way. This work has been well developed also in some European countries. The American Museum of Safety was established in 1907 with a view of enlisting public sympathy with this work, and in 1913 the National Safety Council, membership which is open to all manufacturers engaged in hazardous occupations, was founded.

Accident prevention falls naturally into three divisions: (1) designing and installing protection devices; (2) educational propaganda to make workers more careful of themselves and others; and (3) the collection of data that will show progress and indicate what hazards are most dangerous. In respect of the first item much general good can be accomplished by careful design of buildings, stairs, elevators, etc. As regards the protection of machines there are now on the market all manner of protective devices and much thought is being given to this phase of the work.

Arthur H. Young, while Director of the American Museum of Safety, estimated, however, that not more than 25 per cent of the accidents that occur are preventable by mechanical safeguards, and reasons correctly therefrom that the greatest hope lies in educational efforts which will awaken personal interest in safety work. This work opens a new field of wide scope and of great economic and humane importance for the industrial engineer. Statistics show that this work is already effective.

The U. S. Steel Corporation,[2] for instance, states that from 1906 to 1922, inclusive, its safety measures saved 35,313 employees from death or serious injury as compared with the records of years prior to the introduction of accident prevention work. This same company, which

[1] See Alford, L. P. (Ed.), "Management's Handbook," p. 76, for detailed statement of these totals.

[2] Young, Robert J., "Selling Workers Safety Work," *Management*, November, 1924.

employs about 216,000 men, reports that since 1912 all disabling accidents have been reduced 71.41 per cent, which means that 193,232 men have been saved from injury during that period. The logic of this work is perfectly sound. No one questions the economy of preventing fires. The same arguments apply to accident prevention with the added impetus that it is one of the most humane movements ever inaugurated.

HEALTH CONSERVATION—FACTORY HYGIENE

305. Physical Fitness.—Every progressive factory of any magnitude is equipped with a resident physician and hospital facilities (see Chap. VIII) for caring for the accidents and sickness of those employed. It is even more logical to examine the worker physically at the time of engagement, and many employers are now requiring such an examination. H. L. Gardiner, employment manager for Cheyney Brothers, reported that in a single month 449 applicants were thus examined and 547 cases of accident or disease were treated among those already in the employ. Of the 449 applicants 41 were rejected because of heart disease, tuberculosis, or other physical weaknesses that rendered them unfit for the work in hand. Of those selected and employed, 137 were placed on certain tasks only, their physical condition not permitting them to assume more laborious duties. The importance of this last item should not be overlooked. Physical examination should not be used as a means of excluding all but the very best, but should be used as a basis of classification. Clearly it is a dangerous proceeding to place a man with a bad heart in charge of an overhead crane or a man with bad eyesight in charge of a yard engine. Physical examination at engagement will, no doubt, do much not only to obtain better classification of the force, but will serve as a valuable basis for keeping the force in prime physical condition. A purchaser of horses or cattle would take all of these precautions, yet it is difficult to convince some men of the economic value of these common-sense proceedings.

306. Medical Service.—In no one feature of factory administration has there been such a change in point of view as in this field. The factory manager of a few years ago would take every precaution to protect his horses against disease, but the health of the human worker was his own business. The progressive employer of today, however, knows that it pays to look after the health of his employees and he knows that sick or disabled men are not efficient producers. Dr. Otto P. Gier, medical director of the Cincinnati Milling Machine Company, said regarding this point: "The loss in wages to the workers on account of preventable but unprevented diseases runs annually into the billion dollar mark. The accompanying loss to the employer must surely be twice that amount when it is remembered what a part bad health plays in efficiency." Many industrial plants, therefore, now have a resident physician and a well-equipped dispensary. Such an equipment will most commonly first justify itself and make a place for itself in the factory as a measure for first aid and accident relief. But if this activity is in charge of the proper kind of physician, who can win the confidence of the employees, it will, in a short time, become a center from which will radiate advice and counsel concerning all manner of personal ailments, and the resident doctor will become a confidant and personal adviser to the entire community. The value of such a department in selecting employees has already been discussed, but its greatest good will be with those already in the employ and in following up those who have been examined at engagement. Dr. Gier believed that any plant having 750 men or more can afford a resident physician and a dispensary, and suggests that smaller concerns may accomplish good results by cooperative methods.

The extension of medical service to the families of employees borders on paternalism and is perhaps questionable practice. It is true that an able shop physician with strong social tendencies may do much in a personal way among the families of the workers. But the systematic supervision of such families by the shop physician with the aid of a visiting nurse, as is being done in some places, may result in more harm than good. In any case, that phase of employees' service must be approached with caution, and it may be better to handle it as a community problem, as is being done in many places.

307. Factory Hygiene and Personal Comfort.—The recognition of the value of conserving the health of the employee carries with it a new view concerning his surroundings and equipment. The original idea of a factory was a place to house machinery and the fact that human beings had to spend a large part of their lives in these buildings was given little or no consideration. A very few years ago most machine shops were dark, dingy, and cold, with unspeakable toilet arrangements and a general lack of elementary sanitation. Many such shops still exist, unfortunately, but they are rapidly becoming the exception. It is a well-recognized principle that it pays to provide heat, light, and ventilation and that a worker produces more when his bodily needs are well cared for.

In all progressive states the law fixes a minimum of excellence for sanitary arrangements and in all such states all factory workers are protected against gross negligence on the part of factory owners. Such regulations are in large degree the result of the efforts of reformers and progressive factory owners who find in the law the only force that will compel universal recognition of what is just and right. In fact, welfare work in general has always been the forerunner of protective legislation, and the voluntary reform work of one period often becomes the basis for the legal regulations of a later day.

But there is still much that can be done in this field over and above that required by law, and many of these efforts will pay dividends.

Space will permit of only a brief discussion of a few of the items in this important field, namely, ventilation and lighting, lavatory and dressing facilities, housing and individual equipment.

308. Ventilation and Lighting.—All new modern plants are fully equipped with adequate devices of some kind for insuring a plentiful supply of pure air, and the principles of ventilation are well understood. But many old factories still exist, built long before the need of ventilation was fully appreciated, where the installation of a good system of ventilation would add much to the comfort of the workers and to the dividends of the company. This is especially true where dust or obnoxious vapors are prevalent, as in grinding and buffing rooms and in plating operations. Well-developed apparatus for this purpose is now to be had in the market and there is no excuse for foul or dusty atmosphere in the factory. Such conditions are conducive to ill health, ill temper, and general inefficiency.

Good lighting, aside from its value in preventing accidents, is an economic measure of great importance. In these days of improved electric lighting there is no excuse for the use of candles, such as one still sees in old-fashioned plants. Modern lighting installations aim to reduce all eyestrain by avoiding direct exposure of the lamp, particularly if it be bright. Eyestrain increases accident hazard, and proper lighting and shading pay profits.

309. Lavatory and Dressing Facilities.—Good, modern, lavatory equipment costs so little, comparatively, that there is no excuse for not providing proper washing and dressing facilities. Dr. Gier stated that the worker who leaves the factory in his working clothes, often saturated with perspiration, is 80 per cent more liable to respiratory diseases than the worker who has washed himself and changed his clothes. There is nothing, furthermore, that adds so much to a man's dignity as to appear on the street clean and neatly dressed. If it is desired to encourage workmen to wash themselves and change their clothes, adequate provision must be made so as to avoid crowding at quitting time. Care should be taken, however, to keep the equipment as simple as possible and of a quality consistent with the worker's social status. The worker will place small value on elaborate bathing facilities in the factory if his scanty payroll forbids a bathtub for his family.

The same general arguments apply to toilet facilities. There is absolutely no excuse on the part of any factory owner for not installing modern toilets of fair quality. At least one toilet should be provided for every twenty persons. The facilities, furthermore, should be housed in rooms that are kept clean and are properly warmed and ventilated. The practice of installing them in cold outbuildings is neither humane nor economical. Each toilet should have a screen door. The exposed toilet is a barbarous cruelty that should be prohibited by law. Drinking water should be supplied by bubblers and the common drinking cup should be prohibited.

EMPLOYEES' SERVICE

310. Scope and Origin of Employees' Service.—Under this title is included all efforts of employers and private individuals, in general, that are directed toward the betterment of their employees, physically, mentally, and morally, beyond that which may be considered *at the time* as standard justifiable factory practice. The movement is virtually a recognition that the employing or capitalistic class, as a whole, owes a duty to the employed class over and above that prescribed by law; and that the employer's whole duty is not defined by the agreement regarding wages. While essentially private and individual in its character the movement has no doubt been a powerful furtherer of industrial legislation which, after all, is simply an expression of the will of the community, and the two are closely connected.

The early efforts in this field were known as **welfare work** or **betterment work.** These terms, however, have become identified with certain efforts along this line that savor strongly of philanthropy, paternalism, or reform work incident to the early stages of the movement. Many of these efforts were dismal failures, but they have been useful in showing the true content of successful work along this line, which savors less of philanthropy and more of real service. The name **employees' service** is, therefore, coming into use rapidly as indicating more clearly the true scope of this work. Space forbids more than the listing of the principal features of this work. A more extended discussion will be found in the third edition of this book. A classification of the more common forms of employees' service follows:

1. **Housing and home-making assistance.**
2. **Provision for rest and recreation.**
3. **Educational assistance other than vocational training.**
4. **Financial betterment.**

It will be obvious that under each of these divisions there is scope for much experimentation. In fact, much has already been done and not always with happy results, some of the most comprehensive efforts having been attended with the most discouraging endings. Yet it is clear that this work opens up tremendous possibilities for good or evil, and the question naturally arises whither the movement is tending and what does it portend? Is it a collection of unrelated items based upon personal opinion, experimental in their character, short-lived, and of no lasting value? Or is it a part of a greater movement toward the development of a true and satisfactory industrial democracy? Will these experiments in time point the way to make an equitable distribution of the proceeds of industry? Obviously they are in their essence an effort to do this very thing.

Is this work, in brief, to remain a cheap kind of philanthropy or missionary effort as it so often is, or is it destined to grow into a real service which will be recognized by employer and employee as belonging by right in the field of industrial management? So far as the writer is aware, no real comprehensive attempt has been made as yet to analyze this movement with a view of determining its real place in our industrial fabric. It is more than probable that the recent federal legislation affecting wages, pensions, and collective bargaining (Arts. 242, 318) will have a marked influence upon employees' service. Aside from the natural tendency that may arise on the part of the employer to let the employee look out for himself, the very heavy taxes that are now levied to support governmental expenditures for pensions, etc., may greatly discourage the employer from doing any more than the law requires.

It would be easier to predict the future of employees' service if more were known of the real motives that lie back of this movement. It must be admitted that much of the welfare work, so called, has had selfish motives back of it. Advertising, the hope of distracting discontented employees by athletics, the desire to pose as a benefactor, and similar motives have too often been at the bottom of some of these efforts. Perhaps this is the reason why there have been so many failures up to the present time. Even some of those who have entered this field with the highest of motives have met with failure because their work did not rest upon solid ground and upon the true foundation of this important work. It has already been noted that the only solid ground upon which men can meet and settle their differences is that which might be called justice. And it may be assumed that the time has gone by when men and women will accept any industrial relation upon blind faith. Any educational, religious, recreative, social, or other facility provided by any factory manager that cannot be *justified* before the recipients of such privileges is preordained to fail in this enlightened age. To endure they must be in line with the growth of modern industrial democracy whose watchword is "*justice*" and the "*square deal*." They must rest upon brotherhood and not upon paternalism.

References

Alford, L. P. (Ed.): "Cost and Production Handbook," p. 149.
———: "Management's Handbook."
Blackford, Katherine M. H.: "The Job, the Man, and the Boss."
Bloomfield, Daniel: "Labor Maintenance."
Frankel, L. K., and A. Fleisher: "The Human Factor in Industry."
Kelly, R. W.: "Training Industrial Workers."
Kemble, W. F.: "Choosing Employees by Test."
Morris, J. V.: "Employee Training."
Smith, Elliot Dunlap: "Psychology for Executives."
Tead, Ordway: "Human Nature and Management."
Tead, O., and H. C. Metcalf: "Personnel Administration."
Walters, J. E.: "Applied Personnel Administration."

CHAPTER XXV

INDUSTRIAL RELATIONS CONTINUED—INDUSTRIAL DEMOCRACY

311. General.—The methods of production discussed in the preceding sections, while enabling us to produce the comforts of life as no other people have been able to do, have also rendered our civilization so complex as to make equitable distribution of these comforts an exceedingly difficult problem. With this increasing power of production has come, therefore, an increasing demand that the fruits of industry shall be more equitably divided, or rather, divided in a different ratio, since it is difficult to say just what an equitable division may be. The reasons for industrial discontent are many and deep rooted. First there is the ancient contrast between the very rich and the very poor, which is so great today as to cause even some of those who have great wealth to ponder the desirability of such great extremes. A great contributing cause is found, no doubt, in the utter dependence of those who labor upon organized industry and capitalistic control, due to the complete separation of the worker from the ownership of the tools of industry. A minor but important cause is the lack of opportunity on the part of the worker to take a more intelligent part in industry, because division of labor chains him to the production of a small part and cuts off visualization of the industry as a whole. In other words, the worker, to a large degree, can no longer "express" himself as in the old handicraft industry.

More potent than these is the rising tide of modern industrial ideals that increasingly insist that industry shall be considered less as a personal matter and more as a general support of life, and that personal profit and advantage shall be secondary to the general weal, or as it is sometimes stated, that industry shall be "democratized." Our ideas of democracy in industry will be governed, therefore, largely by our interpretation of this democratic movement; and within the group that is pressing for this democratization a wide variation of opinion will be found and many panaceas are offered for our industrial ills.

The basic tenet of the most important group in this movement is the *restoration to the worker of the ownership of the tools of industry*. This is the tap-root of all socialistic doctrine, though the advocates of socialism differ widely in their ideas as to the degree to which it is necessary or possible to bring about this result. In its most violent form this group would destroy modern industrialism with no adequate substitute to replace it. This had been almost accomplished in Russia, where the extreme view prevailed that the ownership of the tools of industry should be vested in those who actually produce. The brief but dreadful experience of that unhappy land has proved beyond doubt what every student of organized government already knew. *No organized industry that is capable of supporting a modern civilization can be successfully operated by manual labor alone.* The industrial manager, the functionalized worker or specialist, and the financier, are as necessary to modern industry as the actual worker no matter how skillful he may be.

312. Representative Government.—Recognizing, perhaps, these limitations of socialistic doctrines, some industrial reformers have turned to the principle of government by representation as illustrated by our national government. In theory, at least, this form of government is rational and fair. It recognizes that civilization requires many men of many minds; and through the election of those best fitted to represent the varied and conflicting interests of the country it aims to confer the greatest good upon the greatest number. In spite of its failings and limitations, representative government as existing in this country is in many ways the best form of government for our ideas of civilization that has, as yet, been devised. It was quite natural, therefore, that an effort should be made to apply its essential features to industrial management in answer to this demand for democratization. For some time prior to the World War, forward-looking employers and employees who wished to obtain a more adequate means of presenting their desires had, in a number of instances, organized joint committees of various kinds in an effort to reach a better mutual understanding. The labor difficulties incident to the war gave a considerable impetus to this movement, both the National War Labor Board and the Shipbuilding Labor Adjustment Board not only encouraging the formation of joint committees of workers and employers for the discussion of industrial problems but, in some instances, insisting that such agencies be employed.

A report upon this subject by the National Industrial Conference Board in 1919 states that 225 such "works councils," as the report designates them, had been organized since January, 1918. A supplementary report published in 1920 states that the number of works councils which were then in force was upward of 700.

It will be obvious that from the very diversity of industry itself these works councils must necessarily vary widely in character and scope. They have, however, one important common feature, namely, they are all based upon representation chosen by and from the employees of an individual enterprise. Otherwise they vary in size, scope, method of formation, and other specific features of organization. In small plants the works councils are of the simplest and most informal type, while in some of the larger enterprises they are very formal and complex. For convenience of discussion all works councils may be divided into two types.

313. Industrial Democracy.—The first of these types includes those organizations that are modeled after the federal government and known, therefore, as **industrial democracy.** One of the first sponsors of this method of employee representation was John Leitch, who defines this method as:

> . . . the organization of any factory or other business institution into a little democratic state with a representative government which shall have both the legislative and executive phases.

In this plan there is first a "cabinet" consisting of the executive officers of the plant. This body is not elective but owes its existence to the ownership of the enterprise. The cabinet holds a veto power over legislation, but it may suggest measures to the "senate" and "house of representatives." The senate consists of foremen and department heads and may or may not be an elective body, though in one instance this body is elected by the employees from the ranks of the foremen and departmental heads. Lastly there is the house of representatives which is elected by secret ballot by the actual workers on such basis as may seem desirable, the representatives being chosen from the workers themselves. These bodies are organized with the same general legislative machinery, committees, etc., as the federal government, and are expected to transact business in a manner similar to that organization. As a basis of action and as a bond to hold the work of the several bodies in harmony there is a written "Business Policy" corresponding to the constitution of the United States and containing a declaration of principles and reasons why the organization has been called into being.

The basic intent of this form of organization is to provide an opportunity for the workmen to express their views on all matters in which they are competent to do so. Bills or measures may originate in the senate or house, but they must pass both house and senate and be approved by the cabinet before becoming a "law" or shop regulation. Undoubtedly such a plan will provide the opportunity for a free exchange of opinions on many phases of industrial management, and no doubt shop rules and regulations formulated thus, with the aid and consent of the workers, will be more satisfactory than if imposed by the management without conference. If founded in a liberal spirit the deliberations of the house will, no doubt, bring many needed changes and grievances to the attention of the management and assist materially in obtaining a better understanding of the conditions that make for contentment and confidence in the management. Obviously such a comprehensive plan as outlined in the foregoing is possible only in plants of some magnitude. So far as information can be obtained no successful experiment of this kind is known.

314. Works Councils.—One of the greatest defects in industrial democracy, so called, in the opinion of the writer, is the fact that the representatives of the workers meet by themselves in one body, and the representatives of management meet by themselves in two other bodies. While it may be that such an arrangement is conducive to greater freedom of speech on the part of the workmen, it does not tend to restore, in any great measure, the old *personal contact* that has been lost in the great growth of modern industry. The intercourse between the management and the workers is necessarily quite formal.

For this reason there is probably much more hope of securing better industrial relations through the second type of works councils, which is based upon the committee system described in Art. 105. It will be obvious that the committee system offers a wide range of joint activity. Thus the works council may consist of a single joint committee or there may be a number of committees arranged in ascending order of importance and authority, or there may be a number of unrelated committees each having jurisdiction over some special field. Again, these committees may consist wholly of employees or of executives, as in the plan of industrial democracy, or they may be joint committees of employees and executives.

It is this last form of committee system that probably holds out most hope, since this form of council offers more opportunity for personal contact between employer and employee than any other. Many variations of the committee method have been tried. Three points bearing on their successful operation should be noted. In all cases it is necessary to have definite plans for securing fair and satisfactory elections, the method of procedure must be clearly defined, as must be also the function and authority of all committees.

315. Limitations of Employee Participation.—The most difficult and the most important phase of all organization of this kind is to fix the functions and authority of such committees. And it is in this connection that the limitations of democratic government appear most strongly. It is almost obvious that the deliberations of a body such as the "house" in any plan of industrial democracy, or of a corresponding committee under a committee system, must necessarily be confined to the field of *personnel relations*. Such a body is fully competent to discuss working conditions, shop rules, wages, hours of work, and kindred matters, but there appear to be definite limitations in other directions. A report of the National Industrial Conference Board states:

It appears from the foregoing that practically all works councils deal with such subjects of bargaining as hours of work, wages, and piece rates. In addition many such organizations concern themselves with the social and recreative life of the workers and with living and working conditions. In some cases the works councils deal with shop discipline or with hiring, promotion, and dismissals, but usually by way of review and recommendation only. Relatively few works councils concern themselves with improvement of production or with general management.

This last statement is very significant and indicates the direction of possible growth and development of such systems. It indicates clearly, also, the basic truth that *special knowledge and intelligence are not an elective function.* Important as are these matters that come within the scope of elected committees, they constitute only a portion of the problems of management. They do not touch upon the complicated problems of financing the enterprise, deciding upon what shall be manufactured, nor any of the difficult problems met with in devising and furnishing ways and means, purchasing material, and directing the general business activities. These functions require specialized knowledge, which, as before stated, is not an elective function. If from any industrial enterprise there should be taken away the small body of specialists such as the financier, the chemist, the engineer, and those who understand modern industrial methods, the entire structure would collapse in exactly the same manner as did Russian industry when this class of men was eliminated.

There is, nevertheless, an immense amount of industrial knowledge in the possession of any group of skilled workers that, under ordinary methods of management, is largely lost. The joint committee offers a means of cooperative effort that will make this practical knowledge of use, and many such committees are now in use. In a few instances an attempt has been made to secure a more democratic control by permitting the workers to elect representatives to sit with the managing directors and other executive bodies. While such representation may, if wisely directed, tend to a much better mutual understanding by removing any mystery surrounding the administrative methods, and assure the workers that they are getting their share of the profits, the limitations described in the foregoing hold true. In general, workmen are not prepared to assume administrative duties and less prepared to give intelligent decisions on matters requiring special knowledge.

316. Future of Employee Participation.—Actual experience with employee participation in management has been far too limited to permit any very definite conclusions as to the permanent value of the movement. Many questions as to the best procedure to be followed in operating works councils still remain vague and undetermined. Clearly much more experience with the idea will be necessary before its full possibilities and limitations can be evaluated. In all probability this will involve the investigation of the relations between cooperative effort of this kind and financial incentives for increased production. And the attitude of organized labor, which, on the whole, has not been very friendly to employee representation, is another factor that may greatly affect the future of the movement. It may be that the Wagner Act and similar legislation, which tend to separate employers and employees into two clearly separate groups, may not only prevent any further growth in this direction but may destroy the experiments that now exist.

The most important consideration, however, in connection with this movement is not the particular method of forming works councils, nor even their powers and jurisdiction. The main question is whether this *principle* offers a means of securing a better understanding between employer and employee. If the principle is sound the best method of procedure is sure to be evolved. The history of welfare work, so called, is filled with the records of failures and misunderstandings. Yet out of it have come certain basic principles and practices affecting working conditions that today no thinking man questions. Aside from any humanistic motives it has been demonstrated that plenty of sunlight, air, and comfortable and sanitary surroundings for the worker are good business investments. A similar movement is needed that will assist in evaluating these more intangible and more important human relations.

Most industrial troubles have their origin in *distrust,* and distrust usually has its roots in *selfishness.* It would appear that there must be some form of joint activity that will enable capital and labor to sit down together, and setting both of these darksome human characteristics aside, arrive at a decision on any debatable matter that will be acceptable to both sides. Perhaps works councils offer this opportunity; at least they appear to hold a principle that is well worthy of careful consideration.

317. Democratic Ownership.—It should be carefully noted that there is nothing in our laws or in public sentiment that prohibits in any way the joint ownership of productive tools by any group of men in any number. There is, furthermore, no prohibition of any kind that would prevent such a group from operating such tools in the most democratic manner they may choose to elect or devise. The history of such cooperative efforts, except where those participating have been held together by some extraneous bond such as religion, has been, for the most part, a story of failure. While, therefore, socialistic doctrines, looking to the return of the ownership of the tools of industry to those who actually produce, have exercised, and are exercising, a powerful modifying influence upon capitalistic industry, they are not likely to be accepted, in the near future at least, as controlling principles in industrial management.

The widespread lack of thrift among present-day workers and their lack of special knowledge and training in industry and finance will, unless our educational processes work a great change, long remain a great obstacle to cooperative ownership and control of the most democratic kind. Yet there is growth in this direction. The stocks and bonds of all of our great industrial enterprises are very widely scattered throughout the country and this tendency is sure in time to affect materially the viewpoint of great masses of workers as concerns modern industry. And the worker is making some experiments in real democratic ownership, though some of these have met with disastrous results, as illustrated by the banking venture of the Locomotive Brotherhood. The outcome of this venture may profoundly affect the formation of other enterprises by labor both organized and unorganized. Profit-sharing and similar methods of employee participation are discussed in Art. 267.

318. Government and Industry.—It was noted in Art. 76 that many cities own utilities, such as water works, etc., that several states own roads, canals, parks, etc., and the federal government owns many properties of national interest, including several large irrigation projects and several large dams which produce electric energy. For the most part the several states have not entered into competition with private enterprise. The federal government also until very recent years has been very considerate of state rights and has not entered into direct competition with private business or industry. But the hydroelectric by-product of the Tennessee River has brought the government into direct competition with private electric corporations, although the avowed primary purpose of the later dams built upon the river was to develop navigation and to prevent flooding in that area. The federal government, through the Home Owners Loan Corporation, is in the business of insuring loans upon homes; through the Social Security Act (Art. 278) it is in the business of insuring against the insecurity of old age; and through the U. S. Shipping Board it is in the steamship business.

Commenting on these activities Charles C. Abbot[1] in the *Harvard Business Review,* Vol. XVI, No. 4, lists 69 "Federal Corporations and Corporate Agencies," most of which are concerned in some way with industry. He states:

> The activities of these bodies range from loans to individuals as small as $10 made by the Emergency Crop and Feed Loans Division of the Farm Credit Administration to single loans amounting to millions of dollars extended by the Reconstruction Finance Corporation. Their operations comprise such diverse undertakings as the insurance of mortgages as large as $5,000,000 on a single piece of property by the Federal Housing Administration, the manufacture of rum and the raising of chickens and tomatoes by the Virgin Islands Company, and the operation of the Alaska and Panama Railroads. What the ultimate effect of this vast superstructure of corporate and semi-corporate entities will be on American life [he continues], on wage earners and businessmen, on banking and agriculture, on the behavior of the trade cycle and the standard of living of the common man, it is impossible to foresee.

It would appear that we need a redefinition of the functions of government in its relation to business if our present economic system is to

[1] This article will repay reading.

survive. There is a vast difference between governmental *regulation* and governmental *ownership*. The argument advanced by some that government-owned and -operated enterprises can establish "yardsticks" of performance and costs is not borne out by actual experiences. Without in any way questioning the wisdom and necessity of governmental ownership of such projects as are of national interest or are so large as to be beyond the financial strength of a state or private corporation, it would appear that a limit should be placed upon the rapidly expanding bureaucratic control of industry that in the long run must completely throttle the individual enterprise that has built up our efficient industries.

References

Abbott, Charles C.: *Harvard Business Review*, Vol. XVI, No. 4.
Alford, L. P. (Ed.): "Cost and Production Handbook," p. 1386.
Leitch, John: "Man to Man."
Tead, O., and H. C. Metcalf: "Personnel Management."

CHAPTER XXVI

RÉSUMÉ—SCIENCE IN INDUSTRY

ECONOMICS OF SCIENTIFIC MANAGEMENT

319. General.—It is quite obvious that the principles of production discussed in the several chapters of this book can be combined into many different systems of management. The general outlines of Mr. Taylor's system, which was the first of the modern systems of so-called scientific management, have been discussed briefly in Chap. XII. There have been several other similar systems put forward since, and much has been written on the subject of so-called scientific management. To such an extent is this true that the many descriptions of the machinery of these systems have done much to obscure the principles that lie at the bottom. It has been shown here that these principles are few and comparatively simple. Scientific management is really a point of view that is applicable to the building, equipping, and operating of all parts of industrial enterprises and not alone to the work of production in metal-working shops, as one would be led to believe by much of the literature of the subject. It is also applicable to the buying of raw materials and selling of finished product.

Two important economic claims have been made for these new methods: (1) that they will greatly increase production; and (2) that they will solve the wage or labor problem. The truth and limitations of the first claim have been fully discussed. It remains to consider very briefly the second claim.

The ground on which advocates of these new, yet old, methods base this second claim is that because of the vastly increased production per man, when using these methods, unit cost will go down and wages will go up. That is to say, increased productive power *necessarily* means increased profits, and their resulting comforts to the actual producer; for a diligent search through the principles of efficiency engineering fails to disclose any new principles regarding the *distribution* of the fruits of labor. True, great stress is laid on the "square deal" and cooperation of employer and employee in all these systems; but these are not new or peculiar to any system of management.

It is true, of course, that decreased cost of production always gives the employer an *opportunity* to pay better wages, until his competitors obtain the same methods, when the natural law of competition again comes into effect and the employer is again confronted with the choice of smaller profits, lower wages, or still more refined methods and improved tools.

The greatest gain in productive ability that the world has ever witnessed came with the introduction of labor-saving machinery. All the *possibilities* for the physical and mental betterment of humanity offered by the most tremendous gain in productive power mankind has ever witnessed were opened up at that time. The immediate effect of these new methods was to reduce the workers concerned to a state of pauperism and wretchedness which was relieved only by legislation and other reactive measures and not by anything *inherent* in the new methods. These productive methods have been tremendously improved and added to steadily for over 100 years; and what is the net result? Today the skilled mechanic who can save a competence is a rarity. Instead of the individual independence which every man should be able to acquire, governmental and other forms of pensions are in operation on a large scale. In spite of our much vaunted increased educational facilities only a minority of the entire population of this the most favored of countries get the minimum amount of education that is considered necessary to make them intelligent citizens. True, the workman of every calling has benefited very greatly by the improved methods, and it is true that he is better clothed, better fed, and better housed, and particularly better educated, than formerly; but the fact remains that his progress has not been proportionate to our increased productive capacity.

Now labor-saving management, as has been shown, does not differ in its action or ultimate effect from that of labor-saving machinery; and while it must be conceded that it will increase production there is no reason for thinking it possesses any inherent power to change the problem of distribution. It was noted in Chap. I that the *total* wealth that any community could possess depended on its natural resources and on the efficiency of its tools of production; but that the distribution of wealth was quite another matter, and depended on the method by which the fruits of labor were distributed. Labor-saving management will help to increase the total wealth, but it cannot of itself be expected to do more than labor-saving machinery has done in distributing it.

The great problem that confronts us is not that of production but that of *economic distribution.* More manufactured goods can be produced than can be used, and far more than is needed to make all of us comfortable. All the new productive processes that may be invented will throw little light on the problem of why, in many places, at the one time, storehouses are found filled with raw material, idle factories equipped with the finest tools the world has ever seen, and people walking the streets without food or clothing, yet willing to work.

The problem is too complex to be solved by the simple expedient of increased production. There still remain the questions of competition, unfair taxation, wasteful governmental expenditures, tariff and monetary problems, immigration, and a dozen other factors that are not as yet within the control of the employer, be he ever so fair minded, or of the employee, be he ever so strongly organized. It may be that a readjustment of some of these would do as much for all workers, both employer and employee, as would a large increase of productive power. What is most needed is *scientific distribution.* This is true not only of manufactured goods but markedly so of agricultural products where the cost of marketing is a disgrace to our intelligence.

During the last few years we have witnessed a number of legislative experiments affecting industry, agriculture, and our monetary system. However well intentioned these efforts may have been, no well-informed person would claim that they have in any marked degree solved this problem of distribution. In fact so far as agriculture is concerned we appear to be about where we started, although the land still resounds with panaceas. No Moses has arisen to lead us out of these economic difficulties. The problem of production is solved; the problem of equitable and stable distribution awaits solution.

320. Scientific Management and Government.—Scientific methods have long since spread from the engineering and productive phases of industry to all forms of industrial and commercial management. The existence of schools of business, so called, is direct evidence of the efficiency of these methods. Wherever such methods have been intelligently applied they have not failed to produce the desired results. Little attempt has been made, however, to apply these methods to the problems of government. It is true that the strictly engineering problems of city, state, and nation are well handled and both the army and navy have developed splendid line-and-staff organizations, systematic planning of all work, and a procedure to insure its execution that is unsurpassed. But the broader phases of government that have to do with the problems of distribution, taxes, tariffs, and foreign affairs are still administered by "town-meeting" methods by men elected on the basis of expediency and party politics and not because of their scientific knowledge of the matters concerning which they are called upon to legislate. Apparently no science of government has been developed and the situation is exactly that discussed in Art. 317 concerning the administration of industrial enterprises by worker's representatives. As there stated, special skill and knowledge are not elective functions, but are confined to those who have had the requisite training in the special field considered.

Consideration of these facts has led in recent times to some loose thinking and hasty conclusions, notably the proposals made that the engineer, because of his intimate knowledge of the industrial basis of our national life, should have a larger part in government. Quite recently this idea has been put forward seriously under the name of *technocracy*, that is, by inference, government by technicians, or in a more popular sense by engineers. It is true that engineers have the widest knowledge of our industrial basis and also that they use scientific methods with amazing exactness. But it should be remembered that the "patterns" of their problems are very definite, long-established, and rest upon an established body of knowledge. Their problems and the solutions of them are coherent, so to speak, which is far from the case in economic and governmental problems. Unquestionably where facts or tangible evidence can be obtained, the scientific method is very effective in arriving at accurate conclusions, and the engineer is in a peculiarly advantageous position for obtaining such tangible evidence as can be gathered from the industrial field. However, in the case of our more difficult problems in general economics and government, exact facts and tangible evidence are not easy to obtain and oftentimes the evidence is voluminous and conflicting. In many cases the well-trained business man and the lawyer are at least as capable of drawing an accurate conclusion as any one else.

What is needed, apparently, is not government by technicians, but a reorganization of our government both federal and state by **functions** just as has been done in successful industry. The greatest problem would be the means of finding adequate personnel for these functions and yet retain our democratic form of government. At the present time, attempts are made to secure functional advice by the appointment of governmental commissions whose recommendations Congress may or may not adopt. But until government is conducted by men with special training and knowledge such as are to be found in large industrial organizations, there would appear to be little hope of an intelligent national, state or city administration.

321. Scientific Management and Human Relations.—The foregoing discussion of the principles of industrial administration has considered them almost entirely as *machinery* of production, and their possibilities and limitations as such. But with the advance in productive machinery there has come a change in the evaluation of the human interests involved that is far more important than these advances themselves. The principles governing human relations permeate every nook and corner of industry, modifying and controlling other factors as never before in the history of the world. They are ever present and cannot for an instant be forgotten or ignored. Until very recently these relations were looked upon as being entirely personal. It was supposed that personality, as expressed in leadership, was the one great force in controlling the relations of men to each other. It is still true and will always remain true that leadership is a prime essential in the success of any enterprise involving human relations, but even here cold, scientific methods have shown that some of these matters can be **measured** and the results recorded, and this has brought new problems into the administration of human affairs.

Thus it was shown in Chap. XIII that by means of time-study methods it is possible to measure not only a man's possible output, but also to set the most economical rate at which he can work. By this method the law of **human bodily effort** is removed from the qualitative to the quantitative stage of knowledge and the result of bodily effort becomes a definitely known factor that can be measured and recorded.

Again, motion study has shown that inherited methods of doing work are in many cases most wasteful and can be greatly improved by analytical study. Furthermore, experimental data can be recorded here also, thus making it possible to build up synthetically a predicted sequence of operations that is much more efficient than those that come as the result of empirical or inherited methods.

The rewarding of labor, so long a strictly empirical matter, has also been studied analytically, and data showing the ratio of increased reward to increased output are already at hand. Investigations of this character naturally carry the investigator off into psychological measurements of human relations. This field has as yet been barely touched, but what the future holds in store from this form of investigation is difficult to predict, and without doubt the near future will see remarkable developments in the art of measuring factors that affect human relations which now seem intangible.

Many other principles that probably do not admit of quantitative measurement are rapidly becoming a fixed part of all intelligent management. It is now clearly recognized that if men are to put forth their best bodily efforts they must be well fed, well housed, and well clothed. Aside from all philanthropic ideas, it is found that the physical care of men yields dividends. This thought, however, is comparatively new to many; and not many years ago the employer gave far greater attention to the care of his horses than he did to that of his men. If this is true of bodily effort it is even more true of mental effort. The cost of production does not depend upon the wage rate but upon the *unit wage cost* which is a function of *quantity;* and quantity of output depends on mental and physical strength. It is no secret that the well-fed American can easily outwork most of his foreign competitors. But, as noted in Chap. XXV, the caring for the physical welfare of employees is not an act of charity, and if conducted in any spirit of patronage it is fatal to management.

Of equal importance is the principle that it pays to **teach** men the best methods by which work can be done. This is in strict accord with all human experience; yet the backward state of the educational side of factory management is startling. Even the much lauded old apprenticeship systems were not, as a rule, educational in a true sense. The apprentice was given an *opportunity* to learn by *observation* and *absorption*, but was rarely *taught*. Is it any wonder that the accumulated errors and wasteful methods of the trades have persisted? If time and motion studies have done no other service than to call attention to this fact, they have rendered a good service. It is rapidly becoming recognized that increased refinement in methods and higher requirements for the worker can be met only when coupled with proper methods of instruction. It is not sufficient to set standards that only a few men can reach, to the arbitrary exclusion of all others. Every man should be educated industrially to his highest capacity in the work for which he is best fitted, and every man should be given an opportunity to produce to the best of his ability and rewarded accordingly. This implies not only a changed point of view on the part of our public schools,[1] but on the part of factory management also. The work of H. L. Gantt[2] in training men not only in *skill* but in *habits of industry* is worthy of special attention. The setting of standards of performance means very little, after all, unless these standards are high. And if they are high they can be reached by the majority of workmen only after careful training and preparation.

Now it would seem that all would be benefited by the adoption of all fair means of increasing production. The greater the output per man hour the greater will be the surplus of production that *may be* distributed to the worker. It has been demonstrated that in the long run increased production does benefit all men. It would, therefore, seem reasonable that the employer should use such scientific data as he may have to select men properly, matching the requirements of the position with the characteristics of the man. It would seem that he is justified in measuring, if he can, what a fair day's work should be, and paying only a day's wage for a day's work. There is, in fact, no logical argument against the full use of the analytical or scientific method in attacking any problem in industry. If all men could be brought to realize the economic advantages of this method of attack over empirical and rule-of-thumb methods the standard of production would rise tremendously.

But, on the other hand, it must be recognized by the employer that he can no longer introduce any or all methods into his shop at will. It is a far cry to the days of the Industrial Revolution, when the mechanical side of factory equipment could be changed at pleasure and the human portion of the equipment molded to suit the mechanical part. A new industrial day has dawned in which *profits* are not the most important factor. More and more, industry is coming to be looked upon as a *means of supporting human existence* and not as a means of *corporate profit.* The ideal factory so far as producing profits is concerned would be one equipped with the finest of machinery and manned by well-cared-for slaves, whose reward was the best of physical care, and the mental training sufficient only for the needs of the industry. This ideal might well have been imagined a few hundred years ago; but such ideals belong to the past, and as industrial ideals have moved farther and farther away

[1] See "Education for American Life," by the Regents of the State of New York, p. 46.

[2] Gantt, H. L., "Work, Wages, and Profits."

from this standard, employers, workmen, and more important still, public opinion, have become increasingly critical regarding changes in industrial methods. *Men* have become of more interest than *machines.*

The quickness of the Industrial Revolution and its sudden and disastrous effects upon the workman were possible because of his unprepared condition for self-protection. Present-day conditions are vastly different. Labor-saving methods of management differ little in their ultimate economic effect from those of labor-saving machinery. They differ in their application in that labor-saving or scientific management is much more *personal* in its character, and affects the worker much more intimately. Its principles are also of much more widespread application than those of machine production. There is no business so small or no calling so humble or so high to which this *point of view* is not applicable. Yet its adoption must of necessity be slow as compared with that of the principle of machine production.

Because of their economic soundness these new methods will continue to grow in use, just as applied science in general grows in use in all lines of human endeavor. So long as our present ideas of civilization prevail and society holds that the greatest good to the greatest number comes through abundant production of commodities, there can be no reasonable objection to the employer possessing the most refined knowledge of the laws of production. But there is also a constantly increasing objection on the part of society to the use of any such refined knowledge as a means of oppression. Fortunately, progressive employers have no desire so to use these new productive methods, and it is not likely that any degradation of labor, such as followed the introduction of modern machine methods, will result from the introduction of these time-saving methods. Indeed, at times it would appear as though labor and not capital is the more oppressive through the excessive use of protective measures.

Why does the worker naturally resist these new methods?[1] First, because the great majority of men are naturally afraid of all new things that they do not understand and the effects of which they cannot clearly foresee. It is very evident to the worker that time and motion study puts into the hands of the employer a much more powerful *selective* agency than he has hitherto possessed, and the worker is justly afraid of these scientific methods in the hands of the unscientific, the unscrupulous, and the ignorant employer. If this selective power is used solely for the purpose of *sorting* men so as to eliminate the indolent and those that are clearly unfitted for the work in hand, there can be no objection raised against it from the humane standpoint. If, however, it is used to *eliminate all but the very best workers* the effect will be disastrous both

[1] For an exhaustive discussion of the viewpoint of both capital and labor as concerns the effect of scientific management, see "Scientific Management and Labor" by Robert L. Hoxie.

from the humane and from the economic standpoint until an entire readjustment of the field has taken place. What is needed is a scheme whereby *every man can be worked up to his full efficiency whether or not his output be as great as that of his neighbor.*

Secondly, the worker may object to these new methods because of his inherent inertia. The workman who has once learned and long practiced certain methods of doing work is seldom willing to admit that better ways may be devised if these ways appear to be radically different from those to which he is accustomed.

And lastly, he naturally opposes these new methods because his own experience and his inherited point of view naturally lead him to suspect any new methods that promise increased remuneration for increased efforts.

The first two objections may, perhaps, be removed by educational methods, but the third is deep rooted and involves principles that even the advocates of the new methods have not always fully appreciated. The basis of this objection is *distrust* and the root of distrust is usually *selfishness,* sometimes on the part of the employee but more often on the part of the employer; and this can be removed only when employer and employee can agree as to what is a just and equitable division of the profits of industry; which involves, not the application of scientific methods to human relations, but the application of the **fair deal** on the part of all concerned.

Just what changes shall be made in our political and social structure to make this fair distribution possible does not at present seem clear, and prophecies are useless. It is an open question as to whether compulsory bargaining as determined by legislation such as the Wagner Act will accomplish the desired result. One thing is clear, however, and that is that such changes are impending; and impending not only because of unrest among workers of the lower grades but because of a changed point of view among the people at large. The situation is perfectly logical. It would seem incredible that any nation as intelligent as this, with its educational standard rising steadily, and likely to attain a height hitherto unknown, should not arrive at a solution of the division of the profits of industry that will be fair and just, and then compel all men, willing or unwilling, to abide thereby. Labor-saving management, without doubt, will be much used ultimately because its economic principles are valuable. All such principles as lead to multiplied power of production eventually come into use, though the opposition to them may be very great at first. But labor-saving management will have to justify every one of its features much more fully than did its prototype, labor-saving machinery. It will not be enough that it will increase profits, *it must justify its place in our social economy.* Yet the need of improved methods both in our productive processes and in our machinery of distribution is urgent, and the problem of securing these advantages without violent adjustments that cause suffering is not always an easy one. Fortunate, indeed, will it be if some of the reactive influences now at work on social and industrial organization point a peaceful way to this much needed readjustment. Certain it is, however, that no great progress in this direction will be made till workmen are willing to learn forbearance, and employers, setting aside selfishness, will pray as did good old pagan Plato of old, "May my store of gold be such as none but the good can bear."

INDEX

Raymond